❧ Roots of
Scientific
Thought

ROOTS OF SCIENTIFIC THOUGHT

A Cultural Perspective

EDITED BY

Philip P. Wiener
Executive Editor, *Journal of the History of Ideas*

AND

Aaron Noland
Managing Editor, *Journal of the History of Ideas*

BASIC BOOKS · PUBLISHERS · NEW YORK

Q
111
.J6

First Printing October 1957
Second Printing August 1958
Third Printing September 1960

PREFACE

THE CONTRIBUTIONS that comprise this volume trace in various ways certain basic ideas and modes of thought in the historical development of science. Our selections, from the first eighteen volumes of the *Journal of the History of Ideas,* show some of the interrelations of scientific ideas with social, philosophical, religious, literary, and artistic developments in Western culture. Our introductory essays aim to acquaint the reader with the general point of view of the intellectual historian and to fill in some of the background material presupposed by our authors. Their research is essentially interdisciplinary, delving into border regions and twilight zones surrounding every specialist's field of inquiry into the history of man's thought.

Two recent articles in two other journals indicate the ways in which intellectual history impinges on the development of science. In *Nuclear Physics* (II:132, 1957), Alfred Landé notes: "The *search* for the simplest possible laws has occupied scientists from Thales via Leibniz to modern times." In *Isis* (XLVII:48, 1957), Robert C. Stauffer points out that "In the history of science, any speculation, no matter how fantastic, which leads to important experimental discovery, deserves some notice. Thus the stimulus Oersted received from Schelling's 'beautiful and great ideas' and from *Naturphilosophie* in general and also the influence of both the speculations and the experiments of Ritter should be recognized as factors involved in a major discovery of physics. This exemplifies the significance of intellectual factors outside the realm of science as potential influences upon the development of science. Thus in order to have a full account of the history of science, we must also consider not only social and political history, economic history, and the history of technology but general intellectual history as well.''

This volume, then, is not a history of the sciences; instead, it draws upon that history in order to sketch some of the many lines of thought that go beyond the technical minutiae, indispensable as they are, to the major ideas of some of the most significant scientific thinkers of the past twenty-five centuries.

We are greatly indebted to the editors and the many authors of the *Journal of the History of Ideas* for their collaboration in this collection of their scholarly efforts.

To Professor A. C. Crombie, University Lecturer in the History of Science at Oxford University, we owe a special debt of gratitude for permitting us to use parts of his authoritative work on medieval science, *Augustine to Galileo: The History of Science,* A.D. *400–1650,* in our introduction to Part 2, and to Harvard University Press for its concurrent permission.

We wish to thank our colleague Professor Israel Drabkin, distinguished for his work on Greek science, for his valuable suggestions in connection with our introductory essays.

June 28, 1957.   P. P. W.
New York, N.Y.   A. N.

Contents

PART 1

THE CLASSICAL HERITAGE

PART 2

FROM RATIONALISM TO EXPERIMENTALISM

PART 3

THE SCIENTIFIC REVOLUTION

PART 4

FROM THE WORLD-MACHINE
TO COSMIC EVOLUTION

ROOTS OF
SCIENTIFIC
THOUGHT

Roots of Scientific Thought:
A Cultural Perspective

WHEN WE TALK of the "roots" of scientific thought, we are using a metaphor that has a considerable degree of complexity, for the historical antecedents of any science as a cultural product contain both logical, cumulative growths and extralogical, noncumulative (but often persistent) strands. We can perceive both sorts of components, for example, as we trace the roots of Greek mathematical thinking among the Pythagoreans. Intermingled with their talk about friendly and unfriendly numbers, mystic pentagrams, perfect numbers, harmony of the spheres, and so forth, we find the logically clear properties of numbers and spatial figures that found their place later in the neat arboretum of Euclid's *Elements*. Some of the mystical elements reappear centuries later in the writings of such sophisticated scientists as Copernicus and Kepler, and some in the superstitious beliefs of numerologists.

The historian of mathematics has to ignore such emotional excrescences in order to report the internal, logical development of the structure of his science. The historian of ideas, however, is interested not only in the logical, cumulative development of scientific thought but also in the extralogical components and their historical affiliations with other cultural developments in the history of the arts, of social institutions, of religion, and of philosophy. By analyzing minutely the complex interrelations of the scientific with the broader culture in which the scientist lives and works, the historian of ideas aims to shed light on the role played by scientific ways of thinking in shaping the course of civilization.

Of course, the symbolic forms in which these roots attain cultural expression among diverse peoples are varied, but the persistence of certain configurations of thought identifies the non-material components of a culture. The transpositions of such dominant patterns of thought together with their ramifications in the arts and sciences are of prime interest to the historian of ideas. For example, Pythagoreanism, rooted in mathematics and mysticism, is encountered in the history of iconography, literature, and cosmology. Our perspective is focused on the transformations as well as persistence of ideas in the climates of opinion and changing fashions of thought that we discover in the history of literature and the arts, social and political movements, religion, and philosophy—all of which are concomitant with the growth of the sciences.

No doubt such practical needs as food, shelter, commerce, transportation, and the like stimulate the exploration of nature and motivate the acquisition of knowledge. But in the struggle for survival not all peoples have been equally stimulated or successful in coping with the vicissitudes of a changing world. It is clear to the historian of thought that a certain breadth of vision and free play of imagination are as vital as economic factors for scientific growth and cultural survival.

A cursory glance at the history of the ancient Egyptians, Babylonians, and the Greeks may serve to illustrate how the way in which a people conceives of its world and of its relation to the supreme power or powers that govern the universe—*i.e.*, a people's mythology—may either promote or retard the development of a scientific tradition. To the Egyptians, the universe was a well-ordered, unchanging, and beneficent creation of benign powers. These powers, whose chief agent on earth was the divine pharaoh, were constantly concerned with the welfare of man on earth. Thus, the gods made the Nile overflow its banks at regular intervals, flooding the river valley and providing the Egyptian people with fertile deposits of soil as well as sufficient water for irrigation during the long dry season that followed the equally regular recession of the Nile in the late summer. Gods also arranged that the Egyptians be protected from invaders by surrounding the country on three sides with inhospitable deserts.

The divine pharaoh saw to it that justice, order, and truth reigned throughout the land, that harmony marked the relations among the social classes, and that when life on this earth came to an end, all who had been faithful and obedient were rewarded by an eternal afterlife. A well-intrenched and respected priesthood, which enjoyed a long, uninterrupted tenure and a monopoly on all learning, propagated this tidy, comforting mythology.

It was to be expected, therefore, that the Egyptians would feel secure and at home in this world and the next world and would not be particularly motivated to wonder very much about the nature of the universe or the meaning of human experience. Curiosity about the nature of things, about the forces at work in the world, was not a main aspect of their outlook.

The "science" that the Egyptians developed was devoid of speculation: their astronomy, geometry, and arithmetic were all directly related to practical matters of daily life. To be able to predict with some degree of precision when the Nile would overflow, the heavens were studied and a lunar as well as a solar calendar worked out. The sytematic study of the cosmos lay beyond their ken. To re-establish boundaries after the Nile inundation, which obliterated all landmarks, and to solve practical problems in earth-measuring in order to assess taxes on land and to build pyramids for the royal family, the art of land measurement was developed. The Egyptians discovered that the triangle whose sides were 3, 4, and 5 units long was right-angled, but they never asked the general, theoretical question—later raised by the Pythagoreans—concerning the relationship of the sides to the hypotenuse in all right-angled triangles. Likewise, in the Book of Ahmes, a papyrus that is perhaps the oldest scientific work in Western culture, the Egyptians were not able to conceive of a fraction whose numerator was greater than unity, except as the sum of the simplest fractions with numerators always equal to one. The Egyptians, it is apparent, were not given to much theorizing.

The Babylonians, however, were more interested in scientific speculation, and again their mythology is a central clue. In sharp contrast to the Egyptian, who felt secure and comfortable in a world structured by the powers that be to promote his welfare, the Babylonian conceived of the world as an alien and hostile place, devoid of any order other than what careful observations could discern, despite the apparent arbitrariness of the gods.

The Babylonian people, inhabiting an area that lay at the crossroads of continents, were subject to constant invasions. Continuity in government and patterns of life was lacking. Even the elements contributed to the Babylonians' feelings of insecurity. The Tigris and Euphrates rivers were unpredictable in their behavior, overflowing their banks irregularly and often bringing death rather than the gift of life to the inhabitants. Sudden rainstorms would wreak havoc, only to be followed by unanticipated periods of drought and stifling dust storms. In this capricious play of omnipotent gods, man was hard put to find order.

In these circumstances, to conceive of nature as obedient to law and natural phenomena as subject to rational analysis was a brave gesture of the Babylonians, whereas the regulated, less troubled world of the Egyptian discouraged speculation of a rational character. The Babylonians, like the Egyptians, were led by practical considerations to develop the art and skill of land measurement. As Neugebauer has shown in his researches on Babylonian science, it went much farther than the Egyptians and early Greeks in algebra (solving the general quadratic equation, for example, was an achievement of Chaldean algebra). Seeking to divine what the powers had in store for them, the Babylonian priests studied the heavens for signs, and in this way promoted the growth of astronomy.

In contrast to the Egyptians and Babylonians stand the ancient Greeks. Their conception of the world and their relation to the powers that governed nature showed an imagination that promoted rather than retarded the development of a scientific tradition. From early times, as Sir William Dampier observed, the Greek world "was almost untrammeled by theological pre-conceptions" such as those that served to inhibit speculation in Egypt. Moreover, the Greeks did not feel that they were, like the "barbarians," helpless and aimless in a universe without order or meaning. Inheriting the mythologies and scientific attainments of their predecessors, aware of the rich variety of human experience and the complexity of their environment, the Greeks were struck with the "open end" quality of human and natural phenomena, and they felt a freedom and "openness of intellectual outlook" that was without precedent in human history. Respectful, though unafraid, of the gods, the Greeks were at liberty to theorize about the world, to seek to know the why and how of natural processes —to search out what we now call the "laws of nature." Thus it was that the "fluid" mythology of the proud and self-reliant Greeks encouraged the sort of controlled and rigorous speculation and incisive inquiry that heralded the great classical heritage not only in the arts and philosophy and political theory but in the theoretical sciences.

Our collection of studies of the evolution of scientific thought and its cultural impact begins with ancient Greek philosophy, because the pursuit of science was inseparable then from philosophy as the quest or love of wisdom. The debates among the pre-Socratic philosophic schools over Being and Non-Being, Atoms and the Void, Number and Motion, the Limited and the Unlimited, Reality and Appearances, Substance and the Elements seem a far cry from modern experimental and mathematical science. It took several hundred years of speculation, analysis, and argument to reach the monumental attainments of a Euclid or Archimedes. But the intellectual lines of continuity between ancient and modern science are there despite the revolutionary changes that have occurred within the history of science. Modern physicists as distinguished as Heisenberg and Schrödinger, in their search for a unified theory of physics, have been reverting to these ancient Greek speculations, in which they see a general craving of the mind for unity.

Aristotle was the encyclopedist of ancient science, and his interests and scientific attainments in biology led him to an organismic view of nature. It was his genius for systematizing that led him to compose the works on logic on which Euclid drew for his notions of definition, postulates, axioms, and proof. It was this same genius that made Aristotle the authority not only in logic and biology but also in all the other natural sciences, not to dwell on his profound influence on cosmology, ethics, political theory, and esthetics. To most scholars of the Middle Ages he was "the master of all those who know," and it was not until his framework of thought was found inadequate that the sciences took on a different form and pursued new avenues of research.

Aristotle's scheme of physical explanation (*i.e.*, his statics of natural place and dynamics of efficient causes guided by final causes, for nothing happens in nature without a purpose or explanation) was criticized and modified but not totally discarded by Copernicus, Kepler, Galileo, Harvey, Newton, and Leibniz, to mention only a few of the great founders of modern science. It is clear that by the time we reach the seventeenth century the search for "final causes" is abandoned in physics (with the exception of Leibniz, whose Aristotelian ideas failed to convince contemporary scientists) in favor of material causes (corpuscles, chemical elements, protoplasmic cells), efficient causes (elastic forces, gravitational attraction, laws of dynamics), and formal causes (mathematical functions of force, energy, etc.).

The chief reason for the abandonment of final causes was the greater clarity of mathematical analysis and the technical development of successful experiments which measured changes instead of guessing what possible purpose they served. But human desires to have human purposes governing natural events prevented progress in the exploration of the forces actually at work in nature. Copernicus' and Kepler's quasi-mystical sun-worship may have led them toward a new heliocentric astronomy; but they demonstrated their theories by mathematical argument applied to observations. Harvey remarked that "nature doing nothing in vain," the anatomical arrangement of the valves of the heart, arteries, and veins could not exist "without a purpose," before he "began to think whether there might not be *a motion, as it were, in a circle.*" The circle, the most perfect form of geometrical figure in Greek esthetic thought, was preferred not only by all ancient systems of astronomy (Pythagorean, Aristotelian, and Ptolemaic) but

also by Copernicus in his astronomy, until it was modified by Kepler's ellipses; an esthetic as well as a geometric preference for the
sphere is shown by Gilbert in his magnetic experiments. The Hellenic adoration of the circle possessed such an attraction for the
astronomer and physicist (*e.g.,* Huygens formulated the laws of
centrifugal force by use of that geometry) that it took the genius
of a Newton to show convincingly what had been surmised by
Galileo—that it was just as "natural" and even more convenient
to assume as a first law of motion that bodies would move forever
in a straight line with uniform motion if there were no unbalanced
forces acting on them rather than, as the ancients supposed, in
circular paths emulating the eternal motions of the heavenly
bodies.

It is generally admitted that the most exact forms of scientific demonstration will use the simplest and most convenient assumptions in order to "save the appearances," the phrase used
by pre-Copernican astronomers, especially Ptolemy, to describe
the sole function of an astronomical system—that is, to schematize
all observable phenomena in the simplest geometric constructions.
Here, the historian of ideas finds a typical instance of the operation of both continuity and discontinuity in scientific progress.
For although Copernicus clung to the Greek notion that certain
simple and esthetically attractive constructions must be the true
picture of nature, the "breaking of the circle" by Kepler and
Newton prepared the way for the logical relativity of starting
points in modern views of scientific method.

In the history of pure mathematics, too, a cumulative continuity is clearly perceptible amidst the progressive changes within the science.

The Greeks developed geometry more extensively than algebra, first because they were nonplussed by the "irrational" numbers, and then perhaps because their chief arts were architectural,
sculptural, and pictorial. Their philosopher-scientists looked down
upon the menial and commercial arts which had greater need of
arithmetic. Hence, we find their greatest mathematical achievement in the deductive axiomatic system of Euclid's *Elements*.

Arithmetic and algebra—handled geometrically by the Greeks—had to wait until the end of the nineteenth century before receiving a set of axioms.

It is the geometrical approach to nature that links the classical heritage to the seventeenth century, during which everything from the gardens of Versailles to the laws of jurisprudence were arranged in simple geometric fashion (*more geometrico*). The continuity of Greek problems and methods of analysis transmitted through the Middle Ages and Renaissance to the beginnings of modern science owes much to Hebrew, Syriac, and Arabic translators and commentators of Plato, Aristotle, Euclid, Archimedes, Ptolemy, Diophantus, Pappus, and other Hellenistic scientists and philosophers. Their works were made available—thanks also to the important invention of the printing press—in Latin, the universal language of science and scholarship, in which all men of science were trained until the end of the last century. Without the medieval and Renaissance translations and commentaries, there could not have existed the cumulative continuity of scientific thought that nurtured—to take some outstanding examples—Leonardo da Vinci's originality and ingenuity, Gilbert's experiments on magnetism, Galileo's mechanics and laws of falling bodies, Descartes' analytic geometry, Leibniz's and Newton's calculus, Harvey's discovery of the circulation of the blood, and the whole naturalistic approach to the human sciences in modern times.

Of course, the overarching authority of the medieval Church and its official versions of Aristotelian science had to be challenged if scientific thought were to have free rein. Fortunately, the Averroists and the antipapal School of Padua (where Galileo did most of his experimental work) were not bound by Church authority. A neoplatonic intellectual pattern of thought, the idea of the Great Chain of Being (with its component ideas of plenitude, gradation, and continuity, analyzed in the masterly work of Arthur O. Lovejoy), sufficed to provide independent thinkers such as Galileo and Newton with the conceptual framework for their scientific researches without recourse to officially approved conceptions of nature.

The essays in Parts 2 and 3 of this volume exhibit in some detail documentary evidence of the continuity between Hellenic thought and the sixteenth and seventeenth-century surge of emancipated scientific genius. Originality and innovation in what Whitehead has called the "Century of Genius" rode high on the cumulative revival of Hellenic objectivity and mathematical clarity in reading the book of nature, written as it was for minds like Galileo, "in the language of Euclid." Descartes dreamed of a universal mathematics and Leibniz of a universal alphabet and symbolic logic which would translate the eternal truths of nature. They joined with Francis Bacon, so far as their ultimate aims go, in a quest for a direct knowledge of the unity of nature through the sciences without subjection to the scholastic method of authority, which had vainly tried to subordinate scientific to theological thought, mechanical or efficient and formal causes to final causes.

Yet even among these great innovators—"new" sciences proliferate in the titles of seventeenth-century treatises, as Lynn Thorndike shows—there are discernible vestiges of medieval and classical assumptions; for example, that scientific laws express eternal and necessary truths, that the cause is necessarily superior to the effect, that matter cannot originate motion. Despite the contrasting emphasis on experience and reason in the strife between the British empiricists (Bacon, Hobbes, Locke, and Berkeley really continue the nominalism of Ockham) and the Continental rationalists (Descartes, Spinoza, Leibniz), the scientific practice of Huygens, Pascal, Galileo, Boyle, and Newton proceeded either to ignore metaphysical issues, which could not be brought to the test of either experiment or calculation, or to consider such questions outside the province of science. Thus we have in the seventeenth century, long before Comte and later positivism, the beginnings of the separation of physical from unverifiable metaphysical principles. However, the shakiness of the line of separation appears when we find Leibniz objecting to Newton's "action at a distance" in the law of gravitation and Newton's refusal to go into the cause of gravitation (*hypotheses non fingo*).

A clear example of the influence of changing conceptions of nature on the direction and method of science may be seen in the seventeenth-century distinction between primary and secondary qualities. The primary qualities were extension, size, shape, weight, and motion. The secondary qualities were color, sounds, tastes, smells, etc., which were not measurable by any methods known to scientist and were relegated by Galileo, Descartes, Locke, and others to the subjective realm of the mind. This climaxed the famous "bifurcation of nature" (along with the elimination of all but mechanical causes or laws of impact) which Whitehead has condemned in his organismic conception of nature.

The historian of ideas, seeking to understand the historical basis for such a bifurcation, finds it partly in the fact that the primary qualities were those known to be susceptible to geometric analysis and measurement, whereas qualities like color, sound, and warmth were only later analyzed with the aid of tuning forks, prisms, thermometers, etc., and were thus treated objectively. On the other hand, Leibniz regarded all qualities as objectively real or inherent in real things (which for him were spiritual monads) because he thought he had a method in his "universal characteristic" for representing all relations. In his theories of the relational nature of space, time, and physical qualities, he anticipates an objective relativism. The long historical controversy between Cartesians and Leibnizians as to the nature of *vis viva* (living force) is resolved today as a terminological confusion between "momentum" and "energy," so that Descartes is credited by Mach, in his *History of Mechanics,* with the formulation of the law of the conservation of momentum (sum of the masses times velocities is constant) and Leibniz with the law of conservation of energy (mv^2) in closed systems.

The revolutions of scientific thought have interrelations not only with philosophy but also with the literary and other arts. Thus the historian of ideas is concerned with the influence of scientific discoveries and method of thinking as they have affected poetry and literary criticism. It would be a mistake, of course, to read the metaphysical poetry of Donne or Milton as mere documents of intellectual history instead of as artistic creations. But historical knowledge of the poets' intellectual background can be illuminating with regard to the undeniable presence of ideas in their esthetic response to the cross-currents in the thought of their times. The controversy over the Copernican astronomy, for example, was as much alive in Milton's day as Einstein's relativity theory recently was when it became front-page news and when a curious public rushed to hear lectures on a subject they were scarcely prepared to comprehend. No doubt, moral and religious ideas, such as man's fall from grace, original sin, free will, and predestination, were more familiar to Milton's public than the technical points of the new astronomy, but the historical fact remains that moral and scientific ideas, religious and cosmological beliefs were jostled together in new, perplexing patterns to which so sensitive and learned a poet as Milton could hardly avoid alluding. How the experimental temper and spirit of research in science encouraged departures from the traditional rules of literary form in the "quarrel of the ancients and moderns" or "battle of the books" reveals the recurrent cultural tensions arising from the clash of older modes of thought with new discoveries and ways of looking at things due to the advance of science.

It is through the perspectives illustrated in the essays of this volume that the historian of ideas attempts to discern both the continuities and discontinuities that characterize the growth of scientific thought in our culture. In the congeries of ideas that constitute the thought pattern of an individual, of a scientific world-view, of a school of thought, or of a cultural epoch, there are "unit ideas" that are analytically distinguished and studied by our contributors with a constant eye to the transformations that such ideas undergo in diverse historical contexts. Such, for example, are the ideas of atomism, laws of nature, unity of science, saving the appearances, evolution, progress, and so forth, each of which has its several component ideas, with distinct histories, intermingled in the minds of minor as well as major figures in the history of thought. The minor figures are as important for their reflections of the dominant thought patterns of a period as the major ones are for their innovations that mark turning points in the history of ideas.

As we have seen from this brief overview of the intellectual historian's approach to scientific thought, his scope is vast, his subject matter is complex, and his methods are varied. The essays in this volume are representative of a number of these methods. Some essays examine an entire epoch of scientific thought. Others deal with individual figures, their contributions, and their influences—not only upon science but upon adjoining intellectual and cultural areas. Still others analyze the technological and social implications of scientific ideas and methods. And some consider science itself as an evolving social institution. Taken together, they represent a continuously growing interest in exploring the interrelationships of various fields of intellectual enterprise. To be successful, such an effort requires the cooperation of the most productive minds from every area of intellectual effort. The results can do much to break down artificial and stultifying boundaries between these areas.

1 THE CLASSICAL HERITAGE

The Classical Heritage

PIERRE DUHEM begins his monumental history of cosmological doctrines from Plato to Copernicus (*Le Système du Monde*) as follows:

"In the genesis of a scientific doctrine there is no absolute beginning; no matter how far back we trace the line of thought that prepared, suggested or asserted the doctrine, we still come across opinions which in their turn have been prepared, suggested or asserted; and the only reason we stop pursuing this linked procession of ideas is not that we ever grasp the first link, but because the chain disappears buried in the depths of a bottomless past.

"All of astronomy in the Middle Ages contributed to the development of the system of Copernicus; through the intermediary of Islamic science, medieval astronomy is linked to Hellenic doctrines; the most perfected Hellenic doctrines known to us derive from the teachings of ancient schools about which we know very little; these schools in their turn had inherited astronomical theories from the Egyptians, Assyrians, Chaldeans, Hindus, and we know almost nothing about their theories; the night of past centuries is quite impenetrable, and we feel even farther removed from the first men who observed the course of the heavenly bodies, noticed their regularity, and tried to formulate the laws it obeys."

What Duhem has remarked here about the origins of astronomy can equally well be said of the roots of all the sciences. Although the history of a science has no absolute beginning, Aristotle, in dealing with the *logic* of science, found it necessary to posit an absolute beginning of a scientific demonstration in premises ultimately based on universal truths known to reason or particular facts intuitively given to sense observation. For example, to prove that a certain field has a certain area, we break it up into right triangles and sum up the areas. The universal premises are derived from pure geometry and the specific facts from observation and measurement. Aristotle's conception of scientific method was an attempted synthesis of the rational with the empirical elements in the scientific thought of his predecessors and contemporaries as well as of his own systematic investigations of nature.

Not unlike Aristotle, the modern scientist has proceeded to adapt his method to the problems at hand. The historian of ideas, concerned with the evolution of scientific method itself, notes that modern science has abandoned the essences, substances, or first principles which generate all phenomena, and is skeptical about absolute premises or self-evident axioms. It prefers to seek constant relations among events whose functional covariation in a given domain can be expressed mathematically without absolute metaphysical assumptions. Nevertheless, the intellectual historian notes also the common persistent feature that characterizes both Hellenic and modern scientific thought—namely, the idea that nature is not the capricious, senseless jumble of events and things that come and go without rhyme or reason, but that there is order (*cosmos*) and intelligibility (*logos*) in the apparent chaos of phenomena, and that this order and intelligibility can be discovered if we order our thoughts and experiences to harmonize with the order of nature.

The ancient Greek philosophers, especially those schooled in mathematics and astronomy, must be credited with having first formulated the idea of constancy, the root of scientific law, and with having recognized the interplay of sense experience and reasoning in the making of generalizations. When the geometrical laws of optics are brought to bear on conflicting appearances, for example, the stick that appears bent in water becomes an intelligible phenomenon rather than a paradoxical one.

Democritus not only noted that sensory experiences are transitory and our descriptions of qualities arbitrary ("Things are sweet or bitter by convention") but also saw that an atomic theory would make possible the application of mathematics to observation. It was Democritus, too, who, in attempting to find the volume of a cone by resolving it into an infinite number of cylindrical elements formed by planes parallel to the base, sowed the seed of the infinitesimal calculus, nourished by Archimedes but not fully grown until the seventeenth century, and given more rigorous analysis only in the late nineteenth century.

Let us consider briefly what the ancient Greeks meant by scientific thought. Not content with popular, mythical views that changes in nature were due to the whims or passions of implacable deities, these philosophers sought underlying principles (*archai*) of an impersonal sort that would unify man's understanding of the world around him: Water (Thales), Air (Anaximander), the Infinite (Anaximenes), Fire (Heraclitus), Being (Parmenides), Number and the Harmony of the Spheres (Pythagoras), the Atoms (Democritus), the Four Elements (Empedocles). When Xenophanes pointed out that if the oxen had gods they would be pictured as oxen, he was cutting deep into the myth-making and anthropomorphic tendencies of the human mind and thereby opening the way to understanding nature in its own impersonal terms. He sublimated Zeus into pure Being. Some of these germinal ideas of the pre-Socratic schools of thought continued to be argued in the Platonic dialogues and in the systematic treatises of Aristotle.

Aristotle, in the fourth century B.C., summed up the logical outcome of the scientific theories of his predecessors in a doctrine of "four causes" which persisted as a framework of explanation for two thousand years or more. These four causes or principles of explanation, known as the material, efficient, formal, and final causes, throw much light on the direction and framework of scientific thought as it developed historically; hence, they are a guide to the interpretation of ancient, medieval, and Renaissance scientific theories even though they have been discarded by modern science.

The material cause consists of the elements that constitute

the thing to be explained or analyzed. For example, the material cause of the Great Egyptian Pyramid is the stone blocks from which it was built. The efficient cause is the group of agents or forces that put the elements together; in our example, the Egyptian slaves that transported, cut, and placed the stones, plus the gravitational forces that keep the stones in place. The formal cause is the plan or relational form that determines the position and function of each element—*e.g.*, the architect's plans or geometrical structure of the building. The final cause is the end result attained by carrying out a purpose—*e.g.*, the Pyramid's use as the tomb of the royal remains.

Keeping these distinctions in mind, we can see why Aristotle, in his critical review of his predecessors' scientific theories, says that those who considered Water, Air, Fire, and Earth—either separately or collectively—the First Substance, provided only the material cause or explanation; the Pythagoreans, who regarded all things as Number, provided only the formal cause; Democritus' motion of atoms was an efficient cause; and Plato's Idea of the Good was a final cause toward which all things moved. We can also understand why Aristotle explained, or thought he was explaining, magnetism by saying that the iron moves to the magnet as a lover to the beloved, union being the final cause of love and of any form of attraction. Objects fall because they are made of the same elements as the earth, and like attracts like; each element seeking its "natural place," water seeks its own level, the winds circulate above the waters, and smoke rises to the highest "natural place" occupied by fire.

Today it is easier to dismiss this sort of teleological explanation by final causes as absurd than to realize that it was the conceptual matrix of the cultured Greeks' scientific attempt at understanding physical forces and properties.

The continuity and differences between Greek and modern views are perceptible in the biological as well as in the physical sciences. How to explain the self-moving, regenerative, and reproductive properties of living things, already thus distinguished from the properties of inanimate matter by the Greeks, was and to a certain extent still is the fundamental problem of theoretical biology. And to explain the goal-directed phenomena of reproduction, regeneration, and growth the Greeks—drawing upon their own familiar experiences of willing and desiring—concluded that each living thing possessed a soul. The soul was the breath of life, the Greeks believed, but just how it animated matter was the perpetual problem of ancient speculation. It is interesting to note that the modern biologist who defines protoplasm as the physical basis of life cannot simply identify life with any one material element but seeks a concept for the goal-directed activities and functions of living systems. Although such a function of living systems is no longer externally imposed on protoplasmic materials by an *ad hoc* "vital principle," both the problem and the quest for an adequate conceptual scheme of organismic behavior were the contribution of the classical heritage.

The idea that the soul is the form of the body stems from the organismic conception of Plato and Aristotle, and persists in modified form through some of its medieval interpretations, to modern evolutionary and genetic theories. The space and time forms of modern physical science, according to one of our contributors, John E. Boodin, "confirm the Platonic intuition of form and measure everywhere. The building bricks of nature—electrons, neutrons, etc.—are measured, are constant in nature, and this fact indicates cosmic control. The discovery by Moseley of atomic number—a series of atomic forms repeated in nature everywhere—is evidence of cosmic architecture which would have delighted the soul of Plato. There is indication of a life-number—a radiating pattern of life-forms. This order even more obviously than atomic number has reference to time."

Similar speculations of evolutionary cosmologists—who are very often unaware of the history of their ideas—are attempts to combine some of Plato's and Aristotle's ideas with nineteenth-century advances in energetics and evolutionary biology. Obviously, such cosmologists must face the logical difficulties of reconciling the preformationistic biology of Aristotle with modern theories of natural selection, as well as the problem of finding concepts common to physical and biological systems. The history of ideas may be useful in reminding us of the blind alleys of premature synthesis as well as of the fruitfulness of cross-fertilization of ideas common to different scientific disciplines.

In the essays that follow, a number of the main characteristics of ancient science and its methods are examined in considerable detail.

Gomperz' "Problems and Methods of Early Greek Science" analyzes precisely the pre-Socratic conceptions of "Nature" and principles of scientific investigation.

McKeon, in "Aristotle's Conception of Scientific Method," indicates the extent to which this great systematizer of the sciences drew upon the Pythagoreans, the Platonists, and the Democritean atomists for the mathematical and logical elements required in the analysis of an empirical science.

Hall's essay on "The Scientific Origins of the Protoplasm Problem" points out the Greek contribution to the persisting, fundamental biological problem of relating the properties of protoplasm to its functions in the life process.

Boodin's "The Discovery of Form" traces the development of the Greek conception of the soul from its origins in Plato and Aristotle to its modern role in contemporary cosmological theory.

An indication of the continued interest in both the sources and the interpretation of ancient Greek science is offered in the closing essay, Edelstein's review entitled "Recent Trends in the Interpretation of Ancient Science."

[The reader should consult Marshall Clagett's *Greek Science in Antiquity* (London, 1957), published while the present volume was in preparation, for the latest, most competent, study of this period.]

~§ *Heinrich Gomperz*

PROBLEMS AND METHODS OF EARLY GREEK SCIENCE

This paper is based on a careful and prolonged re-examination of the entire material available for the study of the earliest phase of Greek scientific thought, *viz.*, the second half of the sixth century B.C.[1] The paper summarizes the *results* of this re-examination while the re-evaluation of the evidence and the re-interpretation of the fragments and doxographic reports must be reserved for separate treatment. It expresses an approach differing in two respects from the one commonly adopted. It will not be interested primarily in the views of individual thinkers, but will aim at a general description and logical analysis of the intellectual procedures characteristic of the age. And it will disregard the boundary line generally assumed to have separated the "philosophy" of ancient thinkers from their other scientific activities. Indeed, for such a separation there is not even an historical justification, since our chief authority, Theophrastus, presented the entire material indiscriminately as "Opinions of Physicists." And so far as this material itself is concerned, "philosophic" pronouncements could, if at all, be distinguished from others only by the criterion of being unusually sweeping and vague.[2] The following account will be based on the fragments of and doxographic reports on Thales, Anaximander, Anaximenes, Xenophanes,[3] Alcmaeon[4]

[1] Evidently, there would have been many advantages if the study could have been extended to cover the first half of the fifth century as well. Personal and local conditions have rendered this impracticable. Much of what will be said, however, applies to this period likewise.

[2] Indeed, in contrast to metaphysicians as well as anti-metaphysicians who agree in the view that the field of philosophy or metaphysics is different from that of science, I have come to the conclusion that it is rather by being vague and sweeping that philosophic or metaphysical differ from scientific propositions. This explains, on the one hand, why philosophy has so often been capable of exercising a real influence on the development of science but, on the other hand, also accounts for the fact that propositions when duly limited and made precise drop out of philosophy and are incorporated with a particular science. Indeed, this is only another way of stating what has so often been said, *viz.*, that philosophy has been the matrix out of which the particular sciences have gradually been developed.

[3] Xenophanes' theological and moral theories have also been analyzed, but, in order to render the material more homogeneous, have been abstracted from in this paper.

and, in part, of the earliest Pythagoreans.[5]   It will fall into three sections dealing, respectively, with the *problems* discussed, the *methods of explanation* used, and the *methods of research* employed.[6]

I. Problems Discussed

The problems discussed may conveniently be assigned to four fields: Cosmogony, Paradoxology, Cosmology, Anthropology.

1. Cosmogony.

How has the world come to be what it is at present?   This had long been a familiar preoccupation.   But it had prompted preceding generations only to describe the origin and pedigree of the gods who were believed to preside over the sundry regions and phenomena of the universe.   This entire mythological scaffolding was now removed almost at one stroke, with a thoroughness that can hardly fail to surprise us: no traditional divinity is ever mentioned, and not even a passing thought is given to the possibility that earthquakes might be caused by the trident of Poseidon, or a storm by the thunderbolt of Zeus.

In its efforts to reconstruct the development of the universe, speculation was guided by certain presuppositions or postulates, some of which, at least, must be styled *a priori,* since they are in no way obviously suggested by experience.   The most basic of these was the assumption that the development must have started with a state of things almost absolutely simple and homogeneous.   "In the beginning" space was filled with one homogeneous mass: either a simple stuff or an all-inclusive mixture.   This, with a term of Aristotle's, may be designated as the *principle* or *beginning.*

[4] Alcmaeon's lectures were probably given and taken down before the end of the sixth century.   But even if this should not have been the case, we should yet be warranted in regarding him as the representative of the medical school of Croton which, as Herodotus informs us (III 131) flourished at the time of Polycrates of Samos, i.e., about 525 B.C.

[5] The reason why the Pythagorean material could be used in part only is that most of it differs too widely in character from the rest to permit a common description.   In contrast to all other thinkers of the age, the Pythagoreans did not keep science clear of mythology, and their specific approach to science by way of number-theory and, in particular, of the holy *tetraktys* could only be described and analyzed in a separate paper.

[6] Quotations, where no other indication is given, will refer to H. Diels, *Die Fragmente der Vorsokratiker, 5.Auflage, her. v. W. Kranz* (Berlin, 1934 ff.).

From this there must have arisen, in some way or other, a plurality of entities, conceived to be the essential constituents of reality as now known to us: entities which we may style the *fundamentals*. These were of two kinds: either what was generated was a set of *qualities*, such as Hot and Cold, Moist and Dry, or else it was a set of substances, such as fire, air, water and earth, or perhaps we ought rather to say, of states of aggregation, *viz.*, fire, gases, liquids and solids. In either case, these fundamentals were definitely of an abstract or *typical* nature: it was felt that what had to be pointed out was the number and kinds of material that had entered into the structure of the universe—in the same way in which a person who wanted to tell us how a house had been built might begin by stating that the materials available for the purpose had been marble, bricks, wood and iron. From these fundamentals the world was then supposed to have grown by a series of steps described differently by different thinkers, but all conforming to the postulate that these developments must be intelligible by being analogous to events familiar to us from common experience.

It is not always easy to distinguish the qualities from the substances. The Hot, e.g., manifestly tends to be confused with fire, and the Moist with water. Nevertheless, the two kinds of fundamentals differ in one important respect. The substances have definite location and are rather inert, whereas the qualities are all-pervading and possess a more dynamic character. The same duality, about a century later, may be traced in Greek medicine: there was a more materialistic view according to which man consists of the four humors: phlegm, blood, bile and black gall; but there was also a more dynamic theory conceiving the human body as a battle-ground on which the Hot strives to dominate the Cold, and the Moist the Dry.

How do the fundamentals emerge from the principle? Here two cases must be distinguished. Sometimes one of the fundamentals was held to be itself the principle (that is to say, "in the beginning" all was water, or air, or fire); in this case, the other fundamentals must have arisen from it by a process such as condensation and rarefaction, or kindling and extinction. But when the principle was different from all the fundamentals and was conceived rather as a sort of mixture, then the fundamentals must have been segregated or "separated out" from it, and for this process of differentiation some form of movement—perhaps in the nature of a vortex—was mostly held responsible.

2. Paradoxology.

By this I mean the study of what the ancients termed the "paradoxes of nature," i.e., of *unusual* and *irregular* phenomena, such as earthquakes, thunderstorms and eclipses. By these—which formerly mythology had tried to account for—the scientifically-minded were evidently very much puzzled, and their concern with them was almost, if not quite, as great and apparently independent of their preoccupation with cosmogony. At any rate, paradoxology ranked second only to cosmogony among the topics of speculation. It is true, of course, that the unusual and irregular cannot be strictly delimited from the usual and the regular. But it is, I think, a highly significant fact that, for instance, the *eclipses* of the moon appear to have called for an explanation much more urgently than its *phases*. The latter everyone took for granted; they determined the rhythm of private and even of public life; it was the former that took people unawares, startling them and challenging their powers of understanding.

3. Cosmology.

One might have expected that the problem: What is the world like right now, what are its structure and its course? would always and everywhere be in the foreground of scientific thought. That was evidently not the case in sixth-century Greece. At that time and in that area the intellectual effort was directed to the past even more than to the present, and to the extraordinary even more than to the ordinary. The problems of cosmology were definitely felt to be less urgent than those of cosmogony and paradoxology.

Nevertheless, they too could not fail to arise. On the one hand, the cosmogonic tale had, so to speak, necessarily to lead up to a "happy end": it was impossible to recite the steps by which the world had come to be what it is without mentioning what it was like at present. If the account of the transformations heaven and earth had undergone was to be satisfactory, something had also to be said about their present shape and arrangement. On the other hand, the explanation of abnormal phenomena presupposed and called for a background of normality: it was impossible to account for thunderstorms without implying how clouds are formed and how winds arise. And even that was not all. In the cosmogonic accounts certain everyday experiences had to be used as patterns which, sooner or later, to a certain extent at least, became interesting in their own right: a physicist could not, in the long run, go on asserting that all air had originally arisen from water by evaporation or, the other way round, that all water had first been formed from air by precipitation, without realizing that evaporation and precipitation were even now going on before his eyes.   Finally, now and then, a thinker made a statement of a very general and very vague character, evidently meant to apply to present as well as to past developments, such as: "What comes to be, must pass away,"[7] or: "Wherefrom a thing has emerged therein it should again be resolved,"[8] and such pronouncements also may, at least in part, be assigned to the field of cosmology.

4. Anthropology.

Some thinkers occasionally touched on the problem how the human race had arisen and what the first man had been like,[9] and many had something to say about the soul, that is, about the entity supposed to leave men in death and to account for their life and their movements as long as they were alive.[10]   But a systematic study of the human body was first undertaken within the guilds of the physicians.[11]   Within this new field speculation on the process of begetting and on embryology corresponded to cosmogony; pathology to paradoxology; and the investigation of the healthy body, i.e., anatomy and physiology, to cosmology.

II. Methods of Explanation

To explain a phenomenon means to show that, even though at first sight it may appear very unfamiliar, yet, on closer scrutiny, it turns out not to be entirely unfamiliar, since it exhibits certain *analogies* with other phenomena, familiar to us from common experience.   And a phenomenon functioning in this way as an explanatory analogy, may be styled a *thought-pattern.*   Thus we may say that the methods of explanation adopted by the earliest Greek scientists consisted almost exclusively in the use of certain definite thought-patterns.

[7] Xenophanes, A 1 (19).

[8] Thales, A 13 (end); Anaximander, B 1.

[9] Anaximander, A 30; Xenophanes, A 33 (6).

[10] Thales, A 22; Anaximander, A 29; Anaximenes, B 2; Xenophanes, A 50.

[11] Actually, with respect to the field of sixth-century anthropology, the scanty remains of Alcmaeon's lectures constitute our only source material.

So far as I can see, the thought-patterns used by them were chiefly four; but the use of two others may also occasionally be traced.

1. The first of these may be termed the *biological* thought-pattern, and might, were there need, be subdivided into the biological proper, the anthropological and the theological. That is to say, phenomena are accounted for by comparing them to processes such as growth and decay, to the results of design and deliberation and to the achievements of superhuman wisdom and power.

2. A second thought-pattern may be styled *political*. The world is understandable in so far as it is analogous to a city. The regularities of nature correspond to the rules that govern civil life.

3. A third thought-pattern might be designated as that of *artistic creativity*. The scientist takes the attitude of an architect about to found a city or to lay out a temple. He feels that certain forms, measures and proportions are called for under the circumstances, and thence he immediately concludes that the facts actually conform to them.

4. Finally, there is the *mechanical* thought-pattern, that is to say, very often a phenomenon is understood by being assimilated to a procedure used in the crafts.[12]

[12] Two further thought-patterns seem occasionally to have been used. The fifth might be called the pattern of a *well-* or an *ill-ordered household*, or, in more scientific language, of *objective teleology* or *dysteleology*. In a well-ordered household things are so disposed and arranged, from time immemorial, as to serve their purpose; should this not be the case, the household would be out of order. Now, we are told (Anaximander, A 14; comp. Anaximenes, B 3) that the material available for the building of new worlds must be boundless *lest it ever fail;* but we are also told (Xenophanes, A 41a) that the sun sometimes drifts into uninhabited regions where it can do no good and that even according to the ordinary course of things (Xenophanes, A 42) while the sun is useful, the moon is not but just "runs along." The sixth thought-pattern I should term that of *pure factuality*. It is not correct that causality is a universal category of thought. Man is interested in causes only in so far as their knowledge may serve him to bring about the repetition of a desirable or to avoid that of an undesirable experience. But when he feels the occurrence of a phenomenon to be out of his reach he gives little thought to its causes. Of all the persons who state that "this is a nice morning" not one in ten thousand raises the question *why* this is the case, and the same is true with regard to the fact that a breeze is blowing from the North or that the waves of the sea are running high. In all such instances we are completely satisfied to realize that a certain state of things *just happens to be the case.* Now, it appears that the early scientists accounted for at least one type of assumed facts by assimilating them to such as "just happen to

Now, a closer study of the use made of these different thought-patterns has revealed a surprising fact which does not appear to have been given hitherto due consideration. The part played by the different thought-patterns in the investigation of different fields is not at all the same. In cosmogony the biological pattern is used without any reserve: the universe is a living being; it realizes certain schemes; it is hailed as divine. In cosmology the political and the artistic pattern seem to dominate. The kosmos is like a city; it is surrounded by the celestial vault as the city is surrounded by its walls; the order of nature is based on an equilibrium of rights and obligations (day, e.g., has a right to last a certain time, and night a corresponding time),[13] and should this order ever be violated, such violation would have to be avenged.[14] On the other hand, it is assumed to be a fact that the shape of the earth is that of a drum three times as broad as it is high and that the distances of the stars, of the moon and of the sun from the center of the earth are in the ratio of $1:2:3$—not because any measurements have been made to this effect but because it is *fitting* that such should be the case.

But when we come to the field of paradoxology or, to use a still more general expression, when the problem is how to explain any concrete phenomenon whatsoever, all this appears to be forgotten and the mechanistic thought-pattern seems to hold exclusive sway. Generally speaking, the world is divine, just and beautiful; but in the concrete it is all a matter of tossing waves, clouds torn asunder, clods hitting the ground, vapors catching fire. It is well known that this kind of inconsistency (if such it be) was bitterly charged by Plato and Aristotle against Anaxagoras; what is generally not realized is that their attack might, with almost the same degree (or

---

take place": these assumed facts were the first movements or changes (in the nature, e.g., of condensation and rarefaction) supposed to have brought about the development of the fundamentals from the principle. In other words, the original state of things, as it existed "in the beginning," comprised change and motion—in the same sense in which the air and the sea are changing and moving. The significance of this insight consists in this, that it enables us to discard as illegitimate the concept of *hylozoism.* "When a thing x was held to move without being moved by another thing y, it must have been considered to move itself and hence to be a living thing." That is not a valid inference. The Greek scientists no longer believed that winds were moved by gods but neither did they hold them to be living beings.

[13] Heraclitus, B 94.
[14] *Ibid.,* and Anaximander, B 1.

the same lack) of justification, have been directed against any one of his predecessors.[15]

We ought not, however, to speak of the mechanistic thought-pattern indiscriminately, we ought rather to distinguish between the mechanics of solids, of liquids and of gases. The latter were

[15] In order to impress this important fact upon the reader with due emphasis it may be worth while to survey rapidly the chief pre-Anaxagorean thinkers and to show how they all, in some form or another, bear witness to the same antinomy. According to Thales (A 22) "all is full of gods," but (A 15) earthquakes are accounted for by the waves of the waters on which the earth is afloat. According to Anaximander we should suppose that the kosmos is steered by the Unaging and Immortal (B 2) and, at any rate, that what happens must conform to the standards of justice and morality (B 1); but when it comes to the explanation of eclipses (A 11, 4), thunderstorms (A 23) and earthquakes (A 28), it is all a matter of openings obstructed by dirt, of compressed air exploding and rending clouds asunder and of the impact of air-currents that penetrate beneath the surface of the earth and shake it. By Anaximenes the divine nature of the universe may have been somewhat less emphasized (A 7, 1; A 10), but the thoroughly mechanistic character of his explanations is beyond doubt. The case of Heraclitus is particularly instructive: the universe is God and it is steered by wisdom (B 67; B 32; B 41; B 108); but, as far as the phenomena of paradoxology were concerned, Theophrastus informs us that Heraclitus "accounted for almost everything by means of the exhalation arising from the sea" (A 1, 9)—which, however, was not the only one he assumed, since he held that there were exhalations from land as well as from the sea and that in both cases they might be either bright or dark. Similarly, Xenophanes was most emphatic in proclaiming the divine character of the universe, or at least of the heavens: God is all eye, all ear and all thought. But, as is plain from the doxography, the idea never occurred to him that this principle of divine foresight might be used for the purpose of accounting for any details in the natural course of events: this course is determined on the one hand by the law that land and sea are alternately mixed up with and again separated from each other and on the other hand by the fact that from the sea there arise vapors soon transformed into clouds which in part are re-transformed into water, while others catch fire and, being borne along by air-currents, produce the illusion of luminaries moving in permanent orbits. In Parmenides the duality of apparently incompatible points of view has always been felt to be most striking. In "truth" all things are one; there is no change; nothing moves. But according to "appearance" the world has come to be by the interaction of two elements, light and night (B VIII 53 ff) and it is on the prevalence of these that even now the differences of youth and old age (A 46 a), of waking and sleeping (A 46 b) and even of superior and inferior intelligence (B 16) depend. We cannot trace such a duality in Melissos, but if our doxography is reliable, even Zeno after having demonstrated (or before demonstrating) the impossibility of any multiplicity did not disdain to indicate how the universe had been built up out of a plurality of elements (A 1 29). And so we have come down to poor Anaxagoras who was so severely taken to task for an inconsistency which certainly was not specifically his own.

the universal favorite. The boiling of water and the burning of
incense provided the most widely used patterns. Steam and smoke,
vapors and exhalations were felt to be the panaceas for human
ignorance: being for the most part invisible and intangible they
were excellently qualified to play the rôle which later fell to *forces*
and *energies* and which Descartes, for instance, assigned to the
vital spirits.

The most significant scientific issue of the age (and of the ages
to come) concerned the heavenly bodies (whose divine nature was,
in most cases, ignored though not denied). Should their interpretation be based on the mechanics of gases or of solids? One party[16]
held that the world was uniform with regard to stuff and to law;
thence they concluded that the heavens were but part of the atmosphere and their study an extension of meteorology: the celestial
luminaries were burning vapors or clouds. The other party[17] felt
that "the world above the moon" differed essentially from that
beneath her: it was built out of another stuff and on a different
plan; it formed the subject-matter of another science, and the regularity of its revolutions had to be accounted for by mechanical
devices such as wheels and revolving spheres.

And this discussion led up to a further dilemma. If the
heavenly bodies were solids, they were likely to be persistent: today's sun, e.g., would be conceived as identical with yesterday's,
and its orbit would have to be worked out in such a manner as to
account for its daily return from West to East. But if the sun is
but a burning cloud, this intricate and puzzling problem might be
dispensed with altogether, or rather, it would reveal itself as a
pseudo-problem: the sun may then be conceived as being formed
anew each day and instead of assuming a persistent *object* "sun"
it will suffice to posit a meteorological *law* of daily sun-formation.[18]

III. METHODS OF RESEARCH

In a general way, the following statements may, I think, be
made with reasonable assurance. "As might have been expected
in an age whose central problem was cosmogony, i.e., a set of unobservable and unrepeatable phenomena, and which, moreover,

---

[16] Anaximenes, Xenophanes, and later Atomists and Epicureans.

[17] Anaximander, the Pythagoreans and later Plato and Aristotle.

[18] This was the view of Xenophanes, whom Alcmaeon and Heraclitus followed
only in part.

lacked all magnifying devices, the need for increased factual knowledge and for testing assumptions by experience was hardly felt. The facts to be explained were supposed to be matters of common knowledge, and any endeavor to account for them was essentially like the effort to solve a riddle. A scientific hypothesis was a (more or less fortunate) guess and the only criterion of its validity was its intrinsic plausibility. No one, however, could feel quite sure of having guessed aright and hence dogmatic pronouncements were sometimes quaintly introduced by professions of universal agnosticism.''

As soon as we try to be more specific than this, we have to grapple with a very serious difficulty: were two thoughts linked together by an ancient scientist or by a late doxographer? Even with regard to such questions there will be probabilities, but the degrees of these probabilities will be deplorably small.

As a rule it seems that views were stated in a dogmatic fashion. Sometimes such views were in agreement with tradition or with opinions expressed by predecessors. But often there was evidently deliberate disagreement with "what others have held."[19] However, within the domain of science (as distinguished from theology and politics) the grounds for such disagreement were hardly ever stated in so many words. Sometimes the reason why a scientist differed from his predecessor may be inferred from the views by which he replaced the latter's theories;[20] but that is the exception rather than the rule.

The theories themselves do not lack complexity. Very often, several theories are interdependent and express a connected view. And even one and the same theory may sometimes be of considerable complexity. A theory, e.g., concerning the causes of earthquakes is organized in the following way:[21] "All quakes are directly caused by clods breaking away from the mass of the earth. This process of breaking away may itself be due to four or five different causes" (three of which a predecessor had apparently already pointed out). "The breaking away of the clods produces quakes in two different ways. In the first place, while the clods break

[19] Anaximenes, A 7 (6).

[20] Anaximenes' theory of quakes compared with that of Anaximander, according to Seneca, *Nat. Quaest.*, VI 10.

[21] Same passage, for which there are very specific reasons not to hold Seneca responsible.

away, the masses from which they break away are shaken by an effect of recoil. Secondly, when the clods reach the ground, they either hit a solid surface or fall into stagnant waters: in the former case they cause repeated shocks like a ball falling to the ground; in the latter they produce a flood like a stone thrown into a pool.'' In this case as also in a few others *analogies* are adduced with the evident intent of carrying *conviction,* but in more numerous instances the function of analogy is simply to illustrate an alleged state of affairs (e.g., ''the stars move round the earth as the hat moves round the head'').[22]

Arguments are sometimes of a purely tautological character, for instance: ''Clouds, rains, springs, streams all stem from the sea. For if the sea were not, all these would not exist. But actually, the sea does produce them.''[23]   But in the great majority of cases arguments are based on general contentions implied and—if one may say so—dogmatically presupposed, though mostly not explicitly stated. These general contentions are of two kinds: they are either mere *postulates* or *assumptions,* more or less independent of experience; or else they are rather statements of *general facts* based on a more or less sweeping and superficial induction and thus coming close to what we should term *laws of nature.*

The *postulates* again cover statements of various types. Some amount to moral demands and judgments of value. ''Violations of the order of things must in justice be avenged.''[24] ''The material for the building of new worlds must never fail.''[25] ''Whence a thing has arisen, thither must it return.''[26] Some of these postulates that we feel tempted to style purely metaphysical express what we might term exigencies of thought, e.g., ''Qualities persist even when 'dominated' by their opposites and hence not traceable in experience'';[27] ''Where there is apparent change, there must be an unchanging substrate.''[28] Very often a postulate expresses

[22] Anaximenes, A 7 (6). Here is a list of demonstrative and another of merely illustrative analogies. *Illustrative:* Thales, A 14, A 15; Anaximander, A 10, A 11, A 21; Anaximenes, A 7 (6); A 12, A 14, A 15, A 19, A 20. *Demonstrative:* Anaximenes, A 17, A 20 (?); B 2; Seneca, *N. Q.,* VI 10; Alcmaeon, A·5 (25), A 12; Anon. Pyth., B 40 (?).

[23] Xenophanes, B 30.

[24] Anaximander, B 1; Heraclitus, B 28, B 94.

[25] Anaximander, A 14; Anaximenes, B 3.

[26] Thales, A 13; Anaximander, B 1.

[27] Alcmaeon, B 4.

simply a characteristic feature of a scientist's theory which to him appears to be self-evident and not to need any proof, e.g.: "The earth is a flat object";[29] "The earth is freely suspended in the center of the universe";[30] "The distances of the heavenly bodies from the earth correspond to the proportions underlying the musical intervals";[31] "There must have been a first man."[32]   Finally, an hypothesis that affords a possible and convenient explanation of a fact is often dogmatically asserted as true, no thought being given to empirical verification even where this, or rather the falsification of one, would be easy or, at any rate not impossible.   As illustrations, consider the following statements: "Since in death the blood completely recedes from the veins, it must incompletely recede during sleep"[33] (and no one is struck by the fact that a person asleep is neither less warm nor less rosy than one awake).   The female mule is barren because her womb is not sufficiently open to admit the sperm; but the male mule is barren likewise, his sperm being too cold and too light"[34] (and we may be sure the female mule was not dissected nor was any effort made to weigh the sperm of the male or to determine its temperature).   "The child follows the sex of that parent who has contributed 'more' during the act of generation."[35]

Laws of nature, again, exhibit extremely varying degrees of generality, and range from such as are almost true through those that are half-true (or at least contain an element of truth) to the entirely fantastic.   The following list may give an idea of them. "What comes to be, must pass away."[36]   "All things age."[37]   "A thing x does not move another thing y unless x have a soul."[38] "A thing x which is at rest does not move unless it be overpowered by another thing y."   (This, incidentally, is a crude way of empha-

[28] This point of view, definitely over-emphasized by Aristotle, nevertheless doubtless underlies passages like Anaximenes, A 7 and Heraclitus, B 30–31.

[29] Anaximenes, A 20.

[30] Anaximander, A 26.

[31] The fundamental assumption of Pythagorean cosmology.

[32] Anaximander, A 30.

[33] Alcmaeon, A 18.

[34] Alcmaeon, B 3.

[35] Alcmaeon, A 14.

[36] Xenophanes, A 1 (19).

[37] Anaximenes according to Seneca, *N. Q.,* VI 10.

[38] Thales, A 22.

sizing one aspect of the principle of inertia.)   "If a thing x be surrounded by several other things y, z, u . . . , it can be overpowered and moved by that one only to which it is closest in space."[39]   "As a consequence of continuous evaporation the sea must gradually disappear."[40]   "Where there is a break, there is a recoil."[41]   "The factors responsible for the characteristic weather of the different seasons must be such as are capable of causing heat and cold," and hence the stars cannot be such factors.[42]   "Flat objects remain afloat" (on air as on water).[43] "Clouds moved in certain ways begin to glisten."[44]   "It is things hollow that sound."[45]   "Sounds are produced by moving bodies and their pitch is in proportion to the velocity of these bodies." But "a sound may be heard only against a background of silence."[46]

Perhaps the most characteristic feature of sixth-century science, however, is its attitude toward factual verification.   That it tells in favor of an hypothesis or assumption if facts in agreement with it may be pointed out was not at all overlooked.   On the contrary, in a considerable number of instances it is possible to show that facts on which a theory had plainly not been built to begin with were subsequently introduced as supporting or corroborating it, in a spirit that might adequately have been expressed by words such as *"And indeed* it is the case that . . . ."   But two things, it would seem, were never realized.   First, that it makes a great difference whether a corroborating fact is a *real* fact or whether it is itself only *an assumed* and hypothetical fact—indeed perhaps no less hypothetical than the hypothesis it is supposed to corroborate. In the second place, it was completely overlooked that facts may bear out a theory *to a greater or lesser extent.*   A theory was felt to be an indivisible whole and was supposed to be corroborated *in its entirety* by any (real or assumed) fact in agreement with any assumption or belief forming part of the theory.   This important point may perhaps best be illustrated by one particular instance which, moreover, is also of special interest because—quite excep-

---

[39] Anaximander, A 26; Parmenides, A 44.

[40] Anaximander, A 27.

[41] See note 37.

[42] Anaximenes, A 14 end.

[43] Anaximenes, A 20.

[44] Xenophanes, A 39 and 45.

[45] Alcmaeon, A 5 (25).

[46] Anonymous Pythagoreans, B 35.

tionally!—the corroborating facts were not matters of common knowledge, but had been discovered by the scientist himself by means of specific observations and investigations. Xenophanes had figured out a theory according to which sea and land will gradually be mixed up with each other until a state of universal "muddification" is reached, incompatible with the survival of mankind. Then, sea and land will little by little be separated again, the mud will be dried up and a new race will be formed. And such alternating periods will succeed one another again and again, indefinitely. Now, *in support of this theory*,[47] Xenophanes adduced two series of observations. First, shells are found in mid-land and even on hill-tops. Secondly, in certain places (Malta, Syracuse, Paros) the rock exhibits imprints of fossils that could only have originated at a time when the rock was mud and must have been hardened as the mud was dried up. Xenophanes did *not* see that these facts do not bear out either his assumption that "muddification" took place everywhere at the same time or his contention that a new period of "muddification" is impending, but that the facts quoted by him would in themselves tell rather in favor of the view of one of his predecessors, according to which the cosmic process is one of progressive desiccation, ending with the total disappearance of the sea.[48] This was because he compared *his theory as a whole* with the evidence and held the latter to corroborate the former since it was in agreement with *one element* of his hypothesis.

In other instances we are less completely informed, but the methodological situation was probably much the same. I subjoin a list (characterizing such "corroborating" facts as are purely hypothetical by a question-mark.)[49]

"The earth floats on the sea. Quakes take place when it is rocked by the waves. *And indeed,* when there is a quake, new springs appear in most cases, comparable to the water that leaks into a boat rocked by the waves."[50] "The regularity of the celestial movements is due to the fact that the orbits are in truth wheels of opaque vapor containing fire. This fire is visible through circular openings in the wheels and it is these openings that we

[47] "Saying he disposed of the following proofs," Xenophanes, A 33 (5–6).

[48] Anaximander, A 27.

[49] It must be understood that the arguments referred to in the following list are *reconstructions* and are not, *as such,* to be found in the evidence.

[50] Thales according to Seneca, *N. Qu.,* VI 6.

designate as sun, moon and stars. *And indeed,* it is when these
openings are obstructed (?) that the so-called eclipses ensue."[51]
"Earthquakes are due—directly or indirectly—to cracks in the
earth's surface caused either by desiccation or by heavy rains.
And indeed, quakes mostly occur in times either of drought or of
floods."[52] "Heat is the effect of expansion, cold of compression.
And indeed, the breath is cool when compressed by the lips but
warm when allowed to expand."[53] "When the winds tear a cloud
asunder, a flash of lightning is seen. *And indeed,* a flash of white
light is also seen when the water is split by the oars."[54] "The
brain is the general organ of sensation. The sensations are conveyed from the particular sense-organs to the brain by certain
channels. *And indeed,* the senses fail a person who suffers a con-
cussion of the brain because in such a case the brain is displaced
(?) and thereby those channels are interrupted(?)."[55] "We could
not see if there were no fire in the eye. *And indeed,* this fire is seen
when the eye is hit."[56] "Disembodied souls live on mere odors.
And indeed, even some animals (bees) support themselves in this
same way."[57]

Of the five thinkers on whose theories our discussion has mainly
been based the two latest introduced their expositions by a sort of
skeptical proviso. "The precise nature of the gods and of all the
things I am discussing no man has ever beheld nor will there ever
be such a one as beholds it . . . (mere) opinion is spread out over
them all. . . . But in so far as they have revealed themselves to
human vision . . . let us take these opinions as (at least) resembling the truth."[58] "With regard to things mortal the gods attain
to precision, but as far as men may judge by indications. . . ."[59]
And in the following century this chorus was joined by at least two
more voices: "The whole (truth) may not be beheld by men nor
learned about or grasped by their minds and even thou mayst learn

[51] Anaximander, A 11 (4).
[52] Anaximander, A 28.
[53] Anaximenes, B 1.
[54] Anaximenes, A 17.
[55] Alcmaeon, A 5 (26 end).
[56] Alcmaeon, *ibid.* (beginning).
[57] Anonymous Pythagoreans, B 43, taken with Heraclitus, B 98.
[58] Xenophanes, B 34, 36, 35.
[59] Alcmaeon, B 1.

. . . not more than what mortal thinking power reaches up to.''[60] ''True knowledge of reality is not available, but I define it as best I can.''[61] We have good reasons for assuming first, that these skeptical introductions did not weaken or otherwise modify the dogmatic tenor of the subsequent expositions, and furthermore, that they were meant to cast a shade of doubt on particular explanations rather than on general principles, postulates and assumptions.[62] Indeed, we must realize the paradoxality—not to say the enormity—of the undertaking of making pronouncements and even writing books on those regions and domains of nature which were supposed to be, once for all, excluded from human experience or, as one of those authors put it himself, ''on the non-apparent.''[63] If they felt that, here, they were on slippery ground, their feeling was only too justified. And yet it is difficult to believe that the curious unison of four (more or less) independent voices should be due exclusively to the operation of a scientific conscience that made itself felt in four introductions, only to be forgotten or neglected in the works themselves. Perhaps there was an extrinsic motive contributing to the result. To concern oneself with things ''high up and beneath the earth'' was not in good repute. It was the province of diviners, astrologers[64] and treasure-hunters. It is not at all improbable that the earliest scientists found it to be in their interest to draw a line of demarcation between all such people and themselves: ''They may pretend to have certainty concerning these hidden things; we simply communicate our ideas.''[65]

[60] Empedocles, B 2.

[61] Ecphantus, no. 1.

[62] Xenophanes, in particular, certainly exempted theology from the sphere of possible doubt, since here he started from what a god *had* to be in order to be a god. In this I entirely agree with Mr. Deichgraeber, *Rheinisches Museum* (1938), 30.

[63] The title Alcmaeon, B 1, gives as that of his lectures.

[64] Astrologers in the modern sense: Heraclitus, B 105.

[65] But it must also be noted that all the four skeptical utterances come from Lower Italy and Sicily (Elea, Kroton, Akragas, Syracuse). Possibly the motive indicated, or some other motive, operated in those parts with more than its usual force. The region was a hot-bed of religious sects and mysteries. Perhaps a prosecution for impiety might have been more likely and at the same time more dangerous there than elsewhere.

෫ৡ *Thomas S. Hall*

SCIENTIFIC ORIGINS OF THE PROTOPLASM PROBLEM

(Based upon a re-examination of the relations between the concept of life and the doctrine of matter in pre-Socratic Greek science.)*

In 1835, the French microanatomist, Dujardin, performed an experiment which was to have far-reaching consequences for the future of biology.[1] The experiment itself was not a difficult one. It involved crushing the outer envelope of a single-celled animal, with miscroscopic observation of the result. But Dujardin's description of what he saw raised fundamental problems which are still among the central concerns of general physiologists. What Dujardin observed was a colorless, translucent, sticky fluid which oozed out through the breaks in the cellular membrane, forming a kind of foam as it came. Other investigators soon described similar substances in all plants and animals. Gradually the idea arose that the vital properties of every living thing depend directly upon the presence in its cells of fluid substances such as Dujardin had described. The fluids in question were temporarily regarded as identical in their essential aspects for all cells in all organisms[2] and were collectively designated as "protoplasm"[3]—"the physical basis of life."[4]

* Abbreviations used in footnotes: *Diels:* Diels, H., *Die Fragmente der Vorsokratiker,* 5. Aufl. (Berlin, 1934); *Dox:* Diels, H., *Doxographi graeci etc.,* Ed. it. (Berlin and Leipzig, 1929); *L. and S.:* Liddell, H. G. and Scott, R., *A Greek-English Lexikon* (Oxford, 1940); for other authors and titles, the abbreviations appearing in L. and S.

[1] Dujardin, F. *Sur les prétendus estomacs des animales infusoires et sur une substance appelée sarcode,* Ann. des Sci. Nat.: Zool., 2 sér., 4 (1835), 343.

[2] The concept of the universal identity of protoplasm was due especially to Cohn, F. (Nova Acta Acad. Caes. Leop. Carol. Nat. Cur., vol. 22 [Bonn, 1850]), 805; the pertinent fragment is translated in Sharp, L. W., *An Introduction to Cytology* (New York, 1926), 15.

[3] The term makes its appearance somewhat later, being used in a slightly different sense by J. E. Purkinje (*Ueber Analogien in den Strukturelementen des pflanzlichentierischen Organismus,* Verhandl. d. Schlesischen Ges. f. Vaterländ. Kult. [1840], 81); Dujardin, in reporting his experiment, uses the term sarcode.

[4] This expression is probably very old; its wide use was especially stimulated by T. H. Huxley's essay on this subject, *The physical basis of life* (Edinburgh, 1868).

39

When we seek antecedents for this highly generalized notion of a fundamental life substance, an interesting fact presents itself. The protoplasm concept which grew up during the nineteenth century was, except in its detailed formulation, not new. On the contrary, again and again in the history of biology we encounter the proposition that for an object to manifest life a special material composition is indispensable. At times this notion operates only vaguely and implicitly. At other times it becomes explicit and outspoken, and at such times biologists are found actively engaged in an effort to define the character of the requisite substrate. The protoplasm concept which was developed in the nineteenth century was one such effort, but only one of a series.

Our present concern is with protoplasm in its broadest sense. The term will here be used to designate all special substances ever postulated as indispensable to the manifestation of life. The scientific effort to describe these substances we shall call the protoplasm problem. Our particular object will be to trace the origins of the protoplasm problem in early Greek science, and this will necessitate a re-examination of certain familiar aspects of Greek thought, although from a special point-of-view. The nature of this inquiry can be readily understood if we first return briefly to recent developments, particularly those of the past few decades.

For biologists of half a century ago, the proposition "life is localized in the fluid contents of the cells" would, as we have seen, have possessed both meaning and apparent correspondence to fact. At the present time, this proposition is no longer entirely acceptable. This is true for several reasons. For one thing, attention has recently turned more and more upon certain *non-fluid,* thread-like structures which make their appearance in many cells at the time of cell-division. These threads, the "chromosomes," possess the very remarkable faculty of self-duplication.[5] They—or something attached to them—exert powerful chemical influences over the surrounding "protoplasmic fluid"—are, in fact, largely responsible for its essential characteristics. Conversely, the chromosomes are sensitive to changes in the fluids which bathe them, even when these changes originate from causes outside the cell. In short, the chromosomes (and probably other non-fluid entities within the

[5] This centrally important fact attracted the attention of W. Pfitzner and is discussed in his *Beiträge zur Lehre vom des Zellkerns und seinen Teilungserscheinungen,* Arch. f. Mikroskop. Anat., 22 (1883), 616.

cell[6]) now appear as among the very *livest* features of the living organism. Hence, while we may still define protoplasm as living matter or as the physical basis of life if we wish (definitions being arbitrary) we can no longer acceptably describe it as fluid.

This recent revision in our views on this problem is but one of many which have occurred during the same period. But it will serve to illustrate how, for any period, the solution of the protoplasm problem will be highly sensitive to the interpretations of matter prevailing at that time. It suggests, consequently, the necessity for our present purpose of reviewing from a special angle certain aspects of the doctrine of matter which developed in the science of pre-Socratic Greece.

The Concept of Life

First, however, we shall need to reassure ourselves as to the extent to which the question concerning a material substrate for life could even have existed for those thinkers in the sense that it does for us. This depends, to begin with, upon the respective interpretations of life conventional for them and for us. In modern thought *life* has a variety of connotations, of which we must here keep in mind at least three. First of all, life is often thought of as something which *actually exists:* a differentiation of the real world, usually non-material, which makes itself known to us by the behavior of certain material beings (organisms) in relation to which it stands as a cause. It was this idea of life which Lamarck embraced in his quarrel with Richerand: "Life, said Mr. Richerand, is a collection of phenomena which succeed one another for a limited period in organized bodies. He should have said life is a phenomenon which gives rise to a collection of other phenomena, etc.; for it is not these other phenomena which constitute life, but they are themselves caused by life.'"[7]

Richerand's view represents, in fact, the second of those which possess wide currency in modern biology. By this view, *life* becomes an abstraction referring to an ensemble of habitual actions peculiar to a certain category of things—things in which these actions occur as a consequence of their particular material constitution. In Greek times, these actions would have included breathing, growing, moving about, self-duplication. Today, for

[6] This subject has been reviewed in Sections II and III of Hoeber, R., *Physical Chemistry of Cells and Tissues* (Philadelphia, 1945).

[7] In *Philosophie zoologique*, etc., Pt. II, Chap. II (Paris, 1809).

the scholar at least, they would be extended to include metabolic acts (synthesis and hydrolysis, phosphorylation, and the like) whose existence was previously unknown.   This second interpretation of life was current, as we shall see, in the thought of the later pre-Socratic scientists, but it was to await the early 20th century writings of Lloyd Morgan to obtain its most explicit exposition.[8]   The two clearly opposed concepts of life which we have just developed can be conveniently distinguished by the terms *imposed* and *emergent,* the latter term being the one which Morgan popularized.

In addition to these concepts of life as either emergent or imposed, a third idea has acquired considerable currency.   This view, which is strictly a special case of the emergentist idea, proposes that if all organisms are such by virtue of a common substrate, then life should be conceived of as the immediate activities in which this substrate is involved.   One of the most explicit elaborations of this philosophy was made by the nineteenth-century teacher and physiologist, Max Verworn, for whom life comprised the activities of certain hypothetical protein particles which he called biogens.[9]

The degree of parallelism between these modern concepts and those entertained in Greece may be partially approached by a consideration of the Greek words for *life* with special reference to their different uses.   Three of these in particular ($\beta\iota\sigma$, $\psi\upsilon\chi\dot\eta$, and $\zeta\omega\dot\eta$) appear to deserve our attention.   A study of the content of these words reveals a number of striking facts.   To begin with, $\beta\iota\sigma$ was neither plant life nor animal life nor, in fact, anything we are seeking here.[10]   The term appears rather to have referred to: *mode of life* (e.g. a happy life, or the life of a king); or a *living* (the sort one earns—a livelihood); or even a written life (biography).   It would appear, therefore, that the science of biology has been misnamed.[11]   Of the three terms, $\zeta\omega\dot\eta$ undoubtedly most closely corresponds to our abstraction for an ensemble of habitual acts, and the history of this word supplies us with some pertinent information. In Homer, this root does not appear as substantive, but only as par-

[8] In *Emergent evolution* (London, 1923).

[9] See his *Die Biogenhypothese* (Jena, 1903).

[10] We follow here Liddell and Scott; but their view perhaps requires further study.   Thus Heraclitus' famous pun ($\tau\sigma\hat\upsilon$ $\beta\iota\sigma\upsilon$ $\sigma\check\upsilon\nu\sigma\mu\alpha$ $\beta\iota\sigma$ $\check\epsilon\rho\gamma\sigma\nu$ $\delta\epsilon$ $\theta\dot\alpha\nu\alpha\tau\sigma$) posits a life conceived as opposite to death; and for Empedocles air was $\phi\epsilon\rho\acute\epsilon\sigma\beta\iota\sigma$, or "life-bringing."

[11] By Lamarck (see Singer, C., *The story of living things* [New York and London, 1931], 294).

ticiple and verb.   As a substantive it is first encountered in the seventh century.[12]   It is in fact improbable that any word for the whole genus of animals was current until around 550 B. C., and ζωή for *life* came into use only gradually.[13]   In the meantime, therefore, ψυχή carries the load; ψυχή was the life which the Homeric heroes risked,[14] saved, [15] and poured forth with their blood upon the battle field.   For both Hesiod[16] and Homer,[17] this life was the one common to men and animals, and it remained such after the rise of objective science.[18]

The significant point about the use of ψυχή as expressive of life is the rich content of this word when observed in the full variety of its uses.   The common denominator for most of these meanings is something like *consciousness,* motive or perceptive, or both, and to represent this in English, ψυχή is ordinarily translated as *soul.*

The meanings of ψυχή were so numerous as to exhaust, apparently, the full range of possibilities.   Since the protoplasm problem partly resolves itself into a search for the substrate for "soul," some of these meanings are useful to us here.   Souls were either individual (i.e., related to separate entities) or general (pervading or surrounding things in general); and they were either motive, or perceptive, or both.[19]   According to the classical anthropological theory advanced in the nineteenth century by Tylor,[20] primitive men *imputed* souls to animals, to inanimate objects, to nature in general. Tylor supposed that primitive men did this by a positive act of inference; i.e., they decided that things had souls.   For this view, Crawley later substituted a now more widely received hypothesis, more psychological in character, according to which early peoples envisaged souls everywhere because of their failure to make adequate distinctions between objects in general and persons in general.[21]   Crawley's adherents like to point to a similar failure on the part of young children in contemporary society.   We can at least be sure that, by the time the Greek scientists were endeavoring to think objectively about biology, distinctions were drawn between what we now call living and lifeless beings.   This is indicated by the verbal use of ζῶ from Homer onwards.   We may put it forth as an

[12] *E.g.,* Tyrt. 15. 5.   [13] See the uses of the word in L. and S.
[14] *Od.* 9. 255.   [15] *Od.* 9. 423.   [16] *Sc.* 173.   [17] *Od.* 14. 426.
[18] Diels: Anax. B 10.   [19] Arist. *De An.* 404 b.
[20] Tylor, E. P., *Primitive culture: Researches into the development of mythology,* etc., 7th ed. (New York, 1907).
[21] Crawley, A. E., *The idea of the soul* (London, 1909).

hypothesis, however, that the further distinction, that namely between life-as-soul and life-as-action, was only gradually grasped with sufficient clarity to evoke the need for a new substantive to express the latter of these two ideas. Ζωή appears to have supplied this need.

The Doctrine of Matter

The curiosity of natural philosophers repeatedly reverts to two particular aspects of real existences: namely, their *non-homogeneity in space* (their *mixedness*) and their *non-homogeneity in time* (their transformations). Historically, the doctrine of matter may be regarded as the outcome of a constantly renewed effort to comprehend these two phenomena more correctly. Toward this goal, progress has been made, but not always directly. The advance of the investigation is perhaps comparable to that of an ameba which, by numerous extensions of its substance (most of which must be subsequently withdrawn), gradually moves on.

Now the transformations observable in the course of daily experience seem to be of two varieties. In one variety—such, for example, as the transformation of a placid pool into a disturbed one—certain appearances (in this case, fluidity and transparency) are retained. In the other—as of a liquid pool into a frozen one—these appearances are not retained. But it was to become the doctrine of both the Greek and the modern schools that the distinction between these two types of transformation is, in part at least, only apparent, since both, correctly understood, are motion. Both, that is, are mere rearrangements in space. The "real" difference is that the latter sort of change involves the rejuxtaposition of entities too small to see. Aristotle observed that objective science commenced with the recognition that behind appearance lies reality (namely, that which moves) and with the desire to know what that is. Heraclitus observed that nature "loves to hide" and that eyes and ears "are bad witnesses for minds lacking understanding."[22]

For our present inquiry, the most important feature of such speculation is its postulation of "real" entities, often of subvisible magnitude, since it should prove to be something about these entities which in certain instances permits the manifestation of vital activity. For the professional inquirer, the question was bound to arise how many kinds of such entities there are. How many varieties of substrate are required in order to produce, by appropriate

[22] Fairbanks, A., *The first philosophers of Greece*, Fr. 10 (London, 1898).

intermixture, the apparent differentiations of the sensible world? To this question by far the most appealing answers would be: either *very many* (an infinity, it might be) or *very few* (one, for example, or two or four).   An infinity of ingredients, for example, composed the universe of Anaxagoras.[23]   One,[24] two,[25] and four[26] ingredients likewise had their partisans.

Further attention is required in the case of a single substrate; here the inquirer asks the same question as before, only slightly modified.   He now desires to know not *how many substances* but in *how many configurations* the one and only substance should be assumed to exist.   And once again the favorite answers are *very many* and *very few*.   Thus for Thales (according to Burnet[27] the first human being who can rightly be called a man of science) there was but a single substance, which, he said, was water and which he apparently considered capable of assuming an unlimited variety of configurations or states.   Similarly, the much later atoms of Democritus,[28] though all cut out of the same material, varied endlessly in their shapes and movements and hence in the appearances to which they gave rise.   Thales had a famous follower, however, namely Anaximenes, whose basic material, "air," could exist in a more rarefied condition (fire) and two more concentrated ones (water, earth).[29]   Mixtures of these four sufficed to endow the universe with its aspect of complexness.   A view somewhat similar to Anaximenes' in this respect is that of Heraclitus, with fire assuming the fundamental rôle.[30]

Whether many essential substances were assumed or only a few, one of these was usually conceived as in some way more fundamental than the rest and as such was designated a primary substance or material first principle.   First principles are of significance for the present inquiry because the phenomenon of life was

[23] See the section of this paper on *Early ideas of protoplasm*, p. 48.

[24] Thales, Anaximenes, Heraclitus, Democritus, Hippo, Diogenes of Apollonia and others are usually classed as monists.

[25] Xenophanes, vaguely, and more specifically Parmenides (who, however, may have meant to develop the dualistic view chiefly for purposes of exposing its untenability).

[26] Empedocles, Plato.

[27] Burnet, J., *Greek philosophy*, *Pt. 1* (London, 1909).

[28] Diels: A 37 (Simplicius.   Phys. 28, 15 etc.); Arist.   *De An.*   463 b 30.

[29] Arist.   *Met.*   984 a 5; Dox 476.

[30] See this paper, the sect. on early ideas concerning protoplasm.

frequently projected upon, or in some manner attached to, them. The foregoing outline of the doctrine of matter makes it possible for us to understand in exactly what way first principles were considered fundamental. Careful consideration reveals three different criteria for admission to this designation.[31] To begin with, a first principle could be first in time. That is, it could be the original existence out of which all others have arisen or are arising by transmutation or differentiation. Anaximander's first principle, for example, was an undifferentiated existence called ἄπειρον (variously translated as the "boundless," "characterless," "infinite," "indeterminate," etc.). This ἄπειρον was able to resolve itself into two different principles, hot and cold, whose various intermixtures gave rise to the four familiar elements.[31a] In a second sense, a first principle might be that element into which any other element might be most easily transmuted. Or, finally, a first principle could be thought of as designating the only thing which actually exists—the *matter* (especially as in Democritus) whose different dispositions in space produce the differences in the appearances of things.

The study of matter culminates in the problem of the dimensional character of the elements. Unfortunately, very few expositions of this problem remain to us from the pre-Socratic philosophers. In attempts to achieve a solution, the readily observed "mixedness" of things and especially the recoverability of the elements from mixtures has proved basic. The solution is narrowly limited by the fact that in the attempt to visualize the shapes of infravisible entities we are largely limited to comparing them with things we can see. From this point of view mixtures could be visualized only as interlocking reticula, as discontinuous fragments imbedded in a matrix (e.g., the vacuum of Leucippus, the ἄπειρον of Anaximander, and Anaxagoras' νοῦς), or as some combination of these. Of all these possibilities, only the particulate view was ever developed with any real explicitness, and this was the formulation which found acceptance with Anaxagoras, Pythagoras, Parmenides, Heraclitus, and Leucippus. This being so, one wonders why Democritus, although he certainly inherited his idea from a whole galaxy of intellectual ancestors, is, even as early as Aristotle, cited as the founder of the atomic theory. Exactly the same question may be asked, for

---

[31] Our exclusion of matrices (e.g., Anaxagoras' *Nous*) from membership among the first principles is arbitrary and implies no disagreement about the suitability of its inclusion where this would prove useful.

[31a] Diels: A 9, 10, 16; also see Freeman, *op. cit.*, p. 59.

modern science, concerning Dalton. And Dalton himself supplied the answer: "These observations [i.e., of the three states of matter] have tacitly led to the conclusion which seems universally adopted, that all bodies of sensible magnitude, whether liquid or solid, are constituted of vast numbers of extremely small particles, or atoms. It is not my design to call in question this conclusion which appears completely satisfactory; but to shew that we have hitherto made no use of it."[32] It was, in fact, by their *use* of the atomic hypothesis to account for empirical commonplaces (with Democritus diffusion, with Dalton chemical change) that both these thinkers caused a dormant idea to begin to germinate.

Only by understanding the foregoing beliefs concerning material reality can the problem of protoplasm be approached historically in a satisfactorily productive fashion. With these concepts before us, however, it should prove possible in certain instances to predict what theories of protoplasm we shall encounter and then, by surveying the literature, discover which of these theories was actually developed and how explicitly.

For reasons already explained, it is impossible to investigate the material substratum of life separately from that of "soul." We must begin, therefore, by enumerating the possible relations of matter to soul in the same way in which earlier we enumerated those of matter to life. Soul can, apparently, be conceived of either as *imposed* upon matter, as *identical* with it, or as *emergent* from it. The idea of soul as imposed implies its existence independently of matter but does not preclude its occasional residence therein (i.e., since the imposed soul is in itself immaterial, it and matter can co-exist in the same place[33]). The idea of soul as identical with matter contains the two possibilities that *all* matter is soul, or only *some*. And by soul as emergent is meant an activity or activities displayed by matter so composed as to cause such activity to occur. In Lloyd Morgan's theory, for example, at a certain level of constitutional complexity *life* emerges; on a "higher" level, *mind*.[34]

It should be noted, finally, that the concept of life as imposed (i.e., as a real but non-material existence distinct from "soul"),

---

[32] Dalton, J. *A new system of chemical philosophy*, Pt. I (Manchester, 1808) 141. Pertinent passages repr. in *Foundations of the molecular theory* (Edinburgh, for the Alembic Club, 1899).

[33] This whole problem is dealt with by Arist. in the *De An.*, Bk. II.

[34] Lloyd Morgan, *op. cit.*

which is so basic to modern vitalism of the Lamarckian variety, appears not to have presented itself to the early Greek scientific mind, at least not in clear-cut terms. The origin of this idea, a question of the greatest interest, remains, as far as the author is aware, to be discovered.

Early ideas concerning protoplasm

1. The concept of protoplasm which we shall consider first presents us with a universal "soul" conceived as being imposed upon matter. The concept is that of Anaxagoras, remembered among other reasons for bringing science from Ionia to Attica.[35] For Anaxagoras, the universe consisted of an infinity of elementary ingredients, or seeds. Originally, these had existed in a monotonous condition of maximum intermixture.[36] In addition, there existed another entity—that which "alone of all that is simple, unmixed, and pure."[37] The latter entity was apparently viewed by Anaxagoras as a circumambient, motive intelligence which, by giving the seeds an initial twirl, set them to sorting out in orderly arrangements[38]—a process in which, cosmologically speaking, they are still engaged. "All things were mixed up together; then Noῦς came and arranged them all in distinct order."[39] Wherever a group of similar seeds was segregated the result was Anaxagoras' closest approach to an element (homoiomeries), but the variety of these was infinite.

The seeds of special interest from the point of view of protoplasm were certain ones which drifted to earth and, by proper intermixture with others, gave rise to plants and animals.[40] Most authorities agree that Anaxagoras would have "Noῦς *enter into* some things and not others and this explains the distinction between animate and inanimate."[41] The precise nature of "entering into" presents difficulties; that, for example, of reconciling fragment 5 ("In all things there is a portion of everything except Mind;

[35] See Gomperz., Th., *Griechische Denker* (Leipzig, 1896); tr., Magnus, L. (New York, 1907), I, 208.

[36] Fairbanks, *op. cit.*, Fr. 1, p. 237.

[37] Arist. *De An.* 405 a 13.

[38] Fairbanks, *op. cit.*, Fr. 7, p. 243.

[39] Diogenes Laertius (II. 6); see his *Lives of the Eminent Philosophers*, I (London and New York [Loeb Classical Library], 1925), 137.

[40] See Freeman, K., *The Presocratic Philosophers* (Oxford, 1946), 269.

[41] See Burnet, *op. cit.*, 79.

and there are also some things [presumably living ones] in which there is Mind also''[42]), with fragment 12 ("Mind is where all things are, in the surrounding mass and in the things that were separated and in the things that are being separated.''[43]).

We can at least safely limit to two the possibilities for the nature of the relation between matter and mind. Either the germinative seeds themselves incorporated an ingredient of νοῦς or else their nature is such that in them alone does νοῦς still act directly. In both these cases, the distinction between animate and inanimate is the same: viz., that only the former incorporates an ingredient of νοῦς which remains active. The intellectual ingredient of *each* individual would thus be that individual's soul.

Whichever of these two interpretations we adopt, the effective difference between living and non-living in the Anaxagorean system is that in the former alone is Mind capable of direct manifestation of itself in overt activity. The expression "capable of" is intentional, since it was Anaxagoras' view that "all living things, even plants, have a share of mind, although it is not present as a reasoning factor even in all human beings." Evidence is lacking to push the analysis of Anaxagoras' ideas further than this. They are of interest, among other reasons, because of their numerous intellectual descendants. The "archaei" of Paracelsus and van Helmont's hierarchy of immaterial principles[44] are among the intellectual descendants of the animate immaterial particles of Anaxagoras.[45]

2. According to the foregoing doctrine, soul was motive of matter and existed externally by it. By contrast, most pre-Socratic thinkers conceived of soul as internal to matter—as resident in it, i.e., or, in some cases, indistinguishable from it. If not all substantial entities were able to move, breathe, and self-duplicate, then undoubtedly they lacked the material vehicle, or material equivalent, of soul. Or, at any rate, they probably did not possess it in effective apposition with other matter. On this supposition, the primary question in seeking ideas about protoplasm would be to identify the essential element: the element such that only those existences possessing it in proper intermixture could move, breathe, and reproduce. Three solutions to this quest for the key element

[42] Fairbanks, *op. cit.*, 237.   [43] *Ibid.*, 243.

[44] See Singer, C., *op. cit.*, 357.

[45] See Bernard, C., *La définition de la vie* (Paris, 1879).

inescapably suggest themselves: namely air, water, and fire. It will scarcely surprise us that each of these had its proponents in the period with which we are concerned.

Beginning with air, it would be particularly surprising had the establishment of mental connections between air and life awaited the rise of formal science. Actually they were much older and of frequent recurrence. According to the (probably eighth-century) author of Genesis, after man's first formation from dust it remained for God to "breathe into his nostrils the breath of life."[46] A related instance is Isaiah's resuscitation of the Shunamite's son by similar methods, after which the child "opened his eyes and sneezed seven times."[47] Such examples can be multiplied indefinitely. Admittedly vague and difficult to restate in scientifically acceptable terms, these notions make it nevertheless strange that connections between air and soul, and between air and life, should have received as little attention as they did. It has been suggested that the expressions for *soul* (ψυχή) and *to breathe* (ψύχω) were originally equivalent, but this is currently discredited.[48]

The scientific doctrine of air as soul began with the first important Greek scientist after Thales and Anaximander, namely Anaximenes of Miletus, and culminated with Diogenes of Apollonia, eclectic writer of the final days of the Ionian school. As for the views of Anaximenes, only two sure facts remain to us: air was the primary substance,[49] and air was soul.[50] Disappointingly enough, Anaximenes employed this theory, as far as we know, to explain only one of the many interesting characteristics of living bodies, and that by no means their liveliest characteristic: viz., their cohesiveness.[51] This idea is, however, not without its historical importance: life conceived as conservative against natural deteriorative tendencies is prophetic of Stahl's philosophy[52] and of the ideas of several recent theoretical biologists who have claimed that protoplasm somehow evades the working-out of the law of entropy.

[46] Genesis 2.77.   [47] Kings II. 4. 34.

[48] We here follow L. and S.; but see also Ellis, W., *The Idea of the Soul in Western Philosophy and Science* (London, 1940), 26.

[49] Arist. *Met.* 984 a 5.

[50] This idea is contained in the second fragment; see Diels, 95.

[51] Diels gives the fragment in question (B. 2) as follows: *Wie unsre Seele Luft ist und uns dadurch zusammenhalt, so umspannt* (in later editions *umgibt*) *auch die ganze Weltordnung Odem* (later *Hauch*) *und Luft.*

[52] See Wheeler, L. R., *Vitalism, its History and Validity* (London, 1939), 24.

Diogenes compensates in the most abundant fashion for the paucity of explanations offered by his great predecessor, Anaximenes. Air appealed to Diogenes as the common substrate, the first principle, because of the readiness with which it changes its character (its taste, shape, position, temperature, moisture, etc.). Ordinary observations on respiration, and its absence, show that when air is present in the organism, so is life, which Diogenes does not distinguish clearly from intelligence.[53] The unique feature of organic bodies is their admixture with air in its primary form. This theory Diogenes uses to explain innumerable biological details. The ease of these explanations in fact constitutes an egregious example of the danger, where understanding is the goal, of the speculative-deductive form of scientific thought.[54] It seems fairly safe to believe that the special character of protoplasm for Diogenes was the specific degree of condensation of the air it contained. Thus in fragment 5, ''—bei allen Lebewesen ist die Seele ein und dasselbe, Luft, die zwar wärmer ist als die äussere, in der wir uns befinden, jedoch viel kälter als die an der Sonne.'' And if Zeller's interpretation is to be believd, Diogenes further distinguished between merely ''animate'' beings in whom air only existed (entering by diffusion), and fully intelligent ones in whom it existed in much greater amounts (forced in by breathing).

In relation to our present analysis, the essential point about the foregoing views is their imputation of life-as-soul to a specific element, life-as-action emerging in systems containing the soul element properly incorporated. The element in question was, in these cases, air. At least as much to be expected would be the designation of fire as the vehicle of life-as-soul and hence as productive of life-as-action. This is so especially in view of three favoring factors. The first of these is the idea that fire is a substance and hence a proper vehicle. While this notion seems strange in view of the classical physics of the nineteenth century, we must remember that it was not seriously questioned by scientists until around 1800. The second favoring concept is the idea of fire as divine, an idea with a long line of antecedents in prescientific days. And the third is the everyday observation of the coldness of death, and, without doubt, of the heightened activities of ''cold-blooded'' organisms when the temperature rises.

[53] Diels: B4 and 5.

[54] For an admirable summary, see Freeman, *op. cit.*, 282–4, and the corresponding frr. in Diels; also Zeller, in Alleyne's translation (*A History of Greek Philosophy* (London, 1889), 285–93.

The two principal partisans of fire as the animate element were the "dark philosopher (Heraclitus) of Ephesus"[55] (ca. 515) and, somewhat later, the great atomist, Democritus.

Heraclitus' concept of matter provided him with an admirable starting-point toward a notion of protoplasm. Unfortunately, his way of expressing himself makes it difficult to match possible formulations, starting from his premises, with his actual ideas. Heraclitus was, as Gomperz states, "prone to satiate himself in a debauch of metaphors."

Nevertheless, by proceeding cautiously we can piece together at least a skeleton of his ideas. We can, first, be quite sure that the animal body, like all bodies, was composed of earth, water, and fire.[56] These ingredients were involved in a perpetual intertransmutation in the "upward" direction (from earth to water to fire), or "downward" (from fire to water to earth).[56] The special feature of living as compared with other systems is that they are so constituted as to permit their allotment of fire to reveal itself for what it is, viz., the soul. In the body, transmutations upward and downward are ordinarily in equilibrium. Minor downward displacements of this equilibrium make the soul less conscious, as in drunken stupor (the wetter state) or sleep.[57] A major downward displacement renders the whole system unfit as a habitation for its individual soul, which departs to the underworld leaving the body to proceed through water to earth along the downward path. Through the senses, the individual allotment of fire, the soul, may be kindled by the outer, the universal, fire, thus achieving some identity with, some knowledge of, the rationale which governs all.[58]

With Democritus, we come to a view which is both more sophisticated and more distinct. A single matter, chopped up into a huge variety of atoms, underlies all existence. Upon the sizes and shapes of the atoms, never exactly alike, and upon their spatial distributions and redistributions, depends the sensible variety of the known world.[59] From the midst of the infinitely varied types, originally intermixed after the fashion of Anaxagoras' seeds, certain small, rapidly-moving atoms segregated off. In sufficiently

[55] Fr. 20, 21; Fairbanks, *op. cit.,* 31.

[56] See note 55.   [57] Diels: Fr. 68, and 72–4.

[58] This, at least, is Freeman's interpretation (see 118).

[59] The major authority on the metaphysics of Democritus is Simpl., quoting from Arist.'s lost book on D.

pure aggregation, these appear as fire,[60] appropriately intermixed, as soul.[61] Under the right conditions, a soul-filled entity appears as a living organism, arising from the primeval slime.[62] But what are the right conditions? The question presents difficulties. Probably the essential requirement was to keep an adequate population of soul atoms at home. Their tendency to go away (in sleep, in death) is notorious. Breathing serves to counteract their tendency to escape, by drawing others in. One of the unsolved problems in Democritus' thought is how he related the universal to the individual soul. If, as many authorities agree, organisms arise by chance, then Democritus becomes an emergentist in the modern sense. He was considered such, for example, by Claude Bernard. Actually, it is difficult to be sure how Democritus regarded this question.[63]

Even water was designated as a possible vehicle of soul and hence as material cause for life-as-action. A number of everyday observations contributed to this view, especially the dependence of organisms upon water for continued existence, the moist nature of food and of the semen, the abnormal water content of tissue in certain diseases, and the insensibility of the dry parts like hair or the skin of the sole of the foot. Especially connected with this view are the names of Thales, of his student Anaximander, and, later, of the Pythagorean medical practitioner, Hippo.

Thales, for whom water was first principle, conceived of everything as full of soul,[64] presumably by virtue of the presence in it of water.[65] Strictly, the relation of soul to water in Thales is not clear. The two were, according to Aristotle,[66] not equated actually; rather was water "pervaded by soul."[67]

Anaximander's theory is undoubtedly best understood as resulting from his failure to think beyond the soul-water concept and his habit of using it as an explanatory tool in his efforts to interpret things in general. In his cosmogony there is an original infinite and characterless entity, we remember, which first differentiates into a core of cold surrounded by a ring of hot. The cold then differentiates into earth and air and earth into moist and dry. As the latter change occurred, animals arose either "in water"[68] or "through vapors raised by the sea"[69] and climbed, or were stranded

[60] Diels: A 101.   [61] Arist.: *De An.* 404 a 1.   [62] Diels: A 139.
[63] Bernard, *op. cit.*, 115.   [64] Pl.: *Lg.* X, 899B.   [65] See Freeman, *op. cit.*, 54.
[66] See Fairbanks, *op. cit.*, 3.   [67] Aët. Plac. I, 7; and Dox. 301.   [68] Dox. 430.
[69] Fairbanks, *op. cit.*, 113 (Alex. on Meteor.)

on, the land, bursting open to produce terrestrial beings like men.

A final, and once again relatively unsuccessful, effort to make water the vehicle of consciousness was that of Hippo.   He seems to have been influenced by his observation that the sperm, which he believed endowed the future organism with soul, is moist.[70] Freeman suggests that Hippo's views may have arisen as a product of the controversy between the followers of Heraclitus and the members of the Pythagorean medical schools.   Aristotle dismisses him from the company of significant metaphysicians with the statement that "no one would think Hippo fit to be included among these thinkers, because of the paltriness of his thought."[71]

Viewed as a whole, the history of the idea of water as the animate element never earned any considerable success.   Arising at the very beginning of objective thought, it was perpetuated chiefly by thinkers who were seriously interested neither in its origin nor the basis of its validity.   Moreover, although there are many everyday observations that favor the view, there are perhaps as many which make it repugnant.   In fact, no productive solutions of the protoplasm problem were offered by these early founders of the aquatic philosophy, although it was destined to experience a number of later revivals.

Earth as a first principle or as a vehicle for soul appears to have found no especially effective advocate.   For completeness, Xenophanes, reputed founder of the Eleatic school, deserves at least to be mentioned in this connection.   His remark that all things come from and end by becoming earth,[72] seemed to Sabinus,[73] and Aëtius,[74] a postulation of earth as first principle.   Most commentators feel that Xenophanes was not a sufficiently objective metaphysician ever to have committed himself on the subject.   He was intrigued by marine fossils and for all we know may have considered water as important as earth in the origins of animate existence.   Actually, we have no reason to believe that there was a protoplasm in Xenophanes' philosophy nor to disagree, on this subject at least, with Aristotle's complaint that Xenophanes did not "seem to get at the nature of things but merely looked up into the broad heavens and exclaimed 'the unity is God.' "[75]

3. The foregoing ideas are based upon essentially monistic conceptions concerning the nature of reality.   In the Eleatic school, especially with Parmenides, a duality of first principles is encount-

[70] Zeller, *op. cit.*, 282.   [71] Arist. *Met.* 984 a 3.
[72] Fairbanks, *op. cit.*, 69.   [73] Dox. 481.   [74] Dox. 284.
[75] *Met.* 986 b 10.

ered: the warm (related to fire, and to not-being) and the cold (related to earth, and to being).[76] This interesting duality seems to stand ideologically somewhere between Pythagorean matter-and-form and the matter-and-energy of recent physical thought.[77] According to this view, perceptible differences in things are due to their different content of cold and warm.[78] The weakest point in the theory, or in our knowledge of it, is its vagueness as to the way in which complexity emerges from admixtures of but two elements; the dimensional problem, in other words, is not solved. Perceptiveness was, according to Parmenides, a property of everything: warm perceiving warm; cold, cold. For life-as-action, the warm element must be present,[79] as efficient cause, interposed in the cold, as material cause.[80] Life-as-action thus becomes the movements of a specially differentiated variety of the cold under the influence of the warm. The individual mind, in Parmenides, is presumably emergent. He has, at any rate, this to say on the subject: "for as at any time is the blending of the complex members of a man, so is the mind in men constituted."[81]

4. Our survey may most logically end with a brief account of the theory of Empedocles, in whom strikingly modern features appear. Life here is distinctly emergent from the chance temporary intermixture of the four elements. This intermixture exists under the influence of *Love*—the causal principle in response to which elements intermix. (The other principle is Hate, in response to which they segregate.)[82] Organic life began when Love, the mixing influence, predominated. The elements first fused to form separate limbs, which then, still under Love's influence, underwent further fusions, often into monsters. Since then, whole animals have arisen not only in the fashion just described but also biogenetically, by reproduction. We see only those results accidentally fitted to survive and reproduce.[83] The different tissues differ in their composition. One of the difficulties in Empedocles' theory is that the individual soul is transmigratory. One qualification of a successful organic intermixture is thus its fitness to be inhabited by such a

---

[76] Diog. Laert., *op. cit.*, IX 21, 22.

[77] See Ellis, *op. cit.*, 48.

[78] Diels: B 16.

[79] Zeller, *op. cit.*, 602.

[80] Unless Arist., *Met.* 984 b, is crediting Parmenides with a distinction he never clearly made.

[81] Diels: B 16.

[82] Fairbanks, *op. cit.*, 165 (Fr. 51, 55 a) and 171 (Fr. 96).

[83] *Ibid.*, Fr. 242–62, pp. 189–93.

soul.   What this fitness consists in, Empedocles fails to specify.[84]
This troubled Aristotle, who accused Empedocles of failing to specify
the pattern, the λόγος.[85]   Since the intermixing principle acts according to chance and is apparently free from psychic attributes, and
since the organism itself is a product of the way in which intermixtures occur, the Empedoclean theory comes nearer to modern
theory, in these respects, than any other in the period which we are
considering.

Summary

In modern thought, life is ordinarily interpreted either as non-
material and imposed, or as an ensemble of emergent, habitual acts,
or as the peculiar activity of the common material factor for all
"living" things.   In Pre-Socratic Greek science, except in Empedocles and possibly Democritus, life was only gradually and imperfectly distinguished from the motive-percipient soul or consciousness, which in turn was variously regarded as either inherent,
emergent, or imposed.   Some forms of the modern interpretation
of life as non-material and imposed (vitalism) correspond rather
closely to the Greek concept of life as an imposed soul.   In either
system, where life is considered as imposed, the protoplasm problem takes the form of an attempt to determine the metaphysical
character of the system this imposition implies.   Where life is considered as inherent, the problem is to identify the element in which
it inheres.   And where life is considered to be emergent, the problem is to discover the special character of the substrate which such
emergence requires.   The chief differences between ancient and
modern approaches to the problem are: the complete absence from
ancient thought of a concept of life as the intimate activity of the
common material substrate of all living things, and the absence
from modern thought of the view of life as inherent in, or identical
with, any material element of the system as a whole.

---

[84] The doctrine of transmigration is expounded in the *Purification*.
[85] Arist.   *De Part. An.*   642 a 17, *De An.*   408 a 13, and *Met.* 993 a 15.

✒⚯ *John Elof Boodin*

THE DISCOVERY OF FORM

We must go back to the Greeks for the discovery of form. It is not my purpose to give a history of the concept of form. I shall only touch some high points which I think are relevant to the problem today. We may say that Plato is the discoverer of form, one of the most fundamental concepts in the history of thought. There has been an attempt to trace the concept of form back to the Pythagoreans. But this attempt is not supported by Aristotle, who gives us our only relevant information. It is true that the fundamental reality, according to the Pythagoreans, is numbers, and that Plato in his latest phase tried to express the nature of things as numbers. But for the Pythagoreans numbers are sensible things—bodies out of which the world is made, "agreeing apparently with the other natural philosophers in holding that reality was just what could be perceived by the senses, and is contained within the compass of the heavens."[1] Aristotle's interpretation of the relation of the Pythagoreans to Plato is that the Pythagoreans agreed with Plato "in giving numbers an independent reality of their own; while Plato differed from the Pythagoreans in holding that this reality was distinguishable from that of sensible things."[2]

The confusion has come from the fact that the Greek word εἶδος, in popular usage, means *shape* (as does the English word, form) and that is the sense in which the Pythagoreans used it. A geometrical figure has shape, εἶδος. Eurytus, a disciple of Philolaus, in the last generation of the ancient Pythagoreans, tried to express the nature of man "by means of pebbles which he arranged in a figure (εἶδος) having the shape of a man."[3] Form, therefore, could be perceived by the senses.

Plato's form has to do with internal structure, and thus can be grasped only by the mind, and is distinguished from sensible appearance, though the latter may reflect or, in a measure, incarnate structure. This structure is independent of sense ap-

[1] *Metaphysics*, A, 8, 990ª, 3. See John Burnet, *Early Greek Philosophy* (1930), 286 f.

[2] Burnet, *ibid.*, 287.

[3] Burnet, *Greek Philosophy—From Thales to Plato*, 90.

pearances. It exists in its own right—the structure of beauty, the structure of an atom—but by grasping it we grasp the real meaning of the sensible world.   Mainly, what Plato had in common with the Pythagoreans was the word εἶδος, *idea*, but the word was used in a different sense.   The same may be said of Democritus, who also spoke of εἶδος—the shape of the atoms.   Neither the Pythagoreans nor Democritus had any conception of internal structure—structure as such.   Such a conception must wait for the discovery of the concept, which was the work of Socrates and Plato.

The Neo-Pythagoreans were eclectic and helped themselves to what they wanted of the results of the Academy.   But in order to justify their plagiarism they attributed everything to Pythagoras.   The erudite and uncritical Proclus, in the fifth century A.D., was taken in by their propaganda, and A. E. Taylor was taken in by Proclus.

We learn from Aristotle that Socrates was "busying himself with ethical matters, and neglecting the world of nature as a whole but seeking the universal in these ethical matters, and fixed thought for the first time on definitions."   According to Aristotle, he did not hold to the forms, i.e., forms independent of sensible appearance.   To the discerning reader Plato has given a clear account of where Socrates leaves off.   In the *Symposium,* Socrates is represented as familiar with the lesser mysteries—temperance and justice in states and families—but when it comes to the greater mystery, the form of beauty, "absolute, separate, simple, and everlasting," Socrates is ignorant and is obliged to learn from Diotima, an oracle, who knows the future.

For the cosmic significance of form we naturally look to the *Timaeus,* Plato's immortal cosmological dialogue.   Plato informs us that "the father and maker of the universe is past finding out; and even if we found him, to tell of him to all men would be impossible."   It is, therefore, necessary for Plato to convey his meaning of Him in human metaphor.   And the metaphor of the artist is congenial to the Greek mind.   The story of creation is told by the almost mythical Timaeus: "Let us, then, state for what reason becoming and this universe were framed by him who framed them.   He was good; and in the good no jealousy in any matter can ever arise.   So being without jealousy he desired that all things should come as near as possible to being like himself."⁴   (It should

---

⁴ *Timaeus,* 29, Cornford's translation.

be noted that Plato says "as near as possible to being like himself," not to a pre-existent system of forms.) "In the likeness of what animal did the Creator make the world? It would be an unworthy thing to liken it to any nature which exists as a part (*species*) only; for nothing can be beautiful which is like any imperfect (incomplete) thing; but let us suppose the world to be the very image of that whole of which all other animals both individually and in their tribes (*species*) are portions (καθ' ἕν καὶ κατὰ γένη μόρια). For the original of the universe contains in itself all intelligible beings, just as this world comprehends us and all other visible creatures. For the Deity, intending to make this world like the fairest and most perfect of intelligible beings, framed one visible animal comprehending within itself all other animals of a kindred nature."[5]

Plato's dramatic language has, of course, given rise to various interpretations. How are we to understand "that living Creature of which all other living creatures, individually and in their species, are parts"? According to Cornford (who here follows the tradition), "the model called the 'intelligible living creature' is a generic Form containing within itself the Forms of all subordinate species, members of which inhabit the visible world. . . . The generic form must be conceived, not as a bare abstraction obtained by leaving out all the specific differences determining the subordinate species, but as a whole, richer in content than any of the parts it contains and embraces. It is an eternal and unchanging object of thought, not itself a living creature, any more than the Form of Man is a man. It is not a soul, nor has it a body or any existence in space or time. Its eternal being is in the realm of Form."[6] I think the refutation of such a picture of "bloodless categories" is found in the *Sophist:* "And, O heavens, can we ever be made to believe that motion and life and soul and mind are not present with perfect being? Can we imagine that being is devoid of life and mind, and exists in awful unmeaningness an everlasting fixture?"[7]

In the *Philebus,* where Plato does not use metaphorical language, the cosmos, the macrocosm, is conceived as a body gathering up, in their pure states, the elements which are impure in our bodies

---

[5] *Timaeus,* 30, Jowett's translation. Parentheses are mine.

[6] F. M. Cornford, *Plato's Cosmology* (1937), 40. For Plato, the species, man, is a living creature, but a larger form than that of individual man.

[7] *Sophist,* 249 (Jowett's translation.)

and having a soul in every way fairer than our soul and the source of our soul; and having wisdom and mind, which cannot exist without soul, and which is a presiding cause of no mean power. This cosmic organism is not created but is the creator of order. Here we have a development of the original of the *Timaeus*. And surely this is not just a bodiless, soulless, mindless system of forms. It is necessary to grasp the organismic conception of Plato to understand his meaning. This makes analysis a "carving" (though not necessarily a physical carving) which is accompanied by synthesis, retracing the relations to the whole.

In the *Parmenides* we have an explicit statment in regard to the individual forms: "And yet, Socrates," said Parmenides, "if a man, fixing his attention on these and the like difficulties, does away with ideas of things and will not admit that every individual thing has its own determinate idea which is always one and the same, he will have nothing on which his mind can rest; and so he will utterly destroy the power of reasoning as you seem to me to have particularly noted."[8] Here we have a clear statement of the final indivisible form which itself exists within larger wholes. Here we have the key to what Plato hoped to accomplish by the method of division.

In the period of the great ethical dialogues, including the *Republic*, forms are objectively normative. They are structures of the real world. While they transcend the world of becoming, they give beauty and truth to this world which can only imperfectly mirror the real world because of the character of matter or necessity, though the latter lends itself "for the most part" to reflecting the former. In the period of the systematic dialogues, Plato's concern is to show more precisely the relation of forms to the world of becoming, (a) by creation in the *Timaeus*, and (b) by division in the *Sophist, Statesman, Philebus,* and *Phaedrus*. Division[9] is a method of analysis, within the fullness of being, of the living intelligible organic whole, following, like a good carver, the natural joints (*Phaedrus*) until he arrives at the indivisible parts which are also wholes having their own complexity with reference to their

---

[8] *Parmenides*, 35, Jowett's translation.

[9] Julius Stenzel, in *Plato's Method of Dialectic*, trans. D. J. Allan, has a learned discussion of division (διαίρεσις) and "atomic form" and the accompanying synthesis (συμπλεκή εἰδῶν) but it is not clear what he means by "atomic form." See especially chapter V.

distinguishable constituents (letters) and also their relations to the more comprehensive wholes, up to the final comprehensive intelligible organic whole which contains in its living unity all the constituent wholes down to the individual intelligible forms, just as this visible world contains the whole hierachy of visible forms, including us and all living things. This means the existence of the living intelligible whole, not as a mere system of forms, but as a living whole. Otherwise the process of division would fail to give meaning to the world of becoming. Plato has not abandoned the normative ideals as the ultimate structure of reality. The good and the beautiful and the just retain their significance as objective norms in the evaluation of the world of becoming. But the forms now are shown to give structure to the sensible world of individuals. At any rate that is Plato's intention.

The *Seventh Epistle* is now generally recognized as the work of Plato. In 342 d, e, Plato is concerned to distinguish the actual object of knowledge, which is true reality, from the processes by means of which we strive to attain knowledge of it, such knowledge being relative and uncertain (a marvelous analysis). As the actual object of knowledge, he speaks of mathematical objects, "the good and the beautiful and the just," and "every animal." The reassertion of the universal objective norms does not conflict with the assertion of "every animal."

Plotinus feels that he is a true Platonist, and his statement of the relation of the individual forms to the whole reads like a paraphrase of the *Timaeus*. "There is a reason, then, why the soul of this All should be sent into it from God: In the same way the soul of each single one of us is sent, that the universe may be complete; it was necessary that all beings of the Intellectual should be tallied by just so many forms of living creatures here in the realm of sense."[10]

Aristotle corroborates our interpretation, but also points out the difficulty. He discusses the relation of perishableness to the essence of individuals and comes to the conclusion that perishableness must be involved in the essence of some individuals. He points out the problem that this would raise for the believers in forms. "Evidently, then, there cannot be forms such as some maintain, for

---

[10] *Ennead*, IV: 8, 1. Stephen MacKenna's translation. See in this connection, A. O. Lovejoy, *The Great Chain of Being* (1936), 339, Note 35. I am sorry Lovejoy lost his nerve.

then one man [the sensible individual] would be perishable and another [the ideal man] imperishable.   Yet the Forms are said to be the same in form in the individuals and not merely to have the same name; but things which differ in kind [as the imperishable and perishable] are farther apart than those which differ in form.''[11] Aristotle points out rightly that the difference between the intelligible forms and the sensible world still remains.   It also remains for Aristotle, who persistently asserts that forms are eternal.   How could perishableness be a character of an eternal form?   Yet the individual is ultimate for Aristotle, as it is for Plato; for Aristotle it is the only thing that has existence.   Aristotle holds that under the moon, i.e., in the world of becoming, form is never completely realized.   It seems to me that Plato has the advantage over Aristotle, because Plato has an intelligible world in which the forms exist, whether they are realized in the world of becoming or not, but if Aristotle's forms are not realized in the world of matter, where could they exist?

The fundamental difference between Plato and Aristotle is that while Aristotle recognizes only the individual forms as existent (οὐσία), Plato recognizes the existence also of more comprehensive forms.   There are forms of species of living things which in turn are portions of the living whole-form.   Aristotle cannot see how there can be a ''form over forms,'' because for him the individual form is the only form.   But there is more to man than men, there is the history of man, which is part of the history of life.   Plato could express this intuition only as dramatic creation.

We may approach the problem of the individual from its relation to knowledge.   To know the individual is to know how he differs from other individuals.   Plato faces this problem in the *Theaetetus.*   If we try to define the individual in terms of general predicates which also apply to others—nose, eyes, mouth, even snub-nosedness and prominent eyes—we would have no more notion of Theaetetus than of others who resemble him.   ''Surely I can have no conception of Theaetetus until your snub-nosedness has left an impression on my mind different from the snub-nosedness of all others whom I have ever seen, and until your other peculiar-

[11] *Met.*, 1059a.   W. D. Ross' translation.   The explanatory parentheses are also suggested by him.   Ross' translation of the *Metaphysics* is used unless otherwise stated.

ities have a like distinctness; and so when I meet you tomorrow the right opinion will be recalled." "Right opinion implies the knowledge of differences" (209). But this is tautology, not definition. You cannot define the individual in terms of general predicates.

The method of division lands us in the same place. We finally come to the indivisible form—the unique difference. This can only be said to be known in relation to a hierarchical system of forms which gives the individual its place, but it does not define the individual form as such. In the *Sophist* Plato has an elaborate definition of the sophist and in the *Statesman* of the statesman. In each case he uses the method of division, in which he distinguishes narrower forms within larger forms until he thinks he has hunted down his quarry—the sophist or statesman—then recapitulates the larger forms, narrowing the circle until he is supposed to have caught the indivisible form—the sophist or statesman. But the quarry has escaped the net, and Plato has just a generic form— any sophist or any statesman. It is the dilemma of the *Theaetetus*.

Aristotle struggles with the same problem with the same result. For Aristotle only the individual is substance, ultimate reality (οὐσία). Aristotle labors with the conception of substance. "Why is this individual thing, or this body having this form, a man? Therefore what we seek is the cause, i.e., the form, by reason of which the matter is some definite thing; and this is the substance of the thing."[12] In both Plato and Aristotle we have the conception of wholism. In the *Theaetetus* the syllable is not the letters but a unique form. So in Aristotle. "Since that which is compounded out of something, so that the whole is one, not like a heap but like a syllable, now the syllable is not its elements, *ba* is not the same as *b* and *a*. . . ." The syllable is something "other" than its elements. "And this is the substance of each thing, for this is the primary cause for its being."[13] Universals do not exist. There are no universal causes. Only individual causes exist. Not man but Peleus is the "originative principle of Achilles."[14] This rules out medieval realism.

But the logical difficulty of definition still remains. Can substance be defined? Aristotle seems to contradict himself. Only

[12] *Met.*, Bk. VII, 1041b.
[13] *Met.*, Bk. VII, 1041b.
[14] *Met.*, Bk. XII, 1071a, 19–24.

substance is definable.[15]   But substance cannot be defined.[16]   What he means seems to be that substance can be defined in the sense that it can be subject and have predicates.   But substance is not exhausted in its predicates.   There is the form of the individual itself, which is expressed in a formula.   The formula is internal to the individual.   Substance is an atomic form.   It has nothing in common with anything else.[17]   Therefore no universal can be substance.   This rules out species, even *infima species*.   Man or horse is not substance.[18]   On the other hand, contrary to Aquinas, "matter does not create a difference, for it does not make individual men forms of man though the flesh and the bones of which this man and that man consist are other.   The concrete thing is other (ἕτερον, diverse) but not other in form, because in the definition there is no contrariety.   This is the ultimate indivisible form.   Callias is definition + matter."[19]   Predicates are universals; and substance is not a combination of universals, because universals are applicable to more than one thing.[20]

Aristotle tries Plato's method of division.   "There is nothing in the definition except the first named genus and the differentiae."[21]   The differentiae are the important part: "the definition is the formula which comprises the differentiae."   But we must go on in the division to find the differentia of the differentiae, etc.   "Clearly the *last* differentia will be the substance of the thing and its definition."   We thus reach a limit of definition when we reach "forms that contain no differences."   As Aristotle says elsewhere, "the substance of each thing and the essence of each . . . is the limit of knowledge; and if of knowledge, of the object also."   What have we then except what Plato got in the *Theaetetus?*—the perception of differences, which he rejected as definition because the statement of it is tautology or merely verbal.   Aristotle is clear that as regards sensible individuals there can be no knowledge in the logical sense.   Sensible individuals can be reached only through perception and intuitive reason.   But Ideas also are individuals and cannot be defined.[22]

[15] *Met.*, Bk. VII, 1031a, 1.
[16] *Met.*, Bk. VII, 1040a, 28, 29.
[17] *Met.*, Bk. VII, 1038b, 35, 36–1039a; 1040b, 23 ff.
[18] *Met.*, Bk. VII, 1035b, 28, 29.
[19] *Met.*, Bk. XII, 1058, 5 f. (not Ross' translation).
[20] *Met.*, Bk. VII, 1040a, 10 ff.; 1037b, 24 ff.
[21] *Met.*, Bk. VII, 1037b, 28 ff.

I think it is evident that Plato and Aristotle started at the wrong end. Plato started with a large form, ultimately with the form of the universe, and tried to discern smaller forms within it—down to the particular individual form; and according to Xenocrates, he went on dividing until he arrived at the five solids, thus trying to bridge the gap between the organic and the inorganic. In the *Timaeus* he had tried to discover the atomic forms of physics— complex, yet wholes. Modern science starts with small forms— with individual situations and tries to build out from these. It is easier to discover the structure of an atom than the structure of the universe, though Plato was right that they are inter-related, as we are beginning to discover. Aristotle started with a large universal, a genus, and by division and the adding of differences tried to "approach" the individual. But we cannot arrive at the individual by the subject-predicate method; and Aristotle saw this, but gave up. We know that individual form—the structure of an atom, of a personality—is a creative discovery, suggested by the mind, but tried out by observation and experiment. We do indeed proceed from a general background of knowledge and make use of general principles, but the test is creative insight into the particular situation. This procedure required a more refined logic than the subject-predicate logic. For the most part we rely, in practical life, upon common sense, condensed into intuition, as the Greeks did.

Aristotle's great contribution to science is in biology, including psychology. Here he repeats again and again that "the soul is the primary substance and the body its matter," or "the soul is the form of the body." Here there can be no question in regard to the form being an individual form. Here it should not be possible for the most scholastic translator to confuse form (εἶδος) with species. Certainly Callias and Socrates each has a soul. But there is an ambiguity in genetics. Aristotle had stated, again and again, that the father is the adequate cause of the son, at any rate of the form, the mother contributing the matter (the mensis). But the son, too, is an individual with a soul. Aristotle found it necessary to state the relation between generations more accurately. This he does in chapter 5, book XII, of the *Metaphysics*.

Book XII is his final corpus, his third domain of knowledge, theology. (He has three divisions of knowledge, Physics, Mathematics, and Theology.) This book he revised to the end of his

22 *Met.*, Bk. VII, 1036a, 1 ff.; 1040a, 1 ff.

life, as we can see by the eighth chapter, on the plural movers. In chapter 5 we get his most precise statement on form. "But the distinction of actuality and potentiality applies in another way to cases where the matter of cause and of effect is not the same, in some of which cases the form is not the same but different; e.g., the cause of man is (1) the elements (viz., fire and earth as matter, and the peculiar form), and further (2) something else outside, i.e., the father, and (3) besides these the sun and its oblique course." He then goes on to generalize the result: "If the causes of substances are the causes of all things; yet different things have different causes and elements, as has been said; the causes of things that are not in the same class, e.g., of colours and sounds, of substances and quantities are different except in an analogical sense; and those of the things in the same species are different, not in the species, but in the sense that the causes of different individuals are different, your matter and form and moving cause being different from mine, while in their universal definition they are the same."[23] Here we have a precise and final statement in regard to individual forms.

One great stumbling block in the interpretation of Plato and Aristotle is that scholars have approached them with scholastic terminology. Thus γένος has been translated "genus" and εἶδος "species." Since εἶδος and ἰδέα are the words used for form in Plato and Aristotle, it would follow that form is the same as species, at least as the lowest species. This is true in the scholasticism of the thirteenth century. But there is no such established usage in the fourth century B.C. W. D. Ross complains, in a footnote to chapter 10, Book X of the *Metaphysics*: "To translate γένος and εἶδος as genus and species makes nonsense of this chapter. They have therefore been rendered 'kind' and 'form.' "[24] We must not be too hard on Aristotle or Plato. In the fourth century B.C. it was not easy to take a course in scholasticism. It was a

---

[23] Ross translation.

[24] I wish this great scholar, to whom we owe so much, would try the same method on chapter 9 of the same book. I think that would make sense, too. The same could be said of other parts. We need a new approach—an approach from the context of Plato and Aristotle, instead of from scholasticism. At present our translators are out of joint. I cannot say with Hamlet

O cursed spite
That ever I was born to set (it) right!

That must remain for others.

matter of sixteen hundred years of history, which the commentators ignore.

After Aristotle, the Stoics gave a new interpretation of forms in line with the *Sophist* of Plato. Forms are conceived as active or creative forms, λόγοι σπερμάτικοι, what I have called "energy patterns." Pervading all things and giving them rationality is the universal creative reason, λόγος σπερμάτικος, of which the particular forms, λόγοι σπερμάτικοι, including the human reason, are manifestations. Since the Stoics are primarily moralists, the emphasis is on the human soul and its relations to other human souls, and ultimately to the soul of the universe. The Stoics took over from Platonism the hierarchy of forms which is supposed to be repeated in each world cycle, but the individual remained basic, cosmically, psychologically and ethically. Ulpian the Stoic laid down the famous maxim that all men are free and equal, and that slavery is contrary to nature. Salvation is a relation of the individual reason to the world reason. But the Stoic interest in jurisprudence led them to emphasize universal law, and it was this emphasis that commended the Stoics to the Roman empire.

Plotinus follows the Stoics in emphasizing the activity of the forms. They are idea-forces, including individual forms. In the spirit and language of the *Timaeus,* he showed, (as I have already quoted) that the generosity of God must express itself in individual souls. He brought to explicit expression the unity of the soul in its fundamental nature and therefore in its activities. The whole-form of the soul is immortal, backward and forward, in its incarnations. (This is what Plato meant.) Augustine follows Plotinus and indeed repeats his arguments, though since he rejects the pre-existence of the soul (for "lack of evidence," but no doubt because of the Church), he has recourse to con-creation: the soul and body are created together. But the soul is endowed with the Platonic ideas of Truth, Goodness and Beauty. In God all forms exist eternally, and the pure soul can see them in God.

In medieval thought up to the thirteenth century, the ultimate nature of the individual soul was accepted in the spirit of Augustine. The Tree of Porphyry with its Platonic hierarchy of forms was translated into Latin by Boethius and furnished the framework of medieval thought. The hierarchy terminates in individuals—Socrates, Plato and others. Porphyry, in his *Introduction to the Categories,* written for his young pupil, had raised the question whether universals or individuals are to be taken as the ultimately real—in order to whet the interest of his pupil. The young pupil turned out to be the Middle Ages. And the question was debated with great and sometimes tragic zeal. Up to the thirteenth century, the general opinion was that Aristotle was a nominalist, because he had plainly said that only individuals are substances. The trouble arose when Roscellinus carried his nominalism into theology, and said that if linguistic usage permitted we might speak of three gods. By implication, at any rate, the Church would become a collection of individuals, instead of a superhuman reality and the divine source of salvation. A council was called at Soissons; Roscellinus' doctrine was condemned and his book burned, depriving posterity of the knowledge of its contents. We gather from his enemies that he maintained that a universal is a mere word, *flatus vocis,* and that only individuals are real.

From Anselm, who was the energetic accuser, we gather that according to Roscellinus humanity would be just men and color would be just colors.[24a] The juxtaposition is interesting because it shows that the medieval realists did not distinguish between qualitative universals, such as color, and structural forms, such as humanity. This identification is contrary to both Plato and Aristotle. According to Plato sense qualities, such as color, are emergent facts due to the interaction of the motion from the environment with the internal motion of the organism. This is clearly indicated in the *Theaetetus* and developed in the *Timaeus,* for all the sense qualities. For Aristotle sense qualities, such as white, are accidents, and are not part of the nature ($o\dot{v}\sigma\dot{\iota}a$) of the individual. A universal is an abstraction, but form is the very structure of the individual. The Middle Ages never did clear up the confusion of forms with universals. And the confusion has remained to this day.

We may say that the question, which was raised by Porphyry, was not settled on its logical merits. It became a political question, and the Church threw its great power, including the power of the

---

[24a] Qualitative universals are class-concepts. Roscellinus was right that color does not exist. Color is a word symbolizing color discriminations, though particular colors can be grouped into a class or classes on the basis of their affinities. See J. E. Boodin, *Contemporary American Philosophy,* I, 158 ff.; *Cosmic Evolution* (1925), 342 ff. It is different with a structural concept, such as humanity. The human species has objective existence, at any rate when we view it genetically. Humanity must be viewed as a time form. That, of course, was impossible for Roscellinus and the Middle Ages.

State, on the side of universals. The theologians were too pious to antagonize the Church, and, besides, in the twelfth century the pope-maker, St. Bernard, had a passion for purifying heretics by fire. So all united, including Abelard, in denouncing Roscellinus. The Church felt rightly that nominalism would undermine its authority. It was not until its authority was undermined that Ockham could assert frankly the nominalistic doctrine that only individuals are real. He was unintentionally the herald of the Protestant revolt against Catholic authority.

The nominalists were right that the individual form is real. But they did not see, as Aristotle, Abelard and Aquinas did, that the universal has a derived reality as an extract and abstract from individuals, and is important in discourse. A word must be relevant to be significant. Still less did the nominalists see that the living form of the individual is organically related to the larger living form of the species. That means going back to Plato.

The trouble with the medieval realists (including the commentators of today) is that they did not grasp the organismic conception of Plato or Aristotle. The scholastic emphasis is on universals, from being down to *infima species*. The realists did not grasp being as a living organismic form, including individual forms. The nominalists saw rightly the reality of the individual forms, but they were not able, because of the abstract tradition, to see that the individual must be seen in relation to more comprehensive concrete forms such as species. This relationship could be made clear only by the conception of evolution.

The climax was reached in the thirteenth century, when Albertus Magnus and Thomas Aquinas denied individual forms, and made the lowest species, *infima species,* the final form. This result was the outcome of the emphasis on universals, especially the universal church, as the ultimate reality, though they claimed the support of Aristotle. The supposed support was a mistranslation which has persisted to this day.[25] The Aristotelian interpretation was supposed to support the doctrine of transubstantiation, though the Franciscans, who followed the Augustinian tradition, believed in transubstantiation as much as the Dominicans who followed Aquinas. The Thomistic interpretation of the individual, viz., that matter is the principle of individuation and that all men have the same form, would logically have made immortality impossible,

[25] See J. E. Boodin, *Three Interpretations of the Universe*, 362 ff.

as Duns Scotus argued.   But Duns Scotus's weak attempt to save the individual form as a constriction or condensation within the species was discarded for nominalism by Ockham.   In the meantime such doctrines as incarnation and immortality had been grounded upon faith, as they always had been, and removed from the dubious domain of reason.

In the modern period, the medieval confusion of forms with universals has persisted.   The concept of ontological form as structure has played little part in modern philosophy.   It is only recently that there has been a resurgence of Platonism, though generally unconscious.   Claude Bernard showed that the organism functions as a whole in its own economy and in relation to the environment; and the same wholism was worked out more fully by J. S. Haldane, especially in his classic work on Respiration.   He showed how the energy system of the organism determines selectively the action of the atmosphere in breathing, and in turn how the organism could be viewed as part of the larger form of the environment, so that we could say that the universe breathes in us with as much relevance as that we breathe in the universe.   The same could, of course, be said of other vital functions, such as thinking.   Here the dialectic of research, independently of Plato, has thrown fresh light upon Plato's conception of the cosmic inter-relation of forms.[26]

The development of genetics has thrown fresh light upon the relation of generations in the stream of life, and, again, unconsciously, has made scientists take account of a phylogenetic form as well as an ontogenetic form.   It is not possible to account for life merely as individual.   The individual must be understood in his genetic relationship.   It is easy to see that men who took the world as ready-made could look upon man as a universal—an abstraction from the similarities of individual men.   But if we look upon man in evolution, we must recognize that the time-order of development is essential.   There is a time-form of man, which includes a series

[26] There are many indications of form in contemporary science, for example, H. Speman's postulating an "organizing field" to explain the directed activities which result in a highly organized animal.   (*Embryonic Development and Induction*, 1939.) This conception is given a cosmic background in Gustaf Stromberg's genii (another name for Platonic forms) which ingress into the evolutionary process from the world soul.   (See the *Soul of the Universe*, 1940.)

of space-forms, which are transmuted into one another in an orderly way.

The brilliant development in the physical sciences has tended, again unconsciously, by its own dialectic to confirm the Platonic intuition of form and measure everywhere.   The building-bricks of nature—electrons, neutrons, etc.—are measured, are constant in nature, and this fact indicates cosmic control.   The discovery by Moseley of atomic number—a series of atomic forms repeated in nature everywhere—is evidence of cosmic architecture which would have delighted the soul of Plato.   There is indication of a life-number—a radiating pattern of life-forms.   This order even more obviously than atomic number has reference to time.

In modern thought, as in Greek thought, the emphasis has been upon space-form.   Time has been mostly neglected, except as a dimension of space.   The forms of Plato and Aristotle are eternal forms.   Aristotle's biological interest might have led him to discover time-form, if he had not been so completely biased in favor of the eternal.   He does deal with development from potentiality to actuality, but he does not think of realization in terms of time. In the development of the human individual, the form for Aristotle is the same throughout, i.e., is the form of the mature man.   There is no evolution of species in Aristotle.   Plato has an order of creation in nature, but it is stated in a mythical way.   Plotinus interpreted Plato's order of creation as an eternal chain of forms, within a living whole, from the most general forms to the individual soul.

The great need is the development of the idea of time-form. Anaximander and Heraclitus did conceive the cosmos as an order of time, but their insight was killed by Parmenides, and has only recently been revived.   I have tried to develop the concept of time-form ontogenetically, phylogenetically and cosmically.[27]   Plato is right that there is a structure of generations as well as individual structure.   But each is a time form and not merely a space form. And Plato was right that there is a whole-form, ὅλον εἶδος, of the

[27] See the author's *A Realistic Universe* (1931), chapters III and XVIII; *Cosmic Evolution* (1925), chapters III and VIII; *Three Interpretations of the Universe* (1934), chapters IV, V, and VI, esp. V; *God* (1934), chapters II to VI; *The Social Mind* (1939), chapter 1; *Man In His World* (1939); including "Cosmic Implications of Normative Structure," *Proceedings Ninth Internat. Cong. of Philosophy* (1937); "A Revolution in Metaphysics and Science," *Philosophy of Science* (1939).

cosmos, but this whole-form has reference to time as well as to space, to the future as well as to the past, furnishing a guiding field of the multitudinous histories, so far as their inertia and wilfulness permit.   This cosmic whole must be, as Plato felt, in some sense a living whole in order to be self-maintaining and self-regulative.[28] The only alternative would be the conception of fiat creation.   But such a conception is not intelligible and, therefore, cannot be entertained in science or philosophy.

[28] See the author's *God* (1934), Chapter IV.

∽ঌ *Richard McKeon*

ARISTOTLE'S CONCEPTION OF SCIENTIFIC METHOD

I. *Method and the Theories of Philosophers*

In his scientific inquiries and in his demonstration of the conclusions to which they led, Aristotle makes use of carefully elaborated methods which become themselves the object of his attention in three distinct investigations. The differences and interrelations of these inquiries illustrate as well as state the diversifications and unity of his conception of scientific method. Aristotle frequently begins an inquiry or formulates a problem by reviewing the doctrines of other philosophers, for although the method appropriate to a problem is determined by the subject matter on which it is to be employed, the varieties of theory and of theoretical construction may be suggested by historical examination of what men have said concerning a subject of inquiry or by dialectical exploration of possible formulations. The examination of doctrines leads him, in the second place, to the search for principles and the construction of inferences, which are the distinctive marks of methods in the various sciences, and when he pauses in his scientific investigations of phenomena to consider what course he should pursue, his purpose is to discover methods appropriate to particular problems and subject matters and to differentiate them from methods appropriate to other sciences. These considerations of method as reflected in doctrine and opinion and as appropriate to subject matters, finally, depend on distinctions and criteria determined by examination of the logical conditions of statement and inference. The inquiry concerning method in this last stage is itself a kind of science or knowledge. Its subject matter is the terms and propositions, the principles and proofs which are used or constructed in the expression of opinion and knowledge. Since its subject matter is terms, not words, and propositions, not sentences, it is not restricted to the formal study of symbols and language, for the symbolic formulation of the inferences and conclusions of the sciences is inseparable in Aristotle's scientific investigations from the structure of doctrine and belief in which conclusions follow, and that structure in turn reflects the nature of things and causes which the principles of inference express.

The examination of common and expert opinion is therefore an integral part of Aristotle's investigation of the nature of things, and considerations of the controlling influence of the presuppositions of doctrines and the nature of things enter into the determination of the parts and the distinctions of his logic.   In the theoretical sciences Aristotle frequently makes two or more "starts," first to formulate problems in metaphysics, physics, psychology, and biology by examining what has been, and what might be, said about their principles or about specific parts of problems, comparing modes and grounds of statement, and seeking reasons for similarities and differences, before proceeding to "fresh starts" or "returning to the starting point" by directing attention abruptly from the dialectical examination of opinions to the scientific examination of things.

The sequence of inquiry in the treatise *On the Soul* is an excellent example of his use of historical, dialectical, and scientific methods as successive devices of exploration.   After examining the doctrines of other philosophers concerning the nature of the soul in Book I, Aristotle begins Book II by making a fresh start on the definition of the soul,[1] and then, since the definition of the soul which is constructed in the first chapter of Book II is dialectical, a second "return to the beginning of the investigation" is made to construct a definition which will disclose not merely the fact but the cause.[2]   The *Metaphysics* opens with an elaborate dialectical preparation, including the examination of the principles of other philosophers in Book I and the formulation of difficulties and problems in Book III, before proceeding finally to the treatment of the proper problems of first philosophy in Book VI.   The *Physics* makes a "fresh start" in the examination of nature at the beginning of Book II,[3] after the principles of change and motion have been examined dialectically and on the basis of the theories of earlier physicists in Book I.   Like devices are used in the pursuit of inquiries in particular problems when new beginnings are made on the basis of dialectical preparation to avoid the errors consequent on initial false distinctions and to establish the science on natural beginnings or principles.[4]

[1] *On the Soul* ii. 1. 412^{a}3–6.

[2] *Ibid.* 2. 413^{a}11–25.

[3] *Physics* i. 9. 192^{b}1–4.

[4] Cf. *Physics* viii. 5. 257^{a}31–33 and 7. 260^{a}20–21; *On the Heavens* i. 2. 268^{b}11–14 and 12. 281^{b}2–3; *Meteorology* ii. 4. 359^{b}27–28; *Metaphysics* vii. 17. 1041^{a}6–9.

These preliminary devices consist sometimes in examining words, suggesting and analyzing etymologies, enumerating possible meanings, or inquiring into the peculiarities of technical or common usage; they depend sometimes on explaining ideas by their evolution and context as suggested by the interpretation of myth, poetry, and historical circumstances and processes; they turn sometimes on the possibilities of theory disclosed by examining, criticizing, and refuting the arguments and conclusions proposed by philosophers or constructed to complement or balance actual doctrines. The historical portions of these inquiries Aristotle justifies frequently by observing, in mid-course of his historical excursions, that hints and anticipations of true doctrines, as well as tests and refutations of errors, may be found anywhere in the recorded experiences, thoughts, and statements of mankind. The dialectical exploration of the implications of statements supplies the only tests for the principles of theoretic sciences, and previous theories are a useful, and often unique, source of suggestion in the discovery of solutions to particular problems, not only in metaphysics and mathematics, but even in the most empirical branches of the physical sciences.

The same devices are employed in the practical and productive sciences,[5] sometimes with the analogy of the physical and biological sciences clearly in view.[6] Speculation concerning morals, politics, and the arts, however, was of later origin than investigation of nature. Apart from the doctrines of Socrates and Plato, Aristotle found few extensive or developed opinions concerning moral action suited to serve as materials for preliminary dialectical examination, and the history of literature rather than literary criticism supplies the background for poetic analysis.

Method itself, finally, occupies a peculiar place in the development of the arts and the organization of the sciences. It seemed to Aristotle to have come to the attention of philosophers together with the practical sciences and the poetic arts, but since it is the art of constructing scientific proofs it was developed in use before it was formulated in statement. Aristotle examines from time to time in his own scientific treatises the methods which earlier philosophers had used to establish definitions and to justify conclusions,

[5] Cf. *Nicomachean Ethics* vii. 1. 1145ª15–17; *Politics* i. 13. 1260ᵇ20–24; *Rhetoric* i. 1. 1355ᵇ23–25.

[6] Cf. *Politics* ii. 1. 1260ᵇ36–37, where a "natural" starting point is sought for politics, and *ibid.* iv. 4. 1290ᵇ21–37, where a starting place is sought on the analogy of biological inquiry.

and he detected the application of scientific method in the attempts at definition made by Democritus and the Pythagoreans. Explicit doctrines and theories of method are later and less numerous, and Aristotle obviously thought that concern with method had not been conspicuous before his own reports on the varieties of approaches to problems and the similarities and differences among methods. Some problems of method had, however, been the object of direct consideration in Socrates' development of inductive arguments and definitions and in Plato's examination of the processes of division. That these gropings among the forms and grounds of proof, both in theory and in application, are in Aristotle's judgment metaphysical rather than logical in their consequences, is apparent from the fact that he treats them in some detail in the *Metaphysics* but rarely refers to them in his own formulation of the syllogism as a method of proof or in his examination of definition among the principles of proof.

In the last chapter of *On Sophistical Refutations* he contrasts with the history of rhetoric in which a body of teaching, however limited and unsatisfactory, had been developed, the state of inquiry into syllogizing or reasoning where work had been limited to experimental beginnings prior to his own formulation of method; and although the explicit claim to originality is made only in connection with his treatment of dialectical and sophistical argumentation, it applies *a fortiori* to his development of scientific proof and the syllogism in general, where the scanty refutations of a few Platonic doctrines and the silence concerning logic in other philosophers are evidence that Aristotle doubtless thought his own treatises the first systematic inquiries into scientific investigation and proof as well. This claim to originality has more than merely historical or biographical interest, for Aristotle documents the differences which distinguish earlier inquiries from his own scientific method, and the enthusiasm with which later historians of philosophy discover earlier beginnings of his doctrines concerning categories, definitions, propositions, and even syllogisms, depends on distortions of the Aristotelian conception of logic and scientific method which can be rectified by attention to Aristotle's own interpretation of historical data derived by his critics largely from his own works.[7]

[7] The history of scholarly inquiries concerning Plato's logic since the Renaissance, as traced by W. Lutoslawski (*The Origin and Growth of Plato's Logic* [London, 1905], 1–34), turns in good part on balancing the comparative claims of

Philosophers and scientists had first treated problems of method in the course of investigating facts and interpreting sense-perceptions and appearances. The shift of interest from physical to moral and political problems may have stimulated the inquiries into the nature of definition and proof which were contemporary with them, and the analogies and differences of morals and physics, of the arts and the sciences, by which method itself became a subject for investigation in the moral and political disputations of Socrates reported in the dialogues of Plato, reappear in Aristotle as means of distinguishing the theoretic, practical, and productive sciences. The Socratic analogies between arts and virtues doubtless led Aristotle to see in Socrates the beginnings of inquiry into both moral and methodological questions, whereas the Sophists, who dispute moral issues with Socrates and appear as professed masters of all sciences in the dialogues of Plato, are credited in the systematic distinctions of Aristotle, not with practical or theoretic innovations, but only with the elaboration of rhetorical statement and sophistical reasoning. But although Socrates and Plato first analyzed the formal requirements of definition and proof, the scientific method of Democritus alone seemed to Aristotle to have been adequate to the statement of specific scientific problems, and only Democritus seemed to have penetrated below the surface and to have analyzed some problems thoroughly.

Plato and Aristotle. Lutoslawski's own position is that Plato's logic is more independent of the traditional forms of language than the logic of Aristotle, and his range of investigation, if less minute, is scarcely less universal. Even his theory of syllogism, although it was not brought to the precise form which it assumed in the works of Aristotle, prepared for that formulation (*ibid.*, 464, 524). Paul Shorey defends the thesis that "the Platonic dialectic anticipates nearly everything in the Aristotelian logic except the explicit exposition of the syllogism" ("The Origin of the Syllogism," *Classical Phililogy*, XIX [1924], 1; cf. "The Origin of the Syllogism Again," *ibid.* XXVIII [1933], 199–204). Julius Stenzel likewise maintains that Aristotle is throughout his logic building on Plato's results (*Plato's Method of Dialectic*, trans. D. J. Allan [Oxford, 1940], 91, 137 n. 1). Cf. F. Solmsen, *Die Entwicklung der aristotelischen Logik und Rhetorik* (Neue Philologische Untersuchungen, IV, Berlin, 1929) ; Ernst Kapp, *Greek Foundations of Traditional Logic* (New York, 1942), esp. 57–59, 67–70, 73–74; and H. Cherniss, *Aristotle's Criticism of Plato and the Academy* (Baltimore, 1944), esp. 30–31. F. Enriques, on the other hand (*The Historic Development of Logic*, trans. J. Rosenthal [New York, 1929], esp. 4–7, 14–19, 25–28), turns to the mathematicians, the empirical philosophers, and especially Democritus, for the origin and correction of methods and doctrines in the Aristotelian logic.

Earlier developments in scientific method fall, in Aristotle's treatment of them, between the typical extremes of Plato and Democritus: Plato's consideration of method led to the construction of a theory, but he failed to account for phenomena, while Democritus was faithful to phenomena, but he had no theory adequate to account for their causes. Thus, in the investigation of the processes of change Plato restricted his attention to the generation of the elements and paid no attention to the generation of composite bodies or to processes of alteration and growth in them, despite the fact that alteration is a datum of empirical observation.[8] Those philosophers who asserted that the universe is a single something were unable to differentiate generation (or the change by which a substance comes to be) from alteration (or the change of quality in an existing thing), while philosophers like Anaxagoras, Empedocles and Leucippus who asserted a plurality of elements were forced by their theories to differentiate generation from alteration and growth, but were involved in contradictions, since Anaxagoras failed to understand the implications of his own statements and Empedocles contradicted both his own statements and the observed facts.[9]

Democritus alone of Aristotle's predecessors is exempted from this criticism, and he seemed not only to have thought about all the problems involved but also to have been distinguished throughout by his method.[10] The virtue of the procedure of Democritus and of his predecessor Leucippus consisted in its fidelity to observed facts. They came nearest of all previous philosophers to defining according to method by constructing a single formula applicable to all instances and by deriving the principle for their definitions from nature as it is.[11] Their theory, therefore, harmonized with sense perception and did not involve, as did the principles of other philosophers, the necessity of denying generation, corruption, motion, or the multiplicity of things.[12] Although the method of Democritus permitted him to differentiate generation from alteration and growth, however, it had the unfortunate defect that it was inadequate to account for any of the kinds of change and motion which

[8] *On Generation and Corruption* i. 2. 315^{a}29–33.
[9] *Ibid.* 1. 314^{a}6–315^{a}25.
[10] *Ibid.* 2. 315^{a}34–316^{a}1.
[11] *Ibid.* 8. 324^{b}35–325^{a}2.
[12] *Ibid.* 325^{a}23–25.

it distinguished, but yielded a theory in which alteration and growth are strictly impossible.[13]

The failure of Democritus to discover the true method of the physical and biological sciences, in spite of his close approximation to it in use, was due to his lack of any notion of essence or definition.

The reason why our predecessors did not hit on this method was that essence and the defining of substance were unknown in their time. Democritus was the first to touch on the problem, not however because he thought it necessary to natural science, but because he was brought to it, in spite of himself, by the facts. In the time of Socrates the study of this problem advanced, but inquiry concerning nature was abandoned, and philosophers turned their attention to practical virtue and political science.[14]

Most of the ancient physical philosophers sought the principles and causes of natural phenomena in matter, and only a few among them, like Empedocles and Democritus, had any notion of form and essence.[15] Thus, Democritus did not rely on matter alone but defined animals and their parts by means of shape and color; and although Aristotle professes some hesitation in venturing an interpretation of what Democritus meant by that formal addition,[16] he had no doubt of its inadequacy to differentiate living from dead, or actual from potential. But if the method was imperfect in defining natures because of its inadequate treatment of the formal cause, it failed utterly to account for motion because all conception of efficient and final causes was excluded and the differences and modifications of things were traced to the shape, order, and position of the atoms. Like all other philosophers, Democritus seemed to Aristotle to have omitted "lazily" all questions of motion—when it is caused and how it is present in things.[17] The only explanation of motion available to Democritus was the insufficient principle of previous occurrence.

Nor in general is it sound to suppose that it is a sufficient principle that something always is thus or always happens thus. Democritus, thus, reduced the causes of physical phenomena to the fact that things happened in the same way in the past, and did not think it worthwhile to seek a principle

[13] *Ibid.* 10. 327ᵃ14–29; *ibid.* 327ᵃ14–29.

[14] *On the Parts of Animals* i. 1. 642ᵃ24–31.

[15] *Physics* ii. 2. 194ᵃ18–21; *On the Parts of Animals* i. 1. 640ᵇ4–641ᵃ6.

[16] *On the Parts of Animals* 640ᵇ29–35.

[17] *Metaphysics* i. 4. 985ᵇ19–20.

for what is always the case, and so his theory is right in application to certain instances, but it is not right in application to all.[18]

As a result, despite his effort to be faithful to the facts, Democritus assigns causes too generally without investigating the facts in all cases, and in particular he ignores the final cause in the biological sciences, reducing natural phenomena to necessity without recognizing that nothing prevents their being both necessary and for an end.[19]

Democritus' contributions to the advance of scientific method are found in his use of method rather than in a formulation of its requirements. Aristotle praises his method in application to physical phenomena and traces its deficiencies to the overgeneralization which results from the absence of a notion of essence or definition and to the inadequate conception of cause which results from the generalizations of the atomic theory. Socrates, on the other hand, is distinguished according to Aristotle as the first to raise questions concerning the nature of definition, and his interest in that problem is in turn to be traced back to his desire to determine more precisely the nature and use of proof. But his investigation of the conditions of universal definition and of the arguments by which they are validated was pursued in connection with moral rather than physical inquiries, and his method was inapplicable to physical phenomena since it lacked a conception of cause to account for change.

Socrates occupied himself with the moral virtues, and in connection with them was the first to seek universal definition—for in physical questions Democritus barely touched on the problem and defined the hot and the cold after a fashion, while the Pythagoreans, still earlier, had broached it in connection with some few things whose definitions they connected with numbers, such as opportunity, justice, or marriage—but it was natural that Socrates should seek essence, for he was seeking to syllogize, and essence is the principle of syllogisms.[20]

Socrates' inquiries into the principles of science and proof led him to the development of two processes which he was the first philosopher to employ: inductive arguments and universal definition.[21]

[18] *Physics* viii. 1. 252ª32–ᵇ2.

[19] *On the Generation of Animals* v. 8. 788ᵇ9–20; 789ᵇ2–5. Cf. also *On Respiration* 10. 471ᵇ30–472ª25.

[20] *Metaphysics* xiii. 4. 1078ᵇ17–25.

[21] *Ibid.* xiii. 4. 1078ᵇ27–30: "For two processes may rightly be attributed to Socrates: inductive arguments and defining universally, and both of these are

Yet despite innovations in definition, the method which Socrates developed in the *Phaedo* is unsuited to account for motion and change, for it depends on the doctrine that the Forms are the causes of both being and becoming. Aristotle argues that the things which share in Forms will not come into being, even though the Forms exist, unless there is an efficient cause of each generation. The method of Socrates, thus, although it advances beyond the method of Democritus in its treatment of definitions, shares with it the failure to account for the operation of efficient causes, and although Socrates blames everyone else for having given no explanation of generation, he likewise fails to account for generation or motion.[22]

Plato's investigation of method carried the search for the grounds of argument to the further step of separating the Forms, which he called "Ideas," from the changing things which participate in them and, in so doing, making Forms eternal things. This modification of the Socratic doctrine seemed to Aristotle to create new problems of definition without resolving the problems of change and causation. According to Aristotle's account, Plato continued Socrates' interest in moral questions and universal definitions, but differed from him in holding that the common definition could not apply to sensible things, which are constantly changing, but must apply to things of another sort, and it is these changeless things which he called Ideas. The Ideas exist apart from sensible things, and sensible things participate in them and bear the same names as the Forms they share, the application of the same name to both eternal and changing things being univocal or synonymous in the Platonic theory,[23] but equivocal or homonymous if the meanings of terms are different in application to changeless and to changing things, as they are in the Aristotelian criticism.[24]

The development of the doctrine of Ideas in the evolution of dialectic is presented by Aristotle as a consequence of reflection at once on the nature of argument and the nature of things. If the whole sensible world is in a state of constant flux and if scientific

---

pertinent to the principle of science." Cf. also, *ibid.* i. 6. 987[b]1–4: "Socrates, however, was treating of ethical problems and not of the problems of the whole of nature, seeking the universal in those ethical problems and applying thought for the first time to definitions. . . ."

[22] *Ibid.* i. 9. 991[b]3–9; *On Generation and Corruption* ii. 9. 335[b]7–17.

[23] *Metaphysics* i. 6. 987[b]4–10.

[24] *Ibid.* xiii. 4. 1078[b]30–1079[a]4.

knowledge of sensibles is impossible, as Plato was convinced from his contact with Heraclitean doctrines, the search for scientific knowledge must lead to existences of another kind. Dialectic had been so little developed before Socrates' inquiries that not even the requirements of definition had been explored, and in the absence of a conception of essence it had been impossible to investigate contraries or to decide whether contraries came under the same science. Socrates had examined universals and definitions without having been led to think there were any existences apart from sensible things, but in Plato's theory there were Ideas of all terms predicated universally as well as of all particulars.[25] The Pythagoreans, on the other hand, had applied themselves to mathematics and had come to believe that its principles—and in particular numbers, which were by nature first among these principles—were the principles of all things. As Plato had departed from the doctrine of Socrates by supplying entities for his definitions as the subjects to which true arguments applied, so he departed from the doctrine of the Pythagoreans by making their numbers entities as a result of his inquiry into the arguments: "his institution of the One and the Numbers apart from things, unlike the Pythagoreans, and his introduction of the Forms, resulted from his inquiry into arguments, for the earlier thinkers were not practitioners of dialectic."[26]

Aristotle's ascription to Plato of an inquiry into arguments (ἐν τοῖς λόγοις . . . . σκέψις)[27] and the inference from his dialectical method to the nature of Ideas and Numbers carries an echo of Plato's ascription to Socrates of a method of "inquiring into the nature of things in argument" (ἐν τοῖς λόγοις σκοπούμενον τὰ ὄντα)[28] which is suggestive of the altered application which Plato made of the method of Socrates to bring it to bear on the principles of the Pythagoreans. Socrates professes a preference for inquiry in, and by means of, arguments as a second best approximation to the direct contemplation of things and the statement of the highest kind of cause, which he finds impossible of attainment. A second kind of cause may be discovered in argument, and it is related to reality by means of Ideas entertained hypothetically. This method of inquiry in arguments is in turn to be preferred to a third method

[25] *Ibid.* 1078ᵇ25–1079ᵃ4.
[26] *Ibid.* i. 6. 987ᵇ29–33.
[27] *Ibid.* 987ᵇ31–32; cf. *ibid.* vii. 13. 1038ᵇ34 and ix. 8. 1050ᵇ35.
[28] *Phaedo* 100A.

"of inquiring in operations." The method which led Plato to the doctrine of Ideas, as Aristotle formulates it, is not described in the lengthy consideration of its bearing on definition and principles in the *Metaphysics,* and the metaphysical implications of the method, in turn, are not developed in his criticism of the method in the logical treatises. The doctrine of Ideas seemed to Aristotle irrelevant to the purposes of scientific inquiry, although it resulted from a dialectical examination of the nature of arguments and proofs; and the method of division, to which that inquiry led, seemed to him inadequate to validate inference and proof, although it is not without its value as a heuristic device. It is inadequate as a method of proof, since it is a weak syllogism and begs precisely what it ought to prove, but if the division is by differentiae, it is a method of collecting essential natures and discovering definitions, and therefore a useful accessory to proof.[29]

Aristotle makes frequent use of the contrast between the methods of Democritus and Plato to isolate problems of method and to indicate characteristics which he thinks the true scientific method should possess. Both with respect to the devices of analysis and inquiry which they employ and with respect to the metaphysical assumptions on which they are based, the two methods are contrary to each other, and their advantages and deficiencies are opposed and balanced. The true scientific method is distinct from both and should combine their advantages and avoid their errors. Democritus, because of the fidelity of his arguments to his subject matter, made a close approach to a scientific method appropriate to particular problems; but he was unable, within the scope of his method, to find any essence or definition of things beyond material configuration and color or any cause of motion other than the fact that things had been in motion or that what happened had happened in the same way before. He had a rudimentary conception of form, but he wholly neglected efficient and final causes. Plato, on the other hand, treated of essence and definition in his dialectic, but unfortunately his Forms were removed from sensible, changing things and without direct effect on them, and he was therefore unable, in the absence of an efficient cause, to account for motion and change.

The advantage, on the side of facts, lies with the "physical

[29] *Prior Analytics* i. 31. 46ᵃ31–ᵇ37; *Posterior Analytics* ii. 5. 91ᵇ12–92ᵃ5 and 13. 96ᵇ25–97ᵃ6. Cf., also, *On Generation and Corruption* ii. 3. 330ᵇ16–17; *On the Parts of Animals* i. 2. and 3. 642ᵇ5–644ᵃ11; *Metaphysics* vii. 12. 1037ᵇ27–1038ᵃ35.

method," as Aristotle sometimes calls the procedure of Democritus, and, on the side of formal proof, with the "logical method" of Plato.

Lack of experience is the reason why we are less able to take a comprehensive view of the admitted facts. Wherefore those who have dwelt more constantly on investigation of natural phenomena are more able to set up as hypotheses such principles as can be applied coherently to many instances : while those who have been rendered unobservant of the facts by many arguments find it easy to make pronouncements on the basis of a few observations. It is apparent from the methods of investigating the subject under consideration how great the difference is between those who investigate according to a "physical" and according to a "logical" [or "argumentative"] method. For whereas some [sc. the Platonists] argue that there must be indivisible magnitudes because otherwise the Triangle in itself would be many, Democritus seems to have been convinced by appropriate and physical arguments.[30]

The deficiencies of the "physical method" arise from the fact that it is unsuited to explain wholes otherwise than by decomposing them into their parts, as if it were a sufficient explanation of a couch to say that it is made of wood or bronze. Aristotle, therefore, grouped Democritus with the old physical philosophers or physiologists in the judgment that their method was inadequate. This failure to deal adequately with wholes is apparent in biological phenomena as well as in inanimate nature. The true method in biological investigation consists, first, in seeking the definition of the animal as a whole and explaining it both in substance and in form and then treating its several organs in precisely the same fashion; the same procedure must be followed if one is to give a complete description of a couch.[31] The beginnings of the "logical method," on the other hand, may be traced to the Pythagoreans, who had formulated a few definitions and relied in their analyses simply on numbers rather than on physical parts, without, however, concerning themselves with the dialectic of their procedure. The Platonists, who followed the lead of Socrates and who borrowed from the Pythagoreans, developed a dialectic in which the deficiencies of the logical method are apparent, for it removed definitions from application to sensible things and elaborated principles which are useless for the explanation of phenomena or the construction of particular sciences.

[30] *On Generation and Corruption* i. 2. 316ª5–14.
[31] *On the Parts of Animals* i. 1. 641ª14–17.

The difficulties of the sciences, as Aristotle traces the history of the development of method, center about two sets of problems: the problems of inquiry and proof and the problems of definition considered as the product of inquiry and the principle of proof. In neither of these problems did Aristotle profess to find much help in the work of his predecessors. Consequently, contrary to his custom in other investigations, he quotes them little for doctrine, and such use as he finds for their arguments, even as examples, is primarily as illustrations of dialectical or sophistical reasoning. The rejection of their methods is due in part to metaphysical assumptions which are shown to be inadequate and in part to faulty resolution of particular problems of inquiry or definition. The dialectical method of Plato is adapted to the examination of definitions and principles, but at the expense of removing the foundations of truth from relevant application to experience and from plausible explanation of the phenomena of change: it is therefore treated in connection with metaphysics and the more general problems of the natural sciences. The method of Democritus encounters principles and leads to definitions, since both are involved necessarily in the survey and use of data, but the principles which Democritus states do not themselves transcend the indeterminacy involved in infinity and change: his method is therefore encountered more frequently in the treatment of specific scientific problems, although it also involves some implications for the general problems of metaphysics and physics. The demonstrations of Plato consist in simple divisions and combinations of terms, which, since they are useful as part of the method of science, even though they are not inferential or demonstrative, are properly treated in the logic of proof. The method of Democritus, although accurate in application to particular cases, could have no general formulation—and the limits even of the particular case are difficult to determine—in the absence of an adequate conception of definition. It is non-demonstrative since it cannot be extended validly in universal application, and it is incomplete since it omits relevant aspects of phenomena.

Yet the reasons for these deficiencies are to be found in the opposite forms of common errors into which Plato and Democritus had fallen, and the characteristics of the scientific method and logical analyses which Aristotle initiated may be gathered from consideration of his criticisms of the methods of these philosophers, who had been involved in problems of method while treating the subject matters of knowledge, the nature of science, and the principles of arguments. Both Plato and Democritus equated mind and things; both reduced all sciences to a single science; and both sought in mathematics the model of scientific argumentation and indeed made mathematics the whole of science. The logic of Aristotle is based on the denial of all three theses in both of the opposed forms in which Democritus and Plato had advanced them.

In any account of scientific method, the subject matters of the sciences determine and are determined by the psychological processes in which subject matters are known, for the facts are the basis of knowledge, but the manner in which they are known determines whether or not the knowledge is scientific. Reason or nature may be thought to be basic, and they may then be brought into relation with each other by making nature rational or reason physical. The dialectic of Plato led him to set up eternal things, which alone truly are and which are named Ideas; Democritus on the other hand thought that truth lay in appearances or phenomena,[32] and the mind's access to appearances depends on the fact that mind itself is constituted of the atoms and of their motions and conjunctions. Both philosophers therefore equate things and thought, Plato by making things into Ideas in order to preserve in being what is changeless in knowledge; Democritus by making mind a thing in order to preserve in mind what is real in the characteristics of being. Within thought both distinguished sensibles and intelligibles, but when Plato separated Ideas from sensible things, the mind still had direct access to Ideas through reminiscence, while Democritus, recognizing the relativity of sensations caused in the mind by external motions, had greater difficulty in discovering a basis for truth and propounded the dilemma that either there is no truth or it is not evident to us.[33]

The errors of these two statements of the relation of knowledge to things are opposite, yet both result in destroying the subject matter of science by submitting objects to the requirements of knowledge: Plato, in his reliance on dialectic, setting up entities distinct from changing things and therefore useless in furthering the pursuit of science; and Democritus, in his reliance on phenomena, setting up a mind in which the perceptions of sense are irrelevant to science. The dialectic of Aristotle's use of their doc-

[32] *In Generation and Corruption* i. 2. 315^{b}9–10.
[33] *Metaphysics* iv. 5. 1009^{b}11–12.

trines emphasizes these contraries, but their similarity is more apparent in the accounts of later philosophers. They both divided things into intelligibles and sensibles and sought truth by way of intellect rather than sense,[34] and they were associated with each other in their opposition to the sensationalism and relativism of Protagoras and in their defense of the position that only intelligibles are true: Democritus because nothing sensible, but only atoms and the void, exist truly; Plato because sensibles are always becoming and never being, and only Ideas are truly.[35]

The conception of the fundamental nature of reality—whether it consist in Forms or atoms—determines the nature of the principles sought in the sciences; and Aristotle therefore treats Democritus and Plato as opposed in their conception of principles and causes, Democritus seeking the principles of things in matter but achieving some conception of form,[36] and Plato seeking his principles in the Forms and achieving some conception of matter in the indeterminate dyad but, in the process, confusing matter and space.[37] Since neither account provides for efficient or final causes, neither is adequate to account for motion, Democritus denying the reality of chance in natural phenomena and setting up a causal nexus in deterministic explanation of the universe, which as a whole nonetheless derives its origin from chance,[38] Plato employing a dialectical method which is insufficient to account for motion or to differentiate physics from other sciences.[39]

The resulting conception of science is much the same whether things are referred to a single basis of explanation by being reduced to a single underlying matter or whether demonstration, definition, and induction are referred to a single principle and developed in a single dialectical method by which all sciences are reduced to a single science of all things.[40] For the unity of a science is determined by the unity of its subject matter, which consists in a single genus of things, and its scope is determined by the fact that every science deals with both terms of the pair of contraries which falls

[34] Sextus Empiricus vii. 135–144.
[35] *Ibid.* vii. 389–90; viii. 6–7.
[36] *Metaphysics* i. 4. 985^{b}4–20; *Physics* ii. 2. 194^{a}18–21.
[37] *Metaphysics* i. 6. 988^{a}7–17 and 9. 992^{b}1–9; *Physics* iv. 2. 209^{b}11–17.
[38] *Physics* ii. 4. 195^{b}36–196^{a}17; 196^{a}24–^{b}5.
[39] *Metaphysics* iv. 2. 1004^{b}17–26 and xi. 3. 1061^{a}18–^{b}11.
[40] *Ibid.* i. 9. 992^{b}29–33.

under it.[41]   Stated in terms of the principles of science, Democritus and Plato committed a double and antithetical error since both introduced the infinite, which is unintelligible, among their principles, and both were unclear in stating the relation of their principles to phenomena.   Plato made the infinite a principle and made it self-subsistent apart from sensibles, while Democritus made the elements infinite in number and thus made infinity an attribute by which the common body becomes the principle of all things by differing from part to part in infinite diversity of sizes and shapes.[42]

As in the case of the subject matter of the sciences, so too the principles of the sciences as conceived by Democritus and Plato stand in contrast in the dialectical use Aristotle makes of them, but their similarity might likewise be stressed, for both sought a single set of principles or common notions for all sciences and both turned from empirical experience to the independent resources of the understanding for their principles.   Plato viewed actual processes as approximations and imitations of demonstrations and he sought in his dialectic to reduce principles entertained as hypotheses in demonstration to the single Form or principle that underlies them, while Democritus likewise thought sensations mere images and unreliable as knowledge, and he sought criteria for inquiry in the common notions of the understanding.

Finally, if there is a single science or a common body for all things, the science is mathematics and the bodies are magnitudes. Aristotle once more finds Democritus and Plato performing an identical reduction in opposite fashions, Democritus by making the fundamental magnitudes bodies, Plato by making bodies magnitudes.

The principle or the basic question underlying all the problems [concerning the distinction of generation from other kinds of change] is whether things that are are generated thus and alter and grow as well as suffer the contraries to these changes, because the first realities are indivisible magnitudes; or whether there is no indivisible magnitude.   For this makes a very great difference.   And again, if the first realities are magnitudes, it is a fundamental question whether the magnitudes are bodies, as Leucippus and Democritus hold, or planes, as is maintained in the *Timaeus*.   To resolve

[41] *Posterior Analytics* i. 7. 75^b7–20 and 28. 87^a38–^b4; *Metaphysics* vi. 1. 1025^b1–21; x. 4. 1055^a29–33; xiii. 4. 1078^b25–27, and *passim*.

[42] *Physics* iii. 4. 202^b36–203^b2. Cf. also, *Metaphysics* vi. 14.1039^b2–9; *Physics* i. 2. 184^b20–27 and *On the Heavens* iii. 2. 300^b8–11 and 4. 303^a10–12.

bodies only into planes and no further is absurd, as we have already said elsewhere. Therefore, it is more reasonable to hold that there are indivisible bodies. Yet this likewise involves a good deal of absurdity.[43]

In general Aristotle argues that if solids are thought to be composed of planes, the supposition must be carried further and planes must be composed of lines, and lines of points, and he undertook to show that such a theory is absurd in mathematics, since the reduction of a line to points involves both the resolution of a continuity into a collection of discrete quantities and the necessity of an actual infinity of such quantities, and the like absurdities that follow from it are even greater in physics, since mathematics deals with objects known by abstraction and physics with objects known by characteristics collected in observation.[44]

In the particular case of Plato and the adherents to the doctrine of Forms, Aristotle intimates that philosophers had abandoned their proper task of accounting for phenomena or perceptible things and as a result mathematics had become the whole of philosophy for modern thinkers, since the Forms supply neither efficient nor final causes for art or nature, and mathematics requires no consideration of ends and their achievement in its proofs.[45] On the other hand, the doctrine of Leucippus and Democritus, by assuming that the first magnitudes are infinite in number and indivisible in magnitude, makes all existing things to be numbers and to be composed of numbers. Such a view at once conflicts with the mathematical sciences, since it requires the construction of bodies or continuous quantities from numbers or discrete quantities and in so doing necessitates an actual infinity of those primary numbers, and in addition to these mathematical difficulties it confutes many tenets of common opinion and many phenomena of sense perception.[46] Once again, although the errors stressed by Aristotle are opposite, there is a similar tendency in the theories of Democritus and Plato, for both seek the basis for all scientific knowledge in mathematics, the one by examining bodies and motions and reducing them to quantities, the other by examining the processes of demonstration and reducing the principles of the physical sciences to those of mathematics.

*　　　　　*　　　　　*

[43] *On Generation and Corruption* i. 2. 315ᵇ24–33.
[44] *On the Heavens* iii. 1. 299ᵃ1–17.
[45] *Metaphysics* i. 9. 992ᵃ24–ᵇ1 and iii. 2. 996ᵃ22–ᵇ1.   Cf. also, *ibid.* i. 6. 987ᵇ18–22.
[46] *On the Heavens* iii. 4. 303ᵃ3–24; *On Generation and Corruption* i. 8. 325ᵃ34–36; and *Metaphysics* vii. 13. 1039ᵃ3–14.

ᴥ₰ Ludwig Edelstein

RECENT TRENDS IN THE INTERPRETATION OF ANCIENT SCIENCE *

The book by Cohen and Drabkin is a most welcome contribution to the literature on the history of ancient science. No comparable collection illustrating ancient scientific knowledge has ever been attempted. The excerpts brought together by the editors are excellently chosen, and set in sharp relief main aspects of the scientific development in antiquity. The English rendering of the texts is wherever possible taken from available translations, but a great number of passages have been translated by Mr. Drabkin (ix), and translated very well indeed.[1] Ample explanatory notes serve to clarify the content and also refer to the modern debate on specific issues; succinct introductions to each of the various fields of science outline the general background. In short, a work of wide scope and of the devoted labor of years has been completed with great skill, full mastery of the diverse literature, accuracy of detail, and with a view to the broader issues.

In examining such a book it would hardly be useful, I think, to concentrate on minutiae. One may of course always raise the question why a certain passage has been selected, while other evidence has not been included, whether or not the interpretation of a certain detail is correct, and so forth.[2] A discussion of this kind would interest merely the specialist. However, valuable as it is for the specialist, the book is intended mainly for scientists

* A discussion of M. R. Cohen and I. E. Drabkin, *A Source Book in Greek Science* (New York: McGraw-Hill, 1948), pp. xxi, 579; and B. Farrington, *Greek Science,* I, 1944, pp. 154; II, 1949, pp. 181 (Pelican Books).

[1] The translations often amount to a commentary on the text, *e.g.,* the rendering of the passage from Ptolemy (?), *Optics* (271ff.). Variant readings and other textual difficulties are carefully indicated (*e.g.,* 36,5; 66,1; 169,1; 220,1; 252,1; 253,2; 264,1; 282,2; 337,1; 342,4; 364,3; 496,1). In a reprinting of the book an index of the translated passages should be added so that specific authors could be consulted more easily.

[2] To give some examples: the experiments in acoustics (294ff.) should perhaps have been illustrated also by Plato, *Republic,* 531A–C, the oldest evidence (cf. 5,1; 302,5); the chapter on chemistry ought to include excerpts from Aristotle, *Meteorology,* IV (cf. 374, n. 1). Strabo's account of the tides (cf. 390,1) might have been preferable to that of Pliny (389). For the authorship, etc., of the Ps. Hippocratic treatises *On the Nature of the Child* and *On Diseases,* IV (453,2; 489,1) J. Ilberg, *Die Schule von Knidos, S. B. Leipzig* (1925), should have been compared. The essay of Theophrastus quoted on p. 392 is hardly genuine; cf. A. Rehm–K. Vogel, *Exakte Wissenschaften,* in Gercke–Norden, *Einleitung in die Altertumswissenschaft* (1933), 46. Not everybody will agree with the comments on Plato, *Timaeus,* 40 B (cf. *Laws,* VII, 822 A–C), concerning the rotation of the earth (98), nor am I certain that the evaluation of number mysticism and astrology in medicine (500,1; 502,1) is correct. The chapter on acoustics and musical theory, an exceedingly difficult subject, might have profited by a more detailed introduction (286ff.); the remarks on pp. 294 and 302 (notes) do not seem quite sufficient.

or general historians, so that they may see "something of the original sources on which the historian relies" (vii), or for readers "who wish to achieve some understanding not only of the foundations of modern science, but of a vital element of the humanistic tradition" (viii). The *Source Book* will be used, I trust, in courses on the history of science. Rather than deal with the narrower concerns of the work, it seems appropriate, therefore, to inquire into some of the principles which the editors have followed in compiling the material, to draw attention to general problems on which the evidence here assembled has some bearing, and to discuss some recent interpretations of the history of ancient science as a whole, especially that of B. Farrington, as it is expounded in a number of brilliantly written books which have aroused great interest and have exercised a strong influence. In this way I hope to facilitate the use of the material which has now been put at the disposal of all who are interested in the early beginnings of science.

I. ANCIENT SCIENCE AND MODERN SCIENCE

Since the nineteenth century the great majority of scholars have held that ancient science and modern science are worlds apart. But if one reads through the texts collected in the *Source Book*, he can not but agree with the editors that it is an error to date the rise of natural science in the seventeenth century and to consider the Greeks "mere speculators" (vii). In mathematics (1–88), astronomy and mathematical geography (89–181), physics (182–351), chemistry and chemical technology (352–73), geology and meteorology (374–93), biology (394–466), medicine (467–529), physiological psychology (530–58), in all these branches of learning the Greeks developed and followed methods that closely approximate, if they do not equal, the standards of modern science. To be sure, the material assembled in these chapters is mostly outdated. What is presented here is not yet modern science. Nevertheless the link between the ancient investigations and those of modern times is obvious.

The quantitative approach to the analysis of phenomena as well as the method of experimentation were well known to the ancients. This is often denied even nowadays; the evidence available should settle the debate once and for all.[3] The most famous example of the quantitative analysis of observations is the work of the Pythagoreans (294ff.) and of Erasistratus (480; cf. also 239, 280, 312). The experiments known to have been performed are numerous (mechanics: 211, 249–52; optics: 268; acoustics: 294ff.; physiology: 479). It should also be pointed out that references to experiments are to be found not only in classical and Hellenistic authors, but also in books of the archaistic centuries down to the end of antiquity (*e.g.*, 248). Philoponus investigated the laws of falling bodies in the same manner as Galileo (220).[4] Nor were the ancients unacquainted with the

---

[3] Cf. O. Blüh, "Did the Greeks perform Experiments?", *Amer. Journ. of Physics*, 17 (1949), 384ff.

[4] That the experiment of Philoponus was known to Renaissance scientists and played an important rôle in the controversy over Galileo's theories has been shown

concept of " two sets of experiments," as the editors stress in their comment on an experiment in acoustics (298, n. 1). One statement by Philo, the engineer, seems especially remarkable, because it shows the clear awareness of the necessity of repeated experiments, and, in addition, of the " social conditioning " of such an approach: ". . . the ancients did not succeed in determining this magnitude by test, because their trials were not conducted on the basis of many different types of performance, but merely in connection with the required performance. But the engineers who came later, noting the errors of their predecessors and the results of subsequent experiments, reduced the principle of construction to a single basic element. . . . Success in this work was recently achieved by the Alexandrian engineers, who were heavily subsidized by kings eager for fame and interested in the arts " (318).

The statement just cited is interesting also from another point of view. It formulates the concept of scientific progress. Now it is generally held that ancient scientists were unaware of the idea of progress. Philo's words have been called the only clear expression of this concept, and the value of his testimony has been depreciated, since he was an engineer, a man of practical affairs. The practitioners may have been conscious of the necessity of progress, the true scientists, it is maintained, were not.[5] But is not the intent of Philo's assertion identical with that of Hero, who composed his book in the expectation that from his collection of earlier discoveries, to which he added his own, " much advantage will result to those who shall hereafter devote themselves to the study of mathematics " (249)? And if it is objected that Hero is a mechanician, what about Archimedes who writes: " I deem it necessary to expound the method . . . because I am persuaded that it will be of no little service to mathematics; for I apprehend that some, either of my contemporaries or of my successors, will, by means of the method when once established, be able to discover other theorems in addition, which have not yet occurred to me " (71)? Is Archimedes' pronouncement basically different from one by Dürer that is considered characteristic of the Renaissance concept of progress: " I know however that he who accepts it [my doctrine] will not only get a good start, but will reach better understanding by daily practice; he will seek farther and find much more than I now indicate "?[6] Many other passages from

---

by E. Wohlwill, *Physikalische Zeitschrift*, 7 (1906), 23ff., 28ff. Cf. also L. Olschki, *Galilei und seine Zeit, Gesch. d. neusprachlichen wissenschaftlichen Literatur*, III (1927), 160.

[5] E. Zilsel, "The Genesis of the Concept of Scientific Progress," pp. 251–275. He considers Ptolemy, *Almagest*, I, 1 (p. 4 Heiberg), as well as Seneca, *Naturales Quaestiones*, VII, 25, 31, exceptional in the extant literature (see specifically p. 253, n. 3; p. 254, n. 4).

[6] Zilsel, *op. cit.*, 334. That the concept of scientific progress originated in the Renaissance is the commonly accepted view. For the general literature on the idea of progress, cf. Zilsel, 325,1. (F. J. Teggart, *The Idea of Progress*, revised ed. by G. H. Hildebrand [1949], deals with the concept of social rather than scientific progress.)

ancient scientists could be adduced which express the hope that progress will be achieved in the future. Likewise, scientific writings attest that their authors realized their dependence on the work of earlier scientists (*e.g.*, 116, 168f.). Just as the ancients were familiar with experiments and quantitative analysis, so they knew that scientific progress could be attained solely through the cooperation of successive generations.[7]

Modern science and ancient science, then, are not diametrically opposed. I hasten to add, however, that such a claim can be made good only so long as one is willing to do what the editors of the *Source Book* have done, namely to select as evidence that material " which would generally be regarded today as scientific in method, *i.e.*, based, in principle, either on mathematics or on empirical verification " (viii). To put it differently, the impression that ancient science is modern in character is bought at the price of neglecting or omitting all the evidence to the contrary.[8]

The editors, like many other students of antiquity, seem inclined to classify " theories that are now known to be false or even ridiculous " as " magic, superstition, and religion." They speak of " ' pseudo science,' such as astrology and the like," that " can be found in the writings of such sober Greek scientists as Aristotle and Ptolemy " (viii); they refer to " the intrusion of the occult " that is noticeable also in modern scientific writings from Kepler to Eddington (ix). But astrology, the theory of humors, Plato's mathematical scale of music are not " intrusions " in ancient science. Theories like these, which do not pass the muster of modern criticism, constitute in fact the greater part of the preserved material. To the Greeks, they were just as scientific as those other views which happen to seem acceptable to the modern scientist. To be sure, the scientist who says of himself, as Seneca put it, " the day will come when our children will wonder at our ignorance " (*Nat. Quaest.*, VII, 255), may also look in amazement at the ignorance of previous ages. The historian, I think, must try to understand that that which is ridiculous and false in the past is inseparably connected with that which is praiseworthy and true. The errors of the Greeks should teach him as much about their science as do their correct results. What appears to be so " modern " acquires its specific hue only if placed against the setting of the " antiquated."

I should go even one step farther. The " correct " results and methods themselves, if studied more closely, reveal certain implications that are peculiarly their own and are perhaps less correct or modern than one may have supposed at first glance. It is true, empiricism was embraced by many ancient scientists; phenomena were carefully observed and minutely studied

[7] With this problem I intend to deal in detail and to present the pertinent material in a forthcoming essay on *The Influence of Ancient Science on Philosophy*.

[8] In this connection I should emphasize that the chapter headings of the *Source Book* naturally represent the modern divisions of science and were chosen by the editors in the hope that this device " will enable the modern reader concerned with a given special field to find more readily the ancient material that will interest him " (ix).

(*e.g.*, 122, 134, 283); in many ways, ancient empiricism is identical with modern empiricism. Yet it was the empiricists of antiquity who were the first idolators of books, for it is in books, they claimed, that the empirical knowledge of previous generations is stored up. Further verification of results that were once put down and generally agreed upon thus became superfluous. On the other hand, the empirical approach in antiquity prompted the acceptance of sympathetic and antipathetic effects, which earlier rational and speculative science had disregarded. The experiences of superstitious people were acknowledged as valid, since as experiences they were irrefutable.[9] Again it is true, many scientists experimented in a modern fashion. Yet many others did not experiment to test an hypothesis; rather, they restricted experimental proof to the occasional confirmation of a speculative theory, or they might choose to resort to an experiment in order to refute an opponent. The two attitudes existed side by side in the classical age, as well as in the Hellenistic and archaistic periods. And if some of the ancients clearly saw the advantage of repeated, systematic experimentation, others lacked this insight. No less an anatomist than Galen was unwilling to investigate all phenomena, wherever this did not seem to serve his purpose.[10]

Such differences between the modern and the ancient approach must be emphasized not only for the sake of historical objectivity and accuracy, but also in order to forestall new and unwarranted exaggerations in the appraisal of ancient science. Already it is claimed that all scientific progess in antiquity was due to the fact that the ancients " were prepared to abandon theoretical patterns under the impact of new observations and experiments, performed in order to prove or disprove earlier concepts." If relatively little is known of these experiments, one must remember that " much of their knowledge the Greeks considered as *mysteries, i.e.,* as secret knowledge, to be passed on only to a selected few in sacred communities, scientific schools, and trade guilds." [11] I need hardly say that the latter assumption is entirely unfounded. Enough is known about experiments to warrant the claim that they were widely made, contrary to the assertions of earlier scholars. If the available information about them is still scanty, the reason for this is, in addition to the loss of material, that not all ancient scientists experimented and that in some fields the aim of the work undertaken, as well as its literary recording, differed fundamentally from the aim and the literary expression of later generations. Physics, for instance, which in

---

[9] For the book learning of the ancient empiricists, cf. K. Deichgräber, *Die Griechische Empirikerschule* (1930), 298ff., 317ff.; for empiricism and the doctrine of sympathy, cf. L. Edelstein, " Greek Medicine in its relation to Religion and Magic," *Bulletin of the Institute of the History of Medicine,* 5 (1937), 229–38.

[10] For the early history of the experiment, cf. H. Diller, Ὄψις ἀδήλων τὰ φαινόμενα, *Hermes,* 67 (1932), 14ff. In general cf. O. Regenbogen, " Eine Forschungsmethode antiker Naturwissenschaft," *Quellen u. Studien z. Gesch. der Mathematik, Abt. B, Studien,* I (1930), 131ff. For Galen, cf. *Opera Omnia,* ed. G. Kühn, II (1821), 286.

[11] Blüh, *op. cit.,* 385, 387.

antiquity remained closely connected with philosophy, was predominantly concerned with the philosophical category of the " why," rather than with the scientific category of the " how." Physicists, therefore, recording their results started with the logical proof, and then added the factual (experimental) proof, which as a superaddition, so-to-say, could be and actually was limited, no matter how many experiments might have preceded the solution of any given problem. They accepted more or less the philosophical style of discourse, the form of the *quaestiones et solutiones*.[12]

The mention of the influence of philosophy on physics brings up the last question I wish to raise in this connection, that of the relation between philosophy and science in general. The editors of the *Source Book* have omitted the " philosophical speculation on cosmology as well as on human affairs," which is easily available; they have drawn a line " between what should be regarded as scientific material and that which would more properly be considered philosophic or speculative," although, as they admit, " such a line must necessarily be arbitrary, since the Greeks themselves did not draw it very sharply " (viii). Indeed, had the editors decided otherwise, their task would have become well-nigh impossible, and they deserve high praise for the adroitness with which they have handled this thorny problem. I simply want to underline the warning given in their preface and to extend it somewhat farther.

It is at least debatable whether the Aristotelian treatises on zoology, which are included, are the work of the philosopher or of the scientist, Aristotle. Theophrastus, whose botanical writings are excerpted, was a philosopher, too. The philosophical discussion of the concept of analogy decisively influenced his scientific studies. His refusal to compare, where comparison seemed unwarranted on general principle, prevented him from recognizing the bisexuality of plants. In anatomy, the same philosophical discussion of the merit of analogies contributed to the discontinuation of animal anatomy in favor of dissection performed on the human cadaver, and even of human vivisection.[13] Similarly many another author, who in the *Source Book* appears as a scientist, was guided in his research also by his philosophical theories. I am not sure that the astronomical hypothesis of Ptolemy can be designated simply as scientific; I doubt that he accepted the geocentric theory merely on scientific grounds, as the editors hold (107f.). Ptolemy was not averse to using philosophical arguments in proof of scientific data (*e.g.*, 118), and rightly so from his point of view, for in antiquity, science was linked with philosophy much more closely than is true of modern times. It is not by chance that in recent years scholars have paid increasingly more attention to the question as to just when the independent sciences constituted themselves in antiquity, and how far one can

---

[12] Cf. H. Leisegang, *s.v. Physik*, Pauly-Wissowa, *Real-Encyclopädie d. class. Altertumswissenschaft*, XX, 1 (1941), col. 1041.

[13] For Theophrastus, cf. Regenbogen, *op. cit.*, 155–57; for the development of anatomy, cf. L. Edelstein, " Die Geschichte der Sektion in der Antike," *Quellen u. Studien z. Gesch. der Naturwissenschaften u. der Medizin*, 3 (1933), 100ff., 148f.

speak of such an independence at all.[14]

To repeat, modernity is only one of the components of ancient scientific investigation. Reality is more complex than any generalization, any verdict of " modern " or " antiquated " can indicate. The singling out of those trends in ancient development which resemble or foreshadow modern science, permissible and valuable as this procedure may be, tends to give a picture that necessarily remains one-sided. In fact, evaluating the tension between the various tendencies within ancient science is one of the main problems confronting the historian.

II. ANCIENT SCIENCE AND TECHNOLOGY

It is one of the great merits of the *Source Book* that it includes technological material " that seems either to have been a direct application of Greek scientific theory or to have contributed to its subsequent development " (ix). The examples given are drawn from practically every field of knowledge (84f., 134–42, 169–81, 307–10, 314–51). The editors also rightly emphasize the fact that in this context the archaeological material, which necessarily had to be excluded from the book, is especially important (182, 314).[15]

That ancient science failed to lead to technological application is another one of those prejudices that die hard. Yet contrary to the assertions repeated over and over again and made the basis of far-reaching generalizations, like those of Spengler, the Greeks were not hostile to technology.[16] Plato, to be sure, blamed the " corrupters and destroyers of the pure excellence of geometry, which thus turned her back upon the incorporeal things of abstract thought and descended to the things of sense, making use, moreover, of objects which required such mean and manual labor " (315). But Plato is not all of antiquity. Archytas, Eudoxus, Menaechmus constructed instruments and machines (Plutarch, *Quaest. Conv.*, VIII, 2, 1, 718e). Aristotle admired mechanical toys (*Politics*, 1340 b 26f.), Aristoxenus appreciated technical detail.[17] Although Plutarch intimates that Archimedes on account of his " lofty spirit," his " profound soul," that is, on account of his Platonic leanings (cf. 315), did not write on his inventions (317),

[14] E.g., W. Jaeger, *Aristoteles* (1923), 432. F. Solmsen, " Plato and the Unity of Science," *The Philosophical Review*, 49 (1940), 566ff. The problem demands a more detailed investigation than can be given here. I should at least mention that the principles of physics and physiology always formed part of ancient philosophical doctrines.

[15] Much of the evidence known from ancient technological writings is discussed by E. Pernice, *Handbuch der Altertumswissenschaft* (*Archaeologie*), VI, 1 (1939), 250ff. A description of many of the devices used is to be found in G. Childe, *What Happened in History* (1942; Pelican Books), *e.g.*, 235ff., 250ff.

[16] Cf. A. Rehm, " Zur Rolle der Technik in der griechisch-römischen Antike," *Archiv f. Kulturgeschichte*, 28 (1938), 135–62, the best and most recent analysis of the subject.

[17] Cf. J. Geffken, " Antiplatonica," *Hermes*, 64 (1929), 92.

it still remains true that this " geometrical Briareus," as the Romans called him (*ibid.*), did apply his knowledge to practical ends. The list of his inventions is impressive.[18] Geminus, among others, considered mechanics a branch of that part of mathematics which is " concerned with and applied to things perceived by the senses " (2; cf. 5). Carpus, in the first or second century of our era, was one of the many scientists who did not believe that geometry is " harmed by the association with them [the arts] " (185). Pappus held that the science of mechanics " is justly esteemed by philosophers and is diligently pursued by all who are interested in mathematics " (183).

How far applied science advanced in antiquity is quite another question. The various periods differed in their contributions to technology. In the pre-classical era more was accomplished than in the fifth century B.C.; the early Hellenistic period marked a climax; the Romans made great strides, once the Greeks had prepared the way.[19] On the other hand, ancient technical development, no doubt, never went as far as the available knowledge would have permitted. Especially conspicuous is the absence of any consistent attempt to replace human by non-human energy, an attempt not to be carried out before the late Middle Ages, and at that time based largely on the knowledge inherited from antiquity. And yet, on principle the ancients were quite aware of the fact that ropes and cables are means by which " the motion of living beings may be imitated " (5). Nor was the idea alien to them that " vanquished by nature we become masters through technics " (Ps. Aristotle, *Mechanics*, 847 a 20).[20] The more one studies the astounding technological devices discussed in literature (*e.g.*, 329ff., 343ff.) and extant in the archaeological remains, the more one wonders why the ancients did not go farther, why technology did not become more thoroughly integrated into practical life.

The reasons for the relative limitation of ancient technology have been widely debated. As the editors phrase it, " increasing attention has been paid in recent years to the organization of society in antiquity, and in particular the institution of slavery, as affecting the technological development " (314). This problem is of such importance that I feel it necessary to take it up here; naturally it could not be discussed within the scope of the *Source Book* (*ibid.*).

The argument most commonly advanced, and advocated also in the now most widely read histories of ancient science, is that in a slave society labor

---

[18] Cf. Rehm, *op. cit.*, 146, n. 28; he has also interpreted the various accounts given of Archimedes' attitude, 145, n. 27. Farrington's representation of Archimedes (*Greek Science*, II, 75) does not do justice to the divergencies of the tradition.

[19] Cf. Rehm, *op. cit.*, 136, 138f., 146, who follows H. Diels' periodization of the history of technology (*Antike Technik* [1914]).

[20] For the interpretation of this statement (= Antiphon, Fr. 4 [Nauck, *Trag. Graec. Frag.*,² 793]), cf. Rehm, *op. cit.*, 137; also Farrington, *Greek Science*, II, 46. The progress of mediaeval technology is briefly summarized by Farrington, *op. cit.*, II, 168.

is cheap; technical improvements therefore were unnecessary in antiquity.[21] Such an oversimplification seems no longer justifiable, for as the investigations of the past few decades have shown, ancient economy can hardly be called a pure slave economy. Especially in the arts and crafts free labor continued to hold its place. In addition to slaves, metics and citizens were employed as artisans during the classical age; in the Roman empire, the ratio of free labor increased even in big factories. Simple reference to ancient society as a slave economy, then, explains nothing.[22] The exact numerical relation of the various components of the laboring class it is difficult to estimate. What is certain is that the number of slaves in antiquity was much smaller than was thought by historians of the nineteenth century, and this is true above all of the classical and Roman ages.[23] However, even assuming that the percentage of slaves was relatively high, slave labor was neither cheap, nor docile, as is evidenced by slave revolts and strikes. To put it in Rostovtzeff's words: " Why then should the employment of slaves prevent an energetic shop-owner from using new technical devices, which would have been a good way of making his products cheaper and better? "[24]

Another argument that has been proffered is that the insufficient demand for goods, the low buying power of the population hampered the rise of

[21] Cf., *e.g.*, Diels, *op. cit.*, 35. E. Zilsel, " The Sociological Roots of Science," *The Amer. Journal of Sociology*, 47 (1941/42), 559; Farrington, *Greek Science*, II, 166; F. M. Cornford, *The Unwritten Philosophy and Other Essays* (1950), 93.

[22] That slave labor never ousted free labor has been stated by Rehm, *op. cit.*, 153. W. L. Westermann, *s.v. Sklaverei, R.E.*, Suppl., VI (1935), cols. 894–1068, deals most extensively with the question of slavery. Concerning the participation of free men, metics and slaves in fifth- and fourth-century crafts and trades, cf., *e.g.*, M. L. W. Laistner, *A Survey of Ancient History* (1929), 289f.; for conditions in the Roman empire, *ibid.*, 538ff., esp. 540; M. Rostovtzeff, *The Social and Economic History of the Roman Empire* (1926), 303; also Childe, *op. cit.*, 272, who claims however that in the classical period the slave owners " did not want labour-saving devices " (224). Cf. also T. Frank, *An Economic History of Rome* (1927²), esp. 324ff. (The Laborer). The material for the Hellenistic period is scarce; in Greece proper, the majority of slaves seem to have worked in the household (Westermann, cols. 934f.). Factories apparently were manned entirely by slaves (cf. note 24); yet the continuance of free labor is certain.

[23] That the number of slaves in the classical age used to be overestimated, even Rostovtzeff admits, *Social and Economic History of the Hellenistic World*, II (1941), 1258, although he cautions against the tendency to minimize the extent of slave labor in reaction to earlier exaggerations. For the slave trade in Hellenistic times, *ibid.*, 1260ff. For the decreasing number of slaves in the Roman empire, Laistner, *op. cit.*, 535. Some estimates concerning slaves, metics and freemen are given by A. W. Gomme, *The Population of Athens in the fifth and fourth Centuries B.C.* (1933), 19ff.; cf. also Childe, *op. cit.*, 272. Rostovtzeff, *Roman Empire*, 178, considers it impossible to state the exact relation between slaves and freedmen.

[24] Rostovzeff, *Roman Empire*, 303; he adds that " ancient industry reached its highest [technical] level in the Hellenistic period when it was based wholly on slave labour " (*ibid.*).

technology. Mass production hardly existed in antiquity; big export trades flourished only locally and temporarily; in general, wages were low. Whatever was needed and could be afforded by the consumers was easily produced without technical apparatus. These and similar considerations may perhaps explain why in the production of commodities like pottery, metal ware and textiles technical progress was slow, even in the Hellenistic centuries, while in building and in the production of war materials, where the demand was great, progress was more rapid.[25] No one will doubt that economic factors have a certain regulative force. Thus even Pliny, discussing the use of mowing machines in agriculture, remarks that the diversity of procedure depends on the size of the harvest and the availability of workmen (*Nat. Hist.*, XVIII, 300). But can economic considerations alone explain why the ancients, who for their elaborate pageants invented automotive carriages and ships much bigger than the size of their usual warships, did not apply their knowledge to their daily needs? That they constructed water clocks, but failed to make effective use of the water mill, which they also knew how to build (*Source Book*, 350), that they employed the wind wheel to play the hydraulic organ (333), but failed to utilize the power of the wind mill, which they likewise invented? [26]

Moreover, scholars now generally agree that, contrary to earlier views, ancient society was not predominantly a " house economy," but to some extent was also a capitalistic society, no less so at any rate than were some of the societies of the Renaissance. It has been said with regard to the Renaissance artisan that only a man who had " either invented some commercial or technological innovation or who understood the value of the invention of another fellow became a capitalistic manufacturer. Thus the inventive genius of the individual gradually came to the fore." [27] If this were true, it should apply to the ancient craftsman as well. Nor can it be maintained that in antiquity there was no such close cooperation between the scientist and the artisan, as is said to have stimulated interest in inventions during the Renaissance. Those skilled in the theory and construction of machines, the mechanicians, according to Hero, had to learn at least one craft (184). Vitruvius stresses the important relation between theory and

[25] That industrialization in antiquity remained limited on account of the weakness of the internal market, is the thesis of Rostovtzeff, *Roman Empire*, 303ff. The Hellenistic development he has described in *Hellenistic World*, II, 1205ff.; 1230ff. F. M. Heichelheim, *Wirtschaftsgeschichte des Altertums* (1938), 570ff., seems to be inclined to judge the progress during the Hellenistic period more favorably. Rehm, too, explains the lack of technology through the low cost and ample supply of workers, *op. cit.*, 155, 158f. In this connection he pays special attention to the number of metics in classical Athens.

[26] For the milling industry, cf. Childe, *op. cit.*, 235, 252. I have borrowed my examples from Rehm, *op. cit.*, 160f.

[27] Zilsel, "The Genesis of the Concept of Scientific Progress," pp. 251–275. Concerning competitive capitalism in ancient society, cf. Rostovtzeff, *Roman Empire*, 302f., 482ff.; also Rehm, *op. cit.*, 146ff.

practice (I, 1,2). Inventors were held in high esteem, their names were noted and remembered, whether or not they had written about their subjects or achievements.[28] Social conditions, then, although in some respects they may have retarded the rise of technology, were also favorable to its advancement. Their consideration alone will hardly suffice to explain the limitations of ancient technics; was society really so much better off when in the Middle Ages many of the inventions made in antiquity were put to wider use?

It seems to me that in order to understand the attitude of the ancients toward technology, the basic values underlying ancient life must be considered, the fundamental aims and deep-rooted convictions of those who concerned themselves with inventions. As for the scientist, even where he applied his knowledge to practical matters, his true reward remained the insight he had gained into nature. The " sober drunkenness " of cognition was his highest goal. No ancient scientist, I think, could have said what Pasteur said of himself: " To him who devotes his life to science, nothing can give more happiness than increasing the number of discoveries, but his cup of joy is full when the results of his studies immediately find practical applications." [29] It is rather in the words of Ptolemy that the happiness and joy of the ancient scientist is summarized: " I know that I am mortal, a creature of a day; but when I search into the multitudinous revolving spirals of the stars, my feet no longer rest on the earth, but, standing by Zeus himself, I take my fill of ambrosia, the food of the gods " (*Anthologia Palatina*, IX, 577). His own inner enrichment constituted the celebrated humanism of the ancient scientist. He tried to acquire knowledge for knowledge's sake; he applied it when he was asked to do so in the interest of his city or his king, when an occasion offered itself; he hardly ever sought out such an occasion.

Even the work of the mechanician was guided by an unrealistic outlook. To be sure, he propagated inventions, " so that they may be of unlimited usefulness " (351), or in order to " supply the most pressing wants of human life " (249), or to achieve the desired end " without using the laborious and slow method " (342), yet he did not forget the element of wonder, of play or amusement. " The art of those who contrive marvellous devices," " the art of the sphere makers . . . [who] construct a model of the heaven [and operate it] with the help of the uniform circular motion of water," according to Pappus, were subdivisions of mechanics (184). Catoptrics is " clearly a science worthy of study and at the same time produces spectacles

---

[28] It is usually said that ancient society held the inventor in low regard; cf., *e.g.*, Zilsel, *op. cit., Amer. Journal of Sociology*, 559, and Rehm [*op. cit.*, 161 (cf. 143)] who agrees with Diels, *Antike Technik*, 29ff. Yet Diels himself quotes even inscriptions recording the names of inventors. Rostovtzeff's appreciation of the position of the inventor, *Hellenistic World*, 1245, is more positive, and rightly so; cf. also Farrington, *Greek Science*, I, 104; II, 48. The evidence has been surveyed by A. O. Lovejoy and G. Boas, *Primitivism and Related Ideas in Antiquity* (1935), 200, 382ff.

[29] Réné J. Dubos, *Louis Pasteur* (1950), 85.

which excite wonder in the observer. For with the aid of this science mirrors are constructed which show the right side as the right side, and, similarly the left side as the left side, whereas ordinary mirrors by their nature have the contrary property and show the opposite sides" (262). Sentences like these would hardly figure in a modern text book on optics.

As for the artisan and the craftsman, in addition to an innate love of invention which he may have possessed, only self-interest could spur him on to go ahead. The artisans of the Renaissance, as is apparent from their own testimony, justified their inventions by reference "to the glory of God and the Saints, of the craft and the workshop—and to the usefulness of their craft and the public benefit." [30] No ancient artisan could have thought of such a justification. It is true, the development of the arts and crafts was generally recognized as an important part of civilization, and therefore as a common good. The invention of tools, of instruments had served to distinguish human life from animal life. Further progress in the arts and crafts could make life more pleasant and more enjoyable. Specialization and division of labor helped to produce more beautiful objects; they bettered the quality of workmanship.[31] But technical improvement to the ancients was not a value in itself; the moral and political order was supreme. Nor would the ancient craftsman by his inventive genius have enhanced the glory of his art or of his guild. Ancient guilds were private organizations, rather than public institutions; they did not enforce any standards of craftsmanship. The artisan's patron saint was believed by some to have bestowed upon him the knowledge of tools. Yet, while the craftsman owed it to him that he benefited by their use, neither he nor even his god was, in his eyes, a creator rejoicing in ever new manifestations of his creative power. The world was there to live in, not to be used or to be made over.[32]

Among people adhering to such a scheme of values, technological progress, I think, had its natural, its inherent limitations. A change could come and did come about only when another view of the world emerged, when in the later Middle Ages the discrepancy between the two attitudes toward life immanent in Christian thought came to be avowed, when active life began

---

[30] Zilsel, "The Genesis of the Concept of Scientific Progress," pp. 257f.; for the testimony of Renaissance authors, *ibid.*, 258–71.

[31] For specialization and division of labor, cf. Xenophon, *Cyropaedia*, VIII, 2,4ff.; Augustine, *De Civitate Dei*, VII, 4, and Rehm's interpretation of these passages (152f.). That the progress of civilization depended on improvements in the arts was, of course, a commonplace. Contrary to the impression given by J. B. Bury [*The Idea of Progress* (1920), 15ff.], it was held not only by the Epicureans, but also by the classic philosophers (Plato, *Hipp. Mai.*, 281 D; Aristotle, *N.E.*, 1098a23) and by the Stoics (*e.g.*, Cicero, *De Officiis*, II, 3–4).

[32] It was characteristic of the ancient craftsman that he was conscious of the limits of human art. This becomes especially clear in the discussion on the art of medicine; cf. L. Edelstein, *Bull. of the Institute of the History of Medicine* (1937), 224ff. The belief in the periodic destruction of the world probably was another hindrance to unlimited progress (Bury, *op. cit.*, 16). Cf. also note 54 below.

to vie with contemplative life and was finally placed above it, when man at last felt summoned " to participate, in some finite measure, in the creative passion of God, to collaborate consciously in the processes by which the diversity of things, the fullness of the universe, is achieved." [33]

III. PROGRESS AND DECAY OF ANCIENT SCIENCE

Referring to the relation between technology and social factors the editors of the *Source Book* state that social conditions are said to have influenced " possibly also the directions in which science in general developed " (314). The justification of this claim has indeed become the main issue in interpreting ancient science. The various aspects of the problem may conveniently be summed up in the catch phrase " the progress and decay of ancient science."

The expression, of course, is not to be taken too literally. No one will deny that science never became extinct in antiquity, that scientific research was carried on continuously from the turn of the seventh to the sixth century B.C., when scientific studies began, down to the sixth century of our era, when pagan civilization ended and with it what may properly be called Graeco-Roman science. Rather, the terms " progress " and " decay " imply the failure of ancient science " to lead on from its first successes to a continuous growth like that which the modern pioneers of science inaugurated," a failure that " can hardly be attributed to ignorance of scientific method "; or to put it differently, Greek science became sterile, despite the fact that it " had still such vitality that it was capable of a second birth " in the Renaissance.[34] The period of breakdown is variously dated. Some speak of the second century B.C. as the decisive turn; others single out the first century B.C.; still others allow the standstill to have come about only in the second century of our era.[35]

That behind these theories there are facts which need explaining, I readily admit. Ancient science did undergo decisive transformations. After 200 B.C. productive research slowed down; in the second century A.D. the temper of science changed, so that henceforth compilers and commentators usurped the place of original investigators. Needless to add that progress was nevertheless made in the period between 200 B.C. and 200 A.D., and even afterwards. The most ardent proponent of the theory of decay would concede this much; he would not deny that Ptolemy and Galen were original

[33] A. O. Lovejoy, *The Great Chain of Being* (1948[3]), 84. In the words quoted Lovejoy describes the opposing tendencies of the Christian dogma. He has also shown how the mediaeval concept of the poet is determined by the Christian concept of creation (86).

[34] The first two quotations are taken from M. Cary, *A History of the Greek World from 323 to 146* (1932), 352f. (cf. A. J. Toynbee, *A Study of History*, V [1939], 422); the last quotation is from Farrington, *Greek Science*, II, 10f.

[35] Cary, *loc. cit.*, puts the change in the second century B.C.; so do Farrington [II, 163f. (but cf. below, note 46)] and Childe, *op. cit.*, 253, although the latter speaks of a decline of practical application of science as early as after 500 B.C. (224).

scientists, and that the work of Diophantus was of the most far-reaching consequences. Yet generally speaking, the distinctions noted between the various periods seem valid. Can the same be said of the explanations offered?

It is sometimes said that the breakdown of science was due to the " general loss of the spirit of hope and adventure " noticeable throughout ancient society.[36] Even if such a " failure of nerve " had actually occurred, it would be a phenomenon extraneous to science, and I am here concerned only with such factors as could have affected scientific studies specifically. Again, the argument is proposed by some that the decay was accelerated by the lack of precision instruments, an explanation to which the editors of the *Source Book* seem to attribute at least a certain significance (134). The intimate relation between science and technology which I have discussed before, warrants the guess that scientists would have been provided with all the instruments they needed, had they only asked for them.[37]

The view most widely held, however, is that science decayed because of the existence of slavery, or on account of definite political measures imposed to abridge the freedom of science. The foremost exponent of these views in recent years has been Farrington. As he represents the situation in his *Greek Science*, " it was not . . . only with Ptolemy and Galen that the ancients stood on the threshold of the modern world. By that late date they had already been loitering on the threshold for four hundred years. They had indeed demonstrated conclusively their inability to cross it. . . . When we look for the causes of this paralysis it is obvious that it is not due to any failure of the individual. . . . The failure was a social one. . . . The ancients rigorously organized the logical aspects of science, lifted them out of the body of technical activity in which they had grown or in which they should have found their application, and set them apart from the world of practice and above it. This mischievous separation of the logic from the practice of science was the result of the universal cleavage of society into freeman and slave " (II, 164f.).[38]

I am not prepared to enter into a discussion of the question whether or not, as Farrington presupposes, science can develop only if it is closely connected with the world of practice and techniques. Others have seen the rise of technology as an unwilled and incidental outcome of the progress of pure science. Yet, although Farrington mentions Bacon, Vico, Hegel, and Marx

[36] Thus Cary, *loc. cit.;* Toynbee, in spite of his scepticism as to Cary's dating (*op. cit.*, 422, n. 1), seems to be of the same opinion (cf. also *ibid.*, n. 2).

[37] Cary (*loc. cit.*) stresses the lack of instruments as a subsidiary cause for the stagnation of astronomy, botany, and medicine. Farrington (I, 70f.) also mentions the absence of instruments of exact measurement.

[38] Of other scholars who see in slavery the reason for the decline of science I mention, *e.g.*, Zilsel, *op. cit.*, *Amer. Journal of Sociology*, 560f.: " Evidently lack of slave labor is a necessary but not a sufficient condition for the emergence of science "; Childe, *op. cit.*, 253, 258.

among those who have seen that " man makes his mental history in the process of conquering the world " (II, 175), a philosophical debate on this issue is here beside the point. As Farrington rightly insists, " the history of science must be really historical " (I, 149) . He has written " in the conviction that the better understanding of any stage in this long journey [by which man achieves his self-transformation from the animal to the human kingdom] must contribute to the attainment of the final goal " (II, 175). It is, then, the historical facts themselves that need careful scrutiny.

Now, why should science after 200 B.C. have been separated from the world of practice and techniques because of the existence of slavery? That around 300 B.C. " control of techniques, knowledge of the processes of which is essential for many branches of science, passed into the hands of slaves " (II, 8), is merely an assumption which is not borne out by the evidence. I have already summarized the results of modern studies on this problem (cf. above, part II), and I do not intend to rehearse the argument again. Farrington, if I am not mistaken, only once refers to the fact that " historians of society are still disputing the precise degree to which the industrial techniques had, by Plato's time, passed into the hands of slaves." And he adds, " For our purpose it is not necessary to give a more precise answer to this question than to say that for Plato, and for Aristotle, the normal and desirable thing was that the citizen should be exempted from the burden of manual work and even from direct control of the workers " (I, 141). I agree with Farrington that for his purpose, namely, an analysis of Plato's and Aristotle's philosophy, an answer to this question is unnecessary. But can his general assertion concerning the disastrous influence of slavery on science be accepted, unless he, or any one who sides with him, first refutes the results of the sociological investigations which have overturned the very presupposition of his argument? Even after 200 B.C. free men studied and mastered techniques; even at that time it was not considered improper to work with one's own hands for scientific purposes; the gentleman-like attitude of the ancient scholar, so often referred to, did not call for his exclusive occupation with words.[39]

Yet I should inquire also into the positive side of Farrington's argument. The presupposition of his verdict is, after all, his conviction that Greek science arose when, in the sixth and fifth centuries B.C., scientists worked in close cooperation with craftsmen and learned from their techniques. " It was the success with which he applied his techniques that gave the Ionian natural philosopher his confidence that he understood the workings of nature " (I, 77). Thales turned " primarily on techniques " (33); Anaximander and Anaximenes derived proofs from them, and so did Hera-

---

[39] Farrington speaks of " the more gentlemanly pursuit of theory of numbers and geometry " (I, 45); of Aristotle he says that " he was not ashamed to use his hands" at least as a biologist (p. 114). Zilsel, "The Genesis of the Concept of Scientific Progress," also refers to the gentlemanlike disdain for experimentation and dissection; cf., *idem, Amer. Journ. of Sociology*, 559. The situation has been stated correctly by Blüh, *Amer. Journ. of Physics* (1949), 387f.

clitus (33–35). Empedocles and Anaxagoras came to the rescue of observational science, which was threatened by the attacks of Parmenides (50ff.), and they too relied on techniques, as is witnessed by Empedocles' reference to the clepsydra (55) and by Anaxagoras' mention of the same device (58).

Two objections must be raised against such a thesis. First, it can certainly not account for all that the Presocratics called science. Farrington's assumption hardly explains Anaximander's belief in justice as a cosmic force, or Anaxagoras' belief in a divine mind, or Empedocles' mysticism and doctrine of purification, important features of their understanding of the universe, which Farrington fails to mention at all.[40] Secondly, granting that " the doctrine of *Opposite Tension* which Heraclitus applied to the interpretation of nature was derived, as his own words inform us, from his observation of the state of the string in the bow and the lyre " (I, 35), the question arises whether this was properly speaking a scientific procedure. If Heraclitus really based his philosophy on his observations on the tension of the strings and was able to convince others of his conclusions, this was possible only because the universe on speculative grounds was still thought to be uniform, so that everything in it could be compared to everything else. To put it differently, his procedure implies the rather naïve use of analogies. As Farrington himself admits later, the Ionians, " ignorant of the true or even approximate size of the heavenly bodies . . . could argue, without misgiving, from processes going on on earth to processes in the sky; Aristotle felt he could no longer do so " (99–100). Of course, Farrington does not deny that Aristotle was right in refusing to follow the lead of the Presocratics; nor does he deny that this change for the better, by which separate realms of science with specific methods appropriate to their subject matter were constituted, was brought about not by reliance on techniques, but by " the application of mathematics to astronomy " (100; cf. 142).

If, then, it was " the specific originality of the Ionian thinkers . . . that they applied to the interpretation of the motions of the heavenly bodies and all the major phenomena of nature modes of thought derived from their control of techniques " (134), if " the positive content that is decisive " in the Presocratic teaching is " familiarity with a certain range of techniques " (37), this is at the same time the least scientific aspect of their theories. The working model of Anaximander's universe may have been the potter's yard, the smithy, or the kitchen (33). Had subsequent generations not broken away from such analogies and restricted them to their proper scientific use, Greek cosmology might have been free of the influence of the Babylonian god, Marduk, to use a phrase of Farrington (*ibid.*), that is of mythology, but there would hardly have been any science. And what is true of analogies in the field of astronomy and cosmology, is equally true of the other branches of knowledge, as Farrington himself indicates (138–40; cf. also II, 123). The contention that science arose in connection with tech-

---

[40] The same criticism applies to Farrington's representation of Anaximander (*Science and Politics*, 19), as Cornford has pointed out: " This statement, no doubt, represents part of the truth; but it fails to account for those features which Mr. Farrington omits " (*Unwritten Philosophy*, 121).

niques, however important the material which they put at the disposal of the scientist, seems unfounded, and in view of the importance of mathematics in the constitution of science, it seems equally unjustifiable to speak of "the magic wand of Pythagorean mathematics" which "has transformed the natural philosophy of the Ionians into theology" (I, 116).

Even in the later development of science I can find no indication that knowledge of crafts and techniques was a decisive factor. Contrary to the impression one gains from Farrington (II, 27, 30f.), it is not preoccupation with artisan's skills that accounts for the greatness of the accomplishment of Theophrastus and Strato, the representatives of science around 300 B.C. It is not true that in his *Metaphysics* (8a 19–20) Theophrastus demands that in order to understand the behavior of matter "we must in general proceed by making reference to the crafts and drawing analogies between natural and artificial processes" (27); he rather says that "in general we must understand matter by virtue of an analogy with the arts, or any other similarity that may exist," that is, also by analogies of function or structure and the like (cf. 23). In the complicated system of Theophrastus his references to techniques are but one component; he is an adherent of teleology (22)—of his philosophical discussion of analogy I have spoken before.[41] As for Strato, in his mechanical investigations he surely employed analogies drawn from the crafts (30f., 38). Yet again, this one method does not adequately reflect his general outlook. Strato identified nature with the divine, as an Epicurean critic maintained (Cicero, *De Natura Deorum*, I, 13,35), not "the divine with nature," as Farrington puts it (42). In his doctrine of qualities Strato, despite his acceptance of certain Democritean theories, remained an Aristotelian, just as his concept of nature was derived from Aristotle.[42]

Without depreciating the value of practical knowledge accumulated through the arts and crafts, it is fair to conclude that Greek science did more than "sort out the theoretical implications of this practical knowledge and present the resulting body of knowledge as a logically coherent system" (I, 20). Greek science advocated at all times assumptions about an invisible world of law and order; it was theoretical rather than practical. For better or worse it always was "a relaxation, an adornment, a subject of contemplation" (II, 164), and did not become so simply at the end.[43]

But it is time to turn to the consideration of the second factor which in Farrington's opinion was responsible for the decay of ancient science, namely, political pressure interfering with the freedom of scientific research. This thesis Farrington first set forth in his *Science and Politics in the Ancient World*, where the influence of slavery is mentioned only in passing

[41] Cf. p. 95. Farrington's analysis of Theophrastus' system of botany (23), too, is vitiated, I think, by his failure to take into account the difficulties to which Theophrastus' concept of analogy led.

[42] For Strato, cf. H. Diels, "Über das physikalische System des Straton," *S. Ber. Berlin* (1893), 112, 116.

[43] Cf. p. 98f.

(165) ; in his *Greek Science* he has in some measure elaborated the political explanation.[44]

Farrington finds the first signs of political interference with science in Greece. The banishment of Anaxagoras from Athens (61; cf. *Greek Science*, I, 97) was brought about by the masses, though not without the connivance of the upper classes (76ff.). The conflict between Ionian science and the old-established religion had become evident before in Aeschylus' *Prometheus* (69ff.; 84; cf. *Science*, I, 135ff.). It is true, no doubt, that the Athenian democracy was quick in raising the cry of impiety. Yet the banishment of Anaxagoras, the condemnation of Socrates were events that did not halt the progress of science, as Farrington himself admits. After all, in 399, in spite of the trial of Socrates, one could buy Anaxagoras' book for one drachma in the market place at Athens (Plato, *Apology*, 26 D–E).[45]

But the situation changed at the end of the fourth century B.C. " In a city-state, where striking inequalities of wealth prevailed and where in consequence civil war was endemic and often violent, the religion of the State tended more and more to be transformed by the ruling-class into an instrument of mental oppression utterly incompatible with the spread of enlightenment. This was the main reason for the slow strangulation of the great speculative movement of natural philosophy that began in Ionia in the sixth century, flourished for about two hundred years, and then slowly died for about another eight centuries " (*Science and Politics*, 164).[46] And how was this strangulation brought about? By disseminating " such ideas as would make the unjust distribution of the rewards and toils of life seem a necessary part of the eternal constitution of things, and [by] suppressing such ideas as might lead to criticism of this view of the universe " (27). It was essential " to foster the belief that the oligarchical nobility were where they were by the will of heaven, and that any effort to dislodge them would be rewarded by condign punishment in this world and the next. Such a programme, of course, never exists in its naked simplicity as the conscious mental attitude of a whole class in society. It reveals itself only in moments of unguarded candour, or when there is a crisis of thought " (225). And since " in the West the rulers of Rome achieved a degree of success in the control of society through superstition that was denied to the Greek oli-

[44] The thesis of *Science and Politics* (1939) is expressly taken up in *Greek Science*, II, 113. For Childe's acceptance of Farrington's views, cf. *op. cit.*, 225.

[45] Incidentally, the Plato passage just referred to proves, if proof is needed, the incorrectness of Plutarch's contention that astronomy before Plato was taught only in secret and was tainted with reproach (*Nicias*, 23), a contention in which Farrington seems to put great faith (I, 96f.). The story obviously is invented in order to explain the persecution of Protagoras, Anaxagoras, and Socrates mentioned by Plutarch. An answer to Farrington's interpretation of the Aeschylean *Prometheus* is given by Cornford, *Unwritten Philosophy*, 123ff.

[46] The view here expressed slightly differs from Farrington's later assumption that the decay of science began in the second century B.C.; cf. above note 35 and corresponding text.

garchies," the fatal blow was struck with the overthrow of the Roman Republic (231; cf. 202ff.). "The very understanding that there was such a thing as science, except for a few languishing techniques such as medicine or architecture, almost died out under the Empire" (232).

I have no intention to inquire whether those whom Farrington singles out as the protagonists of this program of the oligarchy—Pindar, Plato, Cicero, Virgil, Manilius (225f.) and Aristotle (*e.g.*, 111)—actually had any such aims. Nor shall I raise the question whether ancient religion, even the state cults, could be used for the purposes for which in Farrington's view they were used, either consciously or unconsciously. In my opinion, Farrington is unconvincing on both these counts, just as he is unconvincing in his indictment of Platonism, which to him is unscientific and antisocial.[47] But again, I wish to scrutinize only the historical facts. Is there any evidence that science was repressed by any political movement that allied itself with religion?

As for Greece, Farrington in his first book alludes in passing to Plato's being prepared "to risk" teaching astronomy (110), to Aristotle's opposing the popular myths "behind [the] closed doors" of the Lyceum (111).[48] But in his *Greek Science* Farrington further develops the thesis that astronomy was the science most widely open to political bias. Plato's and Aristotle's astronomical views were shaped by definite political aims (I, 92–98). The fight over the homocentric hypothesis turned out to be not only a scientific, but also, and primarily, a political issue. The thesis of Heraclides, the "daring innovator," already contained "disturbing suggestions" (II, 78). The heliocentric hypothesis caused a "shock" (79). Cleanthes "expressed the opinion that the Greeks ought to indict Aristarchus on a charge of impiety," and these threats "appear to have involved a real danger to the scientist" (79). The "fear of dislodging the earth from the center of the

---

[47] Farrington's analysis of Plato has been criticized by Cornford, *op. cit.*, 127ff.; cf. also P. Shorey, "Platonism and the History of Science," *Proceedings Amer. Philosophical Society*, 66 (1927), 159–82. It is rather strange that Plato, who in the nineteenth century was heralded as the prophet of socialism, as the only one to have fought against the unjust distribution of wealth, and to have advocated mixed government as the sole remedy for the class system, should now be considered the protagonist of reaction. In regard to Farrington's view on religion I should at least mention that even those among the ancient philosophers who distinguished between political and philosophical religion (*Greek Science*, II, 113) did not deny the existence of a deity; they merely distinguished between two different ways of understanding the same truth. To speak of a "police function of religion," which the Epicureans alone abolished (*Science and Politics*, 160; cf. *Science*, II, 113), is quite misleading. Certainly religion in antiquity was sometimes misused for political purposes, by democrats and aristocrats alike. But generally religion held no wordly power over men. And Lucretius' poem, which to Farrington is a source of true and unimpeachable information, attests clearly that aristocrats and masses, in the opinion of the Epicureans, were under the sway of religious beliefs. If the ancient oligarchs tried to deceive the masses by religious means, they were indeed deceived deceivers.

[48] Concerning the risk of teaching astronomy, cf. p. 107, n. 45.

universe was too great " (87). For " the stability of ancient oligarchical society was bound up with a particular view of astronomy [namely, the homocentric or geocentric one]. To hold other views was not a scientific error but a heresy. Astronomy in antiquity was as thorny a subject as biblical criticism in modern times. Observational astronomy was subjected to anxious scrutiny and careful management . . . The astronomers themselves were often torn between two loyalties, like modern historians of religion. They had scientific consciences, but they knew that they were trespassing on a field where opinion involved political and social consequences " (88).

Excepting Duhem's speculations about the accusations of impiety " that ancient Paganism *would* have levelled " against the proponents of a heliocentric theory (88; cf. 79), Farrington does not adduce any evidence in proof of his views. In fact, nothing happened to Aristarchus, or to any one who sided with him. As is well known, trials for impiety became almost extinct after 300 B.C.[49] Hipparchus rejected the heliocentric hypothesis as unscientific, because to him it did not seem to square with observations that had been made. Posidonius opposed Heraclides on the ground that the choice of an astronomical hypothesis lies within the province of philosophy. Others chose to adhere to their respective views because they " had a prejudice in favour of the system which arranges all the spheres concentrically about the centre of the Universe," as Sosigenes suggested, who being himself a Peripatetic accused Eudoxus and his followers of having neglected the data known even to them (86). This explanation apparently is unconvincing to Farrington (cf. 87f., 89). Yet the fact that philosophical prejudices can hamper insight into truth seems very clear in the case of Epicurus and the Epicureans. To Farrington, they were the only ones in antiquity not to hold " two doctrines," that is, one by which to deceive the ruled and another one for the rulers (*Science and Politics*, 171). Through science they tried to liberate men, not to oppress them. They upheld what was the counterposition to oligarchic religion, insisting as they did that believers in unorthodox opinions on the heavenly bodies " were not in danger of being damned for them " either here or in the hereafter (*Science*, II, 89). Nevertheless, they too refused to accept the heliocentric hypothesis. Obviously it did not fit in with their notion of true knowledge.

All the facts, then, militate against Farrington's claim that political reasons can be made responsible for the rejection of correct astronomical views, that they " checked mechanical and chemical speculation on the motion and substance of the heavenly bodies " (II, 89). The silence of ancient writers on this point is the more significant, since they were by no means unaware of·a possible conflict between truth and political exigency. Despite some fervent pleas for the rulers' support of science and research, the suspicion remained that the court was not the place where studies would flourish. Not only did the life of the courtier scholar seem insecure on account of the " irrational wrath " of the tyrant—and occasional expulsions of schol-

[49] Cf. A. B. Drachmann, *Atheism in Pagan Antiquity* (1922), 7ff. The sceptic Carneades, for instance, held high political offices.

ars are known to have occurred in Hellenistic times (II, 100)—it was clearly realized that dependence on governments may jeopardize intellectual integrity and freedom of research. This awareness comes out in a general way in the never-ceasing debate about the question whether or not the philosopher should and could live at the court of a tyrant, or even have any intercourse with prominent political figures. The historian's task, it was said, calls for life in a free city and for independent means; the geographer in the service of the mighty, it was feared, would feel obliged to falsify facts in order to please their whims and ambitions. That rhetoric can survive only in a democracy, while it is bound to decay in an oligarchy, was a commonplace.[50] And yet, it is not attested that strictly scientific opinions were made a matter of persecution, that astronomers or physicists were afraid to hold certain views on the universe.

As for political interference with science under the Roman empire, Farrington, as far as I can see, does not adduce any specific instances. It is indeed hard to imagine how the Roman oligarchy could have put its supposed program into practice. Roman law left it to the gods to punish those who had sinned against them; even the Christians, after all, could be persecuted only as offenders against the emperor. No censorship of publications existed; if at times books were burnt, these were historical or political pamphlets put out by the opposition to the monarchy.[51] It is true, Tiberius ordered the execution of an architect and inventor who had aroused his displeasure, and did not even allow his name to be recorded (Dio Cassius, LVII, 21). Vettius Valens in the second century bewailed the fact that he had not the good fortune " to live in those spacious days [of old] and to breathe the fresh air of their spiritual freedom for research " ; since he is thinking of the days when even " kings and despots . . . were enthusiasts for the science [of astrology] " (*Anthologiae*, VI, Introd.), one can hardly take his testimony at face value.[52] At any rate, Sosigenes in the same century did attack the homocentric hypothesis in favor of the more modern theory of eccentric circles and epicycles, as did the later Peripatetics in general. And although the Roman attitude toward death and burial probably contributed to the decline of human anatomy, nobody objected to Galen's dissections of apes which most closely resembled human beings.[53] It seems fair, then, to say that in Greece as well as in Rome scientists were free to follow the bent of their minds. The decay of science can hardly be attrib-

[50] The general discussion of these topics is summarized by Plutarch, *Maxime cum principibus philosophandum esse.* The ideal conditions for historical research are outlined by Lucian, *Quomodo Historia Conscribenda.* The falsification of geographical facts in order to enhance the glory of political leaders is implied in Posidonius' stricture of Polybius, Strabo, III, 4, 13.

[51] Cf. F. H. Cramer, "Bookburning and Censorship in Ancient Rome," *Journal of the History of Ideas*, 6 (1945), 157ff.

[52] The first reference I owe to Rehm, *op. cit.*, 161, the second to Toynbee, *op. cit.*, V, 423, whose translation I have reproduced.

[53] Cf. Galen, *Opera Omnia*, ed. Kühn, II, 222, and in general Edelstein, *Quellen u. Studien z. Gesch. der Naturwiss. u. d. Medizin*, III, 136ff., 150.

uted to any political conditions that abridged freedom of thought.

Nor can one say with Farrington, I think, that in society as it emerged under the reign of Augustus, resting on Stoicism which itself continued the Platonic tradition, " science . . . was doomed " (*Science and Politics*, 219); that it was incompatible with " the tone and temper " of this society (229). In the first century B.C. the members of the Epicurean school "almost alone . . . fought to rid nature and history of the arbitrary interference of super- natural forces " (*Greek Science*, II, 111). " Wherever men studied nature, not as a manifestation of the mind of a benevolent providence, but as a non- human environment by the control of which men had laid the foundations of civilized life; wherever men studied history, not to trace in it the mys- terious intentions of the gods, but as a record of the trials and errors of mankind; wherever men thought of society as a sphere in which man by the exercise of his political or technical inventiveness might improve his condi- tions of life; wherever human nature was studied as a basis for a rational control of the instinctive life; there the teaching of Epicurus was likely to be at the root of it " (II, 109f.). But the Epicureans were " the defeated party in ancient philosophy " (II, 119), defeated because they did not serve the desired political ends.

Farrington's praise of Epicurus as the " first champion of popular en- lightenment " (*Science and Politics*, 129) does not call for my criticism. It has already been pointed out that Epicurus was not a reformer, he had no interest in politics; great ethical teacher that he was, he wanted to improve man rather than social conditions.[54] I wish to urge, however, that Epicu- reanism was not conducive to scientific research. In recent years, the pic- ture of an Epicurus utterly ignorant of science has rightly been abandoned. To go to the other extreme now and to consider Epicurus the protagonist of science, is in my opinion equally erroneous.

The fact that atomism has become the basis of progress in modern sci- ence should not make one forget the fundamental differences between the ancient and the modern atomic theory. Epicurus' atoms were the elements of rational philosophy, not the working hypothesis of empirical science. The neglect of mathematics in the field of physics is another characteristic of his unscientific approach.[55] More important still, Epicurus' belief in the

[54] Cf. Cornford, *op. cit.*, 93f. (first published in *Background to Modern Science*, ed. J. Needham and W. Pagel [1938]); the tendency to identify progress with Epi- cureanism can be traced at least to the nineteenth century (*ibid.*, 90). Rostovtzeff, *Hellenistic World*, III, 1128ff., has dealt with the general failure of ancient philo- sophical thought to advocate social reform. It is fair, however, to underline the fact that so far as philosophy became active in politics, it was the Platonists and the science, is in my opinion equally erroneous.

[55] For the difference between Epicurus' theory and that of modern science, cf., *e.g.*, W. C. Dampier, *From Aristotle to Galileo* (*Background to Modern Science*, 25f.); also Cornford, *op. cit.*, 122f. For Epicurus' relation to mathematics, I. E. Drabkin, " Notes on Epicurean Kinetics," *Transactions Amer. Philological Ass.*, 69 (1938), 373f. Epicurus' dogmatism, evidenced by his insistence that his pupils should learn his teachings by heart (*Ep.* I, Init.; II, Init.), likewise can hardly be considered a stimulus to further research.

'diversity' of causes makes it impossible to establish that astronomical and mechanical science, the absence of which Farrington laments and attributes to political conditions (II, 89). While in regard to the atoms one cause alone is to be considered (*Epistula* I, Diogenes Laert., X, 78), in astronomy and meteorology, Epicurus holds, as in " all that is unknown, we must take into account the variety of ways in which analogous occurrences happen within our experience " (*ibid.*, 80; cf. *Epistula* II, *ibid.*, 94, 96). " If then we think that an event could happen in one or other particular way out of several, we shall be as tranquil when we recognize that it actually comes about in more ways than one as if we knew that it happens in this particular way " (*Epistula* I, *ibid.*, 80). Has the quest of science not always been the search for the specific explanation of any given phenomenon? [56] And Epicurus' condemnation of specific causality in matters which " are only seen at a distance " (*ibid.*) was not abandoned even by those among his followers who in the first century B.C. scrutinized the structure of empirical science and elaborated the doctrine of inference from observed facts. For they considered this inference applicable only to painting, grammar, rhetoric, music, poetry, as well as to medicine, navigation and mathematics; astronomy and the other natural sciences were not included.[57]

It is therefore not astonishing that Farrington in his history of science, excepting the assertion that the Epicureans were " the best anthropologists of the ancient world " (*Greek Science*, II, 43), cannot name even one Epicurean scientist of note, or one outstanding scientific discovery made within the Epicurean school. Epicureanism during more than five hundred years in which it had devoted adherents made no contributions to science.[58] Wherever atomism as such played a rôle in Greek science, it was after it

---

[56] The Epicurean principle of causation is exemplified in *Ep.* 2; *e.g.*, " Snow may be formed when a fine rain issues from the clouds . . . or again by congelation in clouds . . . And there are other ways in which snow might be formed " (*Diog. Laert.*, X, 107f.). From this, one must distinguish the recognition of a possible multiplicity of causes (*Ep.* II, 96); cf. C. Bailey, *Epicurus, The extant Remains* (1926), 296. For Lucretius' application of the thesis that " all explanations are true and correspond to existing facts, which are not contradicted by phenomena," cf. C. Bailey, *Lucretius, De Rerum Natura* I (1947), 57ff. Even the attempt to find in Epicurus a concept of order that is fundamentally biological (F. Solmsen, " Epicurus and Cosmological Heresies," *Amer. Journ. of Philology*, 72 [1951], 18ff.) leads to the recognition that " the application of the concept of cosmic matters remains problematical " (21).

[57] Cf. Ph. H. De Lacy and E. A. De Lacy, *Philodemus on Methods of Inference* (1941), 136, 152. Appreciation of the method of inference and of the importance which the arguments of Philodemus acquired later, when they were rectified and further worked out, should not deceive one about the shortcomings inherent in the original discussion.

[58] Lucretius' description of the development of civilization is based on Democritus, cf. Farrington, II, 115; by the way, this is not different in principle from that given by the Stoics (cf. above, note 31). Whether Epicurean anthropology should be called the best ever formulated by the ancients (Farrington, II, 43) depends on the point of view of the interpreter.

had been integrated into other systems and considerably modified, as for instance in the case of Strato (II, 41), or Heraclides of Pontus, or Asclepiades, the physician of the first century B.C. Those who furthered research, as far as they belonged to any philosophical sect, were Platonists, Aristotelians, or Stoics, members of those schools which to Farrington represent the unscientific spirit. The achievement of the philosophical dogmatists was even more important than that of the philosophical empiricists or sceptics. When scepticism, which generally withheld all judgment and was hostile to all investigation, at one time allied itself with medical theory, every attempt at generalization was given up and there remained only the observation of individual phenomena.[59]

In every respect, then, Farrington's explanation of the development of ancient science seems to be untenable. His books have done much to arouse interest in the subject. The thesis which they advocate is vitiated however by what, in my opinion, is the basic error in many of the recent evaluations of ancient science, namely, the misapplication of historical analogies. Conditions in antiquity are seen in the light of subsequent events. The conflict between science and religion, which characterized later ages, is injected into the ancient world. Progress and decay of Greek and Roman science are judged by the standards of modern science.

Such an approach not only tends to distort the reconstruction of the actual happenings, it also loses sight of the peculiar problems and solutions which were characteristic of antiquity. The history of ancient science is not merely a history of the more or less correct answers to scientific questions. The very attempt to constitute a scientific view of the universe was beset with difficulties that had to be met. The reaction of society to this attempt, the position of the scientists within the social order, in short, the organization of science had an essential part in shaping the particular way in which science was tackled by the ancients. The achievement of the Greeks, their scientific merit, can be judged more adequately and fairly only if seen within its own setting. Even the various phases of ancient science, the rapid progress at first, the stagnation which set in after the second century of our era and is usually regarded as decay, acquire a meaning of their own if the categories of interpretation are derived from an analysis of the particular and unique historical situation. It is some of these neglected aspects that I propose to discuss in concluding my survey of recent studies.

IV. THE ORGANIZATION OF ANCIENT SCIENCE

The question when science began may at first glance seem as meaningless as the question when poetry and art had their beginning. Yet provided that by science one does not understand just any kind of knowledge or technical skill, however highly developed, but a consistently rational explanation of phenomena, the question is meaningful and allows of an an-

---

[59] For scepticism and science, cf. Edelstein, *Quellen u. Studien z. Gesch. d. Naturwiss. u. d. Medizin*, III, 253ff.; *idem, s.v. Methodiker, R.E.*, Suppl. VI, cols. 367ff. For Heraclides and Asclepiades, cf. K. Lasswitz, *Geschichte der Atomistik*, I (1890), 211ff.

swer. It was with the Presocratic thinkers that such a science came into existence, as the Greeks themselves were well aware. To be sure, there were those who saw in Homer the father of science, of astronomy, geography and history, and who consequently made science coeval with Greek history. But they could make good their claim only by applying to the poet's work the method of allegorical interpretation, that is, by translating his thought, concealed as they believed in poetical language, into the scientific categories of a later period. However, in general it was agreed that a new attitude toward the comprehension of facts began to arise after the heroic age had vanished. On the basis of the hypothesis that the world can be understood by reason some men in Ionia in the early sixth century created a world that reason understands.[60]

Of this new and unprecedented vision society at first took hardly any notice. Xenophanes' angry denunciations of the rewards bestowed on others while he and his kin remained without recognition (21 B 2 Diels) are typical of the situation. In his devotion to learning and insight into nature the scientist was isolated and on his own. A hitherto unknown ideal of human existence—symbolized in Democritus' saying that to find an etiology is greater gain than to become king of Persia (68 B 118 Diels)—challenged the old established ideals of a political or agonistic or acquisitive life. Unrecognized by his contemporaries the scientist found himself outside the confines of the social order. There were no jobs for him; science was not a career. He had to have independent means with which to carry out his investigations or to travel for the sake of his geographical studies. Society had a place for the practicing physician, but not for the biologist. The architect could earn a living, in the builder's workshop mathematical knowledge developed incidentally and empirically; but there was no position for the theoretical mathematician. As interest increased in knowledge as such, the scientist began to teach others who wanted to know about his subject. Occasionally he found a protector who provided for his livelihood. On the whole, even in the classical centuries everything was left to the initiative and courage and determination of individuals who pursued their studies at their own expense and at their own risk. Athens forced her citizens to pay for producing the plays of Aeschylus, Sophocles and Euripides. At the great festivals everywhere, poets and musicians competed for rewards and prizes; no similar opportunity existed for scientists.[61]

[60] The ancient doxographical tradition unanimously attests the Ionian origin of philosophy and science. Here I need not discuss the question whether the Orient had an influence on the beginnings of the Greek development; cf. J. Burnet, *Early Greek Philosophy* (1948⁴), 15ff. For Homer, cf. F. Wehrli, *Zur Geschichte der allegorischen Deutung Homers im Altertum*, Diss. (Basel, 1928).

[61] That it is characteristic of Greek scientific and philosophical achievement that the work was done by individuals without the support of society has been emphasized most strongly by J. Burckhardt, *Über das wissenschaftliche Verdienst der Griechen*, *Vorträge* 1844–1887, ed. E. Dürr (1919⁴), 140ff. Even if one is inclined to speak with Burnet (*op. cit.*, 28ff.) of philosophical schools at the time of the Presocratics, one must admit that these schools were private organizations.

In the Hellenistic age a few research centers were established, notably Alexandria and Pergamum. Some of the kings gave support to scientific investigations, especially to such as were likely to bear practical fruit, further their own interests and enhance their own fame. Yet it was a very limited circle of scholars who profited by royal munificence, who received pay for their work, who were offered the facilities of a library or the resources of scientific collections.[62] In the free cities where the great majority of researchers lived, they still failed to get any help or employment; even public collections of books were rarely at their disposal. The philosophical schools no less than the scientific ones were private organizations, maintained entirely by private contributions. For the acquisition of instruments and all other implements of research the scientists were still forced to fall back on their own resources.[63]

The sober truth, then, is that in the early stages of science, society, far from interfering with the scientist's work, on the whole remained completely indifferent to its value. To the modern interpreter, Greek science may seem to be one of the greatest achievements of the ancients. To the Greeks of the classical and Hellenistic centuries, it was of little consequence. The progress that was accomplished was brought about by individuals fighting against almost insuperable odds. They took up their studies without any proper training in their youth. For even the educational system was impervious to the advance of scientific thought. The instruction of children, a matter left in the hands of parents and private teachers, was concentrated mainly on poetry, music, and gymnastics. The teaching of scientific subjects was rudimentary.[64] Once the scholar had overcome the initial difficulties in acquiring the elementary knowledge which he needed, he could not devote himself exclusively to his work. The constant demands made upon him by the community in the interest of public life curtailed his leisure and diverted much of his energy. Finally, since under the existing conditions only a few were willing or could afford to choose science as their profession, the number engaged in scientific investigations was small indeed. It was a handful of people who had to carry the burden.[65]

That this was the situation and that it impaired the effectiveness of whatever inquiries were made, the ancients realized themselves. " Inasmuch

[62] For the organization of the Museion, cf. *s.v. Museion, R.E.,* XVI, 1 (1933), cols. 807ff. That even the support given by Alexander the Great to scientists has been exaggerated by recent scholars, has been shown by O. Regenbogen, *s.v. Theophrastos, R.E., Supplement,* VII (1950), cols. 1459ff.

[63] For the rare occurrence of public libraries in free cities, cf. W. Christ–W. Schmid, *Geschichte der griech. Literatur,* II, 1 (1920), 19. Concerning the philosophical schools after Plato, cf. U. v. Wilamowitz, *Antigonos von Karystos, Philologische Untersuchungen,* IV (1881), 263ff.

[64] Cf. H. J. Marrou, *Histoire de l'éducation dans l'antiquité* (1948), esp. 160ff., 225ff., 243ff.

[65] The importance of this fact has been underlined by O. Neugebauer, *Exact Sciences in Antiquity* (*Studies in Civilization,* University of Pennsylvania Bicentennial Conference [1941], 25), and pointed out as one of the reasons for the rapid decline of science. Cf. also below, n. 70.

as no city holds [solid geometry] in honor," Plato says (*Republic*, 528 B), "these inquiries are languidly pursued," and he suggests that if the state superintended and honored such studies, " continuous and strenuous investigation would bring out the truth." The historian Diodorus, comparing Greek science with that of the Chaldaeans (II, 29), gives a more comprehensive picture of the state of affairs, which also shows that even in his time no essential improvement had been brought about. In Babylon, he·says, knowledge is handed on from father to son; the pupils " are bred in these teachings from childhood up " ; afterwards they are "relieved of all other services to the state." In Greece, on the contrary, the student "who takes up a large number of subjects without preparation turns to the higher studies only quite late, and then, after laboring upon them to some extent, gives them up, being distracted by the necessity of earning a livelihood; and but a few here and there really strive for the higher studies and continue in the pursuit of them as a profitmaking business, and these are always trying to make innovations in connection with the most important doctrines instead of following in the path of their predecessors." [66]

It is true, Diodorus is an idolator of the Chaldaeans and Egyptians. In the caste system he finds the explanation of the superiority of the Orientals. One may well wonder whether Greek science could have arisen at all, had Greek life been fettered by similar traditions, had Greek society not left it to its members to do whatever they wanted, even if they could not count on the support of their fellow citizens. The admiration for the greatness of Greek scientific achievement should be enhanced by the realization that everything depended on the effort of the individual, unaided by the world in which he lived. Nevertheless, it remains true that what on the one hand constitutes the glory of Greek science, on the other hand accounts for certain of its limitations. Progress necessarily was slowed down and limited by the scarcity of scholars and their insufficient preparation. The lack of social recognition and the consequent lack of permanent and stable forms of organization had a decisive influence, I think, also on the course which science took during the initial phases of its history.

At the outset a few general traits may be emphasized reflecting the insecurity of science within the social order, which was aggravated by the philosophical scepticism concerning the possibility of gaining true knowledge. Such treatises as the Ps. Hippocratic essay *On the Art* inveigh against the detractors of science. The physician who here defends the actual existence of a medical art is well aware of the fact that all the other arts and sciences are also threatened, and expects their representatives to come forth in rebuttal of the attacks made upon them. Obviously written for the élite interested in the new sophistic movement, the treatise shows how the craftsman who intends to be a scientist is fighting for the recognition of his novel aspiration.[67] Nor are later writings devoid of such justifications of the ex-

---

[66] Strictly speaking Diodorus' comparison of Greeks and Chaldaeans concerns their philosophy, but this quite obviously includes the sciences.

[67] Cf. L. Edelstein, περὶ ἀέρων und die Sammlung der hippokratischen Schriften, *Problemata*, IV (1931), 105ff.

istence and truth of knowledge, its value and usefulness, coupled again with a rejection of the philosophical scepticism that undermined science from within. The rhetorical character of many scientific books is an indirect indication of the insecurity of the position of science. One writes with an eye on the public who must be convinced and propagandized. Since the state or the community in no way supervises science and its application—no examinations, no system of licensing existed—the physician for instance develops a technique by which he can convince the layman that he is truly a doctor and not a mere pretender. The greater part of ancient medical prognostic serves this social purpose rather than a scientific one.[68] And it is likely that the insistence on the impressiveness of mechanical devices, the constant emphasis on the marvellous and the astounding, to which I have referred above, is determined also by the wish to gain the approval of public opinion. Thus, a considerable amount of what is, strictly speaking, unscientific matter is integrated into the body of science, naturally to the detriment of more important and strictly scientific features. Finally, no satisfactory solution of the relative position of expert and layman was found. Just as in education no heed was paid to scientific progress, so ancient life in general remained untouched by the results of a scientific understanding of the world. The myth continued to be the prevailing power. In the fifth century B.C. the Athenian general Nicias took an eclipse of the sun for a bad omen; Roman generals or noblemen of the first century A.D. were wont to react similarly. The fundamentals of scientific knowledge were no prerequisite for an official, for the scientific analysis of facts had no authority. The astronomical and geographical views even of the upper strata of society fell far behind the available information, and their lack of knowledge was no matter of reproach. Nowhere did the expert play a rôle or have a clearly defined place in public affairs.[69]

To turn now to questions more intrinsically connected with science proper, I suggest that the failure of the empirical trend to establish itself securely was in great measure due to the lack of a social integration of science. Collecting a vast mass of information presupposes stabilized institutions. Individual effort at assembling data necessarily is limited. To be sure, the Aristotelian school and its members achieved a great deal, and so did the Museion in Egypt. But these were rare exceptions. Historical and geographical studies were hampered by the scholars' tendency to avoid political entanglement and to live as private citizens (cf. above, p. 597).

[68] Cf. Edelstein, *op. cit.*, 60ff. It is in this way, I think, that one must explain " the tendency to popularize science in accordance with the taste of the ruling class," noted by Neugebauer, *loc. cit.*, and regarded by him as the second element responsible for the decay of science. But there is no attempt " to adapt [science] to the teaching level of the schools," *ibid.*; cf. above, note 64 and corresponding text.

[69] Here I have rephrased some of Burckhardt's arguments, *op. cit.*, 146f. The ancients, even in scientific matters, were wont to subordinate the expert's opinion to the judgment of the free citizen, or in Plato's words, to " the user's art " (*Republic*, 601 D). How far the individual wished to go in accepting scientific knowledge, was up to him.

Astonishing though it is how much was accomplished, how documents were assembled and facts were compiled, still the researcher had only as much material at his disposal as he could lay hands on himself. The experimental sciences labored under similar handicaps. No close collaboration in laboratories developed; records were hardly kept beyond the lifetime of the individual scientist. The isolation of the individual and of the private schools was intensified by the difficulties of communication. One seldom knew what other men in the same field were doing. Results gained at one time were forgotten again or not referred to because they were not generally available.[70]

However, the fact that science had originated as an individual endeavor and continued to depend on private initiative even in the Hellenistic centuries had a still more serious consequence: no agreement existed among scientists about the fundamental tenets of science. Science was not yet an aggregate of opinions on which all scientists must and do agree. Of course, there are always periods when revolutionary changes take place in science, so that disagreement may exist for some time. But after the discussion has settled down, unanimity about the basic principles and approaches is reestablished. In its essentials, science in America, England, France, Germany is alike. A very different situation prevailed throughout the early phases of ancient science.

For science as it was elaborated by the various Presocratic philosophers or scientists of the classical age really expressed their individual conviction, which was true in the opinion of its respective proponent and his pupils, but of no validity for anyone else. The evolution of nature as conceived by Anaximander or Anaxagoras had no persuasive power for a Democritean. The physics of Diogenes of Apollonia was anathema to an Empedoclean. There were almost as many kinds of science as there were scientists. The *Corpus Hippocraticum*, the only large bulk of scientific writings preserved from that epoch, illustrates the infinite variety of definitions considered scientific as regards so basic a concept as the etiology of diseases.[71] The Hellenistic age witnessed a gradual change. Not only did schools or organizations now come into existence—thought itself became more uniform. The number of individualistic formulations of science was reduced. Methods and systems that found a wider following coalesced. Still, there remained a great variety of doctrines, and adherence to any one of them was optional, as it were. There was dogmatic and empirical science, the one aiming at establishing causes, the other renouncing the search for an explanation of hidden phenomena. The geography of Polybius differed from that of Eratosthenes not only as regards factual data, but also as regards the basic approach: Polybius, for the sake of the usefulness of geography to the political leader, abandoned the standards of mathematics. Aristarchus

---

[70] Neugebauer, *loc. cit.*, has suggested that "the number of scholars in the ancient world was by far too small to undertake any kind of program based on systematic organized collaboration." I should consider this factor as only one among others that were responsible for the failure of empiricism.

[71] Edelstein, *op. cit.*, 154ff.

and Hipparchus disagreed not only about the heliocentric hypothesis, but also about the principles governing the formulation of astronomical laws. Others doubted the possibility of applying mathematics to astronomy. The debate about the foundation of geometry—whether it was rational or empirical knowledge—jeopardized even the progress of that science which naturally had always been comparatively free of dissension. The medicine of Erasistratus and of Herophilus on the one hand and empirical medicine on the other were as much at cross-purposes, as were Stoic and Epicurean physics. And these divergencies did not imply a distinction between science and non-science; they merely characterized rival systems of thought which continued to exist side by side.[72]

It is this still unreconciled dissension among scientific outlooks which explains why, studying the remains of classical and Hellenistic science, we can detect one type of scientific argument strikingly similar to modern science, while a vast amount of other material, though scientific to the Greeks, does not strike the modern interpreter as scientific at all. Moreover, it should be noted that the reign of rival systems lasted down to the second century A.D. Galen's *Introduction to Medicine,* addressed to beginners, places before them the theories of the three medical sects which at that time competed with one another, that of the Dogmatists, of the Empiricists, and of the Methodists, and the young student is asked to make a choice among them, otherwise he would be at a loss with whom to study.

However, in the same second century—at which time, according to most historians, the decay of ancient science became complete—the confusion of opinions gradually began to disappear. The knowledge gained by previous generations was collected, criticized and, with the addition of new material, synthesized. Such a tendency can be observed in all fields of learning, in grammar, metrics and literary history, no less than in geography, optics, astronomy, algebra and medicine.[73] That it is not by chance that so many works of the new type were composed in this second century, that they were instigated by a conscious effort to dispense with the bewildering diversity of approaches characteristic of earlier periods, follows, I think, from the program which one of these authors, Galen, outlines in his work *On Scientific Demonstration* and in many others of his writings. Oppressed by the " wide

[72] The ancients certainly were well aware of the dissension among scientists, cf., *e.g.,* Diodorus, II, 29, and below, n. 74. Modern scholars, if they pay any attention at all to the phenomenon in question, consider it typical of Greek science generally. Thus Zilsel says, on p. 253, ". . . it would be an overstatement to characterize scientific activity in classical antiquity as a merely individualistic undertaking. Classical science had rather reached, approximately, that degree of continuity and cooperation which in our era is characteristic of philosophy." But as will be shown, this does not apply to the last phase of the ancient development.

[73] For the work of the ancient grammarians and historians of literature, cf. U. v. Wilamowitz, *Euripides Herakles,* I (1889), 179 (*Einleitung in die Tragödie*). It was in the second century too that the classical tragedies and comedies which have survived were selected for use in school.

dissension " that existed he wished not to defend any sectarian dogma, but to show to the physician or to any other scientist how one can establish " the best sect." The doctrine of such a sect in Galen's opinion was to stand above all doctrines and to acknowledge as its criterion not the opinion of any one school, but of truth alone. The method of Euclidean geometry, in praise of which all philosophers agreed, he considered the model of the method of the new science.[74] In other words, as the merely individual views of the Presocratic scientists had been superseded by the more comprehensive Hellenistic systems, so these divergent systems themselves were now to be integrated into a uniform science. It is true, the authors of the second century added relatively little to the knowledge already available. Yet they took a step that had not been taken, they accomplished a task that had not been accomplished before, they solved a problem that called for a solution, if science was to be science. It is their merit to have created the *scientia aeterna*, a science in which all scientists equally share. That is why their books soon became canonical, why they were used, commented upon and excerpted by later generations, while the works of the classical and Hellenistic ages were hardly accorded further study. The scholasticism of late antiquity with its rigid rules for instruction and study, its limitation to certain authors is but the working out of the new ideal of a unified science.[75]

This is not the place to inquire how far certain trends of eclecticism, noticeable even before the second century, or the Roman interest in encyclopedic summaries of knowledge prepared the way for the work done by

[74] The fragments of Galen's treatise *On Scientific Demonstration* have been collected by J. v. Müller, " Über Galens Werk vom wissenschaftlichen Beweis," *Abh. Akad. München,* XX (1894), 405ff., who in his introduction has also surveyed Galen's statements on " the best sect " he contemplated. The specific passages I have referred to are to be found *Opera Omnia,* X, 469 (Müller, 419, n. 17); I, 81 (420, n. 19), 225; *Scripta Minora,* ed. J. v. Müller, II (1891), 117. I should add that in late antiquity and in the Middle Ages Galen was held to be the foremost theoretician of science.

[75] Wilamowitz, *loc. cit.,* claimed that it was due to the weakness and unoriginality of later generations that the second-century authors became canonical, and he considered it the task of historical scholarship to " eliminate the predominance of these men, in order to lay bare the truly scientific and equally important work of the [earlier] Greeks." It is in this spirit that most of the work on ancient science has been undertaken during the past decades, and rightly, in so far as it is only through the work of the later compilers that the content of Hellenistic science and a good deal even of classical science can be recovered. Yet in making such an attempt one should not forget that these later writings also have a value of their own, that their authors with good reason were regarded as great scientists in late antiquity, during the Middle Ages, and even down to the eighteenth century. The unification of science was only one of their merits. For ancient scholasticism in philosophy, cf. K. Praechter, *Byzantinische Zeitschrift,* 18 (1909) 516ff.; in medicine, O. Temkin, " Studies on late Alexandrian Medicine," *Bull. of the Institute of the Hist. of Medicine,* III (1935), 405ff.

men like Galen, Ptolemy, and others. One cannot help feeling that they were inspired also by the political unification of the world. It is surely of significance that Galen prided himself on having unified medicine, just as Trajan had unified Italy by means of the roads that he had built (X, 632f. Kühn). At any rate, the ascendance of the new vision of science was considerably aided by social factors. In the Roman empire the educational system as well as the attitude of society toward science underwent revolutionary changes. The state provided educational facilities. Public schools were founded, universities sprang up. Professorships were endowed, examinations for scholars were introduced. Instruction in the schools all over the empire became standardized. Alexandria, Rome, Massilia, Athens were all part of the same political structure, and consequently also representative of the same science. The varied ancient democracies corresponded to the individualistic systems of science in the classical age; the various Hellenistic kingdoms corresponded to the several schools; the uniform Roman empire came to have one science only.[76]

I am not arguing that these considerations fully explain the course of ancient science. If we wish to understand the development of scientific thought in antiquity, we shall have to take into account a great many other factors, the relationship between philosophy and science, the specific concepts of scientific methods, certain presuppositions that were never challenged, unscientific though they were. Thus in the history of ancient astronomy the prejudice in favor of rest as opposed to motion was as decisive as it was later in the controversy between Galileo and his contemporaries. In the history of ancient physics, the prejudice in favor of the circle as the more beautiful and perfect geometrical form precluded the acceptance of other, more correct views.[77] Theories like these were also responsible for the stagnation of research. Nor am I arguing that ancient science did not suffer through the process of scholastic unification. Progress was retarded; there was a loss of fibre. The " sober drunkenness " which had inspired earlier investigations no longer prevailed; scientists became specialists and officials. I am arguing only that it is incorrect simply to speak of the " decay " of ancient science. Even at the end there was progress, for it was in the final stage of the development that ancient scientists for the first time succeeded in bringing about a satisfactory organization of scientific endeavor. This gain made by the archaistic generation exercised as much influence on all subsequent scientific research as did the discoveries of classical and Hellenistic scientists.

---

[76] For educational institutions in the Roman empire, cf. Marrou, *op. cit.*, 398ff. The importance of the Roman reforms for the whole intellectual development has been succinctly analyzed by W. Dilthey, *Pädagogik, Ges. Schriften*, IX (1934), 72ff.

[77] Cf. E. Goldbeck, " Der Untergang des kosmischen Weltbildes der Antike," *Die Antike*, I (1925), 72ff.; A. E. Haas, *Archiv für Geschichte d. Philosophie*, XXII (1909), 80ff. For other considerations, cf. A. Reymond, *History of the Sciences in Greco-Roman Antiquity* (Engl. ed., 1927), 222ff.; Cornford, *Unwritten Philosophy*, 87.

2 FROM RATIONALISM TO EXPERIMEN-TALISM

From Rationalism to Experimentalism

By A. C. Crombie *

THE HISTORY OF SCIENCE is the history of systems of thought about the natural world. Though the most obvious characteristic of science in modern civilization is the control it has given over the physical world, even while such practical control was being acquired, and certainly for long periods before it became possible, men were trying to bring nature within the grasp of their understanding. The inventions and practical achievements of applied science are of great interest to the historian and so are the effects of natural science on the layman's view of the world as seen in literature, art, philosophy and theology; of even greater interest is the internal development of scientific thought itself. The chief problems before the historian of science are, therefore: what questions about the natural world were men asking at any particular time? What answers were they able to give? And why did these answers cease to satisfy human curiosity? An obsolete system of scientific thought, which may appear very strange to us looking back from the 20th century, becomes intelligible when we understand the questions it was designed to answer. The questions make sense of the answers, and one system has given place to another not always because men discovered fresh facts which made the

* The editors are indebted to Professor A. C. Crombie for providing this discussion of the period.

old theories obsolete, but often because for some reason they began to look at long familiar evidence in a new way.

In ancient Greece men were concerned with trying to discover the intelligible essence underlying the world of change, and they pursued natural science more for understanding than for use. With the rise of Christianity, to this Greek rationalism was added the idea of nature as sacramental, symbolic of spiritual truths, and both attitudes are found in St. Augustine. In Western Christendom in the Dark Ages men were concerned more to preserve the facts which had been collected in classical times than to attempt original interpretations themselves. Yet, during this period, a new element was added from the social situation, an activist attitude which initiated a period of technical invention and was to have an important effect on the development of scientific apparatus. Early in the 12th century men asked how the facts recorded in the book of *Genesis* could best be explained in terms of rational causes. With the recovery of the full tradition of Greek and Arabic science in the 12th and early 13th centuries, and particularly of the works of Aristotle and Euclid, there was born, from the marriage of the empiricism of technics with the rationalism of philosophy and mathematics, a new conscious empirical science seeking to discover the rational structure of nature. At the same time a more or less complete system of scientific thought was provided by Aristotle's works. The rest of the history of medieval science consists of the working out of the consequences of this new approach to nature.

Gradually it was realised that the new science did not conflict with the idea of Divine Providence, though it led to a variety of attitudes towards the relation between reason and faith. Internal contradictions, contradictions with other authorities, and contradictions with observed facts eventually led to radical criticisms of the Aristotelian system. At the same time, extension of the use of experiment and mathematics produced an increase in positive knowledge. By the beginning of the 17th century the systematic use of the new methods of experiment and mathematical abstraction had produced results so striking that this movement has been given the name "Scientific Revolution." These new methods were first expounded in the 13th century, but were first used with complete maturity and effectiveness by Galileo.

The origins of modern science are to be found at least as far back as the 13th century, but from the end of the 16th century the Scientific Revolution began to gather a breathtaking speed. The changes in scientific thought occurring then so altered the type of question asked by scientists that Kant said of them: "a new light flashed on all students of nature." The new science also profoundly affected man's idea of the world and of himself, and it was to have a position in relation to society unknown in earlier times. The effects of the new science on thought and life have, in fact, been so great and special that the Scientific Revolution has been compared in the history of civilisation to the rise of ancient Greek philosophy in the 6th and 5th centuries B.C. and to the spread of Christianity throughout the Roman Empire in the 3rd and 4th centuries A.D. For this reason the study of the changes leading up to that revolution, the study of the history of science from the Middle Ages to the 17th century, is of unique interest for the historian of science. The position of science in the modern world cannot be fully understood without a knowledge of the changes that occurred during that time. . . .

TECHNICS AND SCIENCE IN THE MIDDLE AGES

TECHNICS AND EDUCATION

It has often been pointed out that science develops best when the speculative reasoning of the philosopher and mathematician is in closest touch with the manual skill of the craftsman. It has been said also that the absence of this association in the Greco-Roman world and in medieval Christendom was one reason for the supposed backwardness of science in those societies. The practical arts were certainly despised by the majority of the most highly educated people in Classical Antiquity, and were held to be the work of slaves. In view of such works as the long series of

Greek medical writings, stretching from the first members of the so-called Hippocratic corpus to the works of Galen, the military devices and the "screw" attributed to Archimedes, the treatises on building, engineering and other branches of applied mechanics written during Hellenistic and Roman times by Ctesibius of Alexandria, Athenaeus, Apollodorus, Hero of Alexandria, Vitruvius, Frontinus and Pappus of Alexandria, and the works on agriculture by the elder Cato, Varro and Columella, it may be doubted whether even in Classical Antiquity the separation of technics and science was as complete as has been sometimes supposed. In the Middle Ages there is much evidence to show that these two activities were at no period totally divorced and that their association became more intimate as time went on. This active, practical interest of educated people may be one reason why the Middle Ages was a period of technical innovation, though most of the advances were probably made by unlettered craftsmen. And certainly it was this interest of many theoretical scientists in practical results that encouraged them to ask concrete and precise questions, to try to get answers by experiment and, with the aid of technics, to develop more accurate measuring instruments and special apparatus.

From the Dark Ages, Western scholars showed an interest in getting certain kinds of results for which some technical knowledge was necessary. Medicine was studied in the earliest Benedictine monasteries, and the long series of medical works, written during the Middle Ages, and continuing without a break into the 16th century and modern times, is one of the best examples of a tradition in which empirical observations were increasingly combined with attempts at rational and theoretical explanation, with the result that definite medical and surgical problems were solved. Another long series of treatises was written on astronomy by scholars from the time of Bede in the 7th century for purely practical purposes such as determining the date of Easter, fixing latitude and showing how to determine true North and tell the time with an astrolabe. Even a poet such as Chaucer could write an excellent practical treatise on the astrolabe. Another series of practical treatises is that on the preparation of pigments and other chemical substances, which includes the 8th-century *Compositiones ad Tingenda* and *Mappae Clavicula,* of which Adelard of Bath later produced an edition, the early 12th-century *Diversarum Artium Schedula* of Theophilus the Priest, who lived probably in Germany, the late 13th-century *Liber de Coloribus Faciendis* by Peter of Saint Omer, and the early 15th-century treatises of Cennino Cennini and John Alcherius. Technical treatises were among the first to be translated out of Arabic and Greek into Latin and this was the work of educated men. It was, in fact, chiefly for their practical knowledge that Western scholars, from the time of Gerbert at the end of the 10th century, first began to take an interest in Arab learning. The 13th-century encyclopaedias of Alexander Nequam, Albertus Magnus and Roger Bacon contained a great deal of accurate information about the compass, chemistry, the calendar, agriculture and other technical matters. Other contemporary writers composed special treatises on these subjects: Grosseteste and later writers on the calendar; Giles of Rome in *De Regimine Principum* on the art of war; Walter of Henley and Peter of Crescenzi on agriculture; Peregrinus, in the second part of *De Magnete,* on the determination of azimuths. It took a scholar to write about arithmetic, yet most of the advances that followed Fibonacci's treatise on the Hindu numerals were made in the interests of commerce.

In the 14th century, the Italian Dominican friar, Giovanni da San Gimignano (d. 1323), wrote an encyclopaedia for preachers in which he gave for use as examples in sermons descriptions of numerous technical subjects: agriculture, fishing, cultivation of herbs, windmills and watermills, ships, painting and limning, fortifications, arms, Greek fire, smithing, glass-making and weights and measures. The names of two other Dominicans, Alessandro della Spina (d. 1313), and Salvino degl' Armati (d. 1317), are associated with the invention of spectacles. In the 15th century, a most interesting series of treatises was written on military technology. Beginning with Konrad Kyeser's *Bellifortis,* written between 1396 and 1405, this included a treatise by Giovanni de' Fontana (*c.* 1410–20), the *Feuerwerksbuch* (*c.* 1422), a treatise by an anonymous engineer in the Hussite wars (*c.* 1430), the so-called "Mittelalterliches Hausbuch" (*c.* 1480). The series went on in the 16th century with the treatises of Biringuccio and Tartaglia. These contained descriptions of how to make guns and gunpowder as well as problems of military engineering, which were discussed also by other contemporary writers such as Alberti and Leonardo da Vinci. Some of these treatises dealt also with general technical matters such as the construction of ships, dams and spinning-wheels. The series of practical chemical treatises which, in the earlier Middle Ages, had consisted mainly of recipes for pigments, continued in the 14th and 15th centuries with accounts of distillation and other practical technics and went on in the 16th century with Hieronymus Brunschwig's books on distillation, the metallurgical *Prodierbüchlein* and Agricola's *De Re Metallica*. Examples of the interest shown by medieval scholars in technics could, in fact, be multiplied almost indefinitely. They show not only that they had an abstract desire for power over nature such as Roger Bacon had expressed, but also that they were capable of getting the kind of knowledge that would lead to results useful in practice. . . .

CRITICISM OF ARISTOTLE IN THE LATER MIDDLE AGES

THE SCIENTIFIC METHOD OF THE LATER SCHOLASTICS

The activity of mind and hand that showed itself in the additions of scientific fact and in the development of technology made in the 13th and 14th centuries is to be seen also in the purely theoretical criticisms of Aristotle's theory of science and fundamental principles that took place at the same time and were to lead later to the overthrow of his whole system. Much of this criticism developed from within the Aristotelian system of scientific thought itself and, indeed, Aristotle can be seen as a sort of tragic hero striding through medieval science. From Grosseteste to Galileo he occupied the centre of the stage, seducing men's minds by the magical promise of his concepts, exciting their passions and dividing them, and, in the end, forcing them to turn against him as the real consequences of his undertaking gradually became clear; and yet, from the depths of his own system, providing many of the weapons with which he was attacked.

The most important of these weapons were the result of the development of ideas on scientific method and, in particular, on induction and experiment and on the role of mathematics in explaining physical phenomena, for they gradually led to an entirely different conception of the kind of question that should be asked in natural science, the kind of question, in fact, to which the experimental and mathematical methods could give an answer. The field in which the new kind of question was to produce its greatest effects from the middle of the 16th century was in dynamics, and it was precisely Aristotle's ideas on space and motion that came in for the most radical criticism during the later Middle Ages. The effect of this scholastic criticism was to undermine the foundations of his whole system of physics (with the exception of biology) and so to clear the way for the new system constructed by the experimental and mathematical methods. At the end of the medieval period a fresh impetus was given to mathematics by the translation of some previously unknown Greek texts.

The great idea recovered during the 12th century, which made possible the immediate expansion of science from that time, was the idea of rational explanation as in formal or geometrical demonstration; that is, the idea that a particular fact was explained when it could be deduced from a more general principle. This had come through the gradual recovery of Aristotle's logic and of Greek and Arabic mathematics. The idea of geometrical demonstration had, in fact, been the great discovery of the Greeks in the history of science, and it was the basis not only of their considerable contributions to mathematics itself and to physical sciences like astronomy and geometrical optics, but also of much of their biology and medicine. Their bent of mind was to conceive of science, where possible, as a matter of deductions from indemonstrable premises.

In the 12th century, this notion of rational explanation developed first among logicians and philosophers not primarily concerned with natural science at all but engaged in grasping and expounding the principles, first, of the *logica vetus* or "old logic" based on Boethius and, later in the century, or Aristotle's *Posterior Analytics* and various works of Galen. What these logicians did was to make use of the distinction, ultimately deriving from Aristotle, between experiential knowledge of a fact and rational knowledge of the reason for, or cause of, the fact; they meant by the latter knowledge of some prior and more general principle from which they could deduce the fact. The development of this form of rationalism was, in fact, part of a general intellectual movement in the 12th century, and not only scientific writers such as Adelard of Bath and Hugh of St. Victor, but also theologians such as Anselm, Richard of St. Victor and Abelard tried to arrange their subject-matter according to this mathematical-deductive method. Mathematics was for these 12th-century philosophers the model science and, like good disciples of St. Augustine and Plato, they held that the senses were deceitful and reason alone could give truth.

Though mathematics was regarded in the 12th century as the model science, it was not until the beginning of the 13th century that Western mathematics became worthy of this reputation. The practical mathematics kept alive in Benedictine monasteries during the Dark Ages and taught in the cathedral and monastery schools founded by Charlemagne at the end of the 8th century was very elementary and limited to what was necessary to keep accounts, calculate the date of Easter and measure land for the purposes of surveying. At the end of the 10th century Gerbert had initiated a revival of interest in mathematics, as he did also in logic, by collecting Boethius's treatises on those subjects. Although Boethius's treatise on arithmetic contained an elementary idea of the treatment of theoretical problems based on the properties of numbers, the so-called "Geometry of Boethius" was, in fact, a later compilation from which most of his own contribution had dropped out. It contained certain of Euclid's axioms, definitions and conclusions but consisted mainly of a description of the abacus, the device generally used for calculations, and of practical surveying methods and the like. The writings of Cassiodorus and Isidore of Seville, the other sources of the mathematical knowledge of the time, contained nothing fresh. . . .

SUMMARY

The principal original contributions made during the Middle Ages to the development of natural science in Europe may be summarised as follows:

1. In the field of scientific method, the recovery of the idea of rational explanation and in particular of the use of mathematics raised the problem of how to construct and to verify or falsify theories, and this problem was solved by the scholastic theory of induction and experimental method. Examples of this are seen in optics and magnetics in the 13th and 14th centuries.

2. Another important contribution to scientific method was the extension of mathematics to the whole of physical science, at least in principle, Aristotle having restricted the use of mathematics in his theory of the subordination of one science to another by sharply distinguishing the explicative roles of mathematics and "physics." The effect of this change was not so much to destroy this distinction in principle as to change the kind of question scientists asked. They began, in fact, to show less interest in the "physical" or metaphysical question of cause and to ask the kind of question that could be answered by a mathematical theory within reach of experimental verification. Examples of this method are seen in statics, optics, and astronomy in the 13th and 14th centuries.

3. Besides these ideas on method, though often closely connected with them, a radically new approach to the question of space and motion began at the end of the 13th century. Greek mathematicians had constructed a mathematics of rest, and important advances in statics had been made during the 13th century; the 14th century saw the first attempts to construct a mathematics of change and motion. Of the various elements contributing to this new dynamics, the ideas that space might be infinite and void, and the universe without a centre, destroyed Aristotle's cosmos with its qualitatively different directions and led to the idea of relative motion. Concerning motion, the chief new idea was that of *impetus,* and the most significant characteristics of this concept are that the quantity of *impetus* was proportional to the

quantity of *materia prima* in the body and the velocity imparted to it, and that the *impetus* imparted would persist indefinitely were it not for air resistance and the action of gravity. *Impetus* was still a "physical" cause in the Aristotelian sense and, in considering motion as a state requiring no continuous efficient causation, Ockham came closer to the 17th-century idea of inertial motion. The theory of *impetus* was used to explain many different phenomena, for instance the motion of projectiles and falling bodies, bouncing balls, pendulums and the rotation of the heavens or of the earth. The possibility of the last was suggested by the concept of relative motion, and objections to it from the argument from detached bodies were met by the idea of "compound *impetus*" advanced by Oresme. The kinematic study of accelerated motion began also in the 14th century, and the solution of one particular problem, that of a body moving with uniform acceleration, was to be applied later to falling bodies. Discussions of the nature of a continuum and of maxima and minima began also in the 14th century.

4. In the field of technology, the Middle Ages saw the most rapid progress since prehistoric times. Beginning with new methods of exploiting animal-, water- and wind-power, new machines were developed for a variety of purposes, often requiring considerable precision. Some technical inventions, for instance the mechanical clock and magnifying lenses, were to be used as scientific instruments. Measuring instruments such as the astrolabe and quadrant were greatly improved as result of the demand for accurate measurement. In chemistry, the balance came into general use. Empirical advances were made and the experimental habit led to the development of special apparatus.

5. In the biological sciences, some considerable technical advances were made. Important works were written on medicine and surgery, on the symptoms of diseases, and descriptions were given of the flora and fauna of different regions. A beginning was made with classification, and the possibility of having accurate illustrations was introduced by naturalistic art. Perhaps the most important medieval contribution to theoretical biology was the elaboration of the idea of a scale of animate nature.

6. Concerning the question of the purpose and nature of science, two medieval contributions may be singled out. The first is the idea, first explicitly expressed in the 13th century, that the purpose of science was to gain power over nature useful to man. The second is the idea insisted on by the theologians, that neither God's action nor man's speculation could be constrained within any particular system of scientific or philosophical thought. Whatever may have been its effects in other branches of thought, the effect of this idea on natural science was to bring out the relativity of all scientific theories and the fact that they might be replaced by others more successful in fulfilling the requirements of the rational and experimental methods.

Thus the experimental and mathematical methods were a growth, developing within the medieval system of scientific thought, which was to destroy from within and eventually to burst out from Aristotelian cosmology and physics. Though resistance to the destruction of the old system became strong among certain of the late scholastics, and especially among those whose humanism had given them too great a devotion to the ancient texts and those by whom the old system had been too closely linked with theological doctrines, it was the growth of these 13th- and 14th-century experimental and mathematical methods that brought about the movement which by the 17th century had become so striking as to be called the Scientific Revolution.

Dr. Crombie's illuminating introduction shows clearly the continuity of scientific thought from classical and medieval rationalism to an increasing use of individual observation and experimental techniques, rooted in the crafts of artisans and culminating in the ingenious experimentalism of such Renaissance titans as Leonardo da Vinci and Galileo. In keeping with the point of view of the historian of ideas, the authors of the following essays are primarily concerned with tracing the transmission of Hellenic science and its methodological framework (due to Plato, Democritus, Aristotle and their successors) through the medieval and Renaissance scientific developments. Even though some specific propositions in Aristotle's astronomy and physics were challenged and overthrown, the methods of analysis and synthesis, of deduction and induction, of hypothesis and verification, continued to be used as conceptual tools.

Randall's study of the fourteenth-century School of Padua shows how Aristotle's conception of scientific method was further refined by subtle scholastic logicians sensitive to the complex relations between generalizations and experience. The problem of the relation of universal ideas to particular things was formulated by Boethius in the sixth century and led to the fundamental division of schools of thought between realism and nominalism. The realists argued that universals exist independently of observation; the nominalists claimed that universals are only names or signs of what is common to individual observations. There were many variations of these positions, such as Abelard's conceptualism, which placed univerals in the mind. How these different philosophical positions affected scientific thought and method is the main concern of our authors.

Randall's essay continues the researches of Pierre Duhem, who first traced the influence of the nominalists of Oxford and Paris (*e.g.,* John of Buridan, Albert of Saxony, William of Ockham) on the School of Padua, where Copernicus and Harvey studied and where Galileo did most of his scientific teaching.

In order to understand the studies of Randall, Koyré, and Moody concerning the medieval precursors of Galileo, we must keep in mind Galileo's statement of his method. It consisted of three phases: hypothesis (analysis of mathematical relations among the variables), demonstration (deductive resolution of the consequences of the hypothesis), and verification by experiment.

In the case of falling bodies, Galileo first considered the possibility that the distance varies with the time of fall, and he found by deductive analysis that a contradiction resulted. He then tried the hypothesis that the distance of free fall varies with the square of the time, and numerical analysis showed that a constant increase of velocity would be a consequence of that hypothesis. His final verification by means of his experiments with balls on an inclined plane could yield only an approximation to the uniform acceleration, but it was enough to convince him in his faith that the book of nature was written in the language of Euclid—and, we may add, of Pythagoras. Another evidence of the rationalism in Galileo's method is seen in his disproof of Aristotle's theory that the velocity of a falling body varies with the weight of the body. Two bricks of equal weight, he reports as a "thought experiment," would fall just as fast as either one alone from the same height, if they were tied together by a string, despite the fact that their weight had been doubled. The "leaning-tower experiment" at Pisa of dropping a lead and wooden ball and observing their equal time of descent—even if Galileo did not himself actually do the experiment—would confirm his analysis.

Some logicians still favor his "hypothetico-deductive" method as the most fruitful one for scientific discovery, but when they do so (as does Koyré), they reveal their interest in the rationalistic aspect of scientific work. Hence, it is not surprising to find Koyré interpreting Galileo's dynamics of falling bodies as an embodiment of Platonic rationalism or the quest for eternal forms of natural law.

Moody's essay is a case study of the important role played by an Arabic scientist such as Avempace in medieval science as a transmitter and modifier of Aristotle's scientific work. We still have much to learn about the Averroists at Padua and elsewhere in medieval European universities, where Arabic texts (translated into Latin) in medicine, astronomy, and physics were the means of continuing the scientific researches of the Greeks.

Zilsel's studies of the techniques of the craftsmen of the medieval and Renaissance periods throw light on the social roots of the growth of experimentalism in modern science. The cumulative character of techniques handed down orally from one generation or guild of craftsmen to the next is also a source of the idea of progress which historians have generally attributed to the industrial revolution or to the "heavenly city" of the *philosophes* or to the Baconian spirit ("Knowledge is Power"). In any case, Zilsel's investigations of the scientific ideas of Copernicus, Gilbert, and Francis Bacon constitute a valuable contribution to the "sociology of science" in the late medieval and Renaissance background of the scientific revolution of the seventeenth century. The rise of scientific societies in the sixteenth and seventeenth centuries (the Italian academies, the Royal Society, and the French Academy of Sciences) indicates a sociological shift of centres of scientific research from the medieval, church-dominated university to the secular and freer associations of minds united by the love of experimental inquiry.

Copernicus, a church official, withheld publication of his immortal work until the last year of his life. Only in 1858 was it discovered that he had not written the Preface which presented his heliocentric theory as a mere hypothesis to "save the appearances." Rosen, by means of a philological and historical analysis of the correspondence between the anti-Aristotelian Ramus and the scientific humanist Rhaeticus, shows how the latter defended the scientific truth of Copernicus's theory against the counterfeit Preface of the Protestant theologian Osiander.

⤳§ *John Herman Randall, Jr.*

SCIENTIFIC METHOD IN THE SCHOOL OF PADUA

The Aristotelian science which the thirteenth century had so eagerly worked into its Christian philosophy of life aimed at an understanding of nature divorced from power over things. But during the sixteenth century more and more men began to hold that science should be directed, not merely to understanding and vision, but to a kind of understanding that might give power, action, and an improvement of the practical arts. A leading intellectual enterprise of the time was the search for a fruitful method that could serve this new aim to which knowledge was turning. Those thinkers whose energies were not wholly absorbed by the theological issues in terms of which the major battles were still being fought, concentrated on this problem of method as the paramount scientific task of the day.

Ironically enough, when the fruitful method was finally "discovered" and proved in practice, it turned out to be the least novel of all the elements that went into the formation of the new science. After exploring many a blind alley, men came to realize that one of the great medieval intellectual traditions had already made an excellent beginning at just the kind of practical and useful knowledge they now wanted. In the thirteenth and fourteenth century schools, there had been worked out the idea of an experimentally grounded and mathematically formulated science of nature, and since then much had been done in the way of actual achievement. In Leonardo the penetrating, in the Italian mathematicians and physicists of the sixteenth century, in Copernicus, Kepler, and Galileo, such a science had indeed come of age.

Into this science there entered many different strands, each with its own history. And the powerful stimulus imparted during the sixteenth century by the recovery of the techniques of the Greek mathematicians is not to be minimized. But the conception of the nature of science, of its relation to the observation of fact, and of the method by which it might be achieved and formulated, that was handed on to his successors by Galileo, was not the work of the new seekers after a fruitful method. It appears rather as the culmination of the coöperative efforts of ten generations of scientists inquir-

ing into methodological problems in the universities of northern
Italy.   For three centuries the natural philosophers of the school of
Padua, in fruitful commerce with the physicians of its medical faculty, devoted themselves to criticizing and expanding this conception
and method, and to grounding it firmly in the careful analysis of
experience.   It left their hands with a refinement and precision of
statement which the seventeenth century scientists who used it did
not surpass in all their careful investigation of method.

In contrast with this cumulative and organized elaboration of the
theory and method of science, the many humanist seekers, revolting
from the scholasticism of the Scotists with their technical "termi-
nist" logic, seem to have displayed all the customary ignorance and
futility of intellectual revolutionaries, and to have proposed new
methods distinguished chiefly by the novelty of their ignorance.   As
might be expected, these servants of the word for the most part
sought their new method in language and in rhetoric, and tried to
erect a "natural dialectic" on the basis of Cicero and Quintilian.
Others like Bruno were fascinated by the suggestions of Lully for a
universal language that might reveal all truth.   And still others,
emphasizing the place of a knowledge of nature in human wisdom,
urged men to close their books and observe the world.

The humanists might seek the method of a new science in the
rhetorician's art of persuasion; a Vives or a Bacon, recognizing no
useful knowledge in the investigations of the mathematicians and
astronomers of their day, might counsel experience and ever more
experience.   Their combined onslaught helped to shake men's faith
in the complacent academic traditionalism of the schools, already
sorely disturbed by the new literary and theological movements; it
hardly contributed much guidance to those already busily engaged
upon scientific problems.   Both in its traditional insights and in its
novel guesses the imagination needed the discipline of a critical
method before there could be any significant observation of facts.
The body of ideas which in Galileo and Descartes dared to arrogate
to itself the name of natural science, and which in Newton defini-
tively made good that proud claim, had other and far deeper roots,
stretching back through and beyond the twelfth-century European
appropriation of ancient learning.

History has fallen into error in accepting uncritically the estimate the pioneer thinkers of the sixteenth and seventeenth century
made of their own turning away from the heritage of the past.   Their

consciousness of fresh discovery and radical reorientation obscured the countless bonds of continuity, in materials, methods, and even achievements, uniting them to their predecessors in the late middle ages. In particular the fact that the seventeenth century scientists, in revolt against the humanists' appeal to the authority of the past, preferred to put their trust in "natural reason" alone, and hence cared nothing for historical continuity, has sadly misled our judgment as to the fashion in which their thought was generated. Taking them at their own word, we have assumed that that coöperative criticism and reconstruction of a well-organized system of ideas, shaken from time to time by fresh insights which have had to be worked into the logical structure—that that process which has since the seventeenth century been so characteristic of the procedure of scientific advance, played no part in its earlier stages.

In the present generation much has been brought to light about the organized scientific traditions of the later middle ages in which the sixteenth and seventeenth century pioneers carried on their work. But much more remains to be done. In particular, the fact that several of the most influential investigators have been French has focused attention on the activities of the University of Paris, while the further fact that many of them have been Catholic scholars has made them not unduly appreciative of the work of the free-thinking and anti-clerical Italian schools. For its part, Italian scholarship has been attracted by the spectacular humanistic movement and by the presumably more novel and original literary Platonism of the Florentines. As a result, though it is clear that the thought of the Italian universities forms the immediate background of the sixteenth-century scientific movement that culminated in Galileo, its substantial achievement has as yet received almost no study.

The basic idea of an experimentally grounded science of the mathematical structure of nature appeared as soon as Europeans began to explore the wisdom of the ancients. It developed within the general framework of the first body of ancient materials to be assimilated, the Augustinian philosophy of reason—itself the platonized outcome of Hellenistic thought. It drew specifically upon the Arabic versions of Alexandrian science, though direct contact with the whole of Greek mathematics, astronomy, and mechanics was the last to be established; Archimedes was not known till the sixteenth century. But the idea of such a science, and much of its method and concepts, were in the possession of Europeans from the twelfth century on.

Aristotle's logic, his theory of science and method, was discovered in the *Analytics* during the first half of the twelfth century; his basic concepts and principles of natural science were learned from the *Physics* in the second half. The coming of Aristole introduced a body of materials too impressive to be ignored. Thereafter for centuries the Aristotelian physical writings were taken as the starting-point for all natural science, however far men might eventually depart from them; and the Aristotelian theory of science, however men might interpret it, remained dominant till the time of Newton. From the beginning of the fourteenth century, however, there set in a persistent and searching reconstruction of the Aristotelian tradition, which, when directed to the *Physics,* led by gradual stages to the mechanical and mathematical problems of the Galilean age, and when directed to the *Logic* led to the precise formulation of the method and structure of science acclaimed by all the seventeenth-century scientists.

There were two main critical movements during the later middle ages. The Ockhamites began in Oxford in the thirteenth century, and while persisting there found a new stronghold during the next hundred years in the Faculty of Arts at Paris. The Latin Averroists began in Paris in the thirteenth century, and shifted their seat to Padua early in the fourteenth. Both set out by expressing a secular and anti-clerical spirit, and by undertaking a destructive criticism of Thomism° and Scotism, the thirteenth century syntheses of science and religion. But both soon advanced beyond mere criticism to the constructive elaboration of natural science: they became the two great scientific schools of the later middle ages. The original work of the Ockhamites belongs to the fourteenth century, that of the Paduans, to the fifteenth and sixteenth. The former was done in dynamics, kinematics, and the logic of continuity and intensity; the latter, in methodology and in the further development of dynamics. Both turned from the earlier religious syntheses to the purely natural philosophy of Aristotle himself; and both developed primarily by a constructive criticism of the Aristotelian texts and doctrines. The Ockhamites were at first the more "progressive" and "modern"; they were interested in the free development of the Aristotelian physics, and their works take the form of questions and problems suggested by Aristotle's analyses. The Averroists, though much more secular and anti-clerical, were originally more conservative in their attitude toward Aristotle and his interpreter Averroes: their works are characteristically commentaries on the texts. From 1400 on, however, they knew and taught all the Ockhamite departures from Aristotelian doctrine: Paul of Venice (*1429) is remarkably up-to-date, and his *Summa Naturalis* contains an exposition of all the ideas of the dynamics of the Paris Ockhamites and the Oxford logicians. The works of these fourteenth-century thinkers were printed in many editions so soon as the press reached Italy, all of them by 1490; and in the sixteenth century it was primarily the Italians who advanced by successive stages to the formulations of Galileo.

About 1400, therefore, the interest in the development of scientific ideas shifts from Ockhamite Paris to the Padua Averroists. From the time of Paul of Venice to Cremonini (*1631) the Aristotelian physics and a nascent "Galilean" physics were in definite and conscious opposition at Padua, and this critical conflict contributed greatly to the working out of the latter. Paul of Venice had been sent by his order to Oxford in 1390, where he remained for three years; he then taught for two more in Paris at the time of the last great Ockhamite, Pierre d'Ailly. He thus knew all the Ockhamite developments at first hand, and explained them fully though critically in his encyclopedic writings.

His successor at Padua, Cajetan of Thiene (*1465), was the most radical scientifically of the Averroists, and the most sympathetic to the Paris teachings on dynamics. He initiated a great controversy over the *Calculations* of Suisseth (Swineshead), in which all the arguments for a mathematical as against a qualitative physics are examined, so that the documents of this controversy, in many editions, were among the first works printed in Italy in the 1480's. The fundamental *De latitudinibus formarum* of Nicholas of Oresme, in which the rule for uniformly accelerated motion first appears, came out in 1482, with a discussion by Blasius de Parma de Pelicanis; Albert of Saxony's *Tractatus de proportionibus*, arguing for a quantitative treatment of qualities (already reported in the *Summa Naturalis* of Paul of Venice) also appeared in the same year; in 1496 it was reprinted with the *De intensione et remissione formarum* of Walter Burleigh, a defense of the logic of qualitative change opposed to the spirit of Oresme, and with a full reply to Burleigh in behalf of quantitative analysis by the physician Jacopo da Forlì. Among the most interesting of all these documents, indicative of a lively concern with what was to become the fundamental scientific question, is the

Tractatus de proportionibus of a Milanese physician, Johannes Marlianus (Pavia, 1482), which brings experimental proof to bear on the quantitative side, describes the rolling of balls down an inclined plane to measure their velocity and acceleration, and narrates experiments with pendulums.

The question whether the operation of causes was to be formulated mathematically or qualitatively (whether the "first accident" of substance was to be taken as quantity or not—which happens to be also the way in which Kepler expressed his view that a cause is a mathematical law) was thus vigorously debated at Padua toward the end of the fifteenth century, and the notion of "cause" as a mathematically formulated formal cause won many adherents. In the next century there broke out another great controversy among the Paduans as to whether the "cause" of natural motion was to be sought in a form or in a force, that is, in a definite way of behaving or in something that acted in a definite way. Galileo joined those who identified "cause" with a "force"; but since he also defined force in terms of its way of acting, his divergence was not great. And towards the end of the same century there occurred another dispute, as to whether final causes had any place in natural philosophy. The outcome of these successive debates was to delimit the conception of cause, and to make the Galilean position inevitable. They are here mentioned to suggest certain other strands in the development of Italian Aristotelianism which this study does not presume to set forth in detail, and which in particular illuminate the change from a qualitative to a mathematical treatment of natural operations.

It has become a recent fashion to view the whole "Renaissance," and indeed the very "birth" of modern science itself, as philosophically a turning from the Aristotle of the Schools to Platonism; and Italian thought of the fifteenth century has been represented as dominated by that turning. But it must not be forgotten that the vigorous intellectual life of the Italian universities remained loyal to the Aristotelian tradition. Now in most countries the fifteenth century saw the teaching and refinement of the earlier philosophies, Scotism, Thomism, and Ockhamism, with little basically new. But in northern Italy, at Padua, Bologna, and Pavia, and to a lesser extent at Siena, Pisa, and the brilliant new university of Ferrara, Aristotelianism was still a living and growing body of ideas. What Paris had been in the thirteenth century, what Oxford and Paris together had been in the fourteenth, Padua became in the fifteenth: the center in which ideas from all Europe were combined into an organized and cumulative body of knowledge. A succession of great teachers carried that knowledge to the point where in the next century it could find fruitful marriage with the new interest in the mathematical sciences. In the Italian schools alone the emerging science of nature did not mean a sharp break with reigning theological interests. To them it came rather as the natural outcome of a sustained and co-operative criticism of Aristotelian ideas. If in the sixteenth century the more original minds were led to a formal break with the Paduan teaching, we must not forget that even Galileo occupied a chair there from 1592 to 1610, and that in method and philosophy if not in physics he remained a typical Paduan Aristotelian.

That Italian Aristotelianism was thus able to lead the European schools in the fifteenth and sixteenth centuries was due to several circumstances, not the least of which was the settled commercial prosperity the Italian cities had now achieved. They had long enjoyed and taught in their universities a thoroughly secular and anti-clerical philosophy expressive of the new culture of a this-worldly and commercial society. By 1400 that nice blend of Aristotelian science and Christian faith which Thomas and Duns Scotus had constructed had, in Italy at least, retreated into the monastic orders. At Padua, Bologna, and Pavia there reigned an Aristotelianism that made little attempt to accommodate itself to theological interests. And it is no accident that while the Church-controlled science of the North drove all those who felt the new currents into open rebellion against science itself, the anti-clerical science of the Italian universities could progress steadily in self-criticism to the achievement of a Galileo.

Fundamental also was the close alliance between the study of Aristotle and the study of medicine. At Paris the Faculty of Theology crowned the Sorbonne; at Padua the Faculty of Arts led only to that of Medicine, and Aristotle was there taught as a preparation, not for an ecclesiastical career, but for the study of medicine, with a consequent strong emphasis on his physical writings, his natural history, and his scientific methodology. A physician's Aristotle is bound to differ from a theologian's. The teachers wrote no theological works, no commentaries on the *Sentences*. They normally held medical degrees themselves; they applied Aristotle to medical problems, and to questions of method arising in medical science; they interpreted him in the light of the best medical writers of the Greek and Arabic traditions.

Finally, the liberty of teaching and speculation guaranteed by Venice, the leading Italian anti-papal and anti-clerical state, after its acquisition of Padua in 1404, attracted the best minds from all over Italy, especially the philosophical Southerners. Padua remained to the days of Galileo the leading scientific school of Europe, the stronghold of the Aristotelian qualitative physics, and the trainer even of those who were to break with it. Cusanus, Purbach, Regiomontanus, Copernicus, as well as the Italians, all studied at Padua.

If the concepts of a mathematical physics were arrived at by a long criticism of Aristotelian ideas, the "new method," the logic and methodology taken over and expressed by Galileo and destined to become the scientific method of the seventeenth century physicists, as contrasted with the many noisy proposals of the sixteenth century "buccinators" down to Francis Bacon, was even more clearly the result of a fruitful critical reconstruction of the Aristotelian theory of science, undertaken at Padua in particular, and fertilized by the methodological discussions of the commentators on the medical writers. For three hundred years, after Pietro d'Abano brought the problems to the fore, the Paduan medical teachers were driven by their texts, especially Galen, to a careful analysis of scientific procedure. The great commentators on Galen, Jacopo da Forlì (*1413), who incidentally wrote widely on the methods of the Paris physicists, and Hugo of Siena (*1439), gradually built up a detailed theory of scientific method which the Aristotelian scholars, themselves holders of medical degrees, incorporated into their version of the nature of science. It is possible to trace step by step in rather beautiful fashion the gradual elaboration of the Aristotelian method, in the light of the medical tradition, from its first discussion in Pietro d'Abano to its completed statement in the logical controversies of Zabarella, in which it reaches the form familiar in Galileo and the seventeenth-century scientists.

*　　　　*　　　　*

~~§ *Alexandre Koyré*

GALILEO AND PLATO

The name of Galileo Galilei is indissolubly linked with the scientific revolution of the sixteenth century, one of the profoundest, if not the most profound, revolution of human thought since the invention of the Cosmos by Greek thought: a revolution which implies a radical intellectual "mutation," of which modern physical science is at once the expression and the fruit.[1]

This revolution is sometimes characterized, and at the same time explained, as a kind of spiritual upheaval, an utter transformation of the whole fundamental attitude of the human mind; the active life, the *vita activa* taking the place of the θεωρία, the *vita contemplativa*, which until then had been considered its highest form. Modern man seeks the domination of nature, whereas medieval or ancient man attempted above all its contemplation. The mechanistic trend of classical physics—of the Galilean, Cartesian, Hobbesian physics, *scientia activa, operativa,* which was to render man "master and possessor of nature"—has, therefore, to be explained by this desire to dominate, to act; it has to be considered purely and simply an outflow of this attitude, an application to nature of the categories of thinking of *homo faber.*[2] The science of Descartes—and *a fortiori* that of Galileo—is nothing else than (as has been said) the science of the craftsman or of the engineer.[3]

I must confess that I do not believe this explanation to be entirely correct. It is true, of course, that modern philosophy, as well as modern ethics and modern religion, lays much more stress on action, on πρᾶξις, than ancient and medieval thought. And it is just as true of modern science: I am thinking of the Cartesian physics and its analogies of pulleys, strings and levers. Still the attitude we have just described is much more that of Bacon—whose

[1] Cf. J. H. Randall, Jr., *The Making of the Modern Mind* (Boston, 1926), 220 sq., 231 sq.; cf. also A. N. Whitehead, *Science and the Modern World* (New York, 1925).

[2] This widespread conception must not be confused with that of Bergson, for whom all physics, the Aristotelian just as much as the Newtonian, is in the last analysis the work of *homo faber.*

[3] Cf. L. Labertonnière, *Études sur Descartes* (Paris, 1935), II, 288 sq.; 297; 304: "physique de l'exploitation des choses."

rôle in the history of science is not of the same order[4]—than that of Galileo or Descartes.   Their science is made not by engineers or craftsmen, but by men who seldom built or made anything more real than a theory.[5]   The new ballistics was made not by artificers and gunners, but against them.   And Galileo did not learn *his* business from people who toiled in the arsenals and shipyards of Venice.   Quite the contrary: he taught them *theirs*.[6]   Moreover, this theory explains too much and too little.   It explains the tremendous scientific progress of the seventeenth century by that of technology.   And yet the latter was infinitely less conspicuous than the former.   Besides, it forgets the technological achievements of the Middle Ages.   It neglects the lust for power and wealth which, throughout its history, inspired alchemy.

Other scholars have insisted on the Galilean fight against authority, against tradition, especially against that of Aristotle:

[4] Bacon is the announcer, the *buccinator* of modern science, not one of its creators.

[5] The Cartesian and Galilean science has, of course, been of extreme importance for the engineer and the technician; ultimately it has produced a technical revolution.   Yet it was created and developed neither by engineers nor technicians, but by theorists and philosophers.

[6] "Descartes artisan" is the conception of Cartesianism developed by Leroy in his *Descartes social* (Paris, 1931), and brought to absurdity by F. Borkenau in his book *Der Uebergang vom feudalen zum bürgerlichen Weltbild* (Paris, 1934). Borkenau explains the birth of the Cartesian philosophy and science by that of a new form of economic enterprise, i.e., manufacturing.   Cf. the criticism of the work of Borkenau, a criticism much more interesting and instructive than the book itself, by H. Grossmann, "Die gesellschaftlichen Grundlagen der mechanistischen Philosophie und die Manufaktur," *Zeitschrift für Sozialforschung* (Paris, 1935).

As for Galileo, he is linked with the traditions of the artisans, builders, engineers, etc., of the Renaissance by L. Olschki, *Galileo und seine Zeit* (Halle, 1927), and more recently by E. Zilsel, "The Sociological Roots of Science," *The American Journal of Sociology*, XLVII (1942).   Zilsel stresses the rôle played by the "superior artisans" of the Renaissance in the development of the modern scientific mentality.   It is, of course, perfectly true that the artists, engineers, architects, etc., of the Renaissance played an important part in the struggle against the Aristotelian tradition, and that some of them—like Leonardo da Vinci and Benedetti—attempted even to develop a new, anti-Aristotelian dynamics; yet this dynamics, as was conclusively shown by Duhem, was in its main features that of the Parisian nominalists, the *impetus* dynamics of John Buridan and Nicole Oresme.   And if Benedetti, by far the most remarkable of these "forerunners" of Galileo, transcends sometimes the level of the "Parisian" dynamics, it is not because of his work as engineer and gunner but because of his study of Archimedes and his decision to apply "mathematical philosophy" to the investigation of nature.

against the scientific and philosophical tradition, upheld by the Church and taught in the universities. They have stressed the rôle of observation and experience in the new science of nature.[7] It is perfectly true, of course, that observation and experimentation form one of the most characteristic features of modern science. It is certain that in the writings of Galileo we find innumerable appeals to observation and to experience, and bitter irony toward men who didn't believe their eyes because what they saw was contrary to the teaching of the authorities, or, even worse, who (like Cremonini) did not want to look through Galileo's telescope for fear of seeing something which would contradict their traditional theories and beliefs. It is obvious that it was just by building a telescope and by looking through it, by careful observation of the moon and the planets, by his discovery of the satellites of Jupiter, that Galileo dealt a crushing blow to the astronomy and the cosmology of his times.

Still one must not forget that observation and experience, in the sense of brute, common-sense experience, did not play a major rôle—or, if it did, it was a negative one, the rôle of obstacle—in the foundation of modern science.[8] The physics of Aristotle, and even more that of the Parisian Nominalists, of Buridan and Nicole Oresme, was, as stated by Tannery and Duhem, much nearer to common sense experience than those of Galileo and Descartes.[9]

[7] Quite recently a friendly critic has reproached me for having neglected this side of Galileo's teaching. (Cf. L. Olschki, "The Scientific Personality of Galileo," *Bulletin of the History of Medicine*, XII [1942].) I must confess I do not believe I have merited this reproach, though I do indeed believe that science is primarily theory and not the gathering of "facts."

[8] É. Meyerson, *Identité et réalité*, 3 ed. (Paris, 1926), 156, shows very convincingly the lack of accord between "experience" and the principles of modern physics.

[9] P. Duhem, *Le Système du Monde* (Paris, 1913), I, 194 sq.: "Cette dynamique, en effet, semble s'adapter si heureusement aux observations courantes qu'elle ne pouvait manquer de s'imposer, tout d'abord, à l'acceptation des premiers qui aient spéculé sur les forces et les mouvements. . . . Pour que les physiciens en viennent à rejeter la Dynamique d'Aristote et à construire la Dynamique moderne, il leur faudra comprendre que les faits dont ils sont chaque jour les témoins ne sont aucunement les faits simples, élémentaires, auxquelles les lois fondamentales de la Dynamique se doivent immédiatement appliquer; que la marche du navire tiré par les haleurs, que le roulement sur une route de la voiture attelée doivent être regardés comme des mouvements d'une extrême complexité; en un mot que pour le principe de la science du mouvement, on doit, par abstraction, considérer un mobile qui, sous l'action d'une force unique, se meut dans le vide. Or, de sa Dynamique Aristote va jusqu'à conclure qu'un tel mouvement est impossible."

It is not "experience," but "experiment," which played—but only later—a great positive rôle. Experimentation is the methodical interrogation of nature, an interrogation which presupposes and implies a *language* in which to formulate the questions, and a dictionary which enables us to read and to interpret the answers. For Galileo, as we know well, it was in curves and circles and triangles, in mathematical or even more precisely, in *geometrical language*—not in the language of common sense or in that of pure symbols—that we must speak to Nature and receive her answers. Yet obviously the choice of the language, the decision to employ it, could not be determined by the experience which its use was to make possible. It had to come from other sources.

Still other historians of science and philosophy[10] have more modestly tried to characterize modern physics, as *physics,* by some of its salient traits: for instance, by the rôle which the principle of *inertia* plays in it. Perfectly right, once more: the principle of *inertia,* in contradistinction to that of the Ancients, holds an outstanding place in classical mechanics. It is its fundamental law of motion; it implicitly pervades Galilean physics and quite explicitly that of Descartes and of Newton. But this characteristic seems to me to be somewhat superficial. In my opinion it is not enough simply to state the fact. We have to understand and to explain it—to explain why *modern* physics was able to adopt this principle; to understand why, and how, the principle of inertial motion, which to us appears so simple, so clear, so plausible and even self-evident, acquired this status of self-evidence and *a priori* truth whereas for the Greeks as well as for the thinkers of the Middle Ages the idea that a body once put in motion will continue to move forever, appeared as obviously and evidently false, and even absurd.[11]

I shall not try to explain here the reasons and causes that produced the spiritual revolution of the sixteenth century. It is for our purpose sufficient to describe it, to describe the mental or intellectual attitude of modern science by two (connected) characteristics. They are: 1) the destruction of the Cosmos, and therefore

[10] Cf. Kurd Lasswitz, *Geschichte der Atomistik* (Hamburg und Leipzig, 1890), II, 23 sq.; E. Mach, *Die Mechanik in ihrer Entwicklung,* 8 ed. (Leipzig, 1921), 117 sq.; E. Wohlwill, "Die Entdeckung des Beharrunggesetzes," *Zeitschrift für Völkerpsychologie und Sprachwissenschaft,* vols. XIV and XV (1883 and 1884), and E. Cassirer, *Das Erkenntnisproblem in der Philosophie und Wissenschaft der neueren Zeit,* 2 ed. (Berlin, 1911), I, 394 sq.

[11] Cf. É. Meyerson, *op. cit.,* 124 sq.

the disappearance in science of all considerations based on that notion;[12] 2) the geometrization of space—that is, the substitution of the homogeneous and abstract space of Euclidian geometry for the qualitatively differentiated and concrete world-space conception of the pre-galilean physics. These two characteristics may be summed up and expressed as follows: the mathematization (geometrization) of nature and, therefore, the mathematization (geometrization) of science.

The dissolution of the Cosmos means the destruction of the idea of a hierarchically-ordered finite world-structure, of the idea of a qualitatively and ontologically differentiated world, and its replacement by that of an open, indefinite and even infinite universe, united and governed by the same universal laws; a universe in which, in contradiction to the traditional conception with its distinction and opposition of the two worlds of Heaven and of Earth, all things are on the same level of Being. The laws of Heaven and the laws of Earth are merged together. Astronomy and physics become interdependent, and even unified and united.[13] And this implies the disappearance from the scientific outlook of all considerations based on value, on perfection, on harmony, on meaning and on purpose.[14] They disappear in the infinite space of the new Universe. It is in this new Universe, in this new world of a geometry made real, that the laws of classical physics are valid and find their application.

The dissolution of the Cosmos—I repeat what I have already said: this seems to me to be the most profound revolution achieved or suffered by the human mind since the invention of the Cosmos by the Greeks. It is a revolution so profound and so far-reaching that mankind—with very few exceptions, of whom Pascal was one

[12] The *term* remains, of course, and Newton still speaks of the Cosmos and its order (as he speaks of *impetus*), but in an entirely new meaning.

[13] As I have endeavoured to show elsewhere (*Etudes Galiléennes*, III, *Galilée et la loi d'inertie* [Paris, 1940]) modern science results from this unification of astronomy and physics which enables it to apply the methods of mathematical investigation, till then employed in the study of celestial phenomena, to the study of the phenomena of the sublunar world.

[14] Cf. É. Bréhier, *Histoire de la philosophie*, t. II, fasc. 1 (Paris, 1929), 95: "Descartes dégage la physique de la hantise du Cosmos hellénique, c'est-à-dire de l'image d'un certain état privilégié des choses qui satisfait nos besoins esthétiques. ... Il n'y a pas d'état privilégié puisque tous les états sont équivalents. Il n'y a donc aucune place en physique pour la recherche des causes finales et la considération du meilleur."

—for centuries did not grasp its bearing and its meaning; which, even now, is often misvalued and misunderstood.

Therefore what the founders of modern science, among them Galileo, had to do, was not to criticize and to combat certain faulty theories, and to correct or to replace them by better ones. They had to do something quite different. They had to destroy one world and to replace it by another. They had to reshape the framework of our intellect itself, to restate and to reform its concepts, to evolve a new approach to Being, a new concept of knowledge, a new concept of science—and even to replace a pretty natural approach, that of common sense, by another which is not natural at all.[15]

This explains why the discovery of things, of laws, which today appear so simple and so easy as to be taught to children—the laws of motion, the law of falling bodies—required such a long, strenuous, and often unsuccessful effort of some of the greatest geniuses of mankind, a Galileo, a Descartes.[16] This fact in turn seems to me to disprove the modern attempt to minimize, or even to deny, the originality, or at least the revolutionary character, of Galileo's thinking; and to make clear that the apparent continuity in the development of medieval and modern physics (a continuity so emphatically stressed by Caverni and Duhem)[17] is an illusion. It

[15] Cf. P. Tannery, "Galilée et les principes de la dynamique," in *Mémoires scientifiques*, VI (Paris, 1926), 399: "Si pour juger le système dynamique d'Aristote, on fait abstraction des préjugés qui dérivent de notre éducation moderne, si on cherche à se replacer dans l'état d'esprit que pouvait avoir un penseur indépendant au commencement du XVIIe siècle, il est difficile de méconnaître que ce système est beaucoup plus conforme que le nôtre à l'observation immédiate des faits."

[16] Cf. my *Études Galiléennes*, II, *La loi de la chute des corps* (Paris, 1940).

[17] Cf. Caverni, *Storia del metodo sperimentale in Italia*, 5 vols. (Firenze, 1891–96), particularly vols. IV and V; P. Duhem, *Le mouvement absolu et le mouvement relatif* (Paris, 1905); "De l'accélération produite par une force constante," *Congrès International de l'histoire des sciences, IIIe session*, (Geneva, 1906); *Études sur Léonard de Vinci: Ceux qu'il a lu et ceux qui l'ont lu*, 3 vols. (Paris, 1909–1913), particularly vol. III, *Les précurseurs parisiens de Galilée*. Quite recently the thesis of continuity has been upheld by J. H. Randall, Jr., in his brilliant article "Scientific Method in the School of Padua," *Journal of the History of Ideas*, I (1940); Randall convincingly shows the progressive elaboration of the method of "resolution and composition" in the teaching of the great logicians of the Renaissance. Yet Randall himself states that there was "one element lacking in Zabarella's formulation of method: he did not insist that the principles of natural science be mathematical" (p. 204), and that Cremonini's *Tractatus de paedia* "sounds like the solemn warning of the great tradition of Aristotelian

is true, of course, that an unbroken tradition leads from the works of the Parisian Nominalists to those of Benedetti, Bruno, Galileo and Descartes.   (I myself have added a link to the history of that tradition[18]).   Still the conclusion drawn therefrom by Duhem is a delusion: a well-prepared revolution is nevertheless a revolution, and in spite of the fact that Galileo himself in his youth (as well as at times Descartes) shared the views and taught the theories of the medieval critics of Aristotle, modern science, the science born from his efforts and discoveries, *does not* follow the inspiration of the "Parisian forerunners of Galileo"; it places itself at once on a quite different level—on a level which I should like to call the Archimedian one.   The true forerunner of modern physics is neither Buridan, nor Nicole Oresme, nor even John Philoponos, but Archimedes.[19]

I

The history of the scientific thought of the Middle Ages and of the Renaissance, now beginning to be somewhat better known,[20] can be divided into two periods.   Or better, as the chronological order corresponds only very roughly to that division, the history of scientific thought may be, *grosso modo,* divided into three stages or epochs, which correspond in turn to three different types of thinking: the Aristotelian physics first; then the physics of *impetus,* inaugurated, like everything else, by the Greeks, and elaborated in the current of the Fourteenth century by the Parisian nominalists; and finally modern, mathematical, Archimedian or Galilean physics.

---

rational empiricism to the triumphant mathematicians" (*ibid.*).   As a matter of fact, it is just this "mathematical emphasis added to the logical methodology of Zabarella" (p. 205) which forms, in my opinion, the content of the scientific revolution of the seventeenth century; and, in the opinion of the time, the dividing line between the followers of Plato and those of Aristotle.

[18] Cf. *Études Galiléennes,* I, *A l'aube de la science classique* (Paris, 1940).

[19] The sixteenth century, at least its latter half, is the period of the reception of the study and of the gradual understanding of Archimedes.

[20] We owe that knowledge chiefly to the works of P. Duhem (to the works cited above, n. 17, must be added: *Les Origines de la statique,* 2 vols. [Paris, 1905], and *Le Système du monde,* 5 vols. [Paris, 1913–17]) and to those of Lynn Thorndike (cf. his monumental *History of Magic and Experimental Science,* 6 vols. [New York, 1923–41]).   Cf. equally F. J. Dijksterhuis, *Wal en Worp* (Groningen, 1924).

It is these stages that we find represented in the works of the young Galileo, which thus not only give us information on the history—or the prehistory—of his thought, on the *mobiles* and motives which dominated and inspired it, but present us at the same time, condensed and as it were clarified by the admirable mind of its author, a striking and deeply instructive picture of the whole history of pre-galilean physics. Let us briefly follow this story, beginning with Aristotelian physics.

Aristotelian physics is false, of course; and utterly obsolete. Nevertheless, it is a "physics," that is, a highly though non-mathematically elaborated[21] science. It is not a childish phantasy, nor a brute and verbal restatement of common sense, but a theory, that is, a doctrine which, starting of course with the data of common sense, subjects them to an extremely coherent and systematic treatment.[22]

The facts or data which serve as a basis for this theoretical elaboration are very simple, and in practice we admit them just as did Aristotle. It still seems to all of us "natural" to see a heavy body fall "down." And just like Aristotle or St. Thomas, we should be deeply astonished to see a ponderous body—a stone or a bull—rise freely in the air. This would seem to us pretty "unnatural"; and we would look for an explanation in the action of some hidden mechanism.

In the same way we still find it "natural" that the flame of a match points "up," and that we place our pots and pans "on" the fire. We should be astonished and should seek for an explanation if, for instance, we saw the flame turn about and point "down." Shall we call this conception, or rather this attitude, childish and simple? Perhaps. We can even point out that according to Aristotle himself science begins precisely by looking for an explanation for things that appear natural. Still, when thermodynamics asserts as a principle that "heat" passes from a hot to a cold body, but not from the cold to a hot one, does it not simply translate an intuition of common sense that a "hot" body "naturally" becomes cold, but that a cold one does not "naturally" become hot? And even when we are stating that the center of gravity of a system

---

[21] The Aristotelian physics is essentially non-mathematical. To present it, as Duhem does, *De l'accélération produite par une force constante*, p. 859, simply as based upon another mathematical formula than ours, is an error.

[22] The systematic character of Aristotelian physics is often not sufficiently appreciated by the modern historian of scientific thought.

tends to take the lowest position and does not rise by itself, are we not simply translating an intuition of common sense, the self-same intuition which Aristotelian physics expresses by its distinction of movement into "natural" and "violent"?[23]

Moreover, Aristotelian physics no more rests content than thermodynamics with merely expressing in its language the "fact" of common sense just mentioned; it transposes it, and the distinction between "natural" and "violent" movements takes its place in a general conception of physical reality, a conception of which the principal features seem to be: (a) the belief in the existence of qualitatively determined "natures," and (b) the belief in the existence of a Cosmos—that is, the belief in the existence of principles of order in virtue of which the entirety of real beings form a hierarchically-ordered whole.

Whole, cosmic order, and harmony: these concepts imply that in the Universe things are (or should be) distributed and disposed in a certain determined order; that their location is not a matter of indifference (neither for them, nor for the Universe); that on the contrary each thing has, according to its nature, a determined "place" in the Universe, which is in some sense its own.[24]   A place for everything, and everything in its place: the concept of "natural place" expresses this theoretical demand of Aristotelian physics.

The conception of "natural place" is based on a purely static conception of order. Indeed, if everything were "in order," everything would be in its natural place, and, of course, would remain and stay there forever. Why should it depart from it? On the contrary, it would offer a resistance to any attempt to expel it therefrom. This expulsion could be effected only by exerting some kind of *violence,* and the body would seek to come back, if, and when, owing to such a *violence,* it found itself out of "its" place.

Thus every movement implies some kind of cosmic disorder, a disturbance of the world-equilibrium, being either a direct effect of *violence,* or, on the contrary, the effect of the effort of Being to compensate for the *violence,* to recover its lost and troubled order and balance, to bring things back to their natural places, places where they can rest and remain.   It is this returning to order

[23] Cf. E. Mach, *Die Mechanik,* 124 sq.

[24] It is only in "its" place that a being comes to its accomplishment and becomes truly itself. And that is the reason why it tends to reach that place.

which constitutes precisely what we have called "natural" movement.[25]

Upsetting equilibrium, returning to order: it is perfectly clear that order constitutes a firm and durable state which tends to extend itself indefinitely. There is therefore no need to explain the state of rest, at least the state of a body at rest in its natural, proper place; it is its own nature which explains it, which explains, for instance, the earth's being at rest in the center of the world. It is obvious likewise that movement is necessarily a transitory state: natural movement ends naturally when it reaches its goal. And as for violent movement, Aristotle is too optimistic to admit that this abnormal status could endure; moreover, violent movement is disorder creating disorder, and to admit that it could endure indefinitely would mean, in fact, to abandon the very idea of a well-ordered Cosmos. Aristotle therefore holds the reassuring belief that nothing which is *contra naturam possit esse perpetuum*.[26]

Thus, as we have just said, in the Aristotelian physics movement is an essentially transitory state. Taken literally, however, this statement would be incorrect, and even doubly incorrect. As a matter of fact movement, though it is for *each of the moved bodies*, or at least for those of the sublunar world, for the movable things of our experience, a necessarily transitory and ephemeral state, is nevertheless for the whole of the world a necessarily eternal, and therefore an eternally necessary phenomenon[27]—a phenomenon which we cannot explain without discovering its origin and cause in the physical as well as the metaphysical structure of the Cosmos. Such an analysis would show that the ontological structure of material Being prevents it from reaching the state of perfection implied in the notion of absolute rest, and would enable us to see the ultimate physical cause of the temporary, ephemeral and variable movements of sublunar bodies in the continuous, uniform, and perpetual movement of the heavenly spheres.[28] On the other hand, movement strictly speaking is not a *state:* it is a

[25] The conceptions of "natural places" and "natural motions" imply that of a finite Universe.

[26] Aristotle, *Physics,* VIII, 8, 215 b.

[27] Movement can result only from a previous movement. Therefore every actual motion implies an infinite series of preceding ones.

[28] In a finite Universe the only uniform movement which can persist indefinitely is a circular one.

process, a flux, a *becoming,* in and by which things constitute, actualize and accomplish themselves.[29] It is perfectly true that becoming has Being as its end; and that movement has rest as its goal. Yet this immutable rest of a fully actualized being is something utterly different from the heavy and impotent immobility of a being unable to move itself; the first is something positive, is "perfection and *actus*"; the second is only a "privation." Movement, therefore—a *processus,* a becoming, a change—finds itself placed ontologically between the two. It is the being of everything that changes, of which the being is alteration and modification and which *is* only in changing and in modifying itself. The famous Aristotelian definition of movement—*actus entis in potentia in quantum est in potentia*—which Descartes will find perfectly unintelligible—expresses admirably the fact: movement is the being— or the *actus*—of everything which is not God.

To move is thus to change, *aliter et aliter se habere,* to change in itself and in respect to others. This implies on the one hand a term of relation or of comparison, in respect to which the thing moved changes its being or relation; which implies—if we are dealing with local movement[30]—the existence of a fixed point in respect to which the moved moves itself, a fixed unmovable point; which obviously can only be the center of the Universe. On the other hand the fact that every change, every process needs a cause to explain it, implies that every movement needs a mover to produce it, which, as long as the movement endures, keeps it going. Movement indeed does not maintain itself, as rest does. Rest—a state or a privation—does not need the action of any cause to explain its persistence. Movement, change, any process of actualization (or of decay), and even of continuous actualization or decay cannot dispense with such action. If you remove the cause, movement will stop. *Cessante causa cessat effectus.*[31]

If we are dealing with "natural" movement, this cause, this motor is the very nature of the body, its "form," which seeks to

[29] Cf. Kurt Riezler, *Physics and Reality* (New Haven, 1940).

[30] Local movement—locomotion—is only one, though a particularly important, kind of "motion" (κίνησις), motion in the realm of space, in contradistinction to alteration, motion in the realm of quality, and generation and decay, motion in the realm of being.

[31] Aristotle is perfectly right. No process of change or becoming can dispense with a cause. And if motion, in modern physics, persists by itself, it is because it is no longer a process.

bring it back to its place, and thus keeps the movement going. *Vice versa,* movement which is *contra naturam* requires throughout its duration the *continuous* action of an *external* mover conjoint to the moved. Remove the mover, and the movement will stop. Detach it from the moved, and the movement will equally stop. Aristotle, as we know well, does not admit action at a distance;[32] every transmission of movement implies according to him a contact. Therefore there are only two kinds of such transmission: pressure and traction. To move a body you have either to push or to pull it. There is no other means.

Aristotelian physics thus forms an admirable and perfectly coherent theory which, to tell the truth, has only one flaw (besides that of being false): that of being contradicted by everyday practice, by the practice of throwing. But a theoretician deserving the name does not allow himself to be troubled by an objection from common sense. If and when he encounters a "fact" that does not fit into his theory, he denies its existence. And if he cannot deny it, he explains it. And it is in the explanation of this everyday fact, the fact of throwing, a movement continuing in spite of the absence of a "mover," a fact apparently incompatible with his theory, that Aristotle gives us the measure of his genius. This answer consists in the explanation of the apparently motorless movement of the projectile by the reaction of the ambient medium, the air, or the water.[33] The theory is a stroke of genius. Unfortunately (besides being false), from the point of view of common sense it is utterly impossible. No wonder therefore that the criticism of Aristotelian dynamics turns always to the same *questio disputata: a quo moveantur projecta?*

II

We shall come back in a moment to this *questio,* but we must first turn our attention to another detail of Aristotelian dynamics: the negation of any vacuum and of movement in a vacuum. In this dynamics, indeed, a vacuum does not enable movement to proceed more easily; on the contrary, it renders it utterly impossible; this for very profound reasons.

We have already said that in Aristotelian dynamics, every body is conceived as endowed with a tendency to find itself in its natural

[32] The body *tends* to its natural place, but it is not *attracted* by it.

[33] Cf. Aristotle, *Physics,* IV, 8, 215 a; VIII, 10, 267 a; *De Coelo,* III, 2, 301 b; É. Meyerson, *Identité et réalité,* 84.

place, and to come back to it when, and if, by violence it is moved away from it. This tendency explains its (natural) movement: a movement which brings it to its natural place by the shortest and the speediest way. It follows that every natural movement proceeds in a straight line, and that every body travels to its natural place as fast as possible; that is, as fast as its environment, which resists and opposes its movement, allows it to do. If therefore there were nothing to arrest it, if the surrounding medium did not oppose any resistance to its movement through it (as would be the case in a vacuum) the body would travel to "its" place with an infinite speed.[34] But such a movement would be instantaneous and this—with good reason—seems to Aristotle to be utterly impossible. The conclusion is obvious: no (natural) movement can possibly take place in the void. As for violent movement, that, for example, of throwing, movement in a vacuum would be equivalent to movement without a motor; it is obvious that the vacuum is not a physical medium and cannot receive, transmit and keep up a movement. Moreover, in a vacuum (as in the space of the Euclidian geometry) there are no privileged places or directions. In a vacuum there are not, and there cannot be, "natural" places. Therefore a body put into a vacuum would not know where to go, would not have any reason to move in one direction rather than in any other, and thus would not have any reason to move at all. *Vice versa,* once moved, it would have no more reason to stop here rather than there, and thus it would have no reason to stop at all.[35] Both of which are utterly absurd.

Aristotle is once more perfectly right. An empty space (the space of geometry) is utterly destructive of the conception of a cosmic order: in an empty space there are not only no natural places,[36] there are no *places* at all. The idea of a vacuum is not compatible with the interpretation of movement as change and as process—perhaps not even with that of the concrete movement of concrete "real," perceptible, bodies: I mean the bodies of our common everyday experience. The vacuum is a *non-ens;*[37] and to place things in such a *non-ens* is absurd.[38] Geometrical bodies alone can be "placed" in a geometrical space.

[34] Cf. Aristotle, *Physics,* VII, 5, 249 b, 250 a; *De Coelo,* III, 2, 301 e.

[35] Cf. Aristotle, *Physics,* IV, 8, 214 b; 215 b.

[36] If one likes it better, one can say that in a vacuum all places are the natural places of every kind of body.

[37] Kant called empty space an *"Unding."*

[38] Such was, as we know, the opinion of Descartes; and of Spinoza.

The physicist investigates real things, the geometer reasons about abstractions.   Therefore, contends Aristotle, nothing could be more dangerous than to mingle together geometry and physics, and to apply purely geometrical method and reasoning to the study of physical reality.

III

I have already mentioned that Aristotelian dynamics, in spite— or perhaps because—of its theoretical perfection, was burdened with an important draw-back; that of being utterly implausible and completely unbelievable and unacceptable to plain sound common sense, and obviously contradictory to the commonest everyday experience.   No wonder therefore that it never enjoyed universal recognition, and that the critics and adversaries of the dynamics of Aristotle always opposed to it the common-sense fact of the persistence of movement separated from its original motor.   Thus the classical examples of such movement, for instance the continuing rotation of the wheel, the flight of the arrow, the throwing of a stone, were persistently marshalled against it, beginning with Hipparchus and John Philoponos, through John Buridan and Nicole Oresme, down to Leonardo da Vinci, Benedetti and Galileo.[39]

I do not propose to analyze here the traditional arguments which since John Philoponos[40] have been repeated by the partisans of his dynamics.   *Grosso modo* they can be classified into two

[39] For the history of the medieval criticism of Aristotle cf. the works cited above, n. 17, and B. Jansen, "Olivi, der älteste scholastische Vertreter des heutigen Bewegungsbegriffes," *Philosophisches Jahrbuch* (1920); K. Michalsky, "La physique nouvelle et les différents courants philosophiques au XIVe siècle," *Bulletin international de l'Académie polonaise des sciences et des lettres* (Cracovie, 1927); S. Moser, *Grundbegriffe der Naturphilosophie bei Wilhelm von Occam* (Innsbruck, 1932); E. Borchert, *Die Lehre von der Bewegung bei Nicolaus Oresme* (Münster, 1934); R. Marcolongo, "La Meccanica di Leonardo da Vinci," *Atti della reale accademia delle scienze fisiche e matematiche*, XIX (Napoli, 1933).

[40] On John Philoponos, who seems to be the real inventor of the theory of the *impetus,* cf. E. Wohlwill, "Ein Vorgänger Galileis im VI. Jahrhundert," *Physikalische Zeitschrift,* VII (1906), and P. Duhem, *Le Système du Monde,* I.   The *Physics* of John Philoponos, not having been translated into Latin, remained inaccessible to the scholastics, who had at their disposal only the brief account given by Simplicius.   But it was well known to the Arabs, and the Arabic tradition, directly and through the translation of Avicenna, seems to have influenced the "Parisian" school to a hitherto unsuspected degree.   Cf. the very important article of S. Pines, "Études sur Awhad al-Zamān Abu'l Barakat al-Baghdadi," *Revue des Études Juives* (1938).

groups: a) the first arguments are material and stress the improbability of the assumption that a big and heavy body, a bullet, a revolving mill-stone, an arrow flying against the wind, could be moved by the reaction of the air; b) the others are formal and point out the contradiction involved in attributing to the air a double rôle, that of resistance and that of being a mover, as well as the illusory character of the whole theory which only shifts the problem from the body to the air and is, in fact, obliged to endow the air with the same ability to maintain its movement in spite of its separation from its external cause which it denies to other bodies. If so, they ask, why not assume that the mover transmits to the moved, or impresses it with, something which enables it to move—a something which is called δύναμις, *virtus motiva, virtus impressa, impetus, impetus impressus,* sometimes *forza* or even *motio,* and which is always thought of as some kind of power or force, which passes from the mover to the *mobile,* and which then carries on the movement, or better, which produces the movement as its cause.

It is obvious, as Duhem himself recognized, that we are back with common sense. The partisans of the *impetus* physics are thinking in terms of everyday experience. Is it not clear that we need an *effort,* a deployment and an expenditure of force, in order to move a body, for instance in order to push a carriage along its path, to throw a stone or to bend a bow? Is it not clear that it is this force which moves the body, or better, which makes it move?— that it is this force which the body receives from the mover that enables it to overcome resistance (like that of the air) and to strike at obstacles?

The medieval followers of *impetus* dynamics discuss at great length, and without success, the ontological status of *impetus.* They try to fit it into the Aristotelian classification, to interpret it as some kind of *form,* or as a kind of *habitus,* or as a kind of quality such as heat (like Hipparchus and Galileo). These discussions only show the confused, imaginative nature of the conception, which is a direct product or, if one may say so, a condensation, of common sense.

As such it is even more in accord than the Aristotelian view with the "facts"—real or imaginary—which form the experiential basis of medieval dynamics; and particularly with the well known "fact" that every projectile begins by increasing its speed and acquires the maximum of its velocity some time after its separation from the mover.[41]   Everybody knows that in order to jump an obstacle one has to "make a take-off;" that a chariot which one pushes, or pulls, starts slowly and little by little increases its speed; it too takes off and gathers momentum; just as everybody—even a child throwing a ball—knows that in order to hit the goal hard he has to place himself at a certain distance from it, and not too near, in order to allow the ball to gather momentum.   The physics of *impetus* is not at pains to explain this phenomenon; from its standpoint it is perfectly natural that *impetus* should require some time before it "takes hold" of the *mobile*—just as, for example, heat needs time to permeate a body.

The conception of movement underlying and supporting *impetus* physics is quite different from that of the Aristotelian view. Movement is no longer understood as a process of actualization.

[41] It is interesting to note that this absurd belief, shared and taught by Aristotle (*De Coelo*, II, 6), was so deeply rooted and so universally accepted that Descartes himself did not dare to deny it outright, and as so often with him preferred to explain it.   In 1630 he writes to Mersenne (A. T., I, 110): "Je voudrais bien aussi sçavoir si vous n'avez point expérimenté si une pierre jettée avec une fronde, ou la bale d'un mousquet, ou un traist d'arbaleste, vont plus viste et ont plus de force au milieu de leur mouvement qu'ils n'en ont au commencement, et s'ils font plus d'effet.   Car c'est là la créance du vulgaire, avec laquelle toutefois mes raisons ne s'accordent pas; et je trouve que les choses qui sont poussées et qui ne se meuvent pas d'elles mêmes, doivent avoir plus de force au commencement qu'incontinent après."   In 1632 (A. T., I, 259) and once more in 1640 (A. T., II, 37 sq.) he explains to his friend what is true in this belief: *"In motu projectorum,* ie ne croie point que le Missile aille jamais moins vite au commencement qu'à la fin, à conter dès le premier moment qu'il cesse d'être poussé par la main ou la machine; mais je crois bien qu'un mousquet, n'estant éloigné que d'un pied et demi d'une muraille n'aura pas tant d'effet que s'il en était éloigné de quinze ou de vingt pas, à cause que la bale, en sortant du mousquet ne peut si aisement chasser l'air qui est entre lui et cette muraille et ainsi doit aller moins viste que si cette muraille estoit moins proche. Toutefois c'est à l'expérience de déterminer si cette différence est sensible et je doute fort de toutes celles que je n'ai pas faites moi-même."   Descartes' friend, Beekmann, on the contrary, denies flatly the possibility of an acceleration of the projectile and writes (*Beekmann à Mersenne,* Apr. 30, 1630, cf. *Correspondance du Père Mersenne* [Paris, 1936], II, 437): "Funditores vero ac pueri omnes qui existimant remotiora fortius ferire quam eadem propinquiora, certo certius falluntur." Yet he admits that there must be something true in this belief and tries to explain: "Non dixeram plenitudinem nimiam aeris impedire effectum tormentorii globi, sed pulverem pyrium extra bombardam jam existentem forsitan adhuc rarefieri, ideoque fieri posse ut globus tormentarius extra bombardam nova vi (simili tandem) propulsus velocitate aliquamdiu cresceret."

Yet it is still a change, and as such it must be explained by the action of a definite force or cause. *Impetus* is just that immanent cause which produces the movement, which is *converso modo* the effect produced by it. Thus the *impetus impressus produces* the movement; it *moves* the body. But at the same time it plays another very important rôle: it overcomes the resistance opposed by the medium to the movement.

Owing to the confused and ambiguous character of the *impetus* conception, it is rather natural that the two aspects and rôles should merge together, and that some of the partisans of the *impetus* dynamics should come to the conclusion that, at least in some special cases such as the circular movement of the heavenly spheres, or, more generally, the rolling movement of a circular body on a level plane, or even more generally in all the cases where there is no external resistance to movement, such as would be the case in a *vacuum,* the *impetus* does not weaken but remains "immortal." This seems to be a close approach to the law of inertia, and it is therefore of particular interest and importance to note that Galileo himself, who in his *De Motu* gives us one of the best expositions of *impetus* dynamics, resolutely denies the possibility of such an assumption, and asserts most vigorously the essentially perishable nature of *impetus.*

Galileo is obviously perfectly right. If movement is understood as the effect of *impetus* considered as its immanent—and not natural—cause, it is unthinkable and absurd not to admit that the cause or force which produces it must necessarily spend and finally exhaust itself in this production. It can never remain unchanged for two consecutive moments, and therefore the movement which it produces must necessarily slow down and come to an end.[42] Thus it is a very important lesson that we learn from the young Galileo. He teaches us that *impetus* physics, though compatible with movement in a *vacuum,* is like that of Aristotle *incompatible* with the principle of inertia. And this is not the only lesson that Galileo teaches with regard to *impetus* physics. The second is at least as valuable as the first. It runs that, like that of Aristotle, the dynamics of *impetus* is incompatible with mathematical treatment. It leads nowhere. It is a blind alley.

Impetus physics, during the thousand years that separate John Philoponos from Benedetti, made very little progress. But in the

[42] Cf. Galileo Galilei, *De Motu, Opere,* Ed. Naz., I, 314 sq.

latter's works, and even more clearly, more consistently and consciously, in those of the young Galileo, we find—under the obvious and unmistakable influence of the ''suprahuman Archimedes''[43] a determined attempt to apply to this physics the principles of ''mathematical philosophy.''[44]

Nothing is more instructive than the study of this attempt—or, more exactly, of these attempts—and of their failure. They show us that it is impossible to mathematize, i.e., to transform into an exact, mathematical concept, the rude, vague and confused conception of *impetus*. In order to build up a mathematical physics following the lines of the statics of Archimedes, this conception had to be dropped altogether.[45] A new and original concept of motion had to be formed and developed. It is this new concept that we owe to Galileo.

IV

We are too well acquainted with, or rather too well accustomed to, the principles and concepts of modern mechanics, so well that it is almost impossible for us to see the difficulties which had to be overcome for their establishment. They seem to us so simple, so natural, that we do not notice the paradoxes they imply and contain. Yet the mere fact that the greatest and mightiest minds of mankind—Galileo, Descartes—had to struggle in order to make them theirs, is in itself sufficient to indicate that these clear and simple notions—the notion of movement or that of space—are not so clear and simple as they seem to be. Or they are clear and simple only from a certain point of view, only as part of a certain set of concepts and axioms, apart from which they are not simple at all. Or, perhaps, they are too clear and too simple: so clear and so simple that, like all prime notions, they are very difficult to grasp.

Movement, space—let us try to forget for a while all we have learnt at school; let us try to think out what they mean in mechanics. Let us try to place ourselves in the situation of a contemporary of Galileo, a man accustomed to the concepts of Aris-

[43] Galileo Galilei, *De Motu*, 300.

[44] J. B. Benedetti, *Diversarum speculationum mathematicarum liber* (Taurini, 1585), 168.

[45] The persistence of the terminology—the word *impetus* is used by Galileo and his pupils and even by Newton—must not prevent us from recognizing the disappearance of the idea.

totelian physics which *he* learnt at *his* school, and who encounters for the first time the modern concept of motion. What is it? In fact something pretty strange. It is something which in no way affects the body which is endowed with it: to be in motion or to be at rest does not make any difference for, nor any change in, the body in motion or at rest. The body, as such, is utterly and absolutely indifferent to both.[46] Therefore, we are not able to ascribe motion to a determined body considered in itself. A body is in motion only in relation to some other body which we assume to be at rest. All motion is relative. And therefore we may ascribe it to the one or to the other of the two bodies, *ad libitum*.[47]

Thus motion seems to be a relation. But at the same time it is a *state*, just as rest is another *state*, utterly and absolutely opposed to the former; besides which they are both *persistent states*.[48] The famous first law of motion, the law of inertia, teaches us that a body left to itself persists eternally in its state of motion or of rest, and that we must apply a force in order to change a state of motion to a state of rest, and *vice versa*.[49] Yet not every kind of motion is thus endowed with an eternal being, but only uniform movement in a straight line. Modern physics affirms, as well we know, that a body once set in motion conserves eternally its direction and speed, provided of course it is not subject to the action of any external force.[50] Moreover, to the objection of the Aristotelian that though as a matter of fact he is acquainted with eternal motion, the eternal circular motion of the heavenly spheres, he has never yet encountered a persistent rectilinear one, modern physics replies: of course! rectilinear, uniform motion is utterly impossible, and can take place only in a vacuum.

Let us think it over, and perhaps we will not be too harsh on the Aristotelian who felt himself unable to grasp and to accept this

[46] In the Aristotelian physics, motion is a process of change and always affects the body in motion.

[47] A given body, therefore, can be endowed with any number of different motions, which do not interfere with each other. In the Aristotelian as well as in the *impetus* physics every motion interferes with every other and sometimes even prevents it from taking place.

[48] Motion and rest are thus placed on the same ontological level, and therefore persistence of *motion* becomes just as self-evident and without need of explanation as persistence of *rest* had previously been.

[49] In modern terms: in the Aristotelian and *impetus* dynamics, force produces motion; in modern dynamics, force produces acceleration.

[50] This implies necessarily the infinity of the Universe.

unheard-of notion, the notion of a persistent, substantial relation-state, the concept of something which to him seemed just as abstruse, and just as impossible, as the ill-fated substantial forms of the scholastics appear to us. No wonder that the Aristotelian felt himself astonished and bewildered by this amazing attempt to explain the real by the impossible—or, which is the same thing, to explain real being by mathematical being, because, as I have mentioned already, these bodies moving in straight lines in infinite empty space are not *real* bodies moving in *real* space, but *mathematical* bodies moving in *mathematical* space.

Once more, we are so accustomed to mathematical science, to mathematical physics, that we no longer feel the strangeness of a mathematical approach to Being, the paradoxical daring of Galileo's utterance that the book of Nature is written in geometrical characters.[51]   For us it is a foregone conclusion. But not for the contemporaries of Galileo. Therefore it is the right of mathematical science, of the mathematical explanation of Nature, in opposition to the non-mathematical one of common sense and of Aristotelian physics, much more than the opposition between two astronomical systems, that forms the real subject of the *Dialogue on the Two Greatest Systems of the World*. As a matter of fact the *Dialogue,* as I believe I have shown in my ill-fated volume, is not so much a book on *science* in our meaning of the term as a book on philosophy—or to be quite correct and to employ a disused but time-honored expression, a book on *natural philosophy*—for the simple reason that the solution of the astronomical problem depends on the constitution of a new Physics; which in turn implies the solution of the *philosophical* question of the rôle played by mathematics in the constitution of the science of Nature.

The rôle and the place of mathematics in science is not in fact a very new problem. Quite the contrary: for more than two thousand years it has formed the object of philosophical meditation, inquiry and discussion. And Galileo is perfectly aware of it. No wonder! Even as a young boy, a student in the University of Pisa,

---

[51] G. Galilei, *Il Saggiatore* (*Opere,* VI, 232): "La filosofia è scritta in questo grandissimo libro, che continuamente ci sta aperto innanzi a gli occhi (io dico l'universo), ma non si può intendere se prima non s'impara a intender la lingua, e conoscer i caratteri, ne' quali è scritto. Egli è scritto in lingua matematica, e i caratteri son triangoli, cerchi, ed altre figure geometriche, senza i quali mezi è impossibile a intenderne umanamente parola." Cf. *Letter to Liceti* of Jan. 11, 1641 (*Opere,* XVIII, 293).

he could have learned from the lectures of his master, Francesco
Buonamici, that the "question" about the rôle and the nature of
mathematics constitutes the principal subject of opposition between Aristotle and Plato.[52]   And some years later when he came
back to Pisa, this time a professor himself, he could have learned
from his friend and colleague, Jacopo Mazzoni, author of a book on
Plato and Aristotle, that "there is no other question which has
given place to more noble and beautiful speculations . . . than the
question whether the use of mathematics in physical science as an
instrument of proof and a middle term of demonstration, is oppor-
tune or not; in other words, whether it brings us some profit, or on
the contrary is dangerous and harmful." "It is well known," says
Mazzoni, "that Plato believed that mathematics was quite particularly appropriate for physical investigations, which was the reason

[52] The enormous compilation of Buonamici (1011 pages *in folio*) is an invaluable
source-book for the study of medieval theories of motion.   Though frequently
mentioned by historians of Galileo it has never been utilized by them.   Buonamici's
book is very rare.   I allow myself therefore to quote it at some length: Francisci
Bonamici, Florentini, e primo loco philosophiam ordinariam in Almo Gymnasio
Pisano profitentis, *De Motu, libri X, quibus generalia naturalis philosophiae principia summo studio collecta continentur* (Florentiae, 1591), lib. X, cap. XI.   *Jurene
mathematicae ex ordine scientiarum expurgantur*, p. 56: . . . "Itaque veluti ministri
sunt mathematicae, nec honore dignae et habitae προπαιδεία, id est apparatus quidam
ad alias disciplinas.   Ob eamque potissime caussam, quod de bono mentionem facere
non videntur.   Etenim omne bonum est finis, is vero cuiusdam actus est.   Omnis
vero actus est cum motu.   Mathematicae autem motum non respiciunt.   Haec nostri
addunt.   Omnem scientiam ex propriis effici: propria vero sunt necessaria quae alicui
[?] quatenus ipsum et per se insunt.   Atqui talia principia mathematicae non
habent. . . . Nullum caussae genus accipit . . . proptereaquod omnes caussae de-
finiuntur per motum: efficiens enim est principium motus, finis cuius gratia motus
est, forma et materia sunt naturae; et motus igitur principia sint necesse est.   At
vero mathematica sunt immobilia.   Et nullum igitur ibi caussae genus existit."
Ibid., lib. I, p. 54 "Mathematicae cum ex notis nobis et natura simul efficiant id
quod cupiunt, sed caeteris demonstrationis perspicuitate praeponentur, nam vis
rerum quas ipsae tractant non est admodum nobilis; quippe quod sunt accidentia,
id est habeant rationem substantiae quatenus subiicitur et determinatur quanto;
eaque considerentur longe secus atque in natura existant.   Attamen nonnullarum
rerum ingenium tale esse comperimus ut ad certam materiam sese non applicent,
neque motum consequantur, quia tamen in natura quicquid est, cum motu existit;
opus est abstractione cuius beneficio quantum motu non comprehenso in eo munere
contemplamur; et cum talis sit earum natura nihil absurdi exoritur.   Quod item
confirmatur, quod mens in omni habitu verum dicit; atqui verum est ex eo, quod res
ita est.   Huc accedit quod Aristoteles distinguit scientias non ex ratione notionum
sed entium."

why he himself had many times recourse to it for the explanation of physical mysteries.   But Aristotle held a quite different view and he explained the errors of Plato by his too great attachment to mathematics.''[53]

One sees that for the scientific and philosophical consciousness of the time—Buonamici and Mazzoni are only giving expression to the *communis opinio*—the opposition, or rather the dividing line, between the Aristotelian and the Platonist is perfectly clear.   If you claim for mathematics a superior status, if more than that you attribute to it a real value and a commanding position in Physics, you are a Platonist.   If on the contrary you see in mathematics an abstract science, which is therefore of a lesser value than those— physics and metaphysics—which deal with real being; if in particular you pretend that physics needs no other basis than experience and must be built directly on perception, that mathematics has to content itself with the secondary and subsidiary rôle of a mere auxiliary, you are an Aristotelian.

What is in question in this discussion is not certainty—no Aristotelian has ever doubted the certainty of geometrical propositions or demonstrations—but Being; not even the use of mathematics in physical science—no Aristotelian has ever denied our right to measure what is measurable and to count what is numerable—but the structure of science, and therefore the structure of Being.

[53] Jacobi Mazzoni, Caesenatis, in Almo Gymnasio Pisano Aristotelem ordinarie Platonem vero extra ordinem profitentis, *In Universam Platonis et Aristotelis Philosophiam Praeludia, sive de comparatione Platonis et Aristotelis* (Venetiis, 1597), 187 sq.: *Disputatur utrum usus mathematicarum in Physica utilitatem vel detrimentum afferat, et in hoc Platonis et Aristotelis comparatio.* Non est enim inter Platonem et Aristotelem quaestio, seu differentia, quae tot pulchris, et nobilissimis speculationibus scateat, ut cum ista, ne in minima quidem parte comparari possit.   Est autem differentia, utrum usus mathematicarum in scientia Physica tanquam ratio probandi et medius terminus demonstrationum sit opportunus, vel inopportunus, id est, an utilitatem aliquam afferat, vel potius detrimentum et damnum.   Credidit Plato Mathematicas ad speculationes physicas apprime esse accommodatas.   Quapropter passim eas adhibet in reserandis mysteriis physicis.   At Aristoteles omnino secus sentire videtur, erroresque Platonis adscribet amori Mathematicarum. . . . Sed si quis voluerit hanc rem diligentius considerare, forsan, et Platonis defensionem inveniet, videbit Aristotelem in nonnullos errorum scopulos impegisse, quod quibusdam in locis Mathematicas demonstrationes proprio consilio valde consentaneas, aut non intellexerit, aut certe non adhibuerit.   Utramque conclusionem, quarum prima ad Platonis tutelam attinet, secunda errores Aristotelis ob Mathematicas male rejectas profitetur, brevissime demonstrabo.''

These are the discussions to which Galileo alludes continuously in the course of his *Dialogue*. Thus at the very beginning Simplicio, the Aristotelian, points out that "concerning natural things we need not always seek the necessity of mathematical demonstrations."[54] To which Sagredo, who allows himself the pleasure of misunderstanding Simplicio, replies: "Of course, when you cannot reach it. But, if you can, why not?" Of course. If it is possible in questions pertaining to natural things to achieve a demonstration possessing a mathematical necessity, why shouldn't we try to do it? But is it possible? That is precisely the problem, and Galileo, in the margin of the book, sums up the discussion and formulates the real meaning of the Aristotelian: "In natural demonstrations," says he, "one must not seek mathematical exactitude."

One must not. Why? Because it is impossible. Because the nature of physical being is qualitative and vague. It does not conform to the rigidity and the precision of mathematical concepts. It is always "more or less." Therefore, as the Aristotelian will explain to us later, philosophy, that is the science of the real, does not need to look at details, nor need it have recourse to numerical determinations in formulating its theories of motion; all that it has to do is to develop its chief categories (natural, violent, rectilinear, circular) and to describe its general qualitative and abstract features.[55]

The modern reader is probably far from being convinced. He finds it difficult to admit that "philosophy" had to content itself with abstract and vague generalization and not try to establish precise and concrete universal laws. The modern reader does not know the real reason of this necessity, but Galileo's contemporaries knew it quite well. They knew that quality, as well as form, being non-mathematical by nature, cannot be treated in terms of mathematics. Physics is not applied geometry. Terrestrial matter can never exhibit exact mathematical figures; the "forms" never "inform" it completely and perfectly. There always remains a gap. In the skies, of course, it is different; and therefore mathematical astronomy is possible. But astronomy is not physics. To have missed that point is precisely the error of Plato and of those who follow Plato. It is useless to attempt to build up a mathematical

[54] Cf. Galileo Galilei, *Dialogo sopra i due Massimi Sistemi del Mondo, Opere,* Ed. Naz:, VII, 38; cf. 256.

[55] Cf. *Dialogo,* 242.

philosophy of nature. The enterprise is doomed even before it starts. It does not lead us to truth but to error.

"All these mathematical subtleties," explains Simplicio, "are true in *abstracto*. But applied to sensible and physical matter, they do not work."[56] In real nature there are no circles, no triangles, no straight lines. Therefore it is useless to learn the language of mathematical figures: the book of Nature, in spite of Galileo and Plato, is not written in them. In fact, it is not only useless, it is dangerous: the more a mind is accustomed to the precision and to the rigidity of geometrical thought, the less it will be able to grasp the mobile, changing, qualitatively determined variety of Being.

This attitude of the Aristotelian is very far from being ridiculous.[57] To me, at least, it seems perfectly sensible. You cannot establish a mathematical theory of quality, objects Aristotle to Plato; not even one of motion. There is no motion in numbers. But *ignorato motu ignoratur natura*. And the Aristotelian of Galileo's time could add that the greatest of the Platonists, the *divus* Archimedes himself,[58] was never able to establish more than a statics. Not a dynamics. A theory of rest. Not one of motion.

The Aristotelian was perfectly right. It is impossible to furnish a mathematical deduction of quality. And well we know that Galileo, like Descartes somewhat later, and for just the same reason, was forced to drop the notion of quality, to declare it subjective, to ban it from the realm of nature.[59] This at the same time implies that he was obliged to drop sense-perception as the source of knowledge and to proclaim that intellectual, and even *a priori* knowledge, is our sole and only means of apprehending the essence of the real.

As for dynamics, and the laws of motion—the *posse* is only to be proved by the *esse;* in order to show that it is possible to establish mathematical laws of nature, you have to do it. There is no other way and Galileo is perfectly conscious of it. It is therefore by giving mathematical solutions to concrete physical problems— the problem of falling bodies, the problem of projectile motion—

[56] *Ibid.*, 229, 423.

[57] As we know, it was shared by Pascal, and even by Leibniz.

[58] It is perhaps worth mentioning that for all the doxographic tradition, Archimedes is a *philosophus platonicus*.

[59] Cf. E. A. Burtt, *The Metaphysical Foundations of Modern Physical Science* (London and New York, 1925).

that he leads Simplicio to the confession "that to want to study natural problems without mathematics is to attempt something that cannot be done."

It seems to me that we are now able to understand the meaning of this significant text of Cavalieri, who in 1630 writes in his *Specchio Ustorio:* "How much is added by the knowledge of the mathematical sciences, which the famous schools of Pythagoreans and Platonists considered supremely necessary for the comprehension of physical things, I hope will shortly become clear with the publication of the new science of movement promised by this marvellous Assayer of Nature, Galileo Galilei."[60]

And we understand too the pride of Galileo the Platonist, who in his *Discourses and Demonstrations* announces that "about a most ancient subject he will promote a quite new science," and will prove something that nobody has proven till then, namely that the movement of falling bodies is subjected to the law of numbers.[61] Movement governed by numbers; the Aristotelian objection had at last met its refutation.

It is obvious that for the disciples of Galileo just as for his contemporaries and elders mathematicism means Platonism. Therefore when Torricelli tells us "that among the liberal disciplines geometry *alone* exercises and sharpens the mind and renders it able to be an ornament of the City in time of peace and to defend it in time of war," and that *"caeteris paribus,* a mind trained in geometrical gymnastics is endowed with a quite particular and *virile* strength,"[62] not only does he show himself an authentic

[60] Bonaventura Cavalieri, *Lo Specchio Ustorio overo trattato Delle Settioni Coniche e alcuni loro mirabili effetti intorno al Lume* etc. (Bologna, 1632), 152 sq.: "Ma quanto vi aggiunga la cognitione delle scienze Matematiche, giudicate da quelle famosissime scuole de' Pithogorici et de' 'Platonici,' sommamente necessarie per intender le cose Fisiche, spero in breve sarà manifesto, per la nuova dottrina del moto promessaci dall'esquisitissimo Saggiatore della Natura, dico dal Sig. Galileo Galilei, ne' suoi Dialoghi. . . ."

[61] Galileo Galilei, *Discorsi e dimostrazioni mathematiche intorno a due nuove scienze (Opere,* Ed. Naz., VIII, 190): "nullus enim, quod sciam, demonstravit, spatia a mobile descendente ex quiete peracta in temporibus aequalibus, eam inter se retinere rationem, quam habent numeri impares ab unitate consequentes."

[62] Evangelista Torricelli, *Opera Geometrica* (Florentiae, 1644), II, 7: "Sola enim Geometria inter liberales disciplinas acriter exacuit ingenium, idoneumque reddit ad civitates adornandas in pace et in bello defendendas: caeteris enim paribus, ingenium quod exercitatum sit in Geometrica palestra, peculiare quoddam et virile robur habere solet: praestabitque semper et antecellet, circa studia Architecturae, rei bellicae, nauticaeque, etc."

disciple of Plato, he acknowledges and proclaims himself to be one. And in doing it he remains a faithful disciple of his master Galileo, who in his *Response to the Philosophical Exercitations* of Antonio Rocco addresses himself to the latter, asking him to judge for himself the value of the two rival methods, i.e., the purely physical and empirical method and the mathematical one, adding: "and decide at the same time who reasoned better, Plato, who said that without mathematics one could not learn philosophy, or Aristotle, who reproached this same Plato for having too much studied Geometry."[63]

I have just called Galileo a Platonist. And I believe that nobody will doubt that he is one.[64] Moreover, he says so himself. In the very first pages of the *Dialogue* Simplicio makes the remark that Galileo, being a mathematician, is probably sympathetic to the numerical speculations of the Pythagoreans. This enables Galileo to declare that he deems them perfectly meaningless, and to say at the same time: "I know perfectly well that the Pythagoreans had the highest esteem for the science of number and that Plato himself admired the human intellect and believed that it participates in divinity solely because it is able to understand the nature of numbers. And I myself am well inclined to make the same judgment."[65]

[63] Galileo Galilei, *Esercitazioni filosofiche di Antonio Rocco, Opere,* Ed. Naz., VII, 744.

[64] The Platonism of Galileo Galilei has been more or less clearly recognized by certain modern historians of science and philosophy. Thus the author of the German translation of the *Dialogo* notes the Platonic influence (the doctrine of anamnesis) on the very form of the book (cf. G. Galilei, *Dialog über die beiden hauptsächlichsten Weltsysteme,* aus dem italienischen übersetzt und erläutert von E. Strauss [Leipzig, 1891], p. XLIX); E. Cassirer (*Das Erkenntnisproblem in der Philosophie und Wissenschaft der neueren Zeit,* 2 ed. [Berlin, 1911], I, 389 sq.) insists upon the Platonism of Galileo's ideal of knowledge; L. Olschki (*Galileo und seine Zeit,* Leipzig, 1927) speaks about the "Platonic vision of Nature" of Galileo, etc. It is E. A. Burtt, *The Metaphysical Foundations of Modern Physical Science* (New York, 1925), who seems to me to have given the best account of the metaphysical substructure (Platonic mathematicism) of modern science. Unfortunately Burtt failed to recognize the existence of *two* (and not one) Platonic traditions, that of mystical arithmology, and that of mathematical science. The same error, which in the case of Burtt was a venial sin, was made by his critic, E. W. Strong, *Procedures and Metaphysics* (Berkeley, Cal., 1936), and in this case it was a mortal one.—On the distinction between the two Platonisms cf. L. Brunschvicg, *Les Étapes de la philosophie mathématique* (Paris, 1922), 69 sq., and *Le Progrès de la conscience dans la philosophie occidentale* (Paris, 1937), 37 sq.

[65] *Dialogo,* 35.

How could he be of a different opinion, he who believed that in mathematical knowledge the human mind attains the very perfection of the divine understanding? Does he not say that *"extensive,* that is in respect of the multiplicity of things to be known, which is infinite, the human mind is as nothing (even if it understood a thousand propositions, because a thousand compared with infinity is like zero) : but taking the understanding *intensive,* in so far as this term means to grasp intensely, that is, perfectly a given proposition, I say that the human mind understands some propositions as perfectly and has of them as absolute certainty as Nature herself can have; and of that kind are the pure mathematical sciences, that is, geometry and arithmetic, of which the divine intellect knows of course infinitely more propositions, for the simple reason that it knows them all; but as for those few understood by the human intellect, I believe that our knowledge equals the divine in objective certainty, because it succeeds in understanding their necessity, beyond which it does not seem that there can exist a greater certainty."[66]

Galileo could have added that the human understanding is so excellent a work of God that *ab initio* it is in possession of these clear and simple ideas of which the very simplicity is a guarantee of truth, and that it has only to turn to itself in order to find in its "memory" the true foundations of science and knowledge, the alphabet, i.e., the elements, of the language—the mathematical language—spoken by the Nature God has created. There is to be found the true foundation of a *real* science, a science of the *real* world—not of a science endowed with a purely formal truth, the intrinsic truth of mathematical reasoning and deduction, a truth which would not be affected by the non-existence in Nature of the objects studied by it : it is obvious that Galileo would no more than Descartes ever rest content with such an *Ersatz* for real science and knowledge.

It is of this science, the true "philosophic" knowledge which is knowledge of the very essence of Being, that Galileo proclaims: "And I, I say to you that if one does not know the truth by himself, it is impossible for anyone else to give him that knowledge. It is indeed possible to teach those things that are neither true nor false; but the true, by which I mean necessary things, that is, those for which it is impossible to be otherwise, every average mind

[66] *Dialogo,* 128 sq.

either knows by itself, or it is impossible for it ever to learn them."[67] Assuredly. A Platonist cannot be of a different opinion because for him to know is nothing else than to understand.

The allusions to Plato so numerous in the works of Galileo, and the repeated mention of the Socratic maieutics and of the doctrine of reminiscence, are not superficial ornaments born from his desire to conform to the literary mode inherited from the concern of Renaissance thought with Plato. Nor are they meant to gain for the new science the sympathy of the "common reader," tired and disgusted by the aridity of Aristotelian scholastics; nor to cloak himself against Aristotle in the authority of his master and rival, Plato. Quite the contrary: they are perfectly serious, and must be taken at their face value. Thus, that no one might have the slightest doubt concerning his philosophical standpoint, Galileo insists:[68] "SALVIATI: The solution of the question under discussion implies the knowledge of certain truths that are just as well known to you as to me. But, as you do not remember them, you do not see that solution. In this way, without teaching you, because you know them already, but only by recalling them to you, I shall make you solve the problem yourself."

"SIMPLICIO: Several times I have been struck by your manner of reasoning, which makes me think that you incline to the opinion of Plato that *nostrum scire sit quoddam reminisci;* pray, free me from this doubt and tell me your own view."

"SALV: What I think of this opinion of Plato I can explain by words, and also by facts. In the arguments so far advanced I have already more than once declared myself by fact. Now I will apply the same method in the inquiry we have in hand, an inquiry which may serve as an example to help you more easily to understand my ideas concerning the acquisition of science. . . ."

The inquiry "we have in hand" is nothing else than the deduction of the fundamental propositions of mechanics. We are informed that Galileo judges he has done more than merely declare himself a follower and a partisan of Platonic epistemology. In addition, by applying it, by discovering the true laws of physics, by letting them be deduced by Sagredo and Simplicio, that is, *by the reader* himself, by *us,* he believes he has demonstrated the truth of Platonism "by fact." The *Dialogue* and the *Discourses* give

[67] *Dialogo,* 183.
[68] *Dialogo,* 217.

us the history of an intellectual experiment—of a conclusive experiment, because it ends with the wistful confession of the Aristotelian Simplicio, acknowledging the necessity of the study of mathematics, and regretting that he himself had not learned them in his youth.

The *Dialogue* and the *Discourses* tell us the history of the discovery, or better still, of the rediscovery of the language spoken by Nature. They explain to us the manner of questioning her, i.e., the theory of that scientific experimentation in which the formulation of postulates and the deduction of their implications precedes and guides the recourse to observation. This too, at least for Galileo, is a proof "by fact." The new science is for him an experimental proof of Platonism.

* و§* *Ernest A. Moody*

GALILEO AND AVEMPACE: DYNAMICS OF THE LEANING TOWER EXPERIMENT

Modern science is commonly said to have come into being when men ceased to read the treatises of Aristotle or of his mediaeval commentators, and turned to the Book of Nature for instruction. More precisely, this epochal event is associated with a certain day of the year 1589, when Galileo is said to have dropped two bodies from the summit of the *campanile* of Pisa, in order to demonstrate that the times of their fall, irrespective of their differences in weight or material, would be equal. The simultaneous thud of those two missiles, as they arrived together at the ground, symbolized the death of ancient and mediaeval physics, and the birth of the new science of mechanics. Such is the time-honoured tradition of the modern era, still sacred to the writers of text books and popular expositions of physics.[1]

That the famous Leaning Tower Experiment, thus interpreted, is a sheer myth, has been pointed out by numerous scholars who, like Galileo himself, have felt that school traditions ought to be tested by first-hand study of the evidence.[2] It is questionable whether the experiment was ever performed. But if it did take place, we may be assured on the incontestable authority of Galileo himself that its physical meaning was totally different from that which is ascribed to it by the tradition of our physics books. At the time of the supposed

---

[1] It is not only the elementary schoolbooks that perpetuate this story. Cf. Leonard B. Loeb and Arthur S. Adams, *The Development of Physical Thought* (New York, 1938), 120: " He wanted to discover the nature of this constantly changing velocity downward and to determine the factors upon which the change depended. His famous experiment at the Leaning Tower of Pisa showed that, contrary to the dictum of Aristotle, the change was independent of the nature and weight of the body." Albert Einstein and Leopold Infeld, in *The Evolution of Physics* (New York, 1938), 36–7, also appear to accept the traditional story of the Leaning Tower Experiment.

[2] For an amusing account of the growth of the myth of the Leaning Tower Experiment, in absence of any real evidence of a basis for it in fact, cf. Lane Cooper, *Aristotle, Galileo and the Tower of Pisa* (Ithaca, 1935). Scholars such as Wohlwill, Favaro, Duhem, Cassirer, Koyré, etc., in their studies of Galileo, have of course recognized the legendary character of the story.

experiment, and for a number of years thereafter, Galileo was defending the theory that the velocities of bodies falling freely in a vacuum would differ according to the proportion of the densities, or specific natures, of the bodies. This conclusion was of course abandoned by Galileo in his later period, and his claim to discovery of the correct law of free fall is not disturbed by the fact that this discovery cannot be associated with the Leaning Tower of Pisa or with the year 1589. But the theory of free fall which *can* be associated with Pisa and its *campanile* is of great interest in itself, as a means of determining the point of departure of Galileo's thought, in its historical and philosophical contexts. For what is significant in the legend of the Leaning Tower is the interpretation of the history of ideas, of which it has been a symbol. Is the discontinuity between modern mechanics and the science of the mediaeval Aristotelians, symbolized by the Leaning Tower story, as mythical as the story itself?

In this question, big issues are at stake, and the numerous books concerning Galileo which have appeared during the present century have debated these issues with considerable passion. What were the philosophic foundations of Galileo's physics, and thereby of modern science in general? Was Galileo essentially a Platonist, an Aristotelian, or neither one nor the other? Did he, as Duhem claimed, merely take over and perfect a science of mechanics which had originated within the Christian Middle Ages, and whose essential principles had been discovered and formulated by Jean Buridan, Nicole Oresme, and the other adherents of the so-called "impetus physics" of the fourteenth century? Or did he, as Cassirer and Koyré insist, turn his back on this tradition after giving it a brief trial in his Pisan dynamics, and make a fresh start inspired by Archimedes and Plato? The more recent controversies over Galileo have been in large measure a debate concerning the fundamental value and historical influence of philosophic traditions—Platonist or Aristotelian, scholastic or anti-scholastic.[3]

[3] Cf. Pierre Duhem, *Études sur Léonard de Vinci. III: Les Précurseurs Parisiens de Galilée* (Paris, 1913). Against Duhem, and in defense of the Platonist and anti-scholastic background of Galileo's thought, cf. Ernst Cassirer, "Galileo's Platonism," in *Studies and Essays . . . offered in homage to George Sarton*, edited by M. F. Ashley-Montagu (New York, 1944), 279–97; also Alexandre Koyré, *Études Galiléennes* (Paris, 1939), and "Galileo and Plato," in the *Journal of the History of Ideas* IV, 4 (Oct. 1943). E. A. Burtt, *The Metaphysical Foundations of Modern Physical Science* (revised edition, New York, 1932), also stresses Galileo's Platonism. His view is strongly combatted by E. A. Strong, *Procedures and Meta-*

In these discussions, comparatively slight attention has been given to the determination of the relation between Galileo's Pisan dynamics and the theories of motion found in the mediaeval tradition. It has been taken for granted that this Pisan dynamics, insofar as it reflected mediaeval influences of any kind, reflected that part of the mediaeval tradition which stemmed from the fourteenth century "impetus school." Perhaps this is because J. B. Benedetti, whose dynamics was similar to that of Galileo's Pisan period and has been thought to have influenced it, is generally described as a partisan of the "impetus" physics.[4] Koyré characterizes Galileo's Pisan dynamics as an attempt on his part to achieve a coherent mathematical formulation, through demonstrations modelled after those of Archimedes' statics, of the "impetus physics" of the fourteenth-century Parisian school. The failure of this attempt, according to Koyré, led Galileo to turn his back on the mediaeval tradition and to make a wholly fresh start in his Paduan period.[5]

Now it is undoubtedly true that Galileo's mature dynamics, and consequently the modern classical mechanics which grew from it, was very different from the dynamics which he defended at Pisa. Hence if the Pisan dynamics was in truth Galileo's essay with the fourteenth-century impetus physics, his abandonment of the Pisan dynamics will have been an abandonment of the fourteenth-century tradition, and his mature dynamics, whatever other sources it may have had, will not have been a rediscovery and development of the fourteenth-century impetus physics, as was claimed by Duhem. But is the antecedent assumption true? Was Galileo's Pisan dynamics connected, either theoretically or historically, with the fourteenth-century tradition? It is this question which needs closer examination than has yet been given to it, and to which the pages which follow are

---

physics (Berkeley, 1936). In partial defense of Duhem's thesis, but with special emphasis on the Aristotelian and scholastic basis of Galileo's method as conveyed through the tradition of Padua, cf. J. H. Randall, Jr., "Scientific Method in the School of Padua," *Journal of the History of Ideas* I, 2 (April 1940), 177–206.

[4] This statement about Benedetti was made by Duhem, *op. cit.*, 214, and is repeated by Koyré, *Études Galiléennes*, 41.

[5] A. Koyré, *loc. cit.*, 54–5: "Dans les traités et essais sur le mouvement qu'il compose à Pise . . . Galilée s'efforce de développer d'une façon cohérente et complète la dynamique de la ' force impresse '—de l'*impetus*—dont nous venons de parler assez longuement et, en même temps, de pousser jusqu'au bout la mathématisation, ou mieux, l'archimédisation de la physique dont nous venons de voir les débuts dans l'oeuvre de J. B. Benedetti."

chiefly devoted. The questions to be answered are these: (1) What "laws of motion" were upheld by Galileo at Pisa? (2) Were these same laws of motion known in the Middle Ages, and if so, by whom were they defended? (3) If this dynamics was known and defended by mediaeval philosophers, was it from their writings that Galileo derived his Pisan dynamics? If precise answers can be found to these questions, much light may be cast on the problem of the philosophical tradition which provided the point of departure for Galileo's life work. And if his point of departure is determined, it may then be possible to arrive at a clearer understanding of the direction in which his thought progressed during his life, and of whether, in abandoning his earlier dynamics, he also abandoned the philosophic tradition to which it belonged.

II

The year 1589, date of the supposed Leaning Tower Experiment, was the year in which Galileo was made a Professor of Mathematics at the University of Pisa, at the age of 25.[6] During the previous eight years he had been a student, and probably a private tutor, at the University. Of his earliest writings, published in the first volume of the *Edizione Nazionale*, the fragmentary notes on the *De caelo* probably stem from the student period prior to 1589. They are of interest because of some explicit citations of fourteenth-century authors—Albert of Saxony, Hentisberus, and the "Calculator" (Richard Swineshead) are mentioned. Whether Galileo actually read works by these men cannot safely be determined from these notes, since the class-room notes of a student may well contain citations and references dictated by the teacher, without justifying the inference that he has looked up the references. In any case, these earliest notes do not bear directly on the problem of the law governing the velocities of freely falling bodies, with which the Leaning Tower Experiment was concerned; hence it is not safe to assume that Galileo was familiar with the fourteenth-century treatments of this problem.

It is in a slightly later group of writings that we find Galileo's earliest treatment of the problem of free fall. Among these is an

[6] Cf. *Le opere di Galileo Galilei*, Edizione Nazionale (Firenze, 1890–), XIX, 39, where, in the *Rotolo dello Studio di Pisa* for the year 1589 Galileo's name appears "nunc primum" as Professor of Mathematics, at the pitifully small salary of 60 florins. The three Professors of Philosophy of that year, Francesco Verino, Francesco Bonamico, and Jacopo Mazzoni of Cesena, were receiving salaries of 450 fl., 330 fl., and 500 fl. respectively.

incomplete treatise " On Motion," whose main content was embodied by Galileo in a dialogue, likewise uncompleted, which he perhaps hoped to publish. This dialogue was first published in 1854, when Albèri included it in the eleventh volume of his edition of Galileo's *Opera omnia*. In any case, if the Leaning Tower Experiment did take place in 1589, there is little doubt that the dynamics which Galileo was attempting to confirm through this experiment, was the one formulated in his dialogue *De motu*.[7]

That Galileo did perform such an experiment at the Leaning Tower, in 1589, is not improbable. The earliest historical source for the story seems to be a brief passage in Viviani's biographical sketch of Galileo, written twelve years after his death, in 1654. Viviani states that in 1589 Galileo conducted a number of experiments designed to refute the " commonly accepted opinions " concerning the motions of heavy and light bodies. Among these was one conducted at the *campanile* of Pisa, from which Galileo caused bodies of various weights to be dropped, in order to refute the theory that the velocity of fall of bodies, *of the same material but differing in weight*, is proportional to their weights. The results of this and of the other experiments, Viviani says, were " extremely disconcerting to all the philosophers." [8]

Viviani's brief statement of the purpose of the experiment is sufficient to identify the theory of the proportions of velocities of bodies falling freely in media of the same or of diverse densities, which Galileo himself was defending. It is the theory which Galileo develops, in explicit criticism of the arguments of Aristotle in *Physics* IV, Chap-

[7] In our study of Galileo's Pisan dynamics, we have used the dialogue rather than the incomplete treatise, partly because it presents the Pisan dynamics in more succinct form, and also because it is included in the usually more accessible Albèri edition of Galileo's works, *Le Opere di Galileo Galilei* (Firenze, 1854), XI, 9–55. In the Edizione Nazionale, edited by A. Favaro, the dialogue is found in Vol. I, pp. 367–408. References will here be given to the Albèri edition.

[8] Vincenzo Viviani, *Racconto istorico della vita di Galileo Galilei*, in Albèri's edition of Galileo's works, XV (Florence, 1856), 336. The experiment, says Viviani, was designed to prove " che la velocità dei mobili dell' istessa materia, disegualmente gravi, movendosi per un istesso mezzo, non conservano altrimenti la proporzione delle gravità loro assolute, assegnata loro da Aristotile, anzi che si muovono tutti con pari velocità, dimostrando ciò con replicate esperienze fatte dall' altezza del campanile di Pisa, con l'intervento degli altri lettori e filosofi, e di tutta la scolaresca; e che ne meno le velocità d'un istesso mobile per diversi mezzi ritengono la proporzione reciproca delle resistenze, o densità de' medesimi mezzi, inferendolo da manifestissimi assurdi, che in conseguenza ne seguirebbero contra al senso medesimo."

ter 8, in his dialogue *De motu*. Hence the dialogue, even if composed after 1589, may safely be taken as representing the dynamics that Galileo was defending at Pisa—the dynamics of the Leaning Tower Experiment. If we turn to this dialogue, we shall find many clues to lead us toward answers to our questions concerning Galileo's Pisan dynamics, its mediaeval antecedents, and its immediate sources in the writings accessible to Galileo.

The Pisan dialogue treats of five main problems: (1) the movement of projectiles; (2) the nature of the heavy and light, and the law governing the proportion of velocities of bodies moving freely in corporeal media; (3) whether there is a period of rest between the ascent and descent of a projectile thrown vertically upward; (4) whether natural motion at finite velocity would occur in a void; and (5) the reason of the fact that falling bodies are accelerated in their movement downward. It is the second and fourth of these problems which bear directly on the supposed Leaning Tower Experiment, and which establish Galileo's fundamental conceptions of gravity and natural motion. The other three problems involve the conception of "impressed force," and provide the basis for the assumption made by Koyré and others that the Pisan dynamics reflects the impetus mechanics of the fourteenth century. Since the meaning given by Galileo to the notion of "impressed force" in his treatment of these three problems is determined by the theory of gravity and free fall which he establishes in the second and fourth parts of his dialogue, we may consider this latter theory first.

The discussion of the heavy and light opens when Dominicus, the accommodating respondent of the dialogue, asks Alexander (who is Galileo), to explain in what sense a body is moved, in its free or "natural" motion, by its gravity or levity. Galileo first lays down this postulate:

First of all it is to be assumed that things are so constituted by nature that the heavier bodies rest beneath the lighter, a fact which is most obvious to our senses . . . . To assign the cause of such an order can contribute nothing to our inquiry, since it is obvious that things are related in this way; nor could I assign any other cause than that it was pleasing to nature to establish things in this manner. Unless perhaps we might wish to say that the heavier bodies are nearer to the center than the light ones, because in a way it seems that those things are heavier which, in a smaller space, contain more matter . . . . Since then the spaces which are nearer to the center of the world are smaller than those which are more distant from the center, it was in accord with reason that those spaces should be filled with matter which, being of greater weight, would occupy less space.[9]

In this one paragraph we are introduced to three distinctive and basic assumptions of Galileo's mechanics—assumptions which are still retained in his mature mechanics, and which are of a philosophical order.   These are: (1) the conception of *gravity* as the essential and universal physical property of material bodies; (2) the conception of *space* as of itself empty and weightless and immaterial, though nevertheless real and endowed with mathematical properties as an extended emptiness filled or occupied by material bodies having weight; (3) the assumption of a *center of the world,* or of its space, which determines absolute position for bodies in space, and which determines the direction of their "natural" motions arising from their intrinsic gravity.   The suggestion that the heavier bodies are those which have more matter in a smaller volume of space, assimilates weight to density; or, more accurately, it assimilates differences in the "natures" of elementary bodies and compounds, to differences in their specific gravity.

After making it plain that comparisons of bodies with respect to their heaviness or lightness are to be made on the basis of equal volumes, Galileo then asserts that the heaviness or lightness of a body relative to a fluid medium is the cause of its downward or upward movement in that medium.   He also suggests that the velocity of such movement, or the " degree " of movement, depends on the degree of relative heaviness or lightness of the body in the medium.

Those bodies which are heavier than the medium through which they are moved, are moved downward, since it has ben established by nature that the heavier bodies rest beneath the lighter . . . and so heavy bodies are moved downward to the degree that they are heavier than the medium through which they are moved; therefore their gravity with respect to the medium is the cause of such downward motion.[10]

For Galileo, as for Aristotle and the ancients generally, the "natural" movements of heavy and light bodies are movements toward places or conditions of "natural rest"—of dynamic equilibrium. Equality or inequality of density, as between the body and the medium, define this dynamic equilibrium and disequilibrium.   This assumption is implicit in the Archimedean theorems of hydrostatics,

---

[9] *Le opere di Galileo Galilei,* ed. Albèri, XI (Firenze, 1854), 18–19. All further references to Galileo, unless otherwise indicated, will be to this work, and to this edition.   [10] Galileo, *loc. cit.,* 20.

which use the position at which a floating body comes to rest at the surface of a liquid as a means of calculating the difference in specific gravity between the floating body and the liquid. But to this principle of hydrostatics Galileo adds a further assumption, not derivable from the Archimedean postulates, and belonging to kinetics rather than to statics. This is the assumption that differences in specific gravity determine not merely the *direction* in which one body moves naturally in a fluid medium, and not merely its *position of rest* or of equilibrium, but also its *speed* in moving toward the position of equilibrium. The fundamental measure of gravity, or of "natural" motive power, thus becomes dynamical in the strict sense. Galileo makes this passage from statics to kinetics, and from Archimedes to a law of motion not deducible from Archimedes' statics, with full consciousness.

In the long run I cannot avoid having to demonstrate for you a number of theorems, from which you will clearly understand not only what you are asking about, but also what proportion heavy and light bodies have to the speed or slowness of their motion . . . of which theorems (though similar ones have been demonstrated by Archimedes) I shall set forth demonstrations which are less mathematical and more physical; and I will employ postulates which are clearer and more evident to the senses than those which Archimedes accepted.[11]

The theorems which he undertakes to demonstrate are four, almost identical with Propositions 3, 5, 6 and 7 of Book I of Archimedes' treatise *On Floating Bodies*. But the proofs, and the postulates used in them, are as Galileo says "more physical" than those used by Archimedes. Galileo is not attempting to deduce a law of dynamics from Archimedes' statics, but to use Archimedes' theorems as confirmations of a dynamical theory whose source is not Archimedes, but from which the Archimedean hydrostatic theorems can be derived. The four theorems are the following:

I. Solid magnitudes equal to water in gravity, if placed in water, will be fully submerged, and will not then be borne upward any more than downward.

II. Solid magnitudes lighter than water, if placed in water, will be submerged to the extent that the volume of water equal to the volume of the submerged part of the body, will have the same weight as that whole magnitude.

III. Solid magnitudes lighter than water, if pushed down into the water, will be carried upward with as much force (*tanta vi*), as the weight by

[11] Galileo, *loc. cit.*, 21.

which the volume of water equal to the volume of the submerged magnitude, exceeds the weight of the magnitude.

IV. Solid magnitudes heavier than water, if placed in water, will be carried downward with as much force (*tanta vi*), as the volume of water equal to the volume of the whole magnitude, is lighter than that magnitude.[12]

The crucial shift introduced by Galileo into these theorems occurs in his interpretation of the term *vis,* usually translated as " force " or " power," in the third and fourth theorems.   Archimedes was clearly not considering it as speed or velocity, but only as a factor of disequilibrium measured by the counterbalancing weight which would determine equilibrium.   Galileo, however, construes this *vis* as the power of the body to move at greater or less *speed* through the medium, the speed being determined by the quantity of excess of specific gravity of the body over that of the medium, or, in the case of upward movement, of the density of the medium over that of the body rising through it.   Thus, while Archimedes measures gravity only by gravity, through the statical principle of counterbalancing, Galileo introduces speed (which he calls *velocitas*) as the more basic and general measure of gravity.   After stating that the laws governing the movements of solids in water will apply likewise to the motions of bodies in air or in any other fluid medium, Galileo illustrates his principle as follows:

If then there should be some heavy body, let us say the body A, whose gravity is as 8, while the gravity of a quantity of water equal in volume to A is as 4, then the solid A would be borne downward with a speed and ease corresponding to 4.   If however the same body A should be borne through a lighter medium, such that the gravity of a volume of that medium equal to the volume of A would be as 2; then certainly the solid A, in this second medium, would be borne downward with an ease and speed equivalent to 6 . . . therefore it follows that a medium is to be considered lighter, to just the extent to which heavy bodies are more easily moved downward in it.[13]

[12] Galileo, *loc. cit.,* 22–6.   Each theorem, in the text, is followed by a long and carefully constructed proof.   The method of proof is that of supposing any position or condition other than that asserted by the theorem to obtain, and then showing that in such a condition motion would occur.   To what extent Galileo may have been influenced by the *De ponderibus* of the 13th-century Jordanus Nemorarius, who also derived the statical theorems from dynamical principles, and who used a similar method of proof, is an interesting question on which we cannot enter here. On the tradition of Jordanus and of mediaeval statics, cf. P. Duhem, *Les Origines de la statique,* 2 vols. (Paris, 1905–6).

[13] Galileo, *loc. cit.,* 28–9.   The terms *vis, celeritas, facilitas,* and *velocitas* are used, in the course of this discussion, indifferently and convertibly.   That the funda-

Two basic assumptions are involved in Galileo's theory of the velocities of natural motions in corporeal media, of which one is common to Aristotle and to Galileo, while the other is in sharp opposition to the position of Aristotle. The first of these assumptions is that variation in the speed with which a body moves by its "natural" motion through a corporeal medium is determined by some function whose arguments are the densities of the moving body and of the medium. The second assumption made by Galileo is that this function is the relation of *arithmetical difference* between the densities, such as is represented by the minus sign ("−"). Now this second assumption is radically opposed to the fundamental law of Aristotle's dynamics, according to which the relation between the densities of the mobile body and medium, by which the speed of natural motion is determined, is not arithmetical difference, but *ratio* or *proportion*, such as we symbolize by the sign of division.[14]

When, consequently, we seek to determine the proportion of the speed of one natural motion to that of another by means of the Aristotelian law, we will be stating the proportion of one proportion to another proportion—a relation which, in the tradition of Euclid and of mediaeval mathematics, is one of geometric proportionality. But when we compare two motions according to Galileo's law, we will be stating a simple arithmetic proportion between integers—*i.e.*, be-

---

mental sense given to them by Galileo is that of speed or velocity, rather than that of measure of work done on a mass, is suggested by the fact that he applies his rules directly to the statement of proportions of velocities of natural motions in the void, in which there is no question of *facilitas* or *difficultas* in the sense of pushing through a resistant medium. I shall use the word "velocity" to translate *velocitas*, in the texts of Galileo and of mediaeval writers, it being understood that the technical modern meaning of the word was not understood by these authors.

[14] Cf. Aristotle, *Physics* IV, ch. 8, 215a 24–216a 20. Aristotle uses the notion of density, or "thickness," to characterize the medium, but usually characterizes the differences in the mobile bodies by the terms "weight" or "nature." Yet he takes this to be equivalent to difference in density, at least in the course of his argument in this passage; cf. 215b 30. In other statements of his rules of proportion of velocities, as in *Physics* VII, ch. 5, he speaks of greater or less motive power, in relation to greater or less weight or resistance of the body moved by that power; but here he is considering the case of a body being pushed by an external body moving it by contact, rather than the case of the heavy body falling freely against the resistance of a fluid medium. To attempt to interpret these factors of "motive power" and "resistance" in terms of modern physics is obviously futile and anachronistic. But the fact that the relation determining the velocity is held by Aristotle to be one of *ratio* between power and resistance, and not arithmetical difference, is definite.

tween the units of density which result from the *subtraction,* in each case, of the density of the medium from that of the body falling in it. We can give general expression to Galileo's law, therefore, in the following simple formula, in which "V" represents the speed or velocity of the motion, "P" the motive power measured by the specific gravity of the mobile body, and "M" the resisting medium whose resistive power is measured by its specific gravity.   The formula will then be: $V = P - M$.

Galileo's discussion, up to this point, has been concerned only with the determination of speed by *relative* heaviness or lightness.   But since relative weight, as determining velocity of motion in a medium, is exhibited by Galileo's formula as the remainder, or difference, resulting from the subtraction of the specific gravity of the medium from that of the heavy body, he is committed to the assumption that the density of a body determines for it a definite "natural" velocity which it would have in empty space.   Gravity, and the motion determined for it, are for Galileo absolute and intrinsically determined properties of body.   This is revealed when Dominicus asks for his views concerning heaviness and lightness considered in themselves, and not merely in their relative sense.

If we are speaking of absolute lightness or heaviness, I say that all bodies, whether of mixed or simple nature, have gravity.   If however we are talking of relative weight or lightness, I say that all bodies in this case also have gravity, some however more, and others less.   But we call this lesser gravity lightness, and so we say that fire is lighter than air—not because it lacks gravity, but because it has less gravity than air has.   And in the same manner we call air lighter than water.[15]

When Dominicus then objects to calling fire heavy, saying that everyone holds it to be impossible for fire to move downward by natural motion, the reply is as follows:

Ah! Ah! Another chymaera, another fiction!   Those things are borne downward which are heavier than the medium through which they are to be carried; but fire is not heavier than air, and hence it cannot be borne downward.   But if the air were removed from beneath it, so that a vacuum would be left below the fire, who doubts that the fire would descend into the place of the air?   For since in a void there is nothing, that which is something is heavier than nothing; since therefore fire is something, it would undoubtedly descend beneath the nothing; for it is established by nature that the heavier things remain beneath the lighter.[16]

[15] Galileo, *loc. cit.*, 29.   [16] Galileo, *loc. cit.*, 30.

While this statement probably seems eminently reasonable to most modern readers, who have been reared in the conceptual atmosphere of the Galilean and Newtonian world, it involves a radical difficulty, which might be called the "paradox of the absolute." How can that which, by hypothesis, has no weight whatever, be compared with a ponderable body precisely in respect of weight, and be significantly called "lighter" than the ponderable body? Is not this similar to saying that a point is "shorter" in length than a line, or that the unreal is "less real" than the real? To an Aristotelian, Galileo's statement is paradoxical, since comparisons of "more and less" hold only within some generic character attributable to both of the things compared; for the Aristotelian, the point is not the shortest of lines, because it is not a line at all. And since heaviness and lightness, even on Galileo's assumptions, are properties only of material body, whereas the void is by definition that which is empty of matter or body, his statement is equivalent to the assertion that what is not a body at all is nevertheless the lightest of bodies. This ambiguity and paradox, implicit in Galileo's conception of space, has haunted classical physics ever since his time—to fulfill the needs of physics, space must be both full and empty, corporeal and incorporeal, real and ideal, at the same time.

Why did this paradox not bother Galileo? How was he able to entertain the assumption that ponderable bodies can be compared, precisely with respect to weight, with the weightless void? He could do so, because he conceived relative weight and relative density to be determined by *arithmetical difference,* and not by ratio or proportion. For though we cannot *divide* a finite quantity by zero and get a finite quotient, we can *subtract* zero from a finite quantity and get a finite remainder. But the velocity of a natural motion, for Galileo, was determined by the density of the mobile body, *less* the density of the medium; hence, if the latter is zero, the speed will be of a finite degree, uniquely determined by the density of the mobile body. For Aristotle, by contrast, the speed is determined by the *ratio* of the densities of mobile body and medium; consequently, if the medium is of zero density, the velocity must be infinite. This is immediately evident when we assign zero value to "M" in the two formulae of motion: $V = P/M$ (Aristotle), and $V = P - M$ (Galileo).

On the basis of his arithmetical law of relative velocities, Galileo now proceeds to refute Aristotle's contention that the movement of a heavy body in a non-resistant void would be instantaneous. The discussion in the dialogue commences when Dominicus asks Alexander to give his views about motion in a vacuum, and invokes Aristotle's authority against the possibility of such a motion. To this Galileo replies:

> I could say a great deal about the void, which however I will pass over. . . . I say therefore that in a vacuum, motion would not take place in an instant, which may be seen from what has already been demonstrated. For it has been proved that the velocity of things moved is as great as the weight by which they exceed the medium through which they are moved.[17]

Let the mobile body be called A, he continues, and the medium B. If in comparing equal volumes of A and B, the gravity of A is to the gravity of B as 8 to 3, then the velocity of A's descent in B will be as 5. But if the gravity of B is 2 instead of 3, then A will fall with a velocity of 6; and if the gravity of B is zero, as would be the case if B were a vacuum, then the velocity of A's descent would be, not infinite, but precisely 8. All this obviously follows from the formula: $V = P - M$. As Galileo says:

> The gravity of A exceeds that gravity which is zero, by its own total gravity, which is finite; but the velocity of motion is as the excess gravity. The gravity however is finite, therefore the velocity of the motion will be finite and not infinite.[18]

The refutation of Aristotle, which Galileo now undertakes, is long and detailed, and is clearly the climax and core of the whole dialogue. The Aristotelian text against which his arguments are directed is one which was famous throughout the Middle Ages, and which provided an occasion for each mediaeval commentator to discuss the problem of motion in the void, and of the law governing relative velocities of natural motions in corporeal media of diverse density. This text, which occurs in *Physics* IV, Ch. 8, was known as Text 71 of Averroes' commentary on the fourth book; it was, in a very definite sense, the cradle of mediaeval mechanics. And for Galileo likewise, whose mechanics was so largely developed as a refutation of Aristotle, this text was a constant point of departure. Not only in this Pisan dialogue, but in the great *Discorsi* of Galileo's maturity, it was as a criticism of this Aristotelian text that he developed his dynamic theory of the motion of heavy bodies.

Aristotle's fundamental error, according to Galileo, was that of supposing that the velocity of natural motion in a medium is determined by the ratio or proportion between the gravities or densities of the body and the medium. To show the falsity of this law of propor-

---

[17] Galileo, *loc. cit.*, 38.   [18] Galileo, *loc. cit.*, 39.

tion of velocities, Galileo uses the following argument. Let the mobile body be called " O," he says, and let there be two media, A and B, of which A is water and B is air. Suppose that water is four times as dense as air, and that " O " is such that it will neither rise nor sink in water, though in air it will fall with a velocity of 4 degrees. Then, since the density of air was assumed to be one fourth that of water, it follows that to the velocity of " O " in air, posited as 4, there will correspond a velocity of some substance in water, which will be of value 1. But because the body " O " is moved in air with velocity 4, then, if by Aristotle's law the velocity of an identical body varies inversely as the densities of the media, and if water is four times as dense as air, it follows that " O " will have a velocity in water of 1 degree. But this is in contradiction to the initial assumption that " O " neither sinks nor rises in water. Hence the Aristotelian law is false, since it implies contradictory consequences.[19]

This argument is entirely cogent, insofar as Aristotle's law is construed as a general formula of simple proportionality, of the form $V = P/M$. As so construed, the law is incompatible with the basic dynamic assumption made by Aristotle as well as by Galileo, that when the density or "nature" of the body and its medium are the same, no movement occurs. In Aristotle's language, this is the assumption that an elementary body rests in a medium of its own nature, or in its "natural place." But this assumption is obviously contradicted by the formula $V = P/M$; for by this formula, if $P = M$, V will be, not zero, but 1.

Having thus demolished Aristotle's law, construed as one of simple proportionality, Galileo says that from his own original theorems he will demonstrate the true way of comparing velocities of the natural motion of a body in media of diverse density. Suppose the body to have gravity of 20 degrees, he says, and the two media to have gravities of 8 and 4 degrees respectively. Since then the velocity in each case will be as the excess of the body's gravity over that of an equal volume of the medium, the body will move with velocity 12 in one medium, and with velocity 16 in the other. Hence its speed will be, not twice as great in the medium half as dense, but only 1⅓ times as great.

[19] Galileo, *loc. cit.*, 44. This same argument is found in Buridan's *Questions on the Physics*, Book VII, Qu. 7 (ed. Paris, 1509), fols. CVIIr–CVIIIr, and also in many other 14th-century works. But the conclusion drawn by most of the mediaeval writers was that the interpretation of Aristotle's law as one of simple inverse proportionality could not have been what he had intended.

It is therefore clear that the lighter the medium, the faster will be the motion arising in it from gravity; but since velocity is related to velocity always according to a lesser proportion than rarity to rarity, it follows that when the rarity of a corporeal medium is related to the rarity of the void according to the greatest of all proportions, the velocity in the corporeal medium need not retain that proportion to the velocity in the void, as Aristotle falsely thought.   It also follows, from those things laid down, that the proportion of velocity to velocity is related always *arithmetically, and not geometrically*, to the proportion of lightness of one medium to that of the other.[20]

By his law of arithmetical difference Galileo is thus able to disprove Aristotle's thesis that motion in a void would be impossible, because instantaneous.   He now uses his assumption that differences in the natures of bodies, or in their specific gravities, determine corresponding differences in their "natural velocities" in the void, to refute Aristotle's other statement that if motion were to occur in a void, all bodies, irrespective of their "natures" or gravities, would move at equal velocity.

I say therefore that in a vacuum, heavier bodies would descend more rapidly than lighter ones, because the excess of the heavier bodies over the medium would be greater than the excess of the lighter ones.[21]

This consequence, which is usually said to be just what Galileo's Leaning Tower Experiment was designed to refute, follows clearly from his Pisan law of motion, on the assumption that all bodies are not of the same specific gravity.   For although the *ratio* of a finite number to zero is neither greater nor less than the ratio of any other finite number to zero, so that Aristotle's law would determine equality of velocities in a non-resistant medium, the arithmetical *excess* of one number over zero has a definite proportion to the arithmetical excess of another number over zero—namely, the proportion between the two numbers.   It thus follows for Galileo that it is *only* in the void that the gravities of two bodies exhibit, by the velocities of their free fall, their true proportion.

In summing up, therefore, I will say that the speed or slowness of every downward motion arises from the *proper gravity* of the mobile bodies; and that it is because this gravity is *diminished* by the gravity of the medium,

[20] Galileo, *loc. cit.*, 45–6 (Italics mine).

[21] Galileo, *loc. cit.*, 47: ." Dico itaque quod in vacuo graviora citius descenderent quam leviora, quia excessus graviorum supra medium major esset excessu leviorum."

that the motion becomes weaker. If however the gravity of the medium is as great as that of the mobile body, then, since in such a medium there is no heaviness of the mobile bodies, no motion occurs. And again, if the gravity of the medium is greater, then the gravity of the mobile bodies with respect to the gravity of the medium, becomes lightness, and the body is borne upward. And if there is no gravity of the medium, then the mobile bodies will be moved by their *simple gravity, and in their motions they will follow the same proportion as their proper gravities have to each other.*

And from this is apparent another serious error, which Aristotle upheld absolutely against what ought to be believed. For he said that heavy bodies in a corporeal medium follow in their motions the same proportions as their gravities, but that in a vacuum they would not do so, but that all bodies would be moved at the same speed. But on the contrary, in a vacuum they will follow the proportion of their weights, since the excesses of their weights over the medium are the entire weights of those mobile bodies. In a plenum, however, they will not follow this proportion, as was demonstrated above.[22]

We thus find Galileo rejecting as a " serious error " the theory which he later came to accept as true, attributing this theory to Aristotle, who did indeed conclude that it would follow from the assumption of motion in a void, but who argued from this, not that the theory of equality of speeds *in vacuo* is true, but that because it is false, the assumption of motion in a void is impossible. It is only in passing, at the end of this refutation of Aristotle's " law of motion," that Galileo touches on the issue that was actually at stake in the Leaning Tower Experiment as reported by Viviani. In the second chapter of Book IV of the *De caelo* Aristotle states that of two bodies of the same composition or density, the larger one will fall faster than the smaller. Aside from the fact that Aristotle is not considering the case of bodies falling in a non-resistant vacuum, this statement is offered only as a dialectical premise in the course of Aristotle's argument against those who assumed an internal void as cause of differences in density and rarity of bodies; hence it is highly questionable whether this view can be legitimately ascribed to Aristotle, in the sense in which Galileo does so. In any case, Galileo proves, by very simple arguments, that twenty pounds of lead will not fall faster than ten pounds of lead, since if it did a body as a whole would fall faster than its parts. He then concludes:

It is not therefore true that a large volume is moved more rapidly than a small one, if they are of the same material, although this is what Aristotle

[22] Galileo, *loc. cit.*, 47–8 (Italics mine).

assumed, as if self-evident, throughout his criticism of the ancients in the fourth book of the *De caelo.*[23]

There is no claim in this dialogue of having proved this by experiments with falling bodies; but it was to prove this proposition that the Leaning Tower Experiment, as described by Viviani, was allegedly performed. " A piece of lead," says Galileo, " whose weight is ten pounds, will descend with as much speed as a piece of lead whose weight is one hundred pounds." [24]   But as the discussion has shown, Galileo would have denied that a piece of wood and a piece of iron, if falling in a void, would fall with the same speed. His Pisan dynamics, therefore, was as much opposed to the modern classical mechanics which Galileo approached in his later years, as was the dynamics of Aristotle which he was refuting.

The aim of Galileo's Pisan dialogue, in every one of the problems discussed, is to refute the basic Aristotelian assumption that local motion is essentially a continuously changing external relation between a physical body and a physical medium or " place," such that an external corporeal medium is dynamically necessary to rectilinear local motion.   From the Aristotelian point of view, to posit motion as an act determined solely by the body moved, realizable in the absence of any physical surroundings, is to posit self-motion in an unqualified sense—a conception which Aristotle held to be contradictory.   Motion in a void, or in a purely ideal space, would be a purely ideal or imaginary motion.   A real physical motion, for Aristotle, must involve traversal of a physical medium; and it is in the constantly changing dynamic relation of the mobile body to the corporeal medium immediately surrounding it, rather than in a changing kinematic relation to a merely ideal space-time co-ordinate system, that the essence and reality of movement consists.

Now the hardest problem faced by the Aristotelian, in maintaining that a physical medium is a necessary condition of motion, is that of accounting for the movement of projectiles.   For in this case the medium seems only to hinder, and in no way to produce or sustain the motion.   And since the agent who threw the projectile is no longer in contact with it, and could indeed be annihilated without the projectile ceasing to move, it seems as if no cause of the continuation of the projectile's motion, outside of the projectile itself, can be assigned.

[23] Galileo, *loc. cit.*, 50.   Cf. Aristotle, *De caelo* IV, ch. 2, 309a 19–309b 28.

[24] Galileo, *loc. cit.*, 49.

Self-motion, intrinsically determined by the body in motion, would seem here to be demonstrated by the facts themselves, thereby entailing the ruin of Aristotle's basic assumption that whatever is moved is moved by another. It is for this reason that Galileo opens his dialogue with the question of why projectiles continue to move, after leaving the hand of the thrower. He initiates his attack on Aristotle's fundamental dynamic principle, at the point where its application seems weakest.[25]

Galileo's discussion takes the form of a refutation of Aristotle's efforts to account for the continuation of projectile motion through a propulsive action by the air or medium. The arguments which he uses to this end are not original; they are almost exactly the same as those used by Buridan and Albert of Saxony, and which were used before them by earlier writers and repeated after their time by fifteenth- and sixteenth-century commentators on the *Physics*. Galileo could have read these arguments in numerous books published in his own time, and he no doubt heard them at first hand from Francesco Bonamico, who was teaching at Pisa while Galileo was there, and who discussed the question of projectile motion at great length in his enormous work *De motu*.[26]

These arguments, though used in the Middle Ages by the defenders of the impetus mechanics as well as by many who rejected the impetus explanation of projectile motion, do not of themselves establish, or even imply, any positive theory of the movement of projectiles; they merely serve to show that Aristotle's explanation is incompatible with facts of daily experience. It is to refute Aristotle that Galileo uses these arguments; his own conclusion is little more than a restatement of the projectile problem itself. Since the projectile is not moved by the medium, it must be determined to continuation of its

[25] The problem is discussed on 12–18, *loc. cit.*

[26] For the texts, and a French translation, of the discussions of projectile motion given by Bonamico's *De motu* and by Benedetti's *Diversarum speculationum liber* (published in 1585), see A. Koyré, *Études Galiléennes* (Paris, 1939), 18–54. The history of the earlier treatments of the problem, from Philoponus to Buridan, is sketched by Duhem, *Etudes sur Léonard de Vinci*, Vol. 3 (Paris, 1913), 34–56 and 189–93. This account has been augmented in important respects by Anneliese Maier, *Die Impetustheorie der Scholastik* (Wien, 1940), with full use and quotations of the texts and primary sources. Buridan's discussion, from his Questions on Aristotle's Physics, Book VIII, Qu. 12, was translated by Duhem, *op. cit.*, 35–45; an entirely similar treatment is also given by Buridan in his *Quaestiones de caelo et mundo*, ed. Ernest A. Moody (Cambridge, Mass., 1942), 240–3.

motion by some intrinsic condition or power which it has acquired in consequence of the previous action on it by the thrower.   Galileo uses the expression " impressed force " (*virtus impressa*), rather than the term *impetus,* to designate this intrinsic cause of the projectile's motion.   "What this power may be," he concludes cautiously, " is hidden from us." [27]

It is in the two remaining topics of the dialogue, dealing with the question of intermediate rest between ascent and descent of a projectile, and with the cause of the acceleration of freely falling bodies, that Galileo gives a more definite meaning to his conception of " impressed force."   According to Koyré, the notion of " impressed force " adopted by Galileo is not only not equivalent to the principle of inertia, but is equivalent to a denial of that principle; for Galileo defines this *virtus impressa* as a motive power which is used up by the motion it produces, presupposing the principle that uniform motion requires continuous action of a force for its maintenance.[28]

In order to demonstrate that there is no period of rest between the vertical ascent and descent of a projectile, Galileo lays down two initial axioms: (1) If a heavy body is projected vertically upward, by an impressed force, it will only be moved uniformly (or traverse equal spaces in equal times), on condition that the impressed force remains constant; (2) No body can be moved with violent motion, such as an impressed force involves, through an infinitely great distance.   From these assumptions he then demonstrates that the impressed force does not remain constant as between any two successive parts of the time, or of the trajectory of the motion, but that it is continuously weaker and weaker.[29]   He then reasons as follows: Since the downward force due to the gravity of the projectile is constant, and of itself determines a uniform velocity downward, then, if the upward-directed force of the *virtus impressa* were also to remain constant, the upward movement would be uniform and would endure forever.   For, accord-

[27] Galileo, *loc. cit.*, 18.

[28] A. Koyré, *Études Galiléennes* (Paris, 1939), 54–60.

[29] Galileo, *loc. cit.*, 33: " his autem positis demonstratur, virtutem impressam a motore sucessive in motu violento debilitari, nec posse assignari in eodem motu duo puncta in quibus eadem fuerit virtus impellens." Galileo construes this continuous deceleration as a change in velocity proportionate to *distance,* but appears to assume that this would also be proportionate to time. This erroneous assumption is probably what accounts for the fallacious derivation of the correct kinematic law of acceleration, which Galileo gave when at Padua (after 1604), and only corrected in his later years.

ing to Galileo's law, velocity is determined by $V = P - M$; toward the center of the world when P exceeds M, and away from the center of the world when M exceeds P. Since the consequence of assuming that the *virtus impressa* is constant is in contradiction to the second axiom laid down by Galileo, as well as in contradiction to observed fact, he concludes that the impressed force becomes continuously weaker as the motion proceeds. Hence there will be no period of time, at the point of reversal of direction of the projectile's motion, during which the *virtus impressa* remains equal to the gravity, though this would have to be supposed if it were true that there is a period of intermediate rest between its ascent and descent. This whole argument clearly supposes (a) that uniform motion requires continuous action of a constant force; and (b) that if an accelerated movement occurs, with the motive power remaining constant, then the acceleration must be due to a continuous weakening of the resistance.[30]

Galileo's argument is wholly consistent with his general formula of motion, and is indeed based on it. Precisely the same can be said of his explanation of the *de facto* acceleration of freely falling bodies, to which the last part of the Pisan dialogue is devoted. Since by Galileo's formula the purely natural motion of a body falling freely is a movement at uniform velocity (since its gravity is constant), and since the resistance of the medium causes only a reduction in the degree of this uniform velocity, and not an acceleration, Galileo needs to assign some cause for the commonly observed fact that bodies do increase in speed as they fall. Since the medium is homogeneous, the change in velocity is not due to a corresponding change in the external resistance; it must then be due to a continuously changing internal resistance. Where does this latter come from? Galileo's explanation is ingenious. Before a body is dropped, he says, something must have been supporting it and neutralizing its natural tendency to move toward the center of the world. This resisting factor, as the formula $V = P - M$ indicates, must have been equal in amount, and opposite in direction, to the natural force of the body's gravity. When the impediment to its fall is removed, however, the body initially retains the upward directed *virtus impressa* left in it by the supporting impediment. But with the cause that produced this *virtus impressa* removed, the latter immediately commences to get weaker; consequently the gravity commences to exceed it, and $P - M$ acquires a positive value by reason of the weakening of M. As the impressed

[30] This whole argument occurs on 33–38, *loc. cit.*

force continues to weaken, the value of P – M steadily increases; hence the velocity of the falling body continuously increases. If there were room for the body to fall for a sufficient time, the *virtus impressa* would be wholly used up, and thenceforth the body would fall at uniform velocity—a velocity determined by the constant value of its gravity ("P"), if falling in a void, or by the constant difference P – M, if falling in a medium of uniform density. Normally the fall of easily observed bodies is not long enough for the "natural" uniform velocity to be attained; but in theory every body is determined by its gravity to a limiting uniform velocity of natural motion, and no body, in free fall, could be accelerated indefinitely or beyond any assigned limit, even *in vacuo*.[31]

Such is Galileo's Pisan dynamics—the dynamics of the Leaning Tower Experiment. While consciously developed in opposition to Aristotle, and though involving a "law of motion" radically different from that of the Stagirite, it nevertheless rests on the basic assumption which was rejected in modern classical mechanics. This is the assumption that, in abstraction from all external resistance, a constant motive force is required for continuation of uniform motion at constant velocity. This assumption is usually taken as the distinctive mark of "peripatetic" dynamics. Shall we then call Galileo's Pisan theory Aristotelian, despite its explicit opposition to Aristotle? Or is it merely Greek in its general basis, and anti-Aristotelian in its specific form and character? An examination of the diverse theories of motion, developed in mediaeval treatises and commentaries dealing with the problem of the velocities of freely falling bodies, may help to clarify these questions.

III

The primary aim of Galileo's Pisan dialogue on motion, as our analysis has indicated, was to refute the dynamic theory and "law of motion" on which Aristotle had based his argument against the possibility of motion in a void, in the passage of Book IV of the *Physics* known as Text 71.[32] Here Aristotle states that the proportion between

---

[31] This theory is carefully developed, and proved on the basis of the dynamic assumptions previously established, on 50–55, *loc. cit.*

[32] This text occurs in *Physics* IV, ch. 8, 215a 24–215b 20. The argument continues on to 216a 20, this additional portion being divided by Averroes into Texts 72, 73, and 74. But the main discussion of the problem of the law governing the velocities of freely falling bodies, in Averroes' commentary and in the commentaries of the western scholastics, was regularly given in connection with Text 71.

the speed with which a heavy body falls through a denser medium, and the speed with which the same body falls through a rarer medium, is as the ratio of the rarities (or as the inverse ratio of the densities) of the two media.

For let B be water and D air; then by so much as air is thinner and more incorporeal than water, A will move through D faster than through B. Let the speed have the same ratio to the speed, then, that air has to water. Then if air is twice as thin, the body will traverse B in twice the time that it does D . . . . And always, by so much as the medium is more incorporeal and less resistant and more easily divided, the faster will be the movement.[33]

Since, then, the speed of natural motion of a body through a medium is determined by the *ratio* between the density of the body and that of the medium, as Aristotle supposes here as well as in other passages of the *Physics* and *De caelo,* it follows that if a body of any density at all were to move by its gravity through a medium of zero density, it would move at infinite speed. For no matter how small a positive quantity may be, the quotient of that number divided by zero will be infinite. The two basic assumptions on which Aristotle's argument rests are those which Galileo criticized and rejected in his Pisan dialogue: (1) that the velocity of free fall is determined by the ratio, and not by the difference, between the densities of mobile body and medium; and (2) that in consequence of this, a corporeal medium of some density is essential to the motions of simple bodies at finite velocity.

To determine whether Galileo's Pisan dynamics had a mediaeval ancestry, we need only consult the extensive literature of commentary on Aristotle's *Physics,* and consider the discussions of Text 71 of Book IV. The basis and point of departure of scholastic commentary on the *Physics,* from the time of Albertus Magnus to that of Galileo himself, was the great commentary of Ibn Roschd, or Averroes. Turning to his commentary on Text 71 of the fourth book, we find, immediately following his literal exposition of the text, a lengthy digression, which is devoted to consideration of a criticism of Aristotle's argument, and of the assumptions on which it was based, made by an Arab predecessor of Averroes named Avempace, or Ibn Badga.

Avempace, however, here raises a good question. For he says that it does not follow that the proportion of the motion of one and the same stone

[33] Aristotle, *Physica* IV, ch. 8, 215b 4–12 (Oxford translation, ed W. D. Ross, Vol. II, Oxford, 1930).

in water to its motion in air is as the proportion of the density of water to the density of air, *except on the assumption that the motion of the stone takes time only because it is moved in a medium*. And if this assumption were true, it would then be the case that no motion would require time except because of something resisting it—for the medium seems to impede the thing moved. And if this were so, then the heavenly bodies, which encounter no resistant medium, would be moved instantaneously. And he says that the proportion of the rarity of water to the rarity of air is as the proportion of the *retardation* occurring to the moved body in water, to the *retardation* occurring to it in air.

And these are his own words, in the seventh book of his work, where he says: " And this resistance which is between the plenum and the body which is moved in it, is that between which, and the potency of the void, Aristotle made the proportion in his fourth book; and what is believed to be his opinion, is not so. For the proportion of water to air in density is not as the proportion of the motion of the stone in water to its motion in air; but the proportion of the cohesive power of water to that of air is as the proportion of the *retardation* occurring to the moved body by reason of the medium in which it is moved, namely water, to the *retardation* occurring to it when it is moved in air.

" For, if what some people have believed were true, then natural motion would be violent; therefore, if there were no resistance present, how could there be any motion? For it would necessarily be instantaneous. What then shall be said concerning the circular motion? There is no resistance there, because there is no cleavage of a medium involved; the place of the circle is always the same, so that it does not leave one place and enter another; it is therefore necessary that the circular motion should be instantaneous. Yet we observe in it the greatest slowness, as in the case of the fixed stars, and also the greatest speed, as in the case of the diurnal rotation. And this is caused only by the difference in perfection between the mover and the moved. When therefore the mover is of greater perfection, that which is moved by it will be more rapid; and when the mover is of lesser perfection, it will be nearer (*in perfection*) to that which is moved, and the motion will be slower."

And these are his words. And if this which he has said be conceded, then Aristotle's demonstration will be false; because, if the proportion of the rarity of one medium to the rarity of the other is as the proportion of accidental retardation of the movement in one of them to the retardation occurring to it in the other, and is not as the proportion of the motion itself, it will not follow that what is moved in a void would be moved in an instant; because in that case *there would be subtracted from the motion only the retardation affecting it by reason of the medium, and its natural motion would remain*. And every motion involves time; therefore what is moved in a void is necessarily moved in time and with a divisible motion; and nothing impossible will follow. This, then, is Avempace's question.[34]

This quotation from Avempace's lost work on the *Physics*, preserved for us by Averroes, is worth close study. The speed of natural motion of a body in a medium, according to Avempace, is determined by *subtracting* the accidental retardation caused by the density of the medium, from an essential " natural velocity " which the heavy body would have if falling in the void. The medium is not essential to natural motion at finite speed, as Aristotle held, because the speed is determined by the difference, and not by the ratio, between the densities of body and medium. For Avempace, as for Galileo in his Pisan dialogue, $V = P - M$, so that when $M = 0$, $V = P$.

Avempace's theory of the motions of heavy bodies, moreover, involves the same basic assumptions as Galileo's Pisan theory. Gravity is conceived as an intrinsic motive power acting on the heavy body from within; the true and essential measure of this motive power is conceived to be the speed at which it moves its body through pure geometrical space toward the center of the world; and the essential or " natural " velocities of bodies of diverse nature or density are held to be proportional to the " perfection " of their natures, as to the degree of their densities. If we may use modern terms, it might be said that the force of gravity, for Avempace, is not determined essentially as a relation between the masses of different bodies, but is conceived as an absolute indwelling power of self-motion animating the body like a soul.

This conception is made explicit, in Avempace's case, by his reference to the movements of the celestial spheres, which were thought to be caused by incorporeal substances called Intelligences, distinct from the spheres moved by them, yet operative on them from the inside, like Ideas " motivating " desire. It is this conception of indwelling motive power, or of operative Idea giving motion to a magnitude, that Avempace brings down from the Greco-Arab heavens and extends to the dynamics of terrestrial bodies. He thus conceives a single universal dynamics, breaking down the barrier between the heavens and the earth which is so distinctive of Aristotle's cosmology. Yet this universal dynamics is modelled on the theory of Aristotle's theological astronomy, of celestial rotations caused by immaterial and intellectual " motives." Gravity is conceived as mover of a stone toward the center of the world, in the manner that the separated

[34] *Opera Aristotelis . . . cum Averrois commentariis* (Venetiis, MDLX), Tom. IV, fol. 131 verso. (Italics and parenthetical enclosures mine.)

Intelligences were conceived to be movers of the spheres. In breaking down Aristotle's dichotomy of the universe into the realm of Reason and the realm of Nature, Avempace breaks down Aristotle's distinction between *kinesis* and *energeia*—between motion, which is the act of matter, and thought, which is the activity of mind. He does not, however, reduce thought to motion, but he reduces motion to thought—to the " activity of intelligence which is life " (ἡ γὰρ νοῦ ἐνεργεία ζωή).[35] He does not generalize Aristotle's physics so as to eliminate his theology; on the contrary, he generalizes the theology so as to absorb the physics.

To what degree Avempace was motivated, in his criticism of Aristitle's argument against motion in the void, by a basic philosophic orientation or tradition opposed to that of Aristotle, can only be conjectured. Of Avempace himself, or of the content of his writings, we know very little. His full name was Abou-Bekr Mohammed ben Ya 'hya, but he was commonly known as Ibn-al-Cayeg (son of the clockmaker), or as Ibn-Badga. Born at Saragossa toward the end of the eleventh century of our era, he was at Seville in 1118, and probably lived there until his death in 1138. He was said to be learned in medicine, mathematics and astronomy, and skilled in music and lute-playing. He died at a comparatively early age, poisoned, according to tradition, by his own physicians who were jealous of his medical prowess. Ibn-Tofail, who seems to have been one of his disciples, praised his wisdom and learning highly, but said that his premature death prevented him from publishing any major works, so that his more important writings remained incomplete and known only to a few. He seems to have written commentaries on Aristotle's *Physics, Meteora, De generatione et corruptione,* and *De animalibus,* as well as original treatises in logic, medicine, mathematics and psychology. Manuscripts, in Arabic, of a few of his works are said to be extant; but none of his writings was translated into Latin, and what we know of his teachings in natural philosophy and metaphysics stems from the quotations and references to his doctrines found in the works of Averroes.[36]

[35] Aristotle, *Metaphysica* XII, ch. 7, 1072b 26.

[36] Cf. S. Munk, *Mélanges de philosophie juive et arabe* (Paris, 1857; reprinted by J. Vrin, Paris, 1927), 383–410. Munk gives an analysis of Avempace's " Régime du Solitaire," based on a Hebrew summary of the work; this indicates a rather Neo-Platonic background to Avempace's theory of the soul and intelligence. The Arabic text of this work has recently been edited, with a Spanish translation, by M. Asín Palacios, *Avempace: El régimen del solitario,* published by the Instituto Miguel Asín de Estudios Arabes (1948).

That Avempace's philosophical orientation was in large measure that of the Neo-Platonist wing of Arabian philosophy, is indicated by such scraps of evidence as we possess. Thomas Aquinas, in discussing Avempace's theory of abstraction as recited by Averroes, does not hesitate to classify him as a " Platonist."

Averroes says that a philosopher named Avempace taught that by the understanding of material substances we can be led, according to true philosophical principles, to the knowledge of immaterial substances. For since the nature of our intellect is to abstract the quiddity of material things from matter, anything material residing in that abstracted quiddity can again be made subject to abstraction; and as the process of abstraction cannot go on forever, it must arrive at length at the understanding of a quiddity that is absolutely without matter; and this would be the understanding of immaterial substances.

Now this opinion would be true, were immaterial substances the forms and species of these material things, as the Platonists supposed. But supposing, on the contrary, that immaterial substances differ altogether from the quiddity of material things, it follows that, however much our intellect may abstract the quiddity of a material thing from matter, it could never arrive at anything like an immaterial substance.[37]

St. Thomas' analysis of Avempace's theory of knowledge seems to indicate a metaphysics in which the true natures of sensible things are purely intelligible immaterial substances, just as Avempace's assimilation of the " natures " of heavy and light bodies to the immaterial Movers of the Spheres also indicated. Albert the Great also associates Avempace with the more Neo-Platonic branch of the Arab tradition, to the extent that he ascribes Avempace's theory of natural motion in the void, and his law of velocities, to Avicenna also.[38] Since this eastern Arab school of philosophy drew its guiding principle of unification of Greek philosophy from Plotinus and Proclus, by way of the pseudo-Aristotelian *Liber de causis* and *Theologia Aristotelis*, there would seem to be some support for St. Thomas' classification of

---

[37] Thomas Aquinas, *Summa Theologica* I, Qu. 88, art. 2. The translation is that of *The Basic Writings of St. Thomas*, edited by A. C. Pegis, published by Random House (New York, 1945), I, 848. The citation of Averroes refers to his commentary on the *De anima*, III, comm. 36.

[38] *Alberti Magni Physicorum Libri VIII*, ed. Borgnet (Paris, 1890), III, 288. I have looked through Avicenna's *Sufficientia* for the discussion of the problem, but in the mediaeval Latin version of this work I found only a general metaphysical, treatment, similar in viewpoint to that of Avempace, but without any clear indication of the " law of difference " represented by our formula $V = P - M$.

Avempace as a " Platonist." This is further brought out by Averroes himself, whose analysis and criticism of Avempace's theory turns on fundamental issues, of a philosophic order, on which the Aristotelian and Platonic traditions have been perennially at odds.

Avempace's error, according to Averroes, is to treat the " natures " of heavy bodies as if they were distinct realities from the matter of the bodies, and as if the matter were moved by the form in the way that a celestial sphere is moved by the immaterial Intelligence associated with it, or in the way that an organic body is moved by its soul. According to Averroes, in the natural motions of heavy and light bodies, mover and moved are not distinct entities *in* the body, and the body does not act on itself as efficient cause of its own movement. Rather, the body is mover and moved only with respect to the external medium, its natural motion arising from a reciprocal dynamic interaction between the body and its corporeal surroundings. Self-motion of a simple body is impossible; consequently, if a simple body is in motion, something other than that body is an essential factor and condition of the motion. This other thing is not, as Avempace supposed, an indwelling separate form, called the " gravity " or the " nature " of the body, and operating on it in the way that a separated Intelligence or astral soul operates on its sphere. On the contrary, says Averroes, it is the physical environment or medium which acts on the body, insofar as the latter is said to be moved, and it is the body which acts on the medium, insofar as the body is said to be a mover. Thus the medium is an essential condition, and not merely an accidental impediment, to the body's motion.[39]

Averroes objects to Avempace's assumption that the medium is an impediment and hindrance to the natural movement of the heavy body; because, on that assumption, it would follow that all bodies *de facto* move in a manner unnatural to them, since all do in fact move through corporeal media. But to define the natural as that which never happens, seems to Averroes absurd.

It is to be said that those motions which are of simple bodies, through water and air, are not motions impeded by the medium, as might appear at first sight. For if they were, then natural motions would be those which were never yet observed and which never will be observed—unless it should be possible for those bodies to be moved without a medium, which is impossible if there is no void.[40]

[39] *Opera Aristotelis . . . cum Averrois commentariis* (Venetiis, MDLX), IV, fol. 132v–133r.   [40] Averroes, *loc. cit.*, fol. 132v.

The objection here made by Averroes reflects a major cleavage in the conception of nature, which runs through the whole history of philosophy. Is the "natural" to be identified with the factual, with the concrete? If so, then the abstract and intelligible factors in terms of which we analyze the facts will be attributed to our ways of thinking about things, rather than to the things thought of. Or shall we say that the ideas which permit us to give an intelligible analysis of the facts of experience, however abstract or "ideal" they may be, exhibit the real natures and causes of phenomena, so that the latter are merely "appearances" of the intelligible? This is the issue between "nominalism" and "realism" in mediaeval philosophy, between "empiricism" and "rationalism" in early modern thought, and perhaps between "Aristotelianism" and "Platonism." In any event, Avempace's theory here represents the viewpoint of the mediaeval realist, of the rationalist, and of the Platonist. Averroes, in opposing Avempace's concept of nature and of the natural, represents the nominalist, the empiricist, and, in his own eyes certainly, the "Aristotelian." [41]

It is with these metaphysical implications of Avempace's theory that Averroes is chiefly concerned, rather than with the mathematical problem of formulating a coherent generalized law governing the relative velocities of natural motions. Averroes certainly defends the dynamic *principle* underlying Aristotle's law of motion—that speed depends on the *ratio* of motive power and resistance, rather than being essentially and absolutely determined by the motive power alone. But it is difficult or impossible to determine, from his text, whether he interpreted the Aristotelian law as one of simple inverse proportionality. Thus he says:

[41] It is exactly this basis of philosophical cleavage that is stressed by Cassirer and Koyré, as the criterion distinguishing Galileo's "Platonism" from the "Aristotelianism" of his adversaries. Cf. E. Cassirer, "Galileo's Platonism," *loc. cit.*, 291: "It is easily to be understood, that the Peripatetic adversaries of Galileo completely failed to see his point. They acted in good faith; they could see in Galileo's first principles nothing but a sheer absurdity. How can we explain natural phenomena if, instead of observing and describing nature, we assume something that has never been seen or found in nature?" Cassirer in turn quotes Koyré's article, "Galileo and Plato," p. 171: "No wonder that the Aristotelian felt himself astonished and bewildered by this amazing attempt to explain the real by the impossible, or, which is the same thing, to explain real being by mathematical being, because these bodies moving in straight lines in infinite empty space are not real bodies moving in real space but mathematical bodies moving in mathematical space."

We however say that it is necessary that between the mover and the thing moved there be a resistance. For the mover moves the thing moved, insofar as it is contrary, and the thing moved is moved by it according as it is similar. And every motion will be according to the excess of the potency of the mover over the thing moved, and *the diversity of motions in speed and slowness is according to this proportion which is between the two potencies and these resistances.*[42]

The context clearly shows that by " excess of the potency of the mover over the thing moved," Averroes means the proportion or ratio, and not the arithmetical difference, between the two; he does not accept Avempace's substitution of $P - M$, for P/M, as a correction of Aristotle's formula. But this passage obscurely suggests, in the part italicized, that the proportion of one velocity to another is not determined by the simple ratio of density of one medium to that of the other, but by the *diversity* between the *proportion* of the density of the body to the density of one medium, and the *proportion* of the density of the body to the density of the other medium. What, then, is here meant by " diversity " between two proportions? If it means merely the ratio between them such as we symbolize by the sign of division, then Averroes' statement is fully equivalent to the interpretation of Aristotle's law as one of simple inverse proportionality, represented by the formula $V = P/M$. But if it means some other functional relation, such as geometric proportionality, it could yield a very different formula. This possibility was not explicitly developed, however, until the fourteenth century, when Thomas Bradwardine, utilizing the theorems on geometric proportionality in the fifth book of Euclid's *Elements,* initiated a new stage in the evolution of mechanics with a reformulation of Aristotle's law which required, for generalized statement, a logarithmic function. While Bradwardine modestly characterized his formula as being precisely what Aristotle and Averroes had intended, it is scarcely what either of them said, and may justly be called Bradwardine's Law.[43]

Was Avempace the originator of the theory that velocities of free fall in corporeal media are determined by the difference, rather than

[42] Averroes, *loc. cit.,* fol. 132v (Italics mine).

[43] Cf. Anneliese Maier, " Der Funktionsbegriff in der Physik des 14. Jahrhunderts," in *Divus Thomas* (Freiburg), Vol. 24 (1946), 147–66; republished in her book, *Die Vorläufer Galileis im 14. Jahrhundert* (Rome, 1949). Dr. Maier stresses the significance and novelty of Bradwardine's function, but seems satisfied that it did not represent Aristotle's meaning, which she believes should be represented by the simple formula $V = P/M$.

by the ratio, between motive and resistive powers corresponding to the densities of body and medium? Averroes seems to think so, and he pays his respects to Avempace as an original and profound critic of Aristotle.

Avempace therefore raised doubts in this passage, in two places. . . . And nobody before him had arrived at these questions; and hence he was more profound than any others. And in the copy from which we have written, we found a certain page all by itself, and this was written on it.[44]

But Averroes was mistaken. Avempace's criticism of Aristotle, and his alternative law of velocities, though known to the western scholastics only as "Avempace's theory," had been stated, and its implications developed clearly and fully, by a Christian Neo-Platonist of Alexandria, Joannes Philoponus. For in the commentary which Philoponus wrote on Aristotle's *Physics,* immediately after his exposition of Text 71 of Book IV, we find a lengthy " digression " devoted to criticism of Aristotle's law of velocities and of the dynamic assumptions on which it was based. Philoponus, like Avempace, rejected the assumption that motion essentially depends on a relation between the moved body and a corporeal medium, or that velocity is determined by the ratio of densities of the body and the medium. Like Avempace, he substituted the law of arithmetic difference, represented by the formula $V = P - M$, for Aristotle's law of proportionality represented by the formula $V = P/M$. And he asserted, likewise, that the purely " natural " velocity of a heavy body is that which arises from the absolute gravity of the body moving, alone by itself ($αὐτὴ$ $κατθ'$ $αὐτην$), in the void.[45]

There is no definite evidence that Avempace, or any of his Arab contemporaries or successors, had access to the commentary of Philoponus on the *Physics.* Nevertheless it seems probable that Avempace derived his argument from sources in the Arab tradition which had antecedent links with the late Alexandrian school, and with the ideas of Philoponus. The explanation of projectile motion by an " im-

[44] Averroes, *loc. cit.,* fol. 132v.

[45] P. Duhem, *Le Système du monde,* I, 350–71, gives a full exposition of the discussion of Philoponus, and translates the principal passages into French. Philoponus' commentary, apparently unknown in the Middle Ages, was published, in a Greek text edited by Victor Trincavellus, in 1535. A Latin translation appeared in 1542, or possibly in 1539, followed by several other Latin translations in 1554, 1558 and 1569. The Greek text was edited, in the *Commentaria in Aristotelem Graeca,* Vols. 16–17, by Hieronymus Vitelli (Berlin, 1887–8).

pressed force," whose Greek originator seems to have been Philoponus, was reflected in a passage from Al-Bitrogi's *Theorica Planetarum,* cited by Duhem.[46] It is known, however, that Al-Bitrogi was strongly influenced by the teachings of Ibn-Tofail, who in turn had been a disciple of Avempace. We may therefore surmise that the root source of Avempace's " law of motion," as well as of the theory of "impressed force " as cause of the movement of projectiles, was the Neo-Platonist tradition of Alexandria, represented by Joannes Philoponus in the sixth century of our era. Since both of these theories played a fundamental part in Galileo's Pisan dynamics, there would seem to be not merely theoretical, but historical grounds, for the claims of Cassirer and Koyré that Galileo's science—at least in its Pisan phase—was in the Platonist and Alexandrian tradition. But it remains to determine what influence Avempace's dynamics had in the Christian Middle Ages, and whether the fact that Galileo's Pisan dynamics was Alexandrian and Platonist in its philosophical and historical antecedents, excludes the possibility of its being mediaeval and scholastic as well.

[46] P. Duhem, *Études sur Léonard de Vinci,* II, 191, and III, 34. Al-Bitrogi's text is quoted, in the two Latin versions, by Anneliese Maier, *Die Impetustheorie der Scholastik* (Wien, 1940), 17.

John Herman Randall, Jr.

THE PLACE OF LEONARDO DA VINCI IN THE EMERGENCE OF MODERN SCIENCE

The five-hundredth anniversary of the birth of Leonardo da Vinci is an appropriate time at which to ask the question, In the light of our present knowledge, what is the place of Leonardo in the emergence of modern science? It should, however, be made clear at the outset that I can lay no claims to possessing any expert knowledge of Leonardo. I have not gone carefully through the great Ravaisson-Mollien edition of his notebooks, or the Codice Atlantico. Nor can I really convince myself that I know very much about the emergence of modern science. I have followed eagerly the exciting discoveries made on certain of the strands of thought which came together in the sixteenth century to produce those astonishing results that can well be called the birth of the modern scientific enterprise. One or two strands, which I suspected were quite important, I have even tried to untangle myself, primarily because no one else seemed anxious to do the job.

But nobody, up to the present, seems to me to know enough as yet to judge the relative importance of the many different intellectual traditions whose convergence, in the century from Copernicus to Galileo, led to such momentous results. In the present situation of these studies, we are confronted by many scholars, each of whom has been exploring some one of these traditions, and each of whom has not unnaturally come to be a vigorous partisan of the basic importance of the particular body of ideas he has investigated. It is well to have each of these intellectual currents carefully explored by men vitally interested in it. For if one thing at least has now grown clear, it is that the " emergence of modern science " was a very complicated affair, and involved a great variety of factors. The central problem, however, is that of the judicious appraisal of the relative importance of a number of different " necessary conditions " ; and for such a wise balancing and weighing we seem hardly ready yet. Each of us may have his own suspicions, but they have certainly not as yet produced agreement.

But for an answer to the question proposed, as to the place of Leonardo da Vinci in this complicated process, the fact that one may not know completely everything that Leonardo ever said and wrote and did does not really matter. Like everybody else, I think Leo-

---

[1] The substance of this paper was presented in a symposium in commemoration of the quincentenary of Leonardo's birth, held by the New York Renaissance Club in the Morgan Library on December 6, 1952.

nardo was quite a fellow, no less when he touched on scientific problems than in his many other activities. He could see with great clarity and insight certain features of what it is in his case especially appropriate to call " the anatomy of nature "—for he accepted the Renaissance view that nature is man writ large, and man is a little world, so that the " anatomy " of both is fundamentally alike. And since he could draw quite well, he managed to develop a real knack for getting these features on paper. As every one who has ever seen copies of Leonardo's drawings knows, this talent for scientific illustration is indeed impressive. It impressed Dürer and his friends, and it impressed others; the impressiveness seems somehow to have reached Vesalius. Indeed, Erwin Panofsky has suggested that, for the descriptive sciences at least, the invention of a method of recording observations through revealing drawings, an invention made by the great universal artists of the turn of the fifteenth century, deserves to rank with the invention of the telescope and the microscope in the seventeenth century and of the camera in the nineteenth.

But I think that historical investigation of the process by which modern science came into being has now progressed so far that we can say that, for all his great gifts as a careful observer, Leonardo, strictly speaking, has no place whatever in that process. I am thinking, of course, primarily of that body of ideas in astronomy and physical theory which in the seventeenth century effected so tremendous a revolution in human thought—about Galilean science. In the history of the descriptive sciences, above all in anatomy, Leonardo may well claim a niche—though even here it is still problematic what the difference would have been had he not lived.

We may safely, I think, lay down here three general propositions: 1.) Leonardo was not himself a scientist, in the sense in which he and his contemporaries understood science—or in any sense in which anybody else has ever understood science. He was an artist, every sort of artist—a painter, an engineer, a canal-builder, an architect, an inventor, and all the rest. He got more and more interested in all kinds of scientific problems as he went on—to the detriment of his art, for his concern with worrying these many different problems undoubtedly caused him to leave more and more of his multifarious projects unfinished than he otherwise might have. Of course, his much too fertile mind, teeming with far too many ideas for his own or the world's good —a mind which, like Leibniz's, led him to dash off in another direction before he got one project or idea well started, to say nothing of worked out—would doubtless have made him the master of the incomplete and the unfinished anyway.

2.) There is not discoverable, in Leonardo's Codici, a single theoretical scientific idea that is essentially new, or that was unknown in the organized scientific schools in Italy in his day. The notion that not unnaturally arose when his Codici were first printed after 1881, that they were full of startlingly original insights, arose from the sheer ignorance prevailing at that time of what was familiar to Leonardo's scientific contemporaries.

3.) Even if Leonardo had had original ideas in scientific theory, he would still have no " place " in, and would have exerted no " influence " on, the emergence of modern science. For these ideas of his remained quite unknown until the Paris Codici were published, 1881–91,[2] and the Codice Atlantico in 1894.[3] Even his *Trattato de la Pittura* did not appear until 1651, though a manuscript at Urbino, edited and copied in another hand, indicates that it was known to the Urbino circle at least. · Venturi made the first report on the contents of the Codici in 1797,[4] and Libri followed in 1840.[5] The fact that many of the later sixteenth-century scientific writers in the long progression leading up to Galileo state certain important ideas closely resembling Leonardo's, means merely that they too were familiar with the books he was eagerly reading.

I shall now amplify and comment on these three propositions. I shall then try to state what seems to me to be Leonardo's real genius in science, in the light of the state of science in his time, and in the context of the intellectual events then occurring.

I

Leonardo was not himself a scientist. " Science " is not the hundred-odd aphorisms or " pensieri " that have been pulled out of his Codici and collected, by Richter,[6] Solmi,[7] and others. " Science " is not oracular utterances, however well phrased; it is not bright ideas jotted down in a notebook. " Science " is systematic and methodical thought. As Leonardo himself has it, " Science is that mental discourse which takes as its starting point those first principles to which no other in nature is prior, . . . as the point is the first principle of

[2] Charles Ravaisson-Mollien, M.S.E. de la Bibliothèque de l'Institut, 6 vols. (Paris, 1881–91). [3] *Codice Atlantico*, Accademia dei Lyncei (Rome, 1894).

[4] *Essai sur les Ouvrages de Léonard de Vinci* (Paris, 1797). [5] *Histoire des Sciences mathématiques en Italie* (Paris, 1840), III, 11.

[6] J. P. Richter, *Literary Works of Leonardo da Vinci*, 2 vols. (London, 1883). [7] Edmondo Solmi, *Frammenti letterari e filosofici di Leonardo da Vinci* (Florence, 1899).

geometry." [8]   This is of course the accepted Aristotelian conception prevalent in Leonardo's day.

" Science " is not just the appeal to experience, though it involves such an appeal, as Leonardo stated in answering those critics who had censured him as a mere empiric: " If I could not indeed like them cite authors and books, it is a much greater and worthier thing to profess to cite experience, the mistress of their masters." [9] " Science " is not the mere rejection of authority, the case for which is well put by Leonardo: " He who argues by citing an authority is not employing intelligence but rather memory." [10]   The later medieval schools of the fourteenth and fifteenth centuries had equally come to reject such " memory " for the exercise of original intelligence—and these were just those " auctoritates " or authors whom Leonardo was actually reading, learning from, following and occasionally citing—in the Lokert edition of 1516.

It is true that during Leonardo's youth—the second half of the Quattrocento—the intellectual influence of the non-scientific humanists had been making for a kind of St. Martin's summer of the " authority " of the ancients, and that his life coincides with this rebirth of an authoritarian attitude toward the past.   Leonardo's protests were magnificent, and doubtless pertinent.   But they are not enough to constitute " science."   " Science " is not merely fresh, first-hand observation, however detailed and accurate.

Above all, " science " is not the intuitions of a single genius, solitary and alone, however suggestive.   It is cooperative inquiry, such as had prevailed in the Italian schools from the time of Pietro d'Àbano († 1315; his *Conciliator* appeared earlier)—and such as was to continue till the time of Galileo—the cumulative cooperative inquiry which actually played so large a part in the emergence of modern science.   As a matter of fact, Leonardo seems to represent a kind of throwback to the conditions of the ancient world, where, as Ludwig Edelstein has brilliantly pointed out,[11] the fundamental reason why there was so little steady " progress " or cumulative development to science was largely that the continuity and cooperative character of scientific inquiry had not managed to establish themselves in any institutionalized form.

In practice, Leonardo always becomes fascinated by some particular problem—he has no interest in working out any systematic body of knowledge.   His artist's interest in the particular and the concrete, which inspires his careful, precise and accurate observation, is carried

[8] E. Solmi, *Frammenti, op. cit.,* pp. 76–7.   [9] *Ib.,* 81.   [10] *Ib.,* 83.
[11] "Recent Trends in the Interpretation of Ancient Science," pp. 90–121.

further by his inordinate curiosity into a detailed analytic study of the factors involved. His thought seems always to be moving from the particularity of the painter's experience to the universality of intellect and science, without ever quite getting there.

II

If Leonardo has no place in the emergence of modern science, in that he made no contribution to the body of theory that took classic form with Galileo, he has at least a dominating place in the emergence of our *knowledge* of the history of modern science. After the publication of the Codici in 1881, historians began to trace the antecedents of the Galilean physical ideas through the earlier years of the sixteenth century, back to Leonardo. Since he was where they stopped, he must have been a major influence in the development of scientific method and theory. He was obviously a " genius "; so he must have been the one who thought up out of thin air these ideas, which were then elaborated and criticised in more normal and familiar ways until they reached Galileo. So opinion ran.

It was from Leonardo that the pioneer historian of pre-Galilean science, Pierre Duhem, took his start. The successive volumes of his *Études sur Léonard de Vinci* [12] contain one of the classic detective stories of scholarly investigation—how he was forced back from his original assumption of a single great " Précurseur " of genius [13] to the organized schools of the fourteenth-century Paris Ockhamites and Oxford logicians. This is a story now familiar to every serious student of the history of science, though it has not yet penetrated into the popular manuals and the anecdotes that embroider many of our textbooks. Duhem's judgment ran: " In the mechanical work of Leoardo, there is no essential idea that does not come from the geometers of the Middle Ages." [14]

Duhem's pioneer work has now been subjected to a generation of penetrating criticism. Duhem was a Frenchman, and he liked the University of Paris. He was also a Catholic, and he liked the orthodox faith of his beloved Masters of Paris. He has been challenged on both scores. Ernest Moody, after much painstaking investigation of the astounding school of Oxford Mertonians of the fourteenth cen-

[12] 3 vols. (Paris, 1906–13).
[13] Pierre Duhem, *Origines de la Statique*, 2 vols. (Paris, 1905–6), I, 192: " Il n'est, dans l'oeuvre mécanique de Léonard de Vinci, aucune idée essentielle qui ne soit issue des géomètres du moyen âge et, particulièrement du traité de ce grand mécanicien que nous avons nommé le Précurseur de Léonard."
[14] *Ibid.*

tury, has pushed back a generation earlier the first appearance of many of the ideas which for Duhem seemed to originate with Buridan, to Heytesbury, Dumbleton and Swineshead, pupils of Bradwardine at Merton. He has found that Heytesbury had formulated as early as 1335 the "law of uniformly accelerated motion" which Duhem attributed to Nicholas of Oresme.

Having myself done some reading in the anti-clerical Italian writers on natural philosophy of the Quattrocento, since I suspected that Duhem's stalwart Catholicism had done them less than justice, I have found that all the presumably "novel" ideas associated with Leonardo before Duhem's discoveries were known and taught in the fifteenth-century Italian universities—in Padua, Bologna, Pavia, and the rest. They appear in the *Summa Naturalia* of Paul of Venice († 1429) before 1420. Marshall Clagett, the brilliant historian of medieval science, has found that the Oxford logicians, Tisberus (or Hentisberus, Heytesbury) and Suiseth (Swineshead) were known at Padua and Bologna shortly after 1350. All these ideas are expressed with great force and originality by Cajetan of Thiene († 1465) by the middle of the century. As soon as the printing press reached Italy, the writings of these teachers were at once struck off in various editions, and there was a veritable flood of printed works of the great fourteenth-century Ockhamites, and of Suiseth and Tisberus. It was these printed editions which Leonardo read, and which were read by those he is supposed to have "influenced." For example, Nicholas of Oresme's fundamental *De Latitudinibus Formarum* was printed in Padua in 1482, with a full discussion by Blasius de Parma de Pelicanis (Biagio di Parma). Leonardo cites in his notebooks the G. Lokert edition (Paris, 1516) of Albert of Saxony and Jean Buridan (cf. Duhem, *Études sur Léonard de Vinci*).

Moreover, a generation of research since Duhem has brought out more significant differences between the "impetus theory" which runs like a bright thread through all these writers, and which is the theory of motion set forth in Leonardo's Codici, and the dynamics which Galileo finally worked out in his 1632 *Dialoghi,* than Duhem was himself aware of. The *Études Galiléennes* of Alexandre Koyré [15] have made this clear, as have also the detailed and suggestive writings of Dr. Anneliese Maier.[16] Ernest Moody has shown, in his distinguished study, "Galileo and Avempace,"[17] that Galileo, in his 1590

---

[15] 3 vols. (Paris, 1939). Cf. Moody's statement of Kóyre's mistakes, which appears on pp. 176–206.

[16] *Die Impetustheorie der Scholastik* (Vienna, 1940); *An der Grenze von Scholastik und Naturwissenschaft* (Essen, 1943); *Die Vorläufer Galileis im 14ten Jahrhundert* (Rome, 1949).

[17] Pp. 176–206; *J. H. I.* (1951), 375- 422.

Pisan treatise and dialogue *De Motu,* started his attempts to formulate the law of falling bodies by following the tradition of Avempace (Ibn Badga, † 1138), the Arabian Neoplatonic scientist reported in Averroes (*Commentary on Physica,* Book IV, Text 71), a view itself deriving ultimately from the criticism of Text 71 in the commentary on the *Physica* of Joannes Philoponus (6th century; cf. Moody, *op. cit.,* 205-6). Only later did Galileo develop instead, in his *Dialoghi,* the much more Aristotelian position of Buridan.

But though the antecedents of Galileo's thought in dynamics have been thus clarified, nowhere has there come any evidence that vindicates the originality of Leonardo in physical theory. He remains in this field a wide and extremely intelligent reader of the fourteenth-century Paris and the fifteenth-century Italian scientific tradition—the kind of reader any innovator might well delight to have.

III

No evidence has ever been offered that anybody in the sixteenth century capable of appreciating scientific ideas ever saw the Codici of Leonardo. The incredible history of these notebooks, their wandering about Italy and to Spain and England, awakening interest during this odyssey only for the aesthetic quality of the drawings, is a modern counterpart of the legendary adventures of the Aristotelian writings. When they finally came to rest in the Ambrosiana, the progress of science had made the ideas they contained—aside from the technological inventions so profusely strewn throughout them—of merely historical interest. And it was not till they started their journeys once more—the conquering French took them to Paris in 1796—that anyone ever bothered to try to find out what Leonardo was trying to say in his crabbed mirror-writing. But since the scientific ideas expressed therein were all well-known in the universities of Leonardo's day, and were accessible in much more elaborated form in the books the scientists were reading, there seems to be no " problem " of tracing any presumed " influence " of Leonardo on the development of sixteenth-century scientific thought in Italy.

The *Trattato de la Pittura,* or *Paragone,* was not printed until 1651, but its existence in manuscript form suggests that it had been read much earlier by the Urbino circle. It was put together from various manuscripts of Leonardo by an editor whose identity is not known, but who seems to have been responsible for its systematic organization —an organization which later editors have uniformly tried to improve upon.

With Leonardo's anatomical studies, the story is somewhat different. There is no evidence that Vesalius ever actually saw his drawings; but in view of the marked similarities between them and his own much more systematically planned and organized series of drawings, it is difficult to think that he did not. But this is not the place to work out this story.

IV

Turning now from the things that Leonardo, despite all the adulations of his genius, was clearly not, let us try to state what seems to have been his real genius in scientific matters. During the Renaissance, as a result of the surprising dissolution of the rigid boundaries which had previously kept different intellectual traditions, as it were, in watertight compartments, the many different currents of thought which had long been preparing and strengthening themselves during the Middle Ages managed to come together, and to strike fire. The explanation of this phenomenon can ultimately be only sociological— the breaking down of the fairly rigid boundaries that had hitherto shut off one discipline and one intellectual tradition from another. Whatever its cause, the confluence of many different intellectual traditions in the fertile, all-too-fertile mind of Leonardo renders his views an unusually happy illustration of the way in which very diverse intellectual traditions managed during the Renaissance to unite together to create what we now call " modern science."

There is first the " scientific tradition," the careful, intelligent, cooperative and cumulative criticism of Aristotelian physics, which began with William of Ockham, the most emancipated critic of Aristotelian ideas about the processes of nature, and was continued in unbroken line by the epoch-making analyses of the fourteenth-century Ockhamites—the Oxford Mertonians, Suiseth, Tisberus, and Dumbleton, and the Paris Masters, Jean Buridan, Albert of Saxony, Marsilius of Inghen, and Nicholas of Oresme—and the fifteenth-century Italian natural philosophers. In his reading Leonardo was in touch with this scientific tradition, as Duhem has shown.

There is secondly Leonardo's enthusiasm for mathematics, which goes far beyond its obvious instrumental use. It is very hard to assay the precise sense in which Leonardo thought of mathematics as the alphabet of nature: in this area much work remains to be done. There seems to be in Leonardo no trace of the popular contemporary Pythagoreanism or Platonism. If we examine Leonardo's conception of mathematics as depicted in his drawings, not as inadequately stated in his prose, we find that it differs markedly from the static and very geometrical notion of Dürer. It is movement, not geometrical relations, that Leonardo is trying to capture. There is much in his drawings that suggests a world envisaged in terms of the calculus—like the world of Leibniz—rather than in terms of the purely geometrical vision of the Greek tradition. In his mathematical vision of the world, Leonardo seems to belong to the realm of " dynamic " and " Faustian " attitudes, rather than to the static geometrical perfection of Greek thought.

There is thirdly the tradition of what Edgar Zilsel has called the " superior craftsman "—the man who is not afraid to take an idea and try it out, to experiment with it. Zilsel was committed by his Marxian leanings to attributing the progress of scientific thought to the activities of the " superior craftsman," the technologist. He would have no traffic with the notions of Ernst Cassirer or A. Koyré, that Platonistic influences had had something to do with the development of scientific ideas. On this point he was of course right: the only influence of Platonism on the development of scientific thought has been to distort it and to furnish it with Platonic concepts which necessitate drastic criticism. It was not till I pointed out to him that the Demiourgos of the *Timaeus* was really a " superior craftsman " that Zilsel saw the light.

But it seems to remain a fact that the academic professors, like Paul of Venice and Cajetan of Thiene, and even the teachers of medicine itself, during the fifteenth century merely " discussed " with very acute logical arguments the subtle objections that had been raised since the time of William of Ockham against the Aristotelian physics, and particularly against Aristotle's rather incidental " dynamics." Leonardo was different. Having read of such objections, he at once proceeded to " try them out." He devised experiments to see whether the objections were sound. As a pupil of Verocchio, he had no fastidious objections to sullying his hands with " experiment." This habit of Leonardo's of descending from the academic cathedra and actually trying out the ideas of which he read had broad repercussions: it is one of the activities of Leonardo that seems to have become generally known, and to have awakened emulation. The consequences of Leonardo's willingness to experiment are to be found in the " practical geometry " of Tartaglia, the greatest of the sixteenth-century Italian mathematicians. Galileo, of course, was in this tradition of the " practical geometers "; he too was an indefatigable inventor. Indeed, Leonardo can fairly claim to belong not to the line of scientists but to the noble tradition of the inventors. I am not sure whether it is insulting the Renaissance or our own day to suggest that Leonardo would have found Edison more congenial than Einstein— though he had far more imagination than the rather plodding Thomas

Alva. I have, indeed, a dreadful suspicion that Mr. T. J. Watson is right—were Leonardo alive today, he would be working for International Business Machines—unless he got into the big money with General Motors—he seems to have been quite without conscience or wisdom, quite as a-moral as Machiavelli at his most " scientific."

Many of Leonardo's aphorisms treat the matter of the proper intellectual method. He has much to say on the relation between "reason " and " experience," and what he says used to lead commentators to impute to him the anticipation of Francis Bacon's " inductive method " —God save the mark, as though that had anything to do with the method employed by the pioneering scientists of the seventeenth century!

Neither experience alone nor reason alone will suffice. " Those who are enamored of practice without science are like the pilot who boards his ship without helm or compass, and who is never certain where he is going." [18] On the other hand, pure reasoning is without avail: " Should you say that the sciences which begin and end in the mind have achieved truth, that I will not concede, but rather deny for many reasons; and first, because in such mental discourse there occurs no experience, without which there is no certainty to be found." [19]

But Leonardo does not bother to give any precise definition of what he means by his key terms, " experience," " reason," " certainty," or " truth." Certainty depends on " experience," but " there is no certainty where one of the mathematical sciences cannot apply, or where the subject is not united with mathematics." [20] And—maxim for all inventors!—" Mechanics is the paradise of the mathematical sciences, because in it they come to bear their mathematical fruits." [21]

Actually, of course, the longest statement of Leonardo on method is thoroughly Aristotelian in character:

> To me it seems that those sciences are vain and full of errors which are not born of experience, the mother of all certainty, and which do not end in experience observed, that is, whose origin or middle or end do not come to us through any of the five senses. . . .
>
> But the true sciences are those in which experience has penetrated through the senses and has imposed silence on the tongues of all disputants, and which do not feed their investigators with dreams, but always proceed successively and with true implications from first truths and self-evident principles to the end; as occurs in first mathematics, that is, with number and measure, the sciences called arithmetic and geometry, which treat with highest truth of quantity, both discrete and continuous. . . .

[18] Solmi, *Frammenti,* 65.   [19] *Ibid.,* 84.   [20] *Ibid.,* 86.   [21] *Ibid.,* 86.

Here there will be no argument that twice three make more or less than six, or that a triangle may have the sum of its angles less than two right angles; but with eternal silence there is an end to all disputations, they are settled peacefully by all parties, which the deceptive mental sciences cannot do. . . .

But first I shall appeal to experience, before proceeding further, because my intention is first to cite experience, and then to demonstrate by reason why such experience is constrained to operate in such a way.

And this is the true rule by which those inquiring into natural effects have to proceed; and although nature begins from reason and ends in experience, it is necessary for us to proceed in the opposite direction, commencing, as I have said, from experience, and by its means investigating the reason.[22]

This statement of method is of course completely Aristotelian, and its conception of mathematics as an empirical science, sharing the certainty of " experience," is likewise the traditional Aristotelian, as opposed to the Platonic view of mathematics.   Aristotelian also is the precept: " No effect in nature is without its reason; understand the reason and you will have no need of experience " [23]—a precept Galileo was later to emphasize.

When Leonardo comes in his remarks on painting to defend, in typical humanistic style, his own profession against philosophy, poetry and music, he states his painter's trust in nature observed:

If you look down on painting, which alone is the imitator of all the works nature displays, you will certainly look down on a subtle invention, which with philosophical and subtle speculation considers all the qualities of the forms, airs, sites, plants, animals, herbs and flowers, which are bound by shade and light.   And truly this is science and the legitimate daughter of nature, since painting has been born from nature herself.   But to speak more correctly, we shall call her the granddaughter of nature, because all the things observed have been born of nature, from which first-born things has been born painting in turn.   Therefore rightly shall we maintain that she is the granddaughter of nature and the kinsman of God.

Painting extends over the surfaces, colors and figures of everything whatsoever created by nature, and philosophy penetrates into the same bodies, considering in them their proper virtue; but it does not remain satisfied with that truth which the painter makes, which embraces in itself the first truth of such bodies, since the eye is less deceived.[24]

Painting represents to the senses the works of nature with more truth and certainty than do words or letters: but letters represent words with more truth than painting.   But we shall call that science more admirable which represents the works of nature, than that which represents the works of the worker, that is, the works of men, which are words, like poetry and such things, which come from the human tongue.[25]

[22] *Ibid.*, 94–5.   [23] *Ibid.*, 87.   [24] *Ibid.*, 276–7.   [25] *Ibid.*, 238.

These aphorisms as to the relation between reason and experience are no doubt rhetorically effective. But we have only to compare such vague utterances with the very detailed analyses of precisely the same methodological relation which were being carried out at this very time in the Aristotelian schools of the Italian universities [26] to realize the difference between an artist's insights and the scientist's analysis.

Leonardo was above all else the anatomist of nature. He could see, and with his draughtsmanship depict clearly, the bony skeleton of the world—the geological strata and their indicated past. He could also see everywhere nature's simple machines in operation—in man and in the non-human world alike. This fundamental identity between the microcosm of man and the macrocosm of nature, which Leonardo found essental, was of course to be profoundly disrupted by the science of the seventeenth century, which was to divorce man completely from nature, and while creating the Cartesian dualism that has bedeviled thought down to Ryle, was to keep nature freed from all disturbing and extraneous elements, the better to treat it in purely mechanical and mathematical terms. But the effects of Leonardo's version of this intimate relation between man and nature were not scientifically disturbing, like those of so many Renaissance organicists —Paracelsus is the exemplar—because though Leonardo found nature and man to be alike, he conceived both, in the very spirit of the new science, on the analogy of the machine, and saw the principles of mechanics operating everywhere. Especially did Leonardo, who had early devoted himself to canal-building, see the mechanical forces of water everywhere at work—he had a real genius for the graphic depiction of the operation of hydrodynamic forces.

As a genuine contributor, then, to the descriptive sciences, Leonardo reported with his pencil fundamental aspects of nature the great machine—in anatomy, geology, and hydrostatics. As a writer rather than as a graphic reporter, Leonardo shows himself an extremely intelligent reader. But he was clearly never so much the scientist as when he had his pencil in hand, and was penetrating to the mechanical structure of what he was observing.

[26] J. H. Randall, Jr., " The Development of Scientific Method in the School of Padua, pp. 139–46.

~ఇ Edgar Zilsel

THE ORIGINS OF
GILBERT'S SCIENTIFIC METHOD

William Gilbert's *De Magnete* appeared in 1600, six years before Galileo's first publication, five years before Bacon's *Advancement of Learning;* it is the first printed book, written by an
academically trained scholar and dealing with a topic of natural
science, which is based almost entirely on actual observation and
experiment. In the learned literature of the period, among the
writings of both contemporary university scholars and the humanistic literati, it is an isolated case. An analysis of the origins of
its scientific method, therefore, is not only interesting in itself but
is likely to throw some light on the origins of modern natural
science in general. The results of Gilbert's investigation of magnetism and electricity being generally known, we shall consider
first a few characteristics of his method and shall then try to trace
its sources. Unfortunately very little is known of Gilbert's life
and nothing at all of his way of working. The investigation,
therefore, must be based entirely on his two printed books.[1]

* This essay is part of a study undertaken with the help of grants from the Committee in Aid of Displaced Foreign Scholars and the Rockefeller Foundation.

[1] *De Magnete Magneticisque Corporibus et de Magno Magnete Tellure, Physiologia Nova plurimis et argumentis et experimentis demonstrata,* Londini, 1600. If
no other source is given all quotations in the following paper refer to this work and
this edition. An English page-for-page version by Silvanus P. Thompson has been
edited by the William Gilbert Society, Chiswick Press, London 1900. It contains
valuable notes. Gilbert's second work is quoted from the only edition, *De Mundo
nostro sublunari Philosophia nova, Opus posthumum. Ab Authoris fratre collectum
pridem et dispositum.* . . . Amstelodami, 1651.—*De Mundo* does not shed much light
on the origin of Gilbert's ideas. We are not even sure whether it was composed
before or after *De Magnete.* At the margin of page 139 of *De Mundo* a reference
to *De Magnete* VI, 4 is given and a similar remark is added at the end of the chapter.
But since the author's brother who edited *De Mundo* declares himself in the preface
not to know 'which of the books was composed earlier, obviously both remarks have
been added by the editor later on. On the other hand in *De Mundo* (pp. 118 and
151) two statements of Patrizzi are criticised. These quotations can refer only to
Patrizzi's *Nova de Universis Philosophia,* part Pancosmia, book 26 and book 12
respectively (in the second edition, Venice 1593, fol. 132 col. 2 and fol. 91 col. 3).
The first edition of Patrizzi's work was printed in 1591. *De Mundo,* therefore, must
have been composed after 1591 (Gilbert died in 1603). Altogether *De Mundo* gives

I

1. Gilbert's scientific method combines essentially modern with metaphysical, Scholastic, and animistic elements.   Several of his experimental devices are still in use today.   He dresses the poles of his spherical loadstones with sheet-iron and thus invents the armature of magnets (II, chap. 17).   In order to examine weak magnetic forces he fixes small iron pieces on cork floating on water or suspends them on threads (I, 12 and 13; III, 8; V, 9).   He even uses a few physical instruments.   One of them is of his own invention and is the first of its kind in the history of physics.   It is a— still somewhat imperfect—electroscope which obviously is constructed after the pattern of a magnetic needle (II, 2 p. 49).   Besides Gilbert describes at length and illustrates by woodcuts four magnetic measuring instruments, two declinometers and two inclinometers (IV, 12; V, 1; V, 3).   They had, however, been neither invented nor essentially improved by him, though Gilbert omits that point.[2]

It is significant with respect to the origin of Gilbert's interest in scientific accuracy that all of his physical instruments are actu-

the impression of greater immaturity; it is more pedantic and contains more remnants of Scholastic terminology than *De Magnete*.   The first book of *De Mundo* combats the doctrine of the four elements, the second deals with astronomy, books 3 to 5 discuss "meteorological" problems, beginning with comets, the milky way, and clouds, and ending with the sea and the air.   Very few experiments are given. *De Mundo* contains some modern-looking results—*e.g.,* space above the terrestrial atmosphere is thought to be empty and cold—but the methods and arguments are in no way outstanding.

[2] Gilbert's electroscope consists of a light horizontal metal needle, which is put on a point so that it can be turned easily.   In *De Magnete* it is called by the same name *versorium* that is employed for magnetic needles.—The description of Gilbert's four magnetic measuring instruments must be omitted here.   The declinometer was invented in 1525 by Felipe Guillen.   It was improved before Gilbert by Francisco Falero (*Tratado del Esphera,* Sevilla 1535), Pedro Nunes (*Tratado da Sphera,* Lisbon 1537), William Borough (*A Discourse of the Variation of the Compass,* London 1581), and Simon Stevin (*De Havenvinding,* Leyden 1599).   The inclinometer had been invented by Robert Norman (*The Newe Attractive,* London 1581).   These works are reprinted in G. Hellman: *Rara Magnetica, 1269–1599.   (Neudrucke von Schriften . . . über Erdmagnetismus No. 10)* Berlin 1898.   As quotations at other places of *De Magnete* show, the cited works of Nunes, Borough, Norman, and Stevin were known to Gilbert.   Gilbert also invented and constructed two nomograms.   The first (IV, 12. p. 176) simplifies determination of the astronomical meridian by means of graphic calculus.   The second (V, 8)—which, however, is based on incorrect assumptions—is meant to determine graphically geographic latitude.

ally nautical instruments or are at least nearly related to the mariner's compass. On the whole he performs measurements practically only when he deals with quantities which are important in navigation, such as magnetic declination and inclination, altitudes of stars, and geographical latitudes (*e.g.,* IV, 4 p. 160; IV, 12 p. 176; V, 8; VI, 1 p. 214). In other fields he usually restricts himself to qualitative observations and experiments. His best quantitative experiment verifies the hypothesis that magnetism is imponderable by weighing pieces of iron "on most exact gold scales" before and after magnetization (III, 3). It is taken over, however, from the compass-maker Robert Norman without the source being given. The few quantitative investigations which are original with him are not very outstanding.[3] Altogether, quantitative investigation appears considerably developed in *De Magnete* if compared with physics in the Middle Ages; it cannot compare, however, with the use of scientific measurements in the works of Galileo and his followers. Calculations are lacking entirely.

Mechanics also plays a very small part in *De Magnete*. Twice Gilbert shows some mechanical insight. Once (II, 35) he vehemently attacks medieval attempts to construct a perpetual motion engine. At another time (II, 24 p. 92) he knows that unstable equilibrium cannot persist for a long time and that, therefore, Fracastoro's story of a piece of iron suspended in the air between the earth and a magnet is "absurd." These two passages, however, are the only ones in his book dealing with mechanical questions. Both the interest in mechanics and the mechanical interpretation of all natural phenomena which dominated physics from Galileo to the nineteenth century are still lacking in Gilbert.

2. It is not easy to draw the picture of Gilbert's scientific attitude correctly. He is usually as critical-minded as a modern experimentalist, does not rely on any authority, and always tests reports of others by his own experiments. Superstitious ideas are emphatically rejected by him. He derides the ancient and medieval stories of diamonds and garlic destroying magnetism, the stories of magnets detecting faithlessness of women and unlocking locks (pp. 2 f. and 6 f.). He vehemently attacks alchemists and their obscure language (pref. fol. iij; I, 3 pp. 19 f. and 24). He rejects the explanation of electric and magnetic attraction by

[3] II, 17 p. 86; II, 25 p. 92; II, 29 p. 97; II, 32 p. 99; III, 15 p. 145; III, 17 p. 150.

means of sympathy and, on that account, scoffs at Fracastoro (II, 2 p. 50; II, 3 p. 63 f.; II, 4 p. 65; II, 39 p. 113). On the other hand he believes in horoscopes, like most of his contemporaries: the magnetizing effect of the earth on pieces of iron being forged in the smithy is compared by him to the influence of the stars on a child during its birth (p. 142).[4]

Aristotelian and Scholastic concepts play a major part in his theoretical conceptions. Gilbert believes in the two basic principles matter and form, "out of which all bodies are produced" (II, 2 p. 52). In his opinion electric effects get their strength (*invalescunt*) from matter, magnetic effects from a "distinguished" (*praecipua*) form (p. 53), for he thinks that the spherical form of the stars and especially the earth, being "primary and powerful" (I, 17 p. 42), is "the true magnetic potency" (II, 4 p. 65). Obviously his explanation of magnetism is based on the Scholastic metaphysics of active forms. In all his experiments he uses spherical loadstones, although he himself knows (II, 15 p. 83; III, 31 p. 99) that bar-like magnets are more effective. He calls them "little earths" (*terrellae* I, 3) and presumably clings to the medieval shape of his magnets because he believes in a metaphysical connection of spherical form and magnetism.

Cardanus's story that "the magnet lives and feeds on iron" is derided by Gilbert as old women's talk (I, 16 p. 37; II, 3 p. 63). He refutes it, using experimental methods, by ascertaining that the weight of the iron filings in which a magnet is kept does not diminish. Again he proves himself an empiricist, but he is opposed to vitalistic explanations only in so far as they contradict single empirical facts. His own "philosophy" of magnetism, so far as it can neither be confirmed nor disproved by observation, is as animistic as the theory of Cardanus. A chapter of his book (V, 12) is entitled: "The magnetic force is animated or is similar to soul; it by far surpasses the human soul as long as that is bound to an organic body." The chapter refers to ancient philosophers from Thales to the Neoplatonists, who taught the existence of a soul of the universe, and adds the Egyptians, Chaldeans and (p. 209) even authorities on occult science, such as Hermes, Zoroaster and Orpheus. It explains (p. 209 f.) that the earth and the stars have

---

[4] The astrological theory of correspondence between metals and planets, however, is called "insane" (p. 20). In Gilbert's opinion metals, especially iron, are the very essence of the earth and, therefore, do not depend on the stars.

souls, although they have no sense-organs, and that God himself is soul;[5] and, quoting Thales, it calls the magnet "an animated stone, that is a part and beloved offspring of the animated mother, Earth."

The last quotation shows that Gilbert's theory of magnetism is embedded in a vitalistic philosophy of the terrestrial globe. To him the earth is "the common mother" of all things. Again and again in *De Magnete* this term is repeated, whenever the earth is mentioned.[6] We can therefore scarcely doubt the strongly emotional background of the idea of the maternal earth. The power of the magnet derives directly from the earth in Gilbert's opinion. For nothing but the magnet has preserved (I, 17 p. 42) "this distinguished substance which is homogenous to the internal nature of the earth and most akin to its marrow itself." Iron and magnets are (I, 16 p. 37) "the true and most intimate parts of the earth," because "they retain the first faculties in nature, the faculties of attracting each other, of moving, and of adjusting by the position of the world and the terrestrial globe."

Gilbert was the first to conceive the earth as a large magnet (I, 17; VI, 1). He was the first to teach that the interior of the earth consists of pure iron and that its surface and rim only are "soiled by other impurity" (I, 16 p. 39). Thus he has anticipated important empirical results of modern geophysics. But the resemblance of his magnetic philosophy to modern science is merely a matter of chance. Gilbert's terms "interior" and "intimate" combine spatial and metaphysical meaning and are always used as concepts of value. How near his "magnetic philosophy" still is to medieval vitalism is revealed by the fact that he believes in a metaphysical correlation of magnetism and rotation. He speaks of the "magnetic rotation" of the terrestrial globe (VI, 3 p. 214), and would like to accept the statement of Pierre de Maricourt that a spherical magnet rotates continuously by itself, were it not for his

---

[5] Gilbert's religious belief obviously is rather Neoplatonic than Protestant. The whole chapter is strongly influenced by Patrizzi. *Cf.* below § 4, footnote 13.

[6] *E.g.* pref. at the beginning and pp. 12, 26, 38 (twice), 41, 117, 152, 210.—Moreover Gilbert likes to compare the interior of the earth with the mother's womb. In his opinion all metals originate from exhalations of the innermost part of the earth that are condensed and congeal nearer the surface in warm cavities "as the sperm or embryo congeals in the warm uterus" (I, 7 p. 20). *De Mundo* advocates the doctrine (p. 39) that all kinds of matter originate in earth and that earth, therefore, is the only element.

conscience as a cautious experimentalist. He reproduces Pierre's statement and adds (VI, 4 p. 223): "until now we have not succeeded in seeing this. We even doubt this movement because of the stone's weight and because the whole earth moves by itself, as it is moved by the other stars also. That does not hold proportionally of some part [the *terrella*]." Everyone who remembers how vehemently Gilbert attacks the reports on perpetual motion machines must notice the difference in emphasis.[7]

II

3. The material thus far presented may serve for a general indication of Gilbert's way of thinking. Animistic and Neoplatonic ideas are abundant in his book; the traces of Scholasticism and astrology are scarcer. But it is not these pre-scientific features that are conspicuous, for his work shares them with the whole learned literature of his period. What really counts is that his animistic metaphysics is nothing but the emotional background of his thinking and does not affect the empirical content of his science. The writings both of the Scholastics and the Renaissance philosophers abound with superstitious stories and magic. Gilbert rejects all that with unswerving criticism and bases his findings on experience and experiment only. This attitude is so exceptional in his period that the question arises where it originates. Since critical minded experimentalists appear more and more frequently among the scholars a few decades after Gilbert, a satisfactory answer would at the same time contribute to the solution of the problem of the origin of modern science in general.

Even in a period in which quoting was more favored by scholars than nowadays, Gilbert is remarkable for the number of his references and his wide reading. He stresses, nevertheless, the novelty of his ideas. His attitude to contemporary literature is explained in the preface of *De Magnete*. There Gilbert says:

What business have I in that vast ocean of books? . . . By the more silly ones among them the crowd and most impudent people get intoxicated, insane and haughty. . . . They declare themselves to be philosophers, physicians, mathematicians, and astronomers and neglect and despise the

[7] The story of the rotating spherical magnet is mentioned in *De Mundo* also (p. 138). There Gilbert gives the same reasons why the *terrella* does not rotate "although it is fit and inclined by nature to rotation."—In order to understand Gilbert's argument we have to realize that he was among the earliest adherents of Copernicus in England and was already convinced of the rotation of the earth.

learned men. Why should I add any thing to this disturbed literary republic? Or am I to offer this eminent philosophy that because of its unknown contents, as it were, is new and unbelievable to people who blindly trust authorities, to most absurd destroyers of the good arts, to literary idiots, grammarians, sophists, pettifoggers, and perverse mediocrities? . . . No! I have presented these principles of magnetism that belong to a new kind of philosophy, to you true philosophers . . . who look for knowledge not in books only but in things themselves.

Continuing, he announces that he will not call upon ancient writers for help, "because neither Greek arguments nor Greek words" can assist in finding truth. He promises that he will avoid "the ornament of eloquence" and will not darken things by words "as the Alchemists are wont to do." He plans to write with the same "liberty of mind" (*licentia*) as the ancient Egyptians, Greeks, and Romans. The "sciolists" of present times still keep the errors of the ancients, but Aristotle, Theophrastus, Ptolemy, Hippocrates, and Galen themselves are sources of wisdom. "Yet our own period has discovered and brought to light very many things which those men too would be glad to accept if they were alive."

These vehement attacks on believers in authority and words, and the emphasis on the novelty of his ideas, are characteristic of the period of the expiring Renaissance, and anticipate Francis Bacon, and in some degree Galileo also. As the mention of grammarians, Greek words and eloquence shows, Gilbert's attack is aimed at declining humanism. Similar attacks are repeated several times in *De Magnete*.[8] Gilbert's other book, *De Mundo,* contains less polemics and is written more dispassionately. But it also opposes belief in authority: the slogan "he himself has said so, Aristotle has said so, Galen has said so" is considered a nuisance (*De Mundo* I, 3 p. 5).[9]

4. We shall therefore not expect to meet with much agreement with other authors in Gilbert's book. In fact most of the numer-

[8] Gilbert scoffs (I, 1 p. 2) at "precocious sciolists and copyists" who add fictitious stories to ancient authors. He accuses "the modern philosophers" (I, 10 p. 28) of having drawn their knowledge from books rather than from things. He derides (II, 2 p. 48) the books "cramming the bookshops" that deal with mysterious stories instead of experiments, and are as fond of Greek words as barbers who try to impress people by using scraps of Latin. He charges Fracastoro (II, 39 p. 113) with his predilection for Greek words and reproaches "the crowd of philosophers and copyists" (II, 38 p. 109) with repeating old opinions and errors.

[9] As is generally known, the *ipse dixit* (αὐτός ἔφα) was the slogan of the Pythagorean school by which they referred to their master.

ous references he gives are critical and negative, whereas the real sources of his ideas are chiefly to be sought elsewhere.

Ancient authors are often quoted. Comparatively favorable judgments are pronounced on philosophers who believe in universal animation, such as Plato and most of the Pre-Socratics. Atomists and mechanists are rejected. The Stoics are not mentioned. Although Gilbert is still greatly influenced by the concept of substantial form, he is opposed to Aristotle. In *De Magnete* (p. 116 and 209) Aristotle's astronomical doctrines are chiefly attacked, in *De Mundo* (I, 3) his doctrine of the four elements. The first book of *De Mundo* is even entitled "New Physiology against Aristotle," the third, "New Meteorology against Aristotle."[10]

References to medieval authors are rarer. Thomas Aquinas is twice quoted (I, 1 p. 3 and II, 3 p. 64) and his ingenuity and scholarship are highly praised. Yet Gilbert adds that Thomas did not experiment and consequently committed errors. A few Arabian authors are mentioned, but for the most part their opinions are attacked.[11]

Almost the same holds of the authors of the modern era. Gilbert does not seem to have known the humanists very well. Among modern scholars cited most frequently are the philosopher-physician Fracastoro, the mathematician and physician Cardanus, the philologist and physician Scaliger, and the learned compiler of curiosities, Giambattista Porta. The first three authors were among the most famous scholars of the late Renaissance. Nearly always Gilbert derides all four of them, Fracastoro because of his belief in "sympathy," the others because of their credulity and superstition. Gilbert—he was physician in ordinary to Queen Elizabeth—wrote two chapters (I, 14 and 15) on the medical effects of iron. There he proves to be familiar with modern medical literature, but practically all authors cited are refuted. He vehe-

[10] Thales, Empedocles, Anaxagoras, Pythagoreans, Plato praised V, 1; Plato attacked p 61; Aristotle: his importance admitted (pref. about the end), his (and Galen's) opinions on iron approved, p. 39; Hippocrates praised because he did not advocate the doctrine of the four elements *De Mundo*, p. 5, attacked *De Magnete* p. 35; Galen criticized, p. 35 and 62, his importance admitted, pref. about the end; Strabo, Ptolemy, Tacitus, and Pliny the Elder quoted on iron mines p. 25; Pliny the Elder (on glass-making) attacked, p. 112.

[11] Avicenna is quoted on meteorites, p. 26; the medical opinions of Avicenna, Razes (= Abu Bekr al Rasi), and unnamed Arabian physicians attacked, p. 34f.; the alchemists Geber and Gilgil Mauretanus attacked, p. 19.

mently attacks Paracelsus, who among the physicians was the first to rebel against the authority of Aristotle and Galen, and he twice mentions (pp. 34 f.) the eminent and empirical-minded anatomist Fallopius without bringing him into any prominence. Gilbert's personal medical opinions are remarkably sound and free of superstition. Contemporary astronomical literature is well known to him (*De Mundo* II, 10 and 20) and Copernicus is highly praised in *De Magnete* (VI, 3). In the preface to *De Magnete*, written by Gilbert's friend Wright, the heliocentric theory is defended at length against scientific and religious objections.[12]

More may be learned of the origin of Gilbert's ideas from the references lacking than from those he gives. Among ancient authors three are conspicuous by their absence in *De Magnete:* Euclid, who is most important for the development of geometrical knowledge in the fifteenth and sixteenth centuries; Archimedes, who greatly influenced mechanics in the same period; and Vitruvius, who is the main source of knowledge in the field of ancient engineering. The three omissions show that Gilbert was not concerned with the mathematical literature of the period, that he was not interested in mechanics, and that he had connections neither with the humanists nor the architects of the Renaissance, who often quoted Vitruvius. With artists, presumably, Gilbert did not have any contacts at all. He could have found real experiments in the papers of the Italian artist-engineers (Brunelleschi, Ghiberti, Leonardo), which, however, were not yet printed. He never mentions Biringuccio either, who belonged with the architects of the Renaissance. Biringuccio's work *Della Pirotechnia*, printed in 1540, treats metallurgy quite empirically and by experiments, but still discusses the magnet in a rather superstitious way.

The omission of one more group of authors is instructive. Gilbert's opposition to belief in books and authorities and his pride

[12] Nicolaus Cusanus ("not to be despised"), p. 64; Marsilius Ficinus, p. 3 ("ruminates ancient opinions") and p. 16; Fracastoro *De Sympathia* (1545), mentioned, pp. 5, 9, 110, 113; his theory of planetary movements (given in his *Homocentricorum seu de Stellis Liber*) discussed in *De Mundo* II, 10; Cardanus's *De Subtilitate* (1552) attacked, pp. 5, 27, 37, 42, 63, 107, 110, 169; Scaliger's *Exercitationes Esotericae* (1557) attacked, pp. 5, 27, 37, 42, 63, 107, 110, 169; Porta's *Magia Naturalis* (1589) quoted, pp. 6, 24, 63, 137f., 143f., 166ff.; Paracelsus's "shameless charlatanry" attacked, p. 93, his merits admitted but Paracelsists attacked, *De Mundo* p. 7; the Antiparacelsist *Thomas Erastus* quoted, pp. 3 and 23. Tycho Brahe (on the coordinates of the Polaris) referred to, p. 174.

in the novelty of his ideas, are greatly reminiscent of Bernardino Telesio. Telesio was the first among the scholars of the Renaissance to oppose his "own principles" to Aristotelian natural philosophy (*De Rerum Natura iuxta propria Principia*, 1565 and 1570). Actually the influence of Telesio appears a few years after *De Magnete* in the works of Bacon, in which the anti-Aristotelian rebellion is carried on with even greater impetus. Gilbert, however, neither mentions Telesio nor seems to have known his work. The case of Telesio's pupil Patrizzi is somewhat different. Patrizzi always attacks Aristotle but is not much of a champion of originality: he likes quoting Plato and the authorities of occult science too well. He was known to Gilbert and is twice quoted in *De Mundo* (II, 2, p. 118 and II, 10, p. 151). Both times, however, statements of Patrizzi—on the shape of the globe and on the cause of the motions of the stars—are rejected. In *De Magnete* also both content and wording of the Neoplatonic chapter on universal animation (V, 12) obviously are influenced by Patrizzi, although he is not even mentioned.[13] Campanella and Giordano Bruno are also intellectually related to Telesio. Both attacked Aristotle and rejected the humanistic veneration of books with the same vehemence. Yet they are never mentioned in Gilbert. Bruno lived in England from 1583 to 1585; it would have been easy, therefore, for our author to make contact with him.

Gilbert's ideas—he describes, as we have seen, parts of *De Mundo* as *Physiologia nova contra Aristotelem, Nova Meteorologia contra Aristotelem*—belong to the same intellectual current as those of Telesio, Patrizzi, Campanella, and Bruno. Modern technology and modern economy had changed civilization too thoroughly for the Scholastic belief in Aristotle or the humanistic veneration of antiquity to endure. Telesio, Patrizzi, Campanella, and Bruno, however, were metaphysicians, not experimentalists, though Telesio and Campanella, theoretically at least, emphasized the importance of experience. It is rather instructive to realize that

[13] Patrizzi's main work *Nova de Universis Philosophia* appeared in Venice, 1591. We quote, however, from the second edition, Venice, 1593. The part *Panpsychia*, book 4 refers to the Presocratics, Plato, the Neoplatonists, the Egyptians and Chaldeans, and to Zoroaster, Hermes, and Orpheus; it stresses the fact that stars do not need organs, though they have souls; it three times (fol. 55 col. 2 and 3) calls Aristotle's philosophy a "monstrum," because in his doctrine the whole universe is animated except for the earth. Quite the same theses and references are repeated in *De Magnete* V, 12 and even the term "monstrum" appears there (p. 209).

three of these philosophers exerted no influence at all on Gilbert and only Patrizzi contributed a few Neoplatonic ideas to his philosophy. In a sociological analysis the young experimental science of the early seventeenth century and the antidogmatic but fantastic metaphysics of the late Renaissance might prove to be connected: in both the same rebellion of the nascent modern society against the antiquated erudition and authorities of the past manifests itself. Yet the natural philosophy of the late Renaissance was the older brother of experimental science, not its father. The experimental method did not and could not have descended from the metaphysical ideas of the natural philosophers. We have to look elsewhere and in other social ranks for its immediate predecessors.

Among all the scholars quoted by Gilbert there is one who really did influence his investigation and method a great deal, although he does not at all emphasize this indebtedness. This is the medieval nobleman Pierre de Maricourt, who in 1269 wrote a short but remarkable account of his magnetic experiments. About his life almost nothing is known. Written copies of his letter on magnetism were circulated until the sixteenth century, when it was printed under the title *Petri Peregrini Maricurtensis De Magnete, seu Rota perpetui motus libellus,* Augsburgi, 1558. Gilbert mentions Petrus Peregrinus five times in *De Magnete* and once in *De Mundo.*[14]

The first reference is in the first chapter of *De Magnete* which compiles the opinions on magnetism of the authors of the past. There (p. 5) Gilbert says: "About 200 years before Fracastoro there is a short work, sufficiently learned considering the period, under the name of a certain Petrus Peregrinus, which many think to have originated in the opinions of the Englishman Roger Bacon of Oxford. From that Johannes Taysner of Hainolt excerpted a booklet and published it as a new one."[15] Twice (III, 1 p. 116 and IV, 1 p. 153) Petrus is mentioned among the advocates of the erroneous opinion that "the magnetic needle is attracted by the celestial pole." In a short chapter (II, 35) Gilbert vehemently

[14] On Pierre and his letter *cf.* Silvanus P. Thompson: *Petrus Peregrinus de Maricourt and his Epistola de Magnete, Proc. Brit. Acad.* vol. 2 (1905/6), pp. 377–408, and Erhard Schlund: *Archivum Franciscanum Historicum* vol. 4 (1911) and vol. 5 (1912). The letter on magnetism is reprinted in G. Hellmann: *Rara Magnetica (Neudrucke etc.)* Berlin, 1898.—On the origin of Pierre's scientific method *cf.* below § 8.

[15] As a matter of fact Roger Bacon depends more on Pierre than Pierre on Bacon.—Taysner's plagiarism was printed Coloniae 1562.

rejects the perpetual motion engines of Cardanus, Antonius de Fantis, Petrus Peregrinus, and Johannes Taysner. And, finally, in *De Magnete* VI, 4 (p. 223) and *De Mundo* II, 7 (p. 13) he criticizes Pierre's story of the always rotating *terrella* (*cf.* §2, above). Except for the first passage, which, however, is rather general and rather tepid, Gilbert always differs with and criticizes the opinions of Pierre de Maricourt.

But in fact he owes more to Pierre than his words indicate. Pierre already knew (Chap. 6) that unlike poles attract, like ones repel one another. He knew (Chap. 9) that, when a magnet is divided, the pieces become new magnets with new poles. But Gilbert's knowledge of these facts need not have been taken over directly from the medieval experimentalist. The case is different with the spherical shape of the magnets. This shape is not a matter of course, but is, from the modern point of view, rather inexpedient. Pierre uses spherical loadstones, and the complicated way of determining the magnetic poles of the sphere—short pieces of iron wire are put on them and meridians are drawn with chalk until they intersect—is so completely identical in both authors (Pierre, Chap. 4, Gilbert I, 3, p. 12 f.) that literary influence cannot be doubted. Gilbert is indebted to the outstanding medieval experimentalist as well for one of his experimental devices. Pierre (Chap. 5–7) had already made his loadstones float on water by means of wooden vessels. The cork pieces which are used by Gilbert of course were not yet known to him.

5. Up to this point we have not been able to give many positive contributions in answer to our main question. We have traced numerous authors to whom Gilbert was not indebted for his scientific method and only one—Pierre de Maricourt—to whom he was. The origins of his experimental technique and his scientific criticism are almost as enigmatic as they were before we started collecting his quotations. But we may have proceeded incorrectly. It was wrong, in fact, to look for his intellectual predecessors among scholars and philosophers. One has but to turn over the leaves of *De Magnete* in order to realize that he was interested in unscholarlike people and non-scholastic subjects too. Of the 240 pages of the book only 97 (40%) explain physical experiments. On the other hand 60 pages (25%) deal with nautical instruments and navigation, 25 pages (10%) with mining, melting, and fashioning of iron. The rest discusses astronomical questions (25 pp.), the

opinions of numerous authors (18 pp.), the terrestrial globe as a magnet (11 pp.), and the medical effects of iron (4 pp.). Obviously *De Magnete* differs a great deal from a modern textbook on magnetism. The very first printed book on experimental physics deals so extensively with practical problems, that in some respects it is nearer to a technological than to a physical work of our time. And this gives the clue to the solution of our problem.

We may discuss first Gilbert's interest in mining and metallurgy. The literature on the subject is well known to him. George Agricola, the best known sixteenth century author in this field, is quoted most frequently. Gilbert esteems him highly but corrects errors uncritically taken over by Agricola from antiquity. Not less than three chapters of *De Magnete* (I, 2, 7, and 8) give extensive accounts of the distribution of iron in the world, describe the various ores, and quote ancient, Arabian, and modern authors on the subject.[16] Iron-manufacturing also is discussed at length (I, 7). Gilbert reports (p. 23) on the manufacturing of cast iron, wrought iron, and steel in Styria and Spain, he refers to the description of iron-foundries in Porta's *Magia Naturalis,* and gives (p. 24) a list, eleven lines long, of iron devices. It contains among other things various kinds of guns, ''the plague of mankind,'' and ends with a hint at other ''numerous devices unknown to Latins.'' His reports on England are most interesting, as they are obviously based on

[16] The books of Agricola (1490–1555) on mining and metallurgy are still the best source of knowledge on this branch of technology in the 16th century. Gilbert (I, 1 p. 2) calls him "most outstanding in science," but regrets that he took over the ancient stories of antimagnetic effects of garlic and diamond. He rejects (I, 38 p. 110) Agricola's statement that the magnet is useful in glass-manufacturing and reproaches Agricola for being influenced on this point by the "ignorant philosophy" of Pliny the Elder. Of course Gilbert knows that glass is not attracted by magnets. He approves (I, 7 p. 19) Agricola's chemical opinion that iron is composed of earth and water. Agricola and other—unnamed—"learned metallurgists" are referred to (I, 2 p. 10) on occurrences of iron-ore in Germany and Bohemia. On a special kind of iron-ore the opponent to Paracelsus, Thomas Erastus, is given as literary informant (I, 7 p. 23). *De Magnete* I, 8 quotes Strabo, Ptolemy, Tacitus, and Pliny on iron-mines in various parts of Europe and emphasizes that iron is the most frequently occurring mineral, as "every expert on metallurgy and chemistry" can confirm. Again Agricola is given as a reference for the occurrence and working of meadow-ore (p. 26). "As some authors write," (obviously Spanish cosmographers or mariners), there is iron in the West Indies too, "but Spaniards are looking for gold only." The chapter ends with a report on iron meteorites and quotes on that subject Avicenna, Scaliger, and Cardanus.

personal experience. He tells (I, 2 p. 11) that "newly" in an English mine, owned by the gentleman Adrian Gilbert, magnetic iron ore was found.[17] He reports (I, 7 p. 23) on the handling of iron in English gun foundries. And he knows (I, 8 p. 26) that English clay always contains iron and that, if bricks are baked in open kilns, "which are called *clampa* with us," the bricks next to the fire show "ferruginous vitrification."

Gilbert is also familiar with forging. In a chapter dealing with magnetic experiments (I, 11 p. 29) he describes how he himself manufactures the wrought iron he needs for his experiments, and adds: "out of that the hammersmiths (*fabri*) form quadrangular pieces but mostly ingots (*bacillas*) which are bought by merchants and blacksmiths (*ferrarii*) and out of which various devices are manufactured in the workshops (*officinis*)." In a chapter (III, 12) which explains how iron is magnetized by the magnetic field of the earth he even gives a large woodcut of a smithy with furnace, bellows, anvil, and tools.

That very woodcut, which would be impossible in a modern textbook on magnetism, illustrates the intimate connection of Gilbert's theoretical investigation with practical metallurgy. Moreover, we must not forget that Gilbert did not live in the period of tradition-bound medieval handicraft. The mining and metallurgy he is interested in is the mining and metallurgy of rapidly advancing early capitalism. As we know from Agricola, hauling engines, stamping mills, ventilators, and tracks for the dogs came into use in mining during the sixteenth century. In the same period the introduction of the blast furnace revolutionized the whole technique of iron manufacture. English mining and English metallurgy participated in that development.[18] Since the miners and foundrymen of the period belonged to the lower ranks of society and were uneducated we know neither their names nor their ideas. Yet we cannot doubt that many of them, stimulated to improvements by economic competition, were wont to try new techniques and to observe natural processes. Technology could not have progressed so rapidly if the laborers in the manner of the medieval guilds had simply

[17] The owner was no relation of the author. *Cf.* the family-tree in Silvanus B. Thompson: *The Family and Arms of Gilbert of Colchester*, Trans. Essex Archaeol. Soc., vol. 9, new series (1906) p. 211.

[18] *Cf.* Ludwig Beck: *Geschichte des Eisens*, Braunschweig 1893–95, vol. 2, pp. 879–97.

clung to the traditional working-processes of the past. Obviously, among such manual laborers there were experimentalists, though experimentalists with practical aims only and without theoretical knowledge. With their ranks Gilbert must have had many con- tacts. By a lucky accident we are even able to prove that he must have himself descended into an iron mine. Once (III, 2 p. 119 f.) he tells how he verified the hypothesis that the direction of mag- netism in magnetic iron ore is induced by the earth. He says:

> We had a twenty pounds' heavy loadstone dug and hauled out after having first observed and marked its ends in its vein. Then we put the stone in a wooden tub on water, so that it could turn freely. Immediately the surface which had looked to the North in the mine turned itself to the North on the water.

It is almost symbolic that Gilbert performed a laboratory experi- ment just after having left a pit and talked to miners. Of course Gilbert's experiments were not plain copies of the trials of the min- ers and foundrymen. But his spirit of observing and experiment- ing was taken over not from scholars but from manual workers. Sometimes, however, even his experiments simply repeated the working processes of contemporary iron manufacture. In three chapters of *De Magnete* (I, 9–11) he describes magnetic experi- ments with iron ore and wrought iron: he makes pieces of ore and iron float on water, he suspends them by threads, and has them attracted by magnets; but first he heats the ore for hours in a fur- nace and melts it; then he hammers the product, puts it into a second furnace and so on. All this is described, not as a mere preparation, but as a part of the experiments themselves. At least a part of his laboratory must have looked like a smithy.

6. Navigation and nautical instruments play an even greater part in *De Magnete* than mining and metallurgy. About 32 pages (13%) of the book are dedicated to nautical instruments, about 28 (12%) to general navigation. Already at the very beginning of *De Magnete*, in Wright's preface, geographic discoveries and cir- cumnavigations of the globe are mentioned. In his survey of previous writers on magnetism (I, 1 p. 4) Gilbert reports (errone- ously) the history of the invention of the compass and remarks that "no invention of human arts has ever been of greater use to mankind." He mentions Sebastian Cabot as the discoverer of magnetic declination and gives (p. 7) the names of four men "who

have observed the variety of magnetic declination on long voyages": Thomas Hariot, Robert Hues, Edward Wright, and Abraham Kendall.[19] Gilbert proves to be familiar with mariners also in a chapter on the terrestrial globe. There (I, 17 p. 39) he gives numerical statements on the depth of the ocean according to the soundings of the mariners. He must have been told of their results by personal friends.[20]

The full extent of his nautical knowledge appears in the fourth book of *De Magnete* which deals with magnetic declination. Gilbert knows (IV, 1 p. 152) that declination differs at different places and gives its amount for places dispersed over all oceans and continents.[21] The remarkably wide range of his statements proves his familiarity with the reports of the English, Spanish, Portuguese, and Dutch navigators and the books of the learned cosmographers of the period. Moreover he mentions (IV, 5 and 10) that declination is great in high latitudes and that it is not influenced by the iron mines of the island of Elba in the Mediterranean. He knows

[19] Since Gilbert's authorities on navigation are characteristic of the social soil from which modern natural science has sprung, their activities and occupations are important. The mathematician and astronomer Hariot or Harriot (1560–1621) who was mathematical tutor to Sir Walter Raleigh as a young man, was sent by him as a surveyor to Virginia, and came back to England later. He published a report on Virginia, and mathematical works. The mathematician Robert Hues (1553–1632) accompanied Thomas Cavendish on his circumnavigation of the globe and published a *Tractatus de Globis et eorum Usu,* London 1594, dedicated to Sir Walter Raleigh. The mathematician Edward Wright (1558–1615) accompanied the Earl of Cumberland on his voyage to the Azores. He was lecturer on navigation to the East India Company. In his book *Certaine Errors in Navigation,* London 1599, he introduced the cartographic projection that usually is ascribed to Mercator. Abraham Kendal or Kendall is the only non-scholar among the four men. He was sailing-master of Sir Robert Dudley's ship the Bear and later joined Drake's last expedition (*cf. The Oxford Dictionary of National Biography* and the Chiswick Press translation of *De Magnete,* London 1900, notes p. 19). Wright wrote the second preface to *De Magnete.* Most probably the three other men also were personal friends of Gilbert (*cf.* footnote 22 below).

[20] He states that the depth of the ocean reaches one mile at a few places only and generally is no more than 50 to 100 fathoms. As the greatest depth of mines he gives 400 to 500 fathoms, as the diameter of the earth 6,872 miles.

[21] P. 153f. East coast of the Atlantic from Guinea to Norway, West coast from Florida to Cape Race in New Foundland; p. 161 Azores; p. 163f. London; p. 167 North Cape in Norway, Corvo in the Azores, Plymouth; p. 178f. on the equator and in the South Atlantic (St. Helena); pp. 179–182 Nova Zembla (from Dutch observations), South Pacific, Mediterranean, Indian Ocean.

(IV, 8 p. 165 f.) that the Portuguese royal cosmographer Pedro Nuñes (*Tratado da Sphera*, Lisboa, 1537) disregards declination entirely and that the Spanish historian Pedro de Medina (*Arte de Navegar*, Valladolid 1545) is wrong on it. He complains of the inexactness of most mariners in determining declination and warns especially of the reports of Portuguese navigators on their voyages to the East Indies. He knows that the Portuguese mariner Roderigos de Lagos, the Spanish mariner Diego de Alfonso, the Dutchmen, and "the experienced Englishman" Abraham Kendall contradict each other in their numerical statements (IV, 13 p. 177 f).[22] Since determination of geographic longitude was a difficult and, consequently, an often discussed problem at that period, he tries to solve it by means of the declination of the magnetic needle. He mentions (IV, 9 p. 167) that the learned compiler of curiosities Giambattista Porta (*Magia Naturalis*, 1589), the Venetian geographer Livio Sanuto (*Geografia*, 1588) and the mathematician Giambattista Benedetto give wrong solutions of the problem, since declination does not vary proportionally with the distance on the surface of the earth, as had been assumed by them. In the end he quotes the correct solution of Simon Stevin, the eminent Dutch expert in military engineering, navigation and book-keeping.[23]

Gilbert is familiar with the astronomical aids to navigation too. He knows how geographic latitude is determined astronomically, even takes into account atmospheric refraction, and gives a long list of bright stars with their declinations and right ascensions for the practical use of navigators (IV, 12 p. 174f.).

Gilbert got his nautical knowledge not from reading only. Again, as with the miners, an occasional mention in *De Magnete*

[22] The sailing-master Kendall (*cf.* footnote 19) did not publish any book. Since Gilbert is familiar with his experiences, he must have known him personally.

[23] The (antiquated) solution is: the declinations at the various places of the surface of the earth have to be listed at first and then the geographic position of the ship can be determined by comparing observed declination with the list. Stevin's paper (*De Havenvinding*, Leyden 1599) is reprinted in G. Hellmann, *Rara Magnetica*, Berlin 1899. Gilbert does not quote the original paper but its Latin translation by Hugo Grotius (the elder) *Portuum Investigandorum Ratio*, 1599. It was in the same year translated as well into English by Gilbert's friend, Edward Wright (*The Havenfinding Art*, London 1599) and into French (*Le trouve Port*, Leyden 1599). The four publications in one year, three vernacular, one Latin, illustrate rather well the rapid development in scientific navigation at this period and the kind of people Gilbert was in touch with. He quotes Stevin just one year after his paper had appeared. In this period this is remarkable.

reveals the personal contacts of the author.   Once (III, 1 p. 117f.)
Gilbert explains that the compass works under all latitudes from
the equator up to the 70th and 80th degree N.L., and adds: "This
the most famous captains and also very many of the more intelligent sailors confirm to us.   This our most famous Neptunus
Francis Drake, and the other circumnavigator of the globe, Thomas
Cavendish, have told and confirmed to me."   Obviously he is proud
of the friendship of the two great circumnavigators who by their
naval victories over the Spaniards—and by their successful privateering—had access to the court of Queen Elizabeth.   Cavendish.
was a gentleman by birth, Sir Francis Drake was knighted because
of his naval success: the names of the ordinary master mariners
and helmsmen Gilbert had contact with are not given by him.[24]

At the end of the passage just quoted (III, 1 p. 118) Gilbert
states that the compass works badly only when the needle has
rusted or when the point on which it turns has got blunt.   This
leads us to his interest in nautical instruments.   The measuring
instruments described at length in *De Magnete* have already been
discussed, and it has been mentioned that they are less new than
the reader of Gilbert's description would assume.[25]   After the publication of *De Magnete* Gilbert was still engaged in improving his
instruments and making propaganda for them.   One year before
Gilbert's death a certain M. Blundeville published a booklet
Theorique of the Seven Planets, London, 1602.   It is written in
English and contains as an appendix "the making description and
use of two most ingenious and necessarie Instruments for Sea-
men. . . . First invented by my good friend, Master Doctor Gilbert. . . ."   Obviously Gilbert had suggested the publication in
English.   The two instruments are the nomogram of *De Magnete,*
which is supposed to make possible the determination of geographic
latitude, and a somewhat more simplified inclinometer than the one
in *De Magnete.*[26]   As this improvement shows, Gilbert does not

---

[24] Gilbert himself in the quotation just given distinguishes "illustrissimi nau-
cleri" and "nautae etiam sagaciores plurimi" among his authorities.   The sailing
master Abraham Kendall (*cf.* footnotes 19 and 22) was personally acquainted with
him.   Edward Wright was his friend and so probably were Thomas Harriot and
Robert Hues (*cf.* footnote 19).   These three men, however, were academically trained
mathematicians who had intimate relations with navigators and navigation.

[25] § 1, footnote 2.

[26] Blundeville is one more of the friends of Gilbert.   He wrote popular scientific
books in English for gentlemen.   Besides the quoted work he published treatises on

deal with instruments as a mere theorist, but is familiar with the practical demands master-mariners make. He realizes (*De Magnete* IV, 12 p. 172) that in navigation simply built instruments are necessary which can be handled in spite of the rolling of the ship, and he invents and draws nomograms because he feels complicated calculations and "the exercises of mathematical genius" to be out of place on shipboard. On the method of preparing, magnetizing, and balancing the needle of the compass he gives a few practical hints (III, 17 p. 147 f.). He discusses at length (IV, 8 p. 165 f.) the various types of compasses that are used by the sailors of the various European nations. This chapter, however, is based on statements of Robert Norman without mentioning his name.

7. Norman's influence on Gilbert's investigation is so important that it must be discussed in greater detail. Gilbert himself does not emphasize it at all, but rather hides it. In the first chapter, after mentioning Wright and his friends, Gilbert goes on (p. 7 f.): "Others invented and made public magnetic instruments and expedient methods of observation, necessary to navigators and long-distance travellers, *e.g.*, William Borough in his booklet on the Declination of the Compass, William Barlow in his Supplement,[27] and Robert Norman in his New Attractive." He adds that Norman, "an expert mariner and ingenious artificer," discovered the dip of the needle. A second time also Norman is quoted with approval. There (IV, 6, p. 161f.) Gilbert explains that the adjusting of the magnetic needle with the meridian is not effected by attraction but by some "disposing and turning faculty" of the earth, and adds that this was stressed by Norman as the first.

horsemanship, on Aristotelian logic, on map-making, on morals, and on counsellors of princes. The sub-title of his *Theorique of the seven Planets* illustrates rather well which social ranks outside the universities were interested in astronomy at Gilbert's time. It reads: *A Booke most necessarie for all Gentlemen that are desirous to be skillful in Astronomie and for all Pilots and Sea-men or any others that love to serve the Prince on the Sea or by the Sea to travell into forraine Countries.* This means that astronomical papers—if they were written in English—were of interest to oversea-traders and ship-owners, their master-mariners and helmsmen, and the gentlemen in the Royal Navy. Blundeville's booklet is based not only on Ptolemy but also on the ephemerides of Peurbach, Copernicus, and his followers Reinhold and Mestlin.

[27] Barlow was the son of a bishop and himself a clergyman, and was interested in navigation, though he had never gone to sea. He published among other papers *The Navigators Supply*, London, 1597. He was a personal friend of Gilbert. Cf. Gilbert's letter to him, published in Barlow, *A Brief Discovery of the Idle Animadversions of Mark Ridle,* London, 1618.

Then he describes at length and illustrates by a woodcut an experiment which is supposed to prove the explanation given.[28]   The experiment in every detail (and its incorrect interpretation) is borrowed from Norman's book.   Twice more (I, 1 p. 5 and IV, 1 p. 153) Norman is mentioned in three words as the author who suggested the name "point respective" for the place that all magnetic needles point to, instead of "point attractive."   Strangely enough, three of the four quotations refer to an opinion in which Norman is wrong.   If we wish to learn what Gilbert actually owes to him, we have to examine Norman's treatise.[29]

Norman was a retired mariner who had turned to compass-making.   That can be inferred from his booklet, which is the only source available on his life.   The booklet itself begins with a few mineralogical remarks on magnetic iron ore, and reproduces a story of Paracelsus on loadstones which can be strengthened to such a degree by making them red-hot so that they can draw nails out of a wall.   It is the same story which incites Gilbert to abuse Paracelsus as a shameless charlatan (*De Magnete*, p. 93).   Norman, however, believes it.   It is more important that Norman's very first chapter describes experiments in which magnets are suspended by threads and made to float on water.[29a]   The second chapter discusses earth-magnetism.   Norman does not believe that it can be explained by loadstones at the North Pole of the earth, because he knows that the iron mines at Elba do not deflect the magnetic needle—a statement simply taken over by Gilbert.   Then Norman discusses (chap. 3) the dip of the magnetic needle "not

[28] He makes a magnetic needle float in water by means of a piece of cork and carefully sees to it that it is completely submerged; from the fact that the needle adjusts itself with the direction of earth-magnetism but is not drawn to the rim of the vessel he concludes that there is no attraction. He (and Norman) forget that the needle has two opposite poles which are drawn to opposite directions.

[29] *The Newe Attractive, Containing a short discourse of the Magnes or Lodestone and amongest other his vertues, of a newe discovered secret and subtil propertie concernyng the Declinyng of the Needle touched therewith under the plaine of the Horizon. Now first founde by Robert Norman Hydrographer. Hereunto are annexed certaine necessarie rules for the art of Navigation by the same R.N.*, London, 1581. The book, reprinted in 1585, 1592, 1596, 1614, and 1720, has become a bibliographical rarity.   G. Hellmann, *Rara Magnetica*, Berlin 1898 gives a reprint of the 1720 edition.   The preface, the introductory poems, and the astronomical tables are not reproduced by him.   We quote from the extremely rare second edition, London, 1592.

[29a] Norman did this by means of small pieces of cork. It is to be remembered that these new experimental devices were simply taken over by Gilbert in *De Magnete*.

before having heard nor read of any such matter," and describes (chap. 4) and illustrates by a wood-cut the very first inclinometer.[30] The descriptions of two outstanding and most carefully performed experiments follow, both taken over by Gilbert. The first (chap. 5) proves by means of a gold balance that magnetism is imponderable; this is experimentally and theoretically entirely correct. The second (chap. 6) has been mentioned above (footnote 28); it is meant to prove that the earth does not attract but only turns the magnetic needle. It is illustrated by a woodcut, is even more carefully performed than in Gilbert—Norman stresses that any current of air must be avoided—but its theoretical interpretation is wrong, just as it is with Gilbert. The same chapter (6) introduces the term "point respective" which we have already mentioned.

The rest of the book does not contain experiments. Norman discusses (chap. 7) how the "point respective" might be determined by comparing magnetic needles at different places on the earth. As a simple mariner and instrument-maker he is unable, so he confesses (chap. 8), to explain the cause of terrestrial magnetism. "I will not offer," he says modestly, "to dispute with the Logitians in so many pointes as here they might seeme to overreach me in Naturall causes." So he restricts himself to a reference to "God in his omnipotent providence." He discusses (chap. 9) magnetic declination and its diversity at different places, stressing—again we remember Gilbert—that there is no "equal proportion" in it, as some navigators had believed who, "notwithstanding their travells mostley have *more followed their Bookes than experience* in this matter." He himself refers to the "18 or 20 years that I have travelled the Seas." He complains that most mariners have but confused ideas on declination because of lack of suitable instruments: "wherefore I have devised one very necessarie." The last chapter (10) discusses the different types of compasses in various countries and is the source of the corresponding chapter in

---

[30] As a matter of fact the dip had been observed before, though less exactly, by the German physician Georg Hartmann. Hartmann's unpublished letter (1544) to Duke Albert of Prussia on his discovery, is reprinted by Hellmann, *loc. cit.* By Norman the dip always is called "declination," whereas magnetic declination is called "variation." This terminology also was taken over by Gilbert. Gilbert's inclinometer is a mere copy of Norman's instrument, but Norman proves to be the more experienced instrument-maker. *E.g.* he makes the bearings of the needle's axle of glass. Gilbert neglects that excellent detail.

De Magnete (IV, 8). It follows a second part containing astronomical tables for the use of navigators.

We have already become acquainted with the empirical temper of this simple instrument-maker who, no less than Gilbert, Francis Bacon, and Galileo, prefers observation to books. His intellectual attitude is expressed even more clearly in the remarkable preface to the book. It is addressed "to the Right Worshipfull, M. William Borough, Esquire, Comptroller of her Maiesties Navie." It starts with the anecdote of Archimedes who, while taking a bath, discovers the law of buoyancy, runs naked to the street, and shouts —Norman avoids Greek—"I have found it." Norman continues:

So I (although in other respects and points of learning and knowledge, I will not presume to compare with Archimedes . . . nor with other learned Mathematicians, being myself an unlearned Mathematician) by occasion of my profession, making sundry experiments of the Magnet stone, found at length amongst many other effects this strange and newe propertie of Declining of the Needle : which forgetting or rather neglecting my own nakedness and want of furniture, to set forth the matter, I have heere in simple sorte proposed . . . to the view of the world.

Again he cites an ancient anecdote, the story of Pythagoras and the hecatomb he offered after having discovered his theorem, and continues:

So that we see these men . . . being carried and overcome *with the incredible delight* conceived of their own devices and inventions, though, they follow partly the peculiar contentation of their privat fancies, yet they seme chiefly to respect either the glory of god or the furtherance of some publike commoditie. . . . And seing it hath pleased God to make mee the instrument to open this noble secret, that his name might be glorified, and the commoditie of my Country procured thereby, I thought it my dutie to aduenture my credite and make my name the object of slaunderous and carping tongues rather then such a secrete should be concealed and the use thereof unknown.

Continuing, Norman stresses the utility of navigation to his country and again explains his resolution to publish his discovery "to frame as it were a theorike" for the use of mariners, and. to describe "whatever I could find by exact triall and perfect experiments."

Wherin, although I may seeme to have discouered my nakedness and want of eloquence and orderly Methode to utter my conceits withall, I trust the reader will either of his curtesie take all things for good, that is well ment, or of his grauitie, *not regarding the words but the matter,* dissemble my faults, and accept of my paines.

He mentions that he has communicated his findings before publication to a few learned friends and concludes with respectful words to William Borough as "your worships most humble Robert Norman." In his short preface to the reader he emphasizes also that he will "ground his arguments onlye upon experience, reason and demonstrations." "Many and divers ancient Authors, Philosophers and other" have written on the magnet, but he intends to write "contrary to the opinions of all them." This remarkable man who, twenty-five years before Galileo's first publication, speaks of the "incredible delight" of experimental discovery, was a craftsman. At the end of the first edition of his booklet a kind of advertisement was printed, stating that the instruments described "are made by Robert Norman and may be had at his home in Ratclif."[31] When the seamen of the sixteenth century went to sea, they laid the foundation-stone of the British Empire and when they retired and made compasses, of modern experimental science.

The note just quoted refers to Norman's own inclinometer and to two declinometers constructed by the mariner William Borough and described in Borough's *Discourse of the Variation of the Compass. or Magneticall Needle,* that in all editions was annexed to Norman's booklet. Borough is mentioned in *De Magnete* (I, 1 p. 7) together with Norman as an inventor of magnetic instruments.[32]

Robert Norman is of great importance for our problem. Except for the Latin erudition, the quotations and polemics, and the metaphysical philosophy of nature, he has everything that is pecu-

[31] Quoted from Hellmann *loc. cit.* The note is omitted in the later editions, presumably because Robert Norman had died.

[32] He was born in 1536, travelled to the White Sea, became Comptroller of the Queens Navy in 1583, and was commander of an English ship in the Armada battle of 1588. Socially he belongs to a higher rank of mariners than Norman and is superior to him in education. In the preface to his *Discourse* he urgently recommends mathematics to the seamen, emphasizing that there are sufficient books on that subject written in English. He mentions "Vitriuius" (*sic*), Albert Duerer, and the ship builder Mathew Baker, as outstanding representatives of the "mechanicall sciences" to which also navigation belongs. He praises the good maps of Abraham Ortelius and criticizes the bad ones of the Paris professor Postillus. Ortelius (1527–98), the most famous map-maker of the period, came from handicraft, but became geographer to Philip II of Spain. Guillaume Postel (1505–81) is a learned polyhistor. The navigator Borough with his relations to superior handicraft on the one hand, to practical astronomy, cartography, and a bit of mathematics on the other, illustrates rather well the soil out of which Gilbert's work has grown.

liar to Gilbert.   Norman as well as Gilbert proceeds by experiment and, "not regarding the words but the matter," bases his statements on experience rather than on books.   Moreover, the measuring-instruments and the details of the experimental technique, the most exact experiments, and many single empirical statements of *De Magnete* are already contained in his booklet.   It is true that the compass-maker Norman is a craftsman and Gilbert a scholar; but Norman already feels "incredible delight" at his discoveries and is interested in knowledge for its own sake: neither his experiment on the ponderability of magnetism nor his dilemma concerning "point respective" or "point attractive" has any practical bearing.   In things that are farther away from his occupation he is a little less critical than his follower of higher birth: he modestly believes in the story of Paracelsus which is vehemently criticized by Gilbert.   On the other hand he is more religious than Gilbert: where Gilbert takes to Neoplatonic theories of universal animation, he retreats to God's impenetrable providence and avoids further explanation.   Socially this is the difference between the highly educated scholar of the late Renaissance and the retired mariner.   As to scientific value, however, Norman's attitude does not compare at all unfavorably with Gilbert's.   Far reaching theories are lacking in his book; but is Gilbert's metaphysics of "distinguished spherical form" that brings about magnetism a useful scientific explanation?   The modern scientist may miss it in Norman's paper as little as he does Gilbert's quarrelsome polemics and erudite quotations.   By the absence of all these Renaissance paraphernalia the experimenting compass-maker is even nearer than Gilbert to the sober objectivity of modern natural science. Or, if we may put it the other way round: modern science and the modern mind in general are nearer to the experimenting manual workers of early capitalism, in which they had their origin, than to Renaissance humanism, which still influences even Gilbert.

III

8. The last paragraphs have answered our main question. Gilbert's experimental method and his independent attitude towards authorities were derived, not from ancient and contemporary learned literature, but on the one hand from the miners and foundrymen, on the other from the navigators and instrument-makers of the period.   Alchemistic experiments probably never

were performed by Gilbert, for he always vehemently attacked the alchemists and derided their attempts to make gold.[33]   A rather complete assortment of the sources of his scientific achievements has been given by himself in his discussion of the practical use of the magnetic needle.   There (III, 17 p. 147) he explains that by means of the needle the content of iron can be diagnosed in ores. The needle is the main part in the compass, which is, as it were, "the finger of God," and has made possible the Spanish and English circumnavigations of the globe.   By means of the magnetic needle veins of iron ore can be discovered, subterranean galleries can be driven in sieges, guns can be pointed at night, territories can be surveyed, and subterranean water-conduits can be constructed.[34]

Altogether, the impression of Gilbert's originality is considerably impaired, when he is confronted with his sources and especially with Norman.   In spite of that, Norman is virtually unknown today, whereas Gilbert is counted among the pioneers of natural science.   But this proves to be less unjust when the rise of science is viewed as a sociological process.   Unfortunately we can only give a sketchy and simplified exposition of that view here and, of necessity, must omit a part of the evidence bearing on the point.[35]

[33] He reproaches them (pref. fol. iij) with "veiling things in darkness and obscurity by means of silly words."   They are called (I, 3 p. 19) "cruel masters of metals who torture and harass them by many inventions."   They are "delirious" (p. 20) and their doctrine that metals can be changed into gold is "futile" (p. 24).

[34] The considerable part played by military engineering in this enumeration might be striking.   We have already met with gun-making in Gilbert's discussion of metallurgy (I, 7 pp. 23f.), have been forced to mention naval warfare and privateering several times, and should meet with military engineering even more frequently if we discussed the investigations of Leonardo da Vinci, Tartaglia, Duerer, and Galileo. Military technology has contributed considerably to the rise of the experimental spirit and natural science.   Its influence on Gilbert is comparatively rather slight.

[35] On the following *cf.*: Leonard Olschki, *Geschichte der neusprachlichen wissenschaftlichen Literatur* (vol. 1: *Die Literatur der Technik und der angewandten Wissenschaften vom Mittelalter bis zur Renaissance,* Heidelberg 1918; vol. 2: *Bildung und Wissenschaft im Zeitalter der Renaissance in Italien,* Leipzig-Roma-Firenze-Geneva 1922; vol. 3: *Galilei und seine Zeit,* Halle 1927).   All these volumes abound in valuable information on the scholar-literature and the craftsman-literature of the period and contain many sociological aspects.   The third volume contains statements, until now scarcely used, on the influence of contemporary technology on Galileo (on the relations of the artists to handicraft, mechanics, military engineering and mathematics *cf.* I, 30–447; on mathematics and mechanics III, 72–110; on Galileo III, 117–469).   On a later period *cf.* Robert K. Merton: *Science and Tech-*

From antiquity until about 1600 a sharp dividing-line existed between liberal and mechanical arts, *i.e.*, in the final analysis, between arts needing heads and tongues only and others needing the use of hands also. The former were considered as worthy of well-bred men, the latter were left to lower-class people. Thus the contempt for manual labor tended to exclude experiment (and dissection) from respectable science. The prejudice against manual labor, however, did not prevent the experiments of the alchemists. Alchemy is not an occupation as carpentering, or forging; it is made respectable by the charm of both magic and gold, and even well-bred people may practise it as a hobby. But no respectable scholar who was proud of his position as a representative of the liberal arts even thought of using the methods of the mechanical arts. The case of those craftsmen who aspired to a higher social level is different; they—*e.g.* the Italian artists of the fifteenth century—discussed the social qualifications of manual work again and again, and stressed that they were connected with mathematics, *i.e.* with science.

The social background and the professional conditions of the scholars of the fifteenth and sixteenth centuries can not be discussed here. Nearly all of them had academic degrees and were consequently more or less linked to the universities, or they were humanists. Though several humanists had obtained academic chairs, generally speaking the universities of the period were still dominated by the spirit of Scholasticism. Both the university-scholars and the humanistic literati were accustomed to deal with natural phenomena chiefly in so far as they had been treated before by the authorities of Scholasticism and humanism respectively. On the other hand, since the decay of the guilds and their traditionalism real observation of natural phenomena, and even some experimentation, were to be found among skilled manual workers. Very little, however, is known of their intellectual interests.

nology in the 17th Century, Osiris vol. 4 (1938) pp. 360–630. On the prejudice against manual labor and its intellectual implications *cf.* Edgar Zilsel: *Die Entstehung des Geniebegriffes,* Tuebingen 1926 (pp. 112–130 the humanistic literati, 130–143 the inventors and discoverers, 143–154 the artists and artist-engineers, 310–15 two strata of intellectual activities). On the effects of the prejudice against manual labor on astronomy *cf.* Edgar Zilsel: *Copernicus and Mechanics,* in *Journal of the History of Ideas* vol. I (1940) pp. 113–118. On the effects on anatomy *cf.* Benjamin Farrington: *Vesalio and the Ruin of Ancient Medicine,* in *Modern Quarterly,* London, vol. 1 (1938) pp. 23 ff.

Since they got no education but the practical one in the workshops of their masters, their observations and experiments must have proceeded rather unmethodically.

With the advancement of early capitalistic society two major intellectual developments occurred: on the one hand, by virtue of technological inventions, geographical discoveries, and economic changes, the contrast between present times and the past became so obvious, that in the second half of the sixteenth century rebellion against both Scholasticism and humanism began among the scholars themselves. Representatives of the learned upper ranks, such as Telesio, Patrizzi, Bruno, and Campanella, vehemently attacked Aristotle and the belief in "words," felt enthusiastic about nature and physical experience, but did not experiment. Merely speculative metaphysics was, as it were, the older brother rather than the father of modern experimental science (*cf* above § 4).

On the other hand, among the ranks of manual laborers a few groups of superior craftsmen formed connections with respectable scholars. During the fifteenth century Italian painters, sculptors and architects had slowly separated from whitewashers, stone-dressers and masons. As the division of labor was still only slightly developed, the same artist usually worked in several fields of art, and often in engineering too. The technical problems of their occupations led them more and more to experimentation. Many of them made contacts with humanistic literati, were told of Vitruvius, Euclid, and Archimedes, and a few of them, such as Brunelleschi (1377–1446), Ghiberti, Leone Battista Alberti, Leonardo da Vinci, Benvenuto Cellini (1500–1571), started writing diaries and papers on their achievements. Biringuccio's treatise on metallurgy, *Della Pirotechnia* (1540), Duerer's two treatises on descriptive geometry and fortification, of 1525 and 1527, in some respect even the papers of Stevin, belong to this literature of the artist-engineers. Another group of superior manual workers were the surgeons, who practised dissection and made contacts on the one hand with artists interested in anatomy, and on the other with medical doctors. Others were the navigators, who formed connections with mathematicians, astronomers, and cosmographers and published treatises on navigation; and, finally, the makers of nautical and of musical instruments. These superior craftsmen were the predecessors of modern experimental science, though they were not regarded as respectable scientists by contemporary public opinion.   So far as papers were composed by them, they were written in the vernacular, not in Latin, and were not read by most of the respectable scholars, even if they were printed.   By their colleagues, however, the books, especially those on navigation, were diligently read, as is proved by the five editions of Norman's and Borough's treatises between 1581 and 1614.   One has only to recall the humble apologies in Norman's preface to realize the barrier between craftsmen-literature and scholar-literature at the end of the sixteenth century.   Experimental science could not have come into existence before this barrier was demolished.

But a few learned authors, very few, comparatively, already showed an understanding of mechanical arts before 1600.   The German physician George Agricola published Latin treatises on mining and metallurgy (1544 and 1556); the chaplain at the royal court of Madrid, Peter Martyr, wrote two Latin books on the great geographical discoveries of the period (1511 and 1530); the learned secretary of the Senate of Venice, Ramusio, did the same in Italian (1550); a few Portuguese and Spanish cosmographers, such as Nuñes and Pedro de Medina, wrote mostly vernacular books on navigation.   But especially in England, and in the period of Gilbert, similar studies increased.   The Oxford B.A. Richard Hakluyt (1552–1616) edited Peter Martyr and published his own widely read books on the great English voyages and discoveries; the prebendary of Winchester, William Barlowe, wrote an English treatise on navigation (1597).   The East India Company engaged the Cambridge graduate William Wright as a lecturer on navigation to their master-mariners.   Wright and two more mathematicians, the Oxford graduates Thomas Harriot and Robert Hues, published Latin and English books in the same field (1588, 1594, 1599).

All these half-technical, half-learned activities show that some branches of the mechanical arts had become so important economically that they began to engage and to interest a few scholars. But they dealt with metallurgy and mostly with navigation rather than with experiments.   The first academically trained scholar who dared to adopt the experimental method from the superior craftsmen and to communicate the results in a book not to helmsmen and mechanics but to the learned public was William Gilbert, who was a personal friend of most of these English authors. This is Gilbert's achievement in history. It might have been as difficult for the physician in ordinary to Queen Elizabeth to overcome the prejudice against manual labor as it was for the craftsman Norman to raise and answer his theoretical problems—though the two achievements are of a rather different kind. By his understanding of the scientific importance of experiment Gilbert made it—or helped to make it—respectable among the ranks of the educated. A few years later two other scholars likewise followed the method of the superior craftsmen: Francis Bacon, who ranked the great inventors and navigators above the scholars of his period, and Galileo, who started from military engineering.[36]

But we must deal with an objection. Is it true that experimental science could not come into existence so long as liberal and mechanical arts were kept separate by the contempt for manual labor? The fact that Pierre de Maricourt had already performed experiments does not seem to fit in with our exposition. Yet it is significant that Pierre tries to come to terms with the prejudice against manual work. In chapter 2 of his treatise he emphasizes that the investigator of magnetic phenomena must not only know "the nature of things" and celestial motions, but that he must also be "industrious in manual work" (*industriosum in opere manuum*); only by "manual industry" will he be able to correct errors which by mere reason and mathematics cannot be avoided. Obviously Pierre can not stress the value of experimentation without immediately speaking of and defending manual labor.

Pierre, no doubt, was the best experimentalist of the Middle

---

[36] Galileo had already experimented a few years before *De Magnete* appeared. He became acquainted with Gilbert's book rather soon. We have a letter from Gilbert to William Barlowe, telling that Gilbert met with the Venetian ambassador who brought him a Latin letter of Joannes Franciscus Sagredus. Gilbert continues: "Sagredo is a great Magnetical man and writeth that he has conferred with . . . the Readers of Padua and reported wonderful liking of my booke" (Barlowe, *Magneticall Advertisement*, London 1616). The letter must have been written between 1600 and 1603. Sagredo was a friend of Galileo and later figures as one of the persons of the discourse in Galileo's great dialogues. No doubt, Galileo himself, who was then lecturer on mathematics at the University of Padua, is the "Reader of Padua." Thirty years later, Galileo praises Gilbert highly because of his new and true observations and his habit of examining all statements of authorities by his own experiments. The only thing he misses in him is a little more mathematical knowledge (*Discorsi, Opere*, Edizione nazionale, VII, 432).

Ages.[37]   He probably was not a monk but a nobleman and might
have been in the Orient as a pilgrim or crusader as his surname
Peregrinus suggests.   In 1269 he took part in the siege of Lucera
in Apulia, probably as a kind of military engineer.   Most probably
he is identical with the *magister Petrus,* the *dominus experimentorum,* often mentioned in Roger Bacon.   If this assumption
is correct, we know a little of his scientific and social attitude.
This Petrus was, as Roger Bacon puts it, keen for the experiences
even of "laymen, old women, and country bumpkins"; he was
interested in metal founding, the working of gold and silver,
mining, arms and military engineering, the chase, surveying,
earthworks, the devices of magicians, and the tricks of jugglers.[38]
In short, he was interested in all branches of technology that his
period had developed and was hampered in his interest by the
social prejudices of neither clergy nor nobility.   It is significant
that in the report of Bacon himself some social scruples still are
hinted at ("country bumpkins, old women, jugglers").   Unfortunately we do not know where Petrus' freedom from bias originates.   Altogether Pierre's attitude rather confirms than dis-
proves the importance of manual labor and the mechanical arts
for the history of science.   The extremely rare medieval experimentalists would need an extensive and careful sociological investigation.   We have, however, to return to Gilbert.

The social rise of the experimental method from the class of
manual laborers to the ranks of university scholars in the early
seventeenth century was a decisive event in the history of science.
Natural science needs theory and mathematics as well as experiments and observations.   Only theoretically educated men with
rationally trained intellects were able to supply that other half
of its method to science.   With Gilbert, however, not much of the
superiority of academic training as to the theoretical side of science can be noticed: his general speculations have not proved to be
fruitful.   It is different with Francis Bacon and Galileo.   Bacon's
far-reaching ideas on the advancement of learning and scientific
coöperation could scarcely have been formed by craftsmen, though
they were nothing but generalizations of their own practice.   Galileo, on the other hand, joined mathematics with experiment.

Why did Gilbert himself never reckon, why did he come to **a**

[37] On the following, *cf.* the papers on Petrus Peregrinus quoted in footnote 14.
[38] *Roger Bacon, Opus tertium,* cap. 12, p. 46 (ed. Brewer).

standstill at the first beginnings of quantitative inquiry? Certainly that deficiency is connected with his subject matter. Magnetic and electric processes can be measured only by complicated methods and, in consequence, were first measured almost two hundred years after Gilbert by Coulomb. It is mechanics that was the birthplace of quantitative research, since mechanical processes can be measured comparatively easily. Therefore, authors dealing with mechanics, such as Stevin and Galileo—and centuries before them Archimedes—were the first mathematical physicists. Gilbert on the other hand, as we have seen, is remarkably little interested in mechanics. He almost appears to have been biased against it. In *De Mundo* (II, 10 p. 154) he criticizes mechanistic astronomers who think Ptolemy's spheres to be material. He objects to their hypothesis on the ground that by it the universe is made a great wheelwork and God a mechanic. In the eighteenth century a comparison like this scarcely could have served as an objection to a theory; on the contrary, similar comparisons were commonplaces in the period of mechanistic physics and deism.

Gilbert's pre-mechanical way of thinking and his predilection for a field where measurements are so difficult may be due to his individual characteristics. But they are connected also with the special conditions of his native country. Practically all quantitative investigations in *De Magnete* originate in nautical technique and the work of the compass-maker Norman; Gilbert's interest in iron-making and iron-foundries, on the other hand, does not result in any quantitative inquiry. It was English iron-making and English iron-manufacture, however, that were advancing fast in the late sixteenth century. Instructive inferences can be drawn from the rapid rise of iron-manufacture.[39] Blast-furnaces were introduced in England in the middle of the sixteenth century; the first English wire-mill was built in 1568; iron cannon, which had previously been imported from abroad, began to be exported from England in the same period; in 1581 and 1585 two laws were passed forbidding the construction of more blast-furnaces, in order to prevent devastation of the forests, since blast-furnaces were heated with wood. Certainly these laws show that iron-manufacture was not yet the leading industry of England; wool-trade and cloth-making still were much more important. Altogether, in the six-

[39] Ludwig Beck: *Geschichte des Eisens,* Braunschweig 1893–95, vol. II, pp. 892 and 896.

teenth century iron had not yet reached its dominant part in technology. It still was used in making weapons and simple tools rather than in machinery. And just this point leads us back again to our problem.

The first machines were made of wood and the first mechanical insights, therefore, were acquired from wooden devices—levers, reels, windlasses, inclined planes. There the Italian artist-engineers and Stevin made their studies and found quantitative relations and laws. Galileo, when experimenting on the law of falling bodies, made brass balls roll down an inclined wooden groove. Not before the eighteenth century did iron machines, and not before the nineteenth did metallurgy become subjects of calculation. In the preceding centuries, therefore, predilection for iron prevented rather than promoted application of mathematical methods. Thus England's natural, economic, and social conditions might form, not a sufficient, but a necessary condition for the characteristics of Gilbert's method. When reading *De Magnete* we must never forget that twelve years before its publication English ships and English iron guns annihilated the Spanish Armada, then the most powerful fleet in the world. England, the country of iron mines and advancing navigation, produced the first learned book on experimental physics. It dealt with the mariner's compass, magnets, and iron. And for that very reason it did not introduce mathematical methods into natural science.

Edgar Zilsel

THE GENESIS OF THE
CONCEPT OF SCIENTIFIC PROGRESS*

The modern scientist looks upon science as a great building erected stone by stone through the work of his predecessors and his contemporary fellow-scientists, a structure that will be continued but never completed by his successors. In this work he wants to coöperate. His object is either the mere theoretical aim of constructing this building, or he follows a utilitarian view, links the progress of science with the progress of civilization, and has in mind the benefit to mankind produced by the practical application of theory. No modern scientist, however, would dare to confess personal advantage or fame as his incentive. This means that science, both in the theoretical and the utilitarian interpretation, is regarded as the product of a coöperation for non-personal ends, a coöperation in which all scientists of the past, the present, and the future have a part. Today this idea or ideal seems almost self-evident. Yet no Brahmanic, Buddhistic, Moslem, or Catholic scholastic, no Confucian scholar or Renaissance humanist, no philosopher or rhetor of classical antiquity ever achieved it. It is a specific characteristic of the scientific spirit and of modern Western civilization. It appeared for the first time fully developed in the works of Francis Bacon.

It was shown by J. B. Bury that before Bacon only scanty rudiments of the concept of progress are found in Western scholarly literature.[1] Since Bury, however, is interested in the idea of cultural rather than of scientific progress, he deals chiefly with statements about the general course of history: his discussion of the pre-Baconian period gives an illuminating analysis of the classical

* This article is part of a study undertaken with the help of grants from the American Philosophical Society, Philadelphia, and the Social Science Research Council, New York. So far the following sections have appeared: "The Sociological Roots of Science," *American Journal of Sociology*, XLVII (1942) 544–562 (an outline of the entire study); "Copernicus and Mechanics," *Journal of the History of Ideas*, I (1940), 113–118; "The Origin of William Gilbert's Scientific Method," *ibid.*, II (1941), 1–32; "The Genesis of the Concept of Physical Law," *Philosophical Review*, LI (1942), 245–279.

[1] *The Idea of Progress* (London, 1924). Cf. also Jules Delvaille: *Histoire de l'idée de progrès* (Paris, 1910).

conception of cultural history but does not investigate the classical conception of science. Moreover, the sociological origin of Bacon's ideas is not traced in his excellent book. We shall therefore try to show that the modern idea of progress through coöperation stems, like many other elements of modern scientific procedure, from the superior artisans of the fifteenth and sixteenth centuries. To elucidate the social causes of this specifically modern intellectual development we must, for purposes of comparison, give also a brief analysis of the classical concept of science. This introductory account, however, must be restricted to an outline and will be documented elsewhere.

We shall use the term "the ideal of scientific progress" to include the following ideas: (1) the insight that scientific knowledge is brought about step by step through contributions of generations of explorers building upon and gradually amending the findings of their predecessors; (2) the belief that this process is never completed; (3) the conviction that contribution to this development, either for its own sake or for the public benefit, constitutes the very aim of the true scientist. (This conviction excludes personal advantage and personal fame as ultimate aims.) The breakdown in the early modern era of the unrestricted authority of Scripture, of the church fathers and scholastics, and of Aristotle and classical antiquity, is indeed a necessary condition for the rise of this ideal of scientific progress, but does not yet constitute the ideal itself; it will therefore be discussed only insofar as it is combined with at least one of the more general ideas above. From the fourteenth to the sixteenth century the scholastics, Aristotle, the humanistic veneration for antiquity, and Galen were frequently attacked from very different angles without any clear conception of progress. An author's awareness that his own or a contemporary's achievements have refuted the doctrines of an authority of the past (e.g., Copernicus vs. Ptolemy) does not yet make him an advocate of the ideal of progress.

1. The virtual absence of the idea of progress in classical antiquity is closely linked with the different rôles played by science in classical and in modern civilization. While modern education emphasizes scientific instruction, a characteristic combination of metaphysics and rhetoric was the backbone of higher education in classical antiquity. Even in the post-Alexandrian period there

were fewer special sciences and many fewer scientific specialists than in our time. The six or seven distinct sciences which developed were less separated from philosophy on the one hand, and from literature on the other: apart from the "physicists" and historiographers, it was nothing unusual for an outstanding astronomical specialist, like Ptolemy, to begin a highly technical work with an exposition of the aims and divisions of philosophy, or for Hipparchus to engage in polemics with the author of an astronomical poem.

Yet it would be an overstatement to characterize scientific activity in classical antiquity as a merely individualistic undertaking. Classical science had rather reached, approximately, that degree of continuity and coöperation which in our era is characteristic of philosophy. Findings of predecessors were used most systematically by the astronomers, but the fund of undisputed knowledge remained comparatively small, and scientific "schools" combatting or ignoring each other were the rule. This is especially conspicuous in classical medicine. Systematic efforts to organize research were never made and the theoretical achievements were due to a few eminent individuals—as in modern philosophy. There were neither laboratories in which scientists could coöperate nor learned periodicals in which scientific findings could be discussed. No scientific publications, no astronomical or geographical investigations which are the work of several collaborating scientists are known, and even the cyclopedias and compendia of the Alexandrian and Roman period were composed by single polyhistors.[2]

This difference in organization also manifests itself in a different intellectual attitude among scholars. It was far from the thought of classical scientists to speak of their publications as "contributions" to science[3]—a phrase characteristic of the modern, non-individualistic concept of research. And in the extant literature it is an exception when a popular treatise predicts that the solution of a problem at present unsolved will be regarded as a

[2] The Septuagint is the only literary product of classical antiquity composed by several authors in collaboration.—Otto E. Neugebauer explains the absence of "systematic organized collaboration" through the scarcity of scientists ("Exact Science in Antiquity," in: *Studies in Civilization* [Philadelphia, 1941], 25).

[3] Almagest I, 1 (p. 4, Heiberg) is an exception in the extant literature (προαιρούμενοι . . . προσθήκην συνεισενεγκεῖν).

triviality by generations to come.[4]   The Hippocratic physicians and the astronomers came nearest to the modern idea of scientific continuity. The Hippocratics sought to establish a tradition of knowledge in their corporation and even composed case histories of their patients, which, however, were not intended for publication. And the astronomers composed star catalogues to be used by future scientists. Yet the only passage in the extant literature which clearly expresses the idea of the gradual progress of knowledge, or better, technological skill, occurs in a treatise on artillery. There the author, one Philo of Byzantium (third or second century B.C.), states that the early war machines were rather poor; only the later Alexandrian engineers put artillery on a sound basis "partly by learning from the earlier constructors, partly by observation of later trials."[5] His remark, brief as it is, expresses the gist of the idea of scientific progress: the method of trial and error used by subsequent generations of experts. Philo however was not a scholar but a military engineer, i.e., a superior artisan with some mathematical knowledge. The Alexandrian military engineers (Philo, the two Ctesibius', Hero) were never admitted as fellows to the Alexandrian Museum.

These differences between classical and modern science point to and are rooted in the basic fact that in antiquity, in contrast to the modern era, science was for the most part not put to practical use, and hence hardly influenced everyday life. When classical theorists wanted to apply their findings to practical life, they restricted themselves to morals and politics (like most of the philosophers), war machines (like Archimedes), or medicine. A scientific technology was non-existent and apparently not required. Machines were used in warfare and as toys, but except for the simplest ones, never in the production of goods or in traffic. As has been often pointed out, this basic fact is probably accounted for by the existence of slave labor.[6] Classical culture was, moreover, carried

[4] Seneca, *Nat. quaest.* VII, 25 and 31, on the orbits of the comets. Cf. Bury, *loc. cit.* 13.

[5] *Belopoika,* ed. Diels-Schramm, *Abhandlungen d. kgl. preuss. Akad. d. Wissenschaften* (1918), *philos.-histor. Klasse,* no. 16, p. 9.

[6] Cf., e.g., H. Diels: *Antike Technik* (3rd ed. Leipzig, 1924), 29–35, 40 ff. More recently a well-documented account of classical technology was given in A. Rehm: "Zur Rolle der Technik in der griechisch-römischen Antike," *Archiv für Kulturgeschichte,* XXVIII (1938), 135–162. Rehm's explanation of the absence of machinery (the great number of metics), however, is not satisfactory.

by a rather thin upper class living on incomes derived from landed property. The intelligentsia and the bulk of the writers were either themselves members of this leisure class or were attached to their households as tutors to their sons and dispensers of prestige. Even the fellows of the Alexandrian Museum were basically court-scholars. Teachers of rhetoric and philosophy, attorneys, physicians, and "architects," i.e., engineers, were the only professional men. The engineers, however, can compare neither in education nor number nor influence with their modern colleagues. Small wonder, therefore, that the classical concept of knowledge differs from the modern one. With the simplifications unavoidable in a brief survey of a thousand years, one may state that the educated classes of classical antiquity, looking down upon all manual activities, esteemed speech-making and metaphysical speculation more highly than experimentation and dissection, and scarcely overcame a certain disdain for people who, with their hands or otherwise, worked for a living.[7]

Civil engineers, scientifically trained civil servants, research workers in laboratories and scientific institutes, could have replaced the individualistic desire for fame of the classical aristocrats and literati with the spirit of coöperation for objective ends. They could have taken over, from the artisans, the aim of gradually increasing knowledge through the method of trial and error. This method and this aim develop easily among craftsmen who have freed themselves from the bounds of the mere workshop tradition. But primitive theorists who have just detached themselves from the traditional mythology everywhere and always want to grasp the universe in a few basic insights. And they are much too convinced of the final truth of their speculations to realize that knowledge progresses only step by step. However sophisticated the later Greek philosophers and scholars were, most of them never completely got rid of conscious or unconscious remnants of this archaic attitude of the Ionian seers. There developed various sceptical "schools," but not the ideals of scientific progress and coöperation. In an aristocratic society without machines but with slaves these ideals could apparently not unfold.

2. This sociological analysis of classical science is confirmed by and sheds light on the intellectual development of the early modern

[7] Exceptions: Thucydides II, 40, Socrates, the Cynics, Dio of Prusa, and others.

era.　For obvious reasons the ideal of the progress of knowledge was foreign to the medieval schoolmen.[8]　The Renaissance humanists, the first secular scholars of the modern era, likewise did not stand for scientific progress, since with few exceptions (Benedetto Accolti, Pico della Mirandola), they considered the classical authors unsurpassable.　Viewed sociologically, the humanists were dispensers of prestige who sought by their polished style and their erudition to make their protectors, and themselves, famous.　The open admission that fame is the goal of all literary activity appears even more frequently in the humanists than in the classical literati, either because the purely individualistic conception of the literary profession was actually more developed in the Renaissance or only because more literary testaments are extant.　One example, relating to mathematics, may illustrate this frankness.　In 1621 the French humanist Claude Gaspard Bachet published the first Greek edition of the *Arithmetic* of Diophantus, dedicated to an influential lawyer.　In the preface the humanist explains that, "in honorable emulation for fame," he is thinking day and night how he might become as famous as his patron.　After examining all disciplines he decided to choose mathematics "since it wonderfully delights the mind and since in mathematics the subtlety of the intellect especially comes to light.　This Diophantus will give evidence whether I have deserved fame beyond the ordinary mathematicians."[9]　The possibility that the publication might further science is not mentioned.　Analogous expressions of glory worship occur very frequently in the more literary writings of the humanists.[10]　On the other hand, in the humanist literature of the Renaissance there seems to be no case in which an author states that he is publishing his treatise in order to make further investigations possible.　We shall see how differently the contemporary craftsmen express themselves.

[8] It was, however, known to the scholastics that, "because of the defects of knowledge of those who first invented the sciences," the sciences in the course of time increased (*augmentum factum est*) and that the same is true in practical matters (*in operabilibus*).　Cf. Thomas, *Summ. Theol.* II, 2, qu. 1, art. 7, obj. 2, and II, 1, qu. 97, art. 1.

[9] Reprinted in Beriah Botfield: *Prefaces to the First Editions of the Greek and Roman Classics* (London, 1861), 656.

[10] Examples: Filelfo: *Epistolae familiares* (Venice, 1502), 12 r, 54 v.; Emile Legrande: *Cent-dix lettres greques de Filelfe* (Paris, 1892), 63; Georg Voigt: *Die Wiederbelebung des classischen Altertums,* 3rd ed. (Berlin, 1891), 334, 446, 527; E. Zilsel: *Die Entstehung des Geniebegriffes* (Tübingen, 1926), 111–123.

It is evident that the individualistic professional ideals of the humanists were incompatible with scientific coöperation. Rivalries, quarrels, and personal intrigues accompanied the literary and scholarly careers of almost all of them. Although after the late fourteenth century literary circles and meetings of humanists became frequent in Italy, there exists in the humanist as little as in classical literature any encyclopedia or dictionary composed by several authors in collaboration. Only the great humanist printers and publishers in Venice, Basel, and Paris who employed numerous classical scholars as editors and proofreaders achieved a certain amount of coöperation among their learned assistants.[11] Printing, however, was a "mechanical" art, and the publishers, though themselves classical scholars, were not literary dispensers of glory but business men. Their printing houses were among the biggest and best organized plants of the sixteenth century.

3. In the workshops of the late medieval artisans coöperation resulted quite naturally from the working conditions. In contrast to a monk's cell or a humanist's writing chamber a workshop or dockyard is a place where several people work together. On the other hand the guilds stressed the continuity rather than the progress of craftsmanship. The apprentice learned the workshop tradition from his master and was taught to honor it as the master had honored the tradition of his master's workshop. Rising capitalism and economic competition, however, broke the power of guild tradition. Only the artisan who had either invented some commercial or technological innovation or who understood the value of the invention of another fellow became a capitalistic manufacturer. Thus the inventive genius of the individual gradually came to the fore. The professional ideals of the early capitalistic artisans can be inferred with some probability. As petty manual laborers they could not well strive for literary immortality like the humanists. Social conditions directed them to more impersonal goals. If they wanted to justify their work and their inventions they had to refer to the glory of God and the Saints, of the craft

[11] The first of them was Aldo Manuzio. He founded the *Neo-Academia* in Venice about 1500; most of the members were his assistants. The humanistic "academies" of Ficinus in Florence, of Pomponius Letus in Rome, and of Pontanus in Naples, all of them in the later half of the fifteenth century, held debates and banquets but did not do real research. Cf. Michele Maylender: *Storia delle Accademie d'Italia* (Bologna, 1926), I, 125 ff.; IV, 249 ff, 320 ff, and 327 ff.

and the workshop—and to the usefulness of their craft and the public benefit.

These ideals are in fact expressed in several treatises composed by superior artisans, such as artists, instrument makers, and gun makers. Sometimes the authors even declared that they intended to further through their treatises the craftsmanship of their colleagues. Such statements reveal the social origin of the modern ideal of progress. To modern ears they may sound rather trivial. We must not forget, however, that in classical, scholastic, and humanist literature no statements on the necessity of the gradual improvement of knowledge exist. Naturally only members of the most highly skilled crafts wrote treatises, and only a few of these craftsmen-authors conceived the idea of progress with any clarity. Even in the sixteenth century a considerable number of the manual workers, particularly outside Italy, were illiterate.[12]

An early handbook of a secular craftsman was composed about 1400 by the Florentine painter Cennini. It is still imbued with the medieval guild spirit and deals with the making of pigments and the various techniques of painting; but being the treatise of an artisan it is also concerned with the painting of chests and the make-up of women. It circulated as a manuscript among the painters of the Quattrocento and is, like all similar treatises, written in the vernacular. Cennini composed his booklet as the title or better, *incipit*, explains, in the reverence of God, the Virgin, and the Saints, "and in the reverence of Giotto, Taddeo, and Agnolo and for the use and profit of any one who wants to enter the craft." Giotto was Taddeo's, Taddeo Agnolo's, and Agnolo Cennini's master: the author was well conscious of the continuity of craftsmanship. On the other hand Cennini states that he "will also make note of what he has tried out with his own hand." Although the addition hardly implies the idea of progress, it shows that Cennini no longer considers the mere workshop tradition as sufficient.[13]

---

[12] Johann Neudörfer (*Nachrichten von Künstlern und Werkleuten* [Nürnberg, 1547]; reprinted by G. W. K. Lochner, *Quellenschriften zur Kunstgeschichte*, X [Vienna, 1875]) discusses two illiterate masters even among the contemporary Nürnberg craftsmen: the locksmith Hanns Bulmann (d. 1549), the constructor of an astronomical clock, and the carpenter Georg Weber (d. 1567), the maker of complex wooden clockwork (pp. 65, 79). They were, however, manifestly exceptions (2 among 111 masters) and their illiteracy is mentioned as a curiosity.

[13] Cennini's *Libro dell' arte*, tr. D. V. Thompson, Jr. (New Haven, 1933); chests p. 170, make up 125, "with my own hand" 1.—The *Schedula Theophili* (11th

Almost a century later (1486) the printed treatise of a late Gothic master-builder clearly advocates the advancement of craftsmanship. Mathias Roriczer, an architect of the cathedral of Regensburg, is the author and his booklet is dedicated to his previous employer, the Bishop of Eichstädt. Although Roriczer treats the tradition of the craft with great reverence, his geometrical constructions are, he states, of his own invention. At the end of the dedication he emphasizes that he has not written his book for fame's sake but for the public benefit "and to better wherever something is to be bettered, and to amend and explain the arts." The public benefit (*der gemeine nutzen*) is three times mentioned as the aim of the author.[14] The dedication only expresses what probably all of the more inventive craftsmen of the period might have felt, but neither Plato nor Aristotle ever stated that his work was intended to mend philosophical shortcomings and to improve the state of philosophical knowledge. A hundred and twenty years later Francis Bacon proclaimed the advancement of knowledge for the benefit of mankind as the goal of the scientist. It is this ideal of progress, naturally in an embryonic form and restricted to the craft of the masons, that appears in Roriczer's treatise for the first time. "Progress" however has its limitations in the booklet of the Gothic master-builder. According to the regulations of the guild of the masons the secrets of the art had to be kept from laymen. But since Roriczer himself printed his treatise on his own printing press he could, and probably did, confine its sale to the members of the craft.

A few years before or after Roriczer's booklet, between 1484 and 1489, a similar but briefer treatise appeared in Nürnberg. It has no title and its author is an otherwise unknown Hans Schmuttermayer of Nürnberg.[15] The author treats not only the same

century) is composed by a monk, the sketch-book of Wilars de Honecourt (about 1255) was written only for Wilars' own workshop; in both works progress is not mentioned. For various reasons progress is not mentioned either in a few early modern treatises on the crafts, Ghiberti's *Commentarii* (1477), Lionardo's *Book on Painting* (c. 1496), Biringucci's *Pirotechnia* (1540), and Palissy's *Recepte véritable* (1563) and *Discours admirable* (1580).

[14] *Von der Fialen Gerechtigkeit* (How to build turrets correctly), ed. A. Reichensperger (Trier, 1845). The quoted passages in the dedication, p. 13.

[15] Reprinted with an introduction in *Anzeiger f. Kunde d. deutschen Vorzeit*, Neue Folge XXVIII (1881), 66–78. The quotation, p. 73.

topic but also has almost the same aims. In the initial lines he states that he is writing his book "for the betterment and adornment (*zu besserung und zierungen*) of the holy Christian church buildings, to . . . the instruction of all masters and journeymen who use this high and liberal art of geometry . . . so that they may better (*bass*) apply their imagination to the true reason of tracery. And not for my own honor's sake but rather to the praise of our ancient predecessors and the inventors of this high art." Although Schmuttermayer must have belonged to the craft it is well established that he was not a member of the masonic guild in Nürnberg where he was born and where also his book was printed. This is possibly an explanation of the fact that he published guild secrets.

While the two architects discussed still belonged to the Gothic style their younger contemporary, Albrecht Dürer, is a representative of the Renaissance. Yet Dürer also was of course, like all the artists of the period, a superior artisan. Dürer wrote three treatises. The first, *Unterweisung der Messung mit dem Zirkel und Richtscheit* (Instruction in Measurement with Compass and Rule), printed in 1525, deals with problems of practical and theoretical geometry and perspective. In the dedication to his learned humanist protector, the councillor of Nürnberg Pirckheimer, Dürer states that the German painters lack geometrical instruction. He composed the treatise "to benefit not only painters but also goldsmiths, sculptors, stonedressers, cabinetmakers, and all those requiring measurement." Nobody is forced, he adds as an apology, to use his doctrine. "I know however that he who accepts it will not only get a good start but will reach better understanding by daily practice; he will seek farther (*weitersuchen*) and find much more (*gar viel mehr*) than I now indicate."[16] Even more clearly is the idea of progress expressed in his book *On Human Proportion,* printed in 1528. The treatise gives extensive quantitative data on the proportions of the human body. In the dedication to Pirckheimer Dürer remarks that some people might blame him, because he, a non-scholar, teaches a subject in which he received no instruction. Yet, "risking slander," he published the book "to the public benefit of all artists and to induce also other experts to do the same so that our descendants may have something which they may augment and improve, so that the art of painting, in the

---

[16] Ed. Moriz Thausing, *Quellenschriften z. Kunstgeschichte* III (Vienna, 1872), 55 f.

course of time, may again attain and reach its perfection." Nobody is forced, he adds, to follow his doctrine everywhere, "for human nature has not yet so weakened that another could not invent something better." He goes on to point out the importance of original invention and expresses the conviction that the art will again become perfect "as in olden times"; then the German painters will not be inferior to any other nation.[17] Dürer manifestly put weight on coöperation and progress. In a letter to Pirckheimer he expressly requested the humanist to compose his preface to *On Proportion* so that it would not contain any "talk of glory" (*Ruhmredigkeit*), and to state that Dürer "begs those having something instructive to say on art, to publish it."[18] Progress, however, is not mentioned in his third treatise, *Etliche Unterricht zur Befestigung der Städt, Schloss, und Flecken* (Some instruction in the fortification of cities, castles, and towns), printed in 1527. In the dedication to the King of Hungary and Bohemia Dürer only states that the treatise was written "to the benefit of your Majesty and other princes."[19] Whether the Habsburg was delighted at the idea that other princes also might learn how to fortify their cities is dubious. Two remarks may be added to the three prefaces. Since, in contrast to Cennini, Roriczer, and Schmuttermayer, Dürer had to reckon also with non-artisans as readers, he apologizes for his writing books as a non-scholar. We shall frequently meet with analogous apologies. And it is, secondly, rather improbable that Dürer had ever read the booklets of the two Gothic architects. The fact that he has the same aim, the progress of craftsmanship, is due to the same sociological conditions, and possibly to oral tradition among the craftsmen rather than to literary influence. This applies also to the authors below.

Dürer died in 1528. In the sixteenth century kindred ideas were expressed by several craftsmen, the more clearly expressed the more remote the authors were from guild tradition. In 1547 one Kaspar Brunner, a Nürnberg master of ordnance, previously a locksmith and clock maker, composed a treatise on gunmaking and gunnery. He wrote it, as he states, "for his generation and

[17] *Ibid.*, 63 f. Dürer's opinion that classical painting was "perfect" is borrowed from humanism. Of course no classical painting was known to him.

[18] *Ibid.*, 61, items 1 and 7.

[19] *Ibid.*, 54.

others to come.''[20]   Naturally, this remark is concerned not with
fame but with the advancement of gunfounding.   Since in the middle of the sixteenth century the technique of gunmaking was still
a more or less strictly kept guild secret Brunner did not publish
his manuscript but only presented it in four copies to the council
of Nürnberg.   About 1400 the poem of an anonymous German
master-gunner had stressed secrecy; about 1530 the master-
gunner of the Duke of Bavaria, Franz Helm, refused, for secrecy's
sake, to publish his handbook on gunnery.   On the other hand the
Feuerwerksbuch, composed by an anonymous master-gunner before
1425, was printed in 1529 and, in a French version, in 1561.[21]   This
fading of guild secrecy shows how the idea that technology must
be furthered through publication made headway in the sixteenth
century.

In 1578 William Bourne of Dover in England pleaded the
gradual progress of ''the arts and sciences'' as an excuse for publication.   Bourne was an expert on measuring instruments, but
probably no longer a member of any guild.   Originally an inn-
keeper, he served as a gunner, did some surveying, and wrote several treatises on gunnery, surveying, and navigation.   His style is
sometimes clumsy, but he knew the mathematical and nautical literature as it existed in English and understood his subjects rather
well.   In 1578 he published a booklet, *Inventions and Devices*.   It
deals for the most part with military engineering and is addressed
to ''all Generalles and Captaines.''   As in all his writings Bourne
in the preface humbly apologizes for his lack of learning and his
''rude and barbarous volume.''   And there the idea of progress
appears.   His devices are deficient, as he states, because ''in any
arte or science'' the first inventions are imperfect; ''yet they that
came after them brought it into perfection.''   Looking to the
future he expresses his hope that ''there may be some further matter gathered of his inventions'' and of course emphasizes his ''good
will to profit the commonwealth.''[22]

[20] *Gründlicher Bericht des Büchsengiessens* (Extensive account of gun founding), printed *Archiv f. d. Geschichte d. Naturwissenschaften und Technik,* VII
(1916).   The quoted passage, p. 171 fol. 174 b.

[21] Cf. Max Jähns: *Geschichte d. Kriegswissenschaften* (München, 1889), I, 382,
384, 408, 591, 608.

[22] *Loc. cit.,* Preface to the Reader, about the end.   On Bourne cf. B. G. R.
Taylor: *Tudor Geography* (London, 1930), 153 ff.   *Ibid.,* 155, an example of a

In 1581 the London instrument-maker Robert Norman, a retired mariner, published a treatise on the dip of the magnetic needle, which he had discovered. The booklet describes nautical instruments of his invention and on sale in his workshop; it contains astronomical tables and is intended to further navigation.[23] In a few remarkable sentences Norman discusses "the incredible delight" of the discoverer of new facts at his discoveries. Nevertheless he rejects these personal motives as "private fancies." He is rather convinced, as twenty-five years later Francis Bacon was, that new discoveries benefit society. In Norman's opinion scientific discoverers "chiefly respect either the glory of God or the furtherance of some publike commoditie." He considers it his duty to publish the discovery of the dip and to make his name "the object of carping tongues rather than such a secrete should be concealed and the use thereof unknowen." "Men," he states, "that will search out the secrets of their arts and professions and publish the same to the behoofe and use of others must not be condemned." Norman hardly felt restrained by medieval guild secrets. He rather justifies his publication because he was no scholar. Yet his apologies are characteristic of the early modern era. As we shall see Tartaglia, Peter Apian, and even Descartes deem it necessary expressly to vindicate the publication of their new ideas.

4. The two most important pioneers of scientific mechanics before Galileo, the Italian Tartaglia and the Dutchman Stevinus, were not artisans. Both were familiar with classical mathematics. Tartaglia published from Latin translations Italian versions of Archimedes and Euclid, Stevinus a French version of Diophantus. They had however no academic training but came to science from military engineering and commercial problems. Their writings contain important remarks on scientific progress and scientific coöperation.

Tartaglia (1499–1557) was a self-educated man, the son of a mailcoach groom brought up in direst poverty with little instruction. He made his livelihood as a mathematical adviser to gunners

---

triangulation carried out by Bourne. The method of triangulation had been invented in 1533 by Gemma Frisius of Louvain.

[23] *The Newe Attractive* (London, 1581). Quotations from the second edition (London, 1592), Preface to the Reader about the end, and Dedication to W. Borough, about the beginning. On Norman and his book cf. E. Zilsel: "The Genesis of Gilbert's Scientific Method," pp. 219–250.

and merchants at ten pennies a question. When his customers gave him a worn-out cloak for his lectures on Euclid instead of the payment agreed upon he had to litigate with them. This remarkable man published many books and treatises in the vernacular on gunnery, military engineering and mathematics, which greatly influenced nascent modern science and in which, for the first time in history, an embryonic form of the function concept is used to state a physical law.[24] In the dedication of his *Quesiti et Inventioni* (1546) Tartaglia states the motives of his publications. The man, he points out, who has found something new "and wants to own it for himself alone deserves no little blame. For if all our ancestors had behaved this way we should today differ little from irrational animals. To avoid this blame I have decided to bring to light my *Questions and Inventions* for everybody."[25] Scientific research and publication of the findings are here clearly recognized as a service to the public and prerequisites of progress. Tartaglia could not have taken this idea from the scholars of his period, since it was unknown to them. Though he was hardly regarded as a real member of the craft by the military engineers and gun-founders with whom he was in constant contact, his concept of science mirrors their frame of mind.[26]

Sixty years later Simon Stevinus (1548–1620) had a similar, though more successful career. Originally a bookkeeper of the municipalities of Bruges and Antwerp, Stevinus turned to military engineering, became technical adviser to Maurice of Nassau, and died as quartermaster-general of Holland. His scientific education was higher than Tartaglia's, but he first entered the University of Leyden as a man of thirty-five. Like all engineers of his period he was considerably nearer to manual labor than his modern

[24] On his youth, *Quesiti et Inventioni* VI, no. 8; "ten pennies (scudi)," *ibid.*, III, no. 10; "function concept," *ibid.*, I, no. 1 (cf. E. Zilsel: "The Genesis of the Concept of Physical Law," *The Philosophical Review*, LI [1942], 264); the worn-out cloak: *Travagliata Invenzione* (Venice, 1551), sig Fij v.

[25] 2nd ed. (Venice, 1554), fol. 4 r. In the dedication of his *Travagliata Inventione* (Venice, 1551), he claims the benefit of Venice as the purpose of his publication. His printer, Troiano, states in the dedication of Tartaglia's version of Euclid (Venice, 1565), that he published the posthumous manuscript "to benefit the world and to make illustrious this author's name" (Tartaglia's? Euclid's?). This is a nice compromise between the modes of speech of the humanists and the craftsmen.

[26] Advising gun-founders, *Ques. et Inv.*, I, no. 22 f.; military engineers (architects), *ibid.*, II, no. 9.

colleagues. Once he reports how he learned the technical terms of his profession from dikers, carpenters, masons, and metal work-ers.[27] He introduced decimal fractions and the parallelogram of forces and first stated the condition of equilibrium on the inclined plane.

Stevinus had the same utilitarian and "progressive" concept of science as Tartaglia. This becomes evident in the preface to his collected papers on applied mathematics, published at the same time in the Dutch original (*Wiscontighe Ghedaechtnissen*) and in Latin and French versions (*Hypomnemata mathematica, Mémoirs Mathématiques*, 1605–1608). Here Stevinus states that he has published the papers in order to make possible "the correction of his errors and the addition of other new inventions profitable to the public." He adds two other motives. Through publication he also wants to forestall plagiarists and to further the use of the mother-tongue in the scientific literature of the great nations.[28]

Stevinus also advocates scientific coöperation. He points out that at present experiments are lacking, "which are the solid basis on which the arts must be built. For this experience, however, the joint effort and the work of many people are required." As an example he cites astronomy. One man cannot carry out the neces-sary observations day and night for years, whereas if several observers collaborate, "the error or negligence of the one is com-pensated by the accuracy of the other." Observations of one observer, however good they may be, are always open to doubt and

[27] *Hypomnemata Mathematica*, I, 41 (*Oeuvres Mathém.*, ed. Girard [Leyden, 1634], II, 126). On Stevinus cf. George Sarton, *Isis*, 21 (1934), 241–262.

[28] Stevinus states (*loc. cit.*) that, without use of the mother-tongue, "the arts and sciences can not reach the perfection of the learned century." He believes in the existence of a pre-Greek "learned century" in which science flourished because it was based on experience rather than on belief in authority (*Hyp. Math.*, I, 11 f.; ed. Girard, II, 106 ff.). Only scanty remnants of this golden age are, according to Stevinus, extant in the Hermetic literature, but it can be awakened to new life "since human ingenuity has by no means diminished." Stevinus is convinced that science can and must be steadily improved. He is still ignorant, however, of the progressive interpretation of history and places the golden age of science in the past. Naturally Stevinus did not invent the "learned century" himself; he rather refers for its existence to his scholarly friends, the jurist Hugo Grotius the Elder, and the hu-manist Joseph Justus Scaliger. From them he also must have picked up the strange esteem of Hermes Trismegistus. His own scientific analyses are strictly mechanistic and entirely free from any influence of occult science—in contrast to nearly all learned natural philosophers of the period.

cannot be accepted as the basis for a theory by other astronomers. Only observations of various observers, if they agree well, can be relied upon.   This applies to the observations of the Landgrave William of Hessen and Tycho Brahe.   Many observers at many places are required also because the sky is sometimes overcast at one place.   There may arise rivalry among the observers, each striving to make his observations best; "but only great advancement for the arts proceeds from this, though ambition also has its pitfalls."   And what is true for astronomy is true for all sciences: science, concludes Stevinus, "requires the joint efforts of many people."   This is the first detailed exposition of the necessity of scientific coöperation.[29]   Tycho Brahe (d. 1591), and Wilhelm IV of Hessen (d. 1592), here mentioned, were the first in Europe to employ a staff of assistants at their observatories in Denmark and Prague and at Cassel respectively.   It is significant that Stevinus can give only astronomical examples although his exposition applies generally; it will be remembered that a certain amount of coöperation had been traditional in astronomy since antiquity. Yet Stevinus' appeal for the advancement of knowledge and coöperation is undoubtedly inspired by rising modern technology and its requirements.

The founder of modern surgery, Ambroise Paré (chronologically between Tartaglia and Stevinus, 1509–90) had a somewhat similar social position to Stevinus.   In sixteenth-century Paris there were four groups of medical men: the academically trained medical doctors who wrote in Latin and did not do manual work like operating and dissecting; the "surgeons of the long robe," organized in the *Collège de Saint-Côme;* the corporation of the "barber-surgeons"; and the quacks who practiced illegally without belonging to any guild.   The Collège of Saint-Côme had been founded in the fourteenth century as a corporation of artisans but had in the course of time successfully assimilated itself to the corporation of the doctors, demanding knowledge of Latin from its members and giving up any real medical work.   The barber-surgeons remained artisans; they had shops and did shaving, leeching, venesection, and operating.   Yet their corporation took care to transmit, under supervision of the doctors and the surgeons of the long robe, a certain amount of anatomical knowledge to the apprentices.   Paré, the son of a maker of strong boxes, was as a

[29] *Hyp. Math.*, I, 17 f. (ed. Girard II, 111 f.).

youth such an apprentice. In his twenties he worked as a kind of surgical intern at the only Paris hospital, and in the field as a military surgeon. Returned to Paris. he became a master in the guild of the barber-surgeons, and with the help of aristocratic protectors whose favor he had gained in the field, he was also admitted to the corporation of the surgeons of the long robe. He died as Surgeon to the King. In his works, all written in French, his connection with handicraft is conspicuous. He frequently scoffs at doctors "cackling in chairs" and "turning over the leaves of books"; he is proud of the manual work in surgery and emphasizes that he has not learned Latin. Yet he has gained from translations a very considerable knowledge of the classical medical literature. Socially he can be compared to Stevinus or the map-maker Ortelius: he was a superior artisan who through his thirst for knowledge ascénded to scholarship and entered the service of a prince. Paré invented entirely new methods in the treatment of fractures and in obstetrics, and introduced the binding of arteries to stop bleeding in operations; previously wounds had been burned with boiling oil. Paré's emphasis on experience and originality, his opposition to classical authorities and the overestimation of words deserve an extensive discussion. We shall, however, restrict ourselves to his conception of scientific progress.

Paré wrote all his works for his young colleagues. In his first publication, *La méthode de traicter les playes* (1545), he addresses the preface "to the young surgeons of good will." He has published the treatise, as he states like Dürer seventeen years earlier, "to stimulate superior minds to write on this subject so that we may all have greater knowledge"; and he concludes with the wish that God to whose honor he is writing may ordain "that some fruit and benefit to the support of the weakness of human life" issue from his labor. His *Collected Works,* frequently reprinted, appeared first in 1575. In the preface Paré promises that he will give case histories "so that young surgeons may take courage to proceed as or, if they can, better than I do (for it is they to whom I address these writings rather than to the scholars)." And he affirms that he has not spent his life in idleness but working "for the republic, always seeking the advancement of the young apprentices of surgery to whom my writings are addressed." His interest in the training of his colleagues obviously derives from medieval craft ideals. Paré had however overcome any ideas of guild secrecy.   His colleagues had accused him of having with his publications given everybody the means of practicing surgery.   To this reproach he replies that he "is extending the gifts given him by God liberally to everybody," wishing "that there may be no one who will not become through my writings much more skillful than I am"; he does not belong to those "who make a cabala of the arts." Thus he can widen his enthusiasm for his craft to the ideal of scientific progress.   "The arts," he says, "are not yet so perfected that one cannot make any addition: they are perfected and polished in the course of time.   It is sloth deserving blame to stop with the inventions of the first discoverers, only imitating them in the manner of lazy people without adding anything and without increasing the legacy left to us. . . . More things are left to be sought after than have been found."   Paré explains this idea at length, cautiously but decidedly assailing the overestimation of classical medicine.   God, he states, "did not give us judgment to let it rot and to stop at the first outlines of the art drawn by our ancestors." Usually Paré gives the public benefit, the benefit of France, the benefit of the patients, and the honor of God as his goals.   He never speaks of glory and literary immortality, although as a good craftsman he is rather proud of his reputation and even of his earnings.   He is the most outspoken advocate of scientific progress before Francis Bacon.   His "progressive" statements, however, although they speak of "the arts" in general, relate only to surgery.   Once he even complains that men are too much interested in astronomy, which in contrast to anatomy will never overcome the stage of mere conjectures.[29a]

5. We have studied a number of artisans, a highly instructed barber-surgeon, and two men with extensive mathematical knowledge, Tartaglia and Stevinus, who were close to the artisans.   University graduates have not been discussed.   In the sixteenth century, however, under the pressure of advancing technology the wall which since antiquity had separated the "liberal" from the "mechanical" arts began to crumble.   In many countries, particularly in England, a few academically trained scholars began to be inter-

[29a] On the Paris surgeons and Paré's life, conf. Ambroise Paré: *Oeuvres,* ed. J. F. Malgaigne (Paris, 1840), Introduction; his interest in the training of his colleagues, *ibid.,* I, pp. CCCIV, 11 f., and 16; on guild secrecy, I, 12 and 14; on progress, I, 8 f.; on astronomy, I, 15.

ested in technological problems.[30]   Their treatises are for the most part written in the vernacular, since they were intended to be used by navigators, gunners, surveyors, and craftsmen, or at least by their employers, the merchants, generals, and princes.   It is often hard to determine who in sixteenth-century technological literature gives and who receives the ideas.   Mathematical knowledge stems of course from the scholars.   Actually the artisans mentioned above, Bourne and Norman, learned mathematics from the works of the scholars Recorde and Digges.   On the other hand, the scholars were in the closest contact with manual workers, and several of them even earned their living, for a time or permanently, as instrument-makers.   They shared of course the utilitarian concept of science with the artisans.   Otherwise they would have written neither on technological subjects nor in the vernacular.   In most of these works the humanist ideal of fame is no longer mentioned and it is expressly stated that the author published the book to benefit the public or his country.[31]

A few anti-individualistic and "progressive" remarks deserve a more extensive discussion.   In 1532 the professor of mathematics at the University of Ingolstadt, Peter Apian, a contemporary of Tartaglia, published a Latin treatise on a measuring instrument of his invention for astronomers and surveyors.   In the booklet is a vindication of invention which somewhat anticipates Baconian ideas.   Those, Apian points out, "who reject the best things be-

[30] A list of authors in E. Zilsel: "The Sociological Roots of Science," *Amer. Journal of Sociol.*, XLVII (1942), 554 n.

[31] Luca Pacioli's *Summa de Arithmetica* (Venice, 1494), is probably the first book of a learned author to stress practical utility in the preface.   The text discusses for the most part problems of commercial arithmetic and contains the first printed account of double-entry bookkeeping.   Luca was a monk and mathematics professor at various Italian universities, but must have had close contacts with artist-engineers and merchants.   Practical utility is also expressly emphasized: in Recorde's dedication of his textbook on algebra, *The Whetstone of Witte* (1557); in Thomas Digges' prefaces to his English treatises on applied geometry and measuring instruments (*Tectonicon*, 1556; *Pantometria*, 1571); in Jacques Besson's works on measuring instruments and machines (*Le Cosmolabe*, 1567; *Theatrum Instrumentorum et Machinarum,* 1569); in John Dee's preface to Billingsley's English version of Euclid (1570); in Thomas Hood's inaugural address as mathematical lecturer of the City of London (1588, edited by Francis R. Johnson, *Journal of the History of Ideas,* III, 1942, 94 ff.).   All these authors were academically trained.   Most of them combine utilitarian with humanistic, Pacioli and Recorde also with scholastic ideas.

cause they are new, err, for without new inventions life would return to the state of the ancients who lived lawless and uncivilized like beasts.'' Countless still hidden astronomical facts could be brought to light if only we did not fail in our zeal for investigation. The author states that, though an admirer of classical antiquity, he does not despise the present; he rather is convinced that Nature is not yet tired and effete and is still able to produce praiseworthy things. In the following year Apian published an enlarged version of the booklet in German since, as he states, he often found better mathematical understanding among laymen than scholars. Here he affirms that he has invented his quadrant ''to benefit the whole of Christianity and almost the whole world.'' He also promises further treatises on measuring instruments since, ''as the proverb states, I am not born to myself alone but also to those with and after me.''[32] Professor Apian (1495–1522) was a skillful mechanic. After his graduation from the University of Leipzig he made his living for several years as a maker of globes and measuring instruments. As a young and badly paid mathematics professor at Ingolstadt he ran at the same time a printer's shop. Later he became astronomy teacher to Charles V and was knighted for a mechanical planetarium.

In 1570 the Dutchman Abraham Ortelius made a not unimportant contribution to the development of scientific method in his atlas, *Theatrum Orbis Terrarum*. Ortelius wanted, as the preface states, to benefit the students of geography rather than to aspire for fame through the works of others. He therefore gave a list of about eighty cartographers and maps used in his book. The writings of the scholastics and humanists abound with references to previous authors. Yet the list of Ortelius is the first extensive bibliography in modern scientific literature. Although bibliographical lists are not the cornerstone in the building of science

---

[32] *Quadrans Astronomicus* (Ingolstadt, 1532), dedication. *Instrument Buch* (*ibid.*, 1533), dedication and part 5.—Apian's polemic against overestimating antiquity is manifestly inspired by Pico della Mirandola. The passage on Nature which is not yet effete is an almost literal allusion to Pliny the Younger, *ep.* VI, 2. This passage was often quoted by Giovanni Pico della Mirandola, his nephew Giovanni Francesco, and other precursors of the *querelle des anciens et des modernes* that developed in the following century. Cf. E. Zilsel, *Entstehung des Geniebegriffs*, 215, 302, 305. On Apian's life, cf. *Allgemeine Deutsche Biographie*, and "Die Apianus Druckerei in Ingolstadt" in *Veröffentlichungen der Gutenberggesellschaft*, Mainz, XXI (1930), 59–82.

they too manifest the modern idea of scientific coöperation. Ortelius (1527–98) was a map-maker, a dealer in maps and antiquities, and became imperial geographer to Charles V. In his youth he had been, together with the engravers, painters, and the renowned Antwerp pianomakers, a member of the St. Luke guild in Antwerp. He was, however, not an ordinary craftsman but an erudite classical scholar despite his lack of academic training.[33]

In 1595 Ortelius' friend, Gerard Mercator, stated in his *Atlas* that in the composition and arrangement of his work he kept his eye on the benefit of the republic; "we are not born to ourselves alone but the Creator ordered us to live for the common weal." Mercator (1512–94) studied at the University of Louvain, but entered a geographer's office in Antwerp after his graduation. These offices composed· itineraries for merchants since reliable maps were rare, and procured heads of caravans. Often they also made maps and nautical instruments. Later Mercator established his own workshop and became the best instrument-maker, surveyor, and map-maker of the century. The editor of the later editions of Mercator's *Atlas,* the cartographer Hond, also emphasized the utilitarian viewpoint. He expressly demands that authors endeavor to benefit the republic and posterity, and blames those who "sing only for themselves and the Muses."[34]

The progress of knowledge was proclaimed as a controlling scientific and philosophical program by Francis Bacon (*Advancement of Learning,* 1605; *Novum Organum,* 1620; *De Augmentis Scientiarum,* 1623). Bacon emphasizes also the importance of scientific coöperation. In his *New Atlantis* (1627) he describes an ideal state ruled by a body of scientists organized, according to the principle of division of labor, in nine groups. Technological and physical laboratories and agricultural stations are at the disposal of the scientists. Such institutes for research were unknown in Bacon's lifetime. There existed only observatories, which of course were not affiliated with the universities but were establishments of rich scholars (Tycho Brahe) or princes (William IV of Hessen, emperor Rudolph II). Bacon's scientific ideas were in

[33] Cf. *Biogr. Nat. Belg.*

[34] Mercator's remark in the introduction to the maps of France (4th edition of the *Atlas* [Antwerp, 1630], 121). Hond's remark in the preface, *ibid.* The editor of the smaller edition, Petrus Montanus, also stressed the public benefit (*Atlas Minor* [Antwerp, 1607], pref.). On Mercator's life cf. *Biogr. Nat. Belg.*

marked contrast to the program of the contemporary universities; he himself set up the "mechanical" arts as a model for the scientist.

Bacon's ideas have been so often set forth that another discussion would be superfluous. It has however not been noted that his idea of progress through coöperation appeared before him in the sixteenth-century literature on applied mathematics, navigation, and cartography. The question of Bacon's literary sources is of minor importance. Since he was not interested in mathematics and quantitative investigation he probably did not read treatises on measuring instruments. On the other hand, it seems improbable that a scholar at the court of Queen Elizabeth, where so much was done for the promotion of navigation, should not at least have been in touch with the scientific tradition of Recorde, Digges, and John Dee. These however are merely biographical questions. What really matters is the sociological origin of Bacon's ideas. Bacon and Stevinus did not know each other. Yet Stevinus' plea for scientific coöperation appeared a few years before the *New Atlantis*. And Tartaglia and Robert Norman, Apian and Mercator held utilitarian views on science and deliberately worked for the gradual advancement of. knowledge, whether Bacon knew their books or not.

Manifestly, the idea of science we usually regard as "Baconian" is rooted in the requirements of early capitalistic economy and technology; its rudiments appear first in treatises of fifteenth-century craftsmen. However, it makes a considerable difference whether notions are advanced in prefaces and casual remarks or whether they are presented as a philosophical platform to revolutionize the whole of science. Bacon used the ideas of his "predecessors" as a battering ram against scholasticism and humanism and was the first to develop their philosophical and cultural implications. The concept of scientific progress was known before him, the ideal of the progress of civilization begins only with Bacon. On the other hand, Bacon fell considerably behind the military engineers and cartographers in the understanding of scientific particulars.[35]

[35] In Campanella's utopia, *Civitas Solis* (composed in 1602, published in 1623) there are public museums but no institutions for research. Scientific progress and coöperation are not mentioned. They are not mentioned either in Campanella's interesting account of his scientific aims, *De libris propriis et recta ratione studendi*

Perhaps the clearest statement of the ideas the genesis of which we have been considering, is found eleven years after Bacon's death in the Cartesian *Discourse on Method* (1637).[36]   In his matter-of-fact style Descartes here explains why he has published "the little that he has found."   He wants, as he puts it, "to induce intelligent men to try to advance farther by contributing, each according to his inclination and ability, to the necessary experiments and by also publishing all their findings.   Thus the last would start where their predecessors had stopped and, by joining the lives and the work of many people, we would all proceed much farther together than each would have done by himself."   Manifestly this procedure, advocated by Albrecht Dürer a hundred and fifty years before, was not yet a matter of course in the Cartesian period.   It is noteworthy that this passage is not a casual remark. It concludes a lengthy explanation of the author's reluctance to communicate his ideas to the public.   Descartes states that he would never have published his ideas so long as they concerned only the "speculative sciences"; when, however, he saw that his new method would revolutionize physics also, he considered its concealment a violation of the law enjoining furtherance of the common weal upon us.   With the help of this method, he adds, we shall understand the actions of fire, water, and all other bodies "as distinctly as we understand the various trades of our artisans, and by application of this knowledge to any use to which it is adapted we could make ourselves masters and possessors of nature." Wherever in the seventeenth century the idea of scientific progress through coöperation appears, the application of science to technology is also emphasized.   The modern textbooks on the history of philosophy often disregard these Baconian traits in Descartes.

The further development of the concepts of progress and scientific coöperation is familiar.   Soon after Bacon's death his program was put into effect, to a large extent under the direct influ-

---

syntagma (composed in 1632, published in 1642; ed. Spampanato, Florence, 1927), where they would have been discussed if Campanella had known these ideas.   In Johann Valentin Andreae's utopia *Christianopolis* (Strassburg, 1619, tr. F. E. Held, New York, 1916) there is a library, an anatomical theatre, a chemical and a physical laboratory, and an observatory.   Andreae is, however, not interested in research but in education and does not mention scientific progress.   He was a German protestant minister, a friend of Comenius, and a Rosicrucian.

[36] *Oeuvres* (Adam-Tannery), VI, 63.

ence of his writings, in scientific organizations and periodicals. The Academy of the Lynxes in Rome (1603–30), established while Bacon was still alive, owed nothing to his ideas. It had no laboratory and was nearer to the sixteenth-century "academies," which were actually aristocratic literary clubs, than to a modern scientific society. Yet the Lincei published a scientific work composed by several authors in collaboration, the *Nova plantarum, animalium, et mineralium Mexicanorum historia* (Rome, 1651). On the other hand, in the laboratories of the *Accademia del Cimento* in Florence (1657–67), the *Royal Society* (founded in 1660), and the *Académie des Sciences* in Paris (founded in 1666) scientists for the first time in history systematically collaborated. The progress of science through coöperation was the aim of these organizations. It is explained with particular clearness in the introduction to the first issue of the *Philosophical Transactions* (1666), edited by the *Royal Society*. Here Oldenburg, the secretary of the Society, states that the new periodical is being published "to the end that such Productions being clearly and truly communicated, desires after solid and useful knowledge may be further entertained . . . and those, addicted to . . . such matters, may be invited and encouraged to search, try, and find out new things, impart their knowledge to one another, and contribute what they can to the Grand design of improving Natural knowledge. . . . All for the Glory of God, the Honour and Advantage of these Kingdoms, and the Universal Good of Mankind." Like Descartes, Oldenburg invites explorers to "contribute" their part to a common design. Knowledge is no longer the business of literati greedy for personal fame and disputing schoolmen: the modern Western concept of scientific research has been reached.[37]

[37] On the first scientific societies and periodicals, cf. primarily Martha Ornstein: *The Rôle of Scientific Societies in the Seventeenth Century*, 3rd ed. (Chicago, 1938). Recent additions in: Harcourt Brown: *Scientific Organizations in 17th Century France* (Baltimore, 1934), and "Martin Fogel e l'idea Accademica Lincea," *Reale Accad. Naz. dei Lincei, Scienze Morali, Rendiconti*, VI/11, (1935), 814 ff.; Giuseppe Gabrielli: "Il Carteggio Linceo," *ibid., Mem.*, VI/1 (1925), 137 ff. and VI/7 (1938/39), 1 ff., and "Le Schede Fogeliane," *ibid., Rendiconti*, VI/15 (1939) 141 ff.; Francis R. Johnson: "Gresham College, Precursor of the Royal Society," *Journal of the History of Ideas*, I (1940), 413 ff. Michele Maylender: *Storia delle Accademie d'Italia*, 5 vols. (Bologna, 1926); Robert Merton: "Science and Technology in the 17th Century," *Osiris*, IV (1938), 360 ff. (on the Royal Society). A sociological analysis of the precursors of the modern scientific organizations and of the first books composed by several authors in collaboration will be published elsewhere.

We have tried to show that this concept made its first appearance in the intellectual attitude of superior artisans. In classical literature similar ideas appear in the treatise of a maker of war-machines. In antiquity, however, they were not taken over by scholars; in early modern capitalism they were. It would be interesting to investigate the Arabic, Persian, Indian, and Chinese literatures. It is not impossible that in these cultures also superior artisans advocated in technological treatises the gradual progress of craftsmanship—if they wrote any. Such ideas were certainly not adopted and developed by the oriental scholars, theologians, and literati. The absence of slavery, the existence of machinery, the capitalistic spirit of enterprise and economic rationality seem to be prerequisites without which the ideal of scientific progress cannot unfold.

ᴈ& *Edgar Zilsel*

COPERNICUS AND MECHANICS

Copernicus overthrew the medieval conception of the solar system by starting from the scanty reports on heliocentric theories in antiquity, by specifying the implications of these geometrically in every detail, and by thus furnishing the exact foundations for ephemerides that far surpassed the exactness of the older tables of planetary movements based on the theory of Ptolemy.[1] His outstanding contribution to astronomy was a mathematico-geometrical one. It is, however, sometimes not sufficiently noticed how far removed Copernicus still is from modern physical and especially mechanical thinking. A few remarks on this point, therefore, may be useful. They refer to the first book of *De Revolutionibus Orbium Coelestium* (1543), in which Copernicus explains the basic ideas of his theory and where, consequently, Pythagorean and Scholastic ideas predominate. Ancient and medieval philosophic ideas recede into the background in the following five books (II–VI) in which the mathematical details are explained.[2]

(1) Copernicus uses again and again concepts of value in his general arguments. The third sentence of Book I asks the rhetorical question "What is more beautiful than the sky? . . . Because of its preëminent excellence most of the philosophers have called it the Visible God." In chapter 8 he supports the statement of the immobility of the sun in the following way (p. 24, ll. 2 *ff*.): "Furthermore the condition of immobility is considered more noble and divine than the condition of change and instability which, therefore,[3] is more fitting to the earth than to the universe. I add that it would seem rather absurd to ascribe movement to the containing and locating and not to the contained and located, which is the earth." In chapter 10 he explains (p. 30, ll. 1 *ff*.): "The sun is stationed (*residet*) in the middle of the universe. In this most beautiful temple who could put this lamp in another or better place than the one from which it can illuminate the whole universe at once?" The sun, he continues, therefore is called by some "mind" and "ruler," and he ends by quoting the chief authority of occult science, alchemy, and Neo-Platonism: "Trismegistus calls the sun

---

[1] *Cf.* Angus Armitage: *Copernicus. The Founder of Modern Astronomy.* London 1938, pp. 90 and 161 *f.*

[2] All quotations from *De Revolutionibus* refer to the Thorn edition, 1873 (ed. M. Curtze).

[3] The idea that immobility is nobler than movement is Platonic and Pythagorean (*cf.* the well-known Pythagorean table of values, Diels, *Fragmente der Vorsokratiker* 45 B 5). Ultimately it goes back to the Eleatic school (Xenophanes, Diels *FVS* 11 B 26).

the Visible God, Sophocles' Electra, Him who sees everything. The sun, indeed, sitting on a royal throne rules (*gubernat*) the family of stars moving around it."

(2) Copernicus is inclined to apprehend inanimate objects as living beings striving to reach aims. Sometimes he expresses himself in an almost animistic way, more often he gives teleological explanations in the more rational way of Aristotle and the Scholastics. A few sentences after the passage just quoted he remarks (p. 30, line 9): "The Earth conceives from the Sun and is impregnated with annual birth." In chapter 1 he explains the spherical form of the universe as follows (p. 11): "This form is the most perfect one, does not need any joint (*nulla indigua compagine*), . . . and is the most capacious figure. . . . All objects strive (*appetant*) to be bounded in this way. This is seen in drops of water and other liquids when they wish (*cupiunt*) to be bounded by themselves." Gravity he explains in the following way (chap. 9, p. 24, line 25): "I think gravity is nothing else but a natural appetency (*appetentia*) given to the parts by the divine providence of the maker of the universe in order that they may establish their unity and wholeness (*ut in unitatem integritatemque suam se conferant*), by combining in the form of a sphere. It is probable that this affection (*affectionem*) also belongs to the sun, the moon, and the planets in order that they may, by its efficacy, remain in their roundness (*ut eius efficacia in . . . rotonditate permaneant*)." On the phenomenon of terrestrial gravitation he says (chap. 7, p. 19, line 28): "The element of the earth is the heaviest, and all heavy things are driven towards it, striving (*contendentia*) to its innermost center."

(3) Closely related to this teleological conception of nature is the opinion of Copernicus that objects of the same kind exert "sympathetic" influences on each other. In chapter 8 he discusses the fact that the surrounding air rotates with the earth and gives two explanations which he considers to be equally admissible, a medieval-sympathetic one and a modern mechanical one. The air rotates, he explains (p. 22, ll. 18 *ff.*), "either because it is mixed with earthen and watery matter and, therefore, follows the same nature as the earth (*eandem sequatur naturam quam terra*), or because the motion of the air is acquired and the air participates in it without resistance, since the air is contiguous to the constantly rotating earth." A few lines later, discussing loose heavy objects (which rotate with the earth as well), he repeats the "sympathetic" explanation alone (p. 22, line 31): "Since the objects which are depressed by their weight are mainly earthen, there is no doubt that the parts retain the same nature as their whole (*eandem servent partes naturam quam suum totum*)." It becomes perfectly clear that in the opinion of Copernicus, "equality of nature" is the point that matters in the whole argument when he discusses flames: they par-

ticipate in the rotation (p. 22, l. 33) "because this fire is earthly and is nourished mainly by earthen matter."[4]

(4) The teleological, half-animistic conception of nature appears also in his theory of motion, which is based on the Aristotelian distinction of "natural" and "artificial" movements. Copernicus explains the falling of bodies by the Aristotelian theory of "natural place" (*locus naturalis,* chap. 8, p. 23, l. 10). He continues (p. 23, l. 13 *ff.*): "Rectilinear movement belongs with objects which wander or are expelled from their natural places. . . . Nothing is so contrary to the order of the universe and the form of the world as for a thing to be out of its place (*extra locum suum . . . esse*). Rectilinear motion, therefore, occurs only if things are not rightly ordered (*rebus non recte se habentibus*)." Obviously Copernicus fully accepts the theory of Aristotle and classical astronomy[5] that celestial bodies move in circles and that this movement is something "natural," whereas rectilinear motion belongs only to terrestrial bodies and is "artificial," as it were.

The medieval idea that everything natural is endowed with an, as it were, spiritual power which is lacking in artificial and imperfect objects and processes leads Copernicus to a discussion of centrifugal force which contradicts modern mechanics in a remarkable degree. Already Ptolemy had objected to the rotation of the earth that by it all objects would have to be thrown off the earth.[6] Copernicus has to defend his theory against this objection. He does it as follows (chap. 8, p. 21, l. 5): "Things governed by nature produce effects contrary to those governed by violence. Things upon which force and impetus are conferred must dissolve and they cannot subsist for a long time; but what is done by nature is rightly ordered (*recte se habent*) and is preserved in its best composition. Ptolemy, therefore, is wrong in fearing lest the earth and all terrestrial things might be dispersed in a rotation brought about by the efficacy of nature. This is something quite different from art or what human ingenuity can carry on." Obviously Copernicus thinks centrifugal force appears only in "artificial" not in "natural" rotation.

The modern answer to Ptolemy's objection, the argument that the effects of centrifugal force may be neglected compared with gravity, would not have been entirely out of the way. Copernicus himself uses the analogous argument against the objection that the revolution of the earth around the

---

[4] It may be mentioned that the medical prescriptions of Copernicus also—he was for a time physician in ordinary to his uncle, the bishop of Ermland—show an entirely medieval spirit. For examples *cf.* M. Curtze, *Inedita Coppernicana,* Leipzig 1878 (*Mittheilungen des Coppernicus-Vereins,* 1 Heft) p. 56 *ff.* E.g., Copernicus thinks that the seeds of water-cress cause "unhealthy humidity" because water-cress grows in humid places. *Loc. cit.,* p. 64, 15.

[5] Aristotle, *De caelo* I, 23; Ptolemy, *Almagest* III, 3.

[6] *Almagest* I, 7.

sun must bring about parallactic shiftings of the fixed stars. There he argues quite correctly that these cannot be observed (with the insufficient instruments of his period, as we have to add) because of the great distance of the fixed stars (I, chap. 10, p. 30, l. 24).[7] Certainly positions of stars could already be measured in antiquity, whereas in the time of Copernicus no way was available of measuring centrifugal forces and comparing them quantitatively with gravitation. The lack of methods of measurement rather often has resulted in metaphysical explanations of physical phenomena. At any rate the quoted passages may have shown sufficiently how much Copernicus is imbued with Pythagorean, Aristotelian, and Scholastic metaphysics.

A correct quantitative theory of centrifugal force was developed for the first time by Huyghens, one hundred and twenty years after Copernicus. Galileo, however, already ninety years after Copernicus, discussed the centrifugal force connected with the rotation of the earth in an entirely unmetaphysical way. Certainly his explanation[8] is not yet correct—he thinks the centrifugal force must at any rate be smaller than gravitation, however fast the earth would rotate, and produces a would-be geometrical proof of this assertion—but he knows that the centrifugal effects in question cannot be observed for the reason that they are too small. The idea that "artificial" rotations behave differently from "natural" ones is not even mentioned by him. This is highly important, for in the last consequence the entirely non-mechanical distinction between "natural" and "artificial" movements excludes experimental research on natural objects. Also with Galileo some teleological ideas still persist, but they form nothing but the general background of his explanations. He almost always uses purely mechanical arguments when he proves his single statements and is strongly opposed to explanations of natural phenomena by means of sympathy and antipathy.[9]

Copernicus is interested in the exact formulation of the mathematical regularities of celestial movements; he is a Pythagorean, and advances not one real mechanical idea. Galileo, on the other hand, is a mechanist: in his dialogue on the theory of Copernicus he is so little interested in the exact details of the planetary movements that he does not even mention the laws of Kepler.[10] He considers it much more important to support the basic ideas of Copernicus by new observations, to show that there is no fundamental difference between celestial phenomena and terrestrial mechanics and

[7] Copernicus gave the same argument previously in his *Commentariolus*: M. Curtze, *op. cit.*, p. 6, Quarta petitio. Translated by Edward Rosen, *Three Copernican Treatises*, 1939, p. 58, assumption 4.

[8] *Dialogo sopra i due massimi sistemi del mondo*, 1632. *Opere*, Edizione nazionale VII, 221, 7 *ff*.

[9] *Cf. Dialogo*, Ed. naz., VII, 436, 17 *ff.; Discorsi*, Ed. naz., VIII, 116.

[10] The dialogue appeared in 1632, Kepler published his laws in 1609 and 1619.

physics, and to refute the pre-mechanical ideas and objections of the Aristotelians of his period.

The difference between Copernicus and Galileo is not a difference of individual psychology only, and even less can it be explained by the mere difference of time. Kepler, who was a contemporary of Galileo, was, as is generally known, at least as Pythagorean and thought at least as teleologically as Copernicus. There rather seems to be a difference between astronomy and mechanics as to their historical evolution and sociological origins. The very first astronomers were Babylonian priests and this connection with priesthood was never quite interrupted; and from antiquity through the Middle Ages up to the end of the sixteenth century, astronomy belonged to the "liberal" arts, as contrasted with the "mechanical" ones. This might explain why metaphysical, Pythagorean and teleological ideas could persist in astronomy until Copernicus and Kepler. It is scarcely mere chance that Copernicus starts his work (I, p. 9) with a eulogy of astronomy "which is the chief of the liberal arts, is most worthy of free men, and rests upon almost all kinds of mathematics." And it is not mere chance that, by enumerating these, Copernicus gives mechanics as the last one. For mechanics belonged to the "mechanical arts," to those which required the use not only of head and tongue, but also of hands, and therefore were left to lower-class people. It may be that in the modern era the experimental method and the elimination of teleological and animistic by causal thinking originated in those ranks of mechanicians and craftsmen. Certainly scientific mechanics and physics did not appear in modern times before the way of thinking of the craftsmen was adopted by academically trained scholars of the upper class, as happened in the period of Galileo. A more extensive inquiry, however, than could be given in this short note on Copernicus, would be necessary to verify this sociological explanation.

≈§ A. C. Keller

ZILSEL, THE ARTISANS, AND THE IDEA OF PROGRESS IN THE RENAISSANCE

The work of the late Edgar Zilsel, whose study of the sociological roots of science stressed the view that modern science owes its origin to the work and writings of artisans in the Renaissance rather than to humanists or scholars, was an important contribution to the history of the beginnings of modern culture. Unfortunately for the world of scholarship, Zilsel could not carry his work to completion, and many points of detail remain to be supplied or clarified within the framework which he built.[1]

One of the characteristics of scientific thought, according to Zilsel, is the belief in progress. This complex idea involves "(1) the insight that scientific knowledge is brought about step by step through contributions of generations of explorers building upon and gradually amending the findings of their predecessors; (2) the belief that this process is never completed; (3) the conviction that contribution to this development, either for its own sake or for the public benefit, constitutes the very aim of the true scientist."[2] But in his effort to emphasize the rôle of the artisans in the formation of this idea, Zilsel gave little consideration to the fact that the same idea was asserting itself in more academic pursuits. He says, for example, that "in classical, scholastic, and humanist literature no statements on the necessity of the gradual improvement of knowledge exist. Naturally only members of the most highly skilled crafts wrote treatises, and only a few of these craftsmen-authors conceived the idea of progress with any clarity."[3]

[1] The following is a complete list of Zilsel's writings, as nearly as the present writer can determine:

Die Geniereligion: Ein kritischer Versuch über das moderne Persönlichkeitsideal mit einer historischen Begründung, Wien, 1918; *Die Entstehung des Geniebegriffes: Ein Beitrag zur Ideengeschichte der Antike und des Frühkapitalismus*, Tübingen, 1926; "Copernicus and Mechanics," *JHI*, I (1940), 113–18; "History and Biological Evolution," *Philos. of Sci.*, VII (1940), 121–8; "The Origins of W. Gilbert's Scientific Method," *JHI*, II (1941), 1–32; "Phenomenology and Natural Science" *Philos. of Sci.*, VIII (1941), 26–32; "Physics and the Problem of Historico-Sociological Laws," *Philos. of Sci.*, VIII (1941), 567–79; "Problems of Empiricism: Experiment and Manual Labor," *International Encycl. of Unified Science*, II, 8 (Chicago, 1941), 53–94; "The Genesis of the Concept of Physical Law," *Philos. Rev.*, LI (1942), 245–79; "The Sociological Roots of Science," *Amer. J. of Sociol.*, XLVII (1942), 544–62; "The Genesis of the Concept of Scientific Progress," *JHI*, VI (1945), 325–49.

[2] "Genesis of the Concept of Scientific Progress," pp. 251–275.

[3] *Ibid.*, p. 257.

He cites an impressive number of such treatises, in which the craftsmen-authors were transmitting their knowledge or discoveries to posterity with the conscious aim of promoting the understanding of their fields of work. In some of the treatises one reads the statement, which was to play so important a part in the seventeenth-century quarrel of ancients and moderns, that nature, far from being exhausted, is still able to produce praiseworthy things now and in the future. This dynamic view is closely associated by Zilsel with the rising capitalist economy, the spirit of competition, and the revolt against authority.

Modern science was born, then, in Zilsel's view, when academic learning and the attitudes of the artisans joined forces, roughly about 1600. What stood in the way before that time was the social barrier which led scholars to look with scorn upon the mechanical arts. However, W. E. Houghton, Jr., has called attention to the importance of the mechanical arts in the learned writers as early as Rabelais and Vives, writing in the 1530's.[4] I should like now to point out that the general notion of progress was not as unknown to the bookish writers of the sixteenth-century as Zilsel thought, and that the notion was evident both in technological and in scholarly writings, separated though they were to a certain extent by the barrier of social prejudice. Nor should this be surprising. The revolt against authority on all fronts, visible in Ramus and Montaigne as well as in Galileo and his precursors, was (and Zilsel understood this, as few have) an expression of a changing society. It would therefore be strange that the idea of progress should have made its appearance in the pre-scientific writings alone. The technological advances, which corresponded to the needs of the age and which inspired confidence in the continuing development of technology, were paralleled by advances in scholarship and academic learning, with parallel effects. The power which the scholars, historians, and political theorists of the sixteenth century felt that they had acquired by the editing of texts and the increased accessibility of the sages of antiquity was not unlike that of the artisans in the face of the improvements in their tools and their technical knowledge. If the growth of capitalism had a more powerful and direct impact on the artisans than on the scholars and made the thought of the former the more significantly "progressive," the bookish men nevertheless were not so isolated from the movement of history as not to share the views attributed by Zilsel to the artisans alone. The attack against tradition was carried on equally in science and philosophy, and the intellectual independence of the artisans is of a piece with that of the speculative thinkers.

Specifically, the general concept of progress appears fairly clearly, among the best-known authors, in Rabelais, Bodin, and Leroy, from the

---

[4] Houghton, Walter E., Jr., "The History of Trades: Its Relation to Seventeenth-Century Thought," pp. 354–381.

1540's to the 1570's.[5] Were their statements isolated from the rest of their work and from their times, they might be regarded as exceptions, like Seneca, in antiquity. But in all three cases, the statements were supported by attitudes of intellectual independence, by vigorous departures from and criticisms of ancient authorities, and by a keen awareness of the dawning of a new age.

Rabelais' *Gargantua and Pantagruel* is too well known to need much comment. It is enough to quote from the last chapter of his book to see how aptly he expressed in general and philosophical terms the sentiment expressed in particular matters by the technological writers. "Your philosophers," he says, "who complain that the ancients have left them nothing to write of or to invent, are very much mistaken. Those phenomena which you see in the sky; whatever the surface of the earth affords you, and the sea, and every river contains, it is not to be compared with what is hid within the bowels of the earth."[6] As far as the beginnings of science are concerned, such statements are not comparable in importance with the work and writings of the artisans, which led in an unbroken chain to Gilbert and Bacon; but they merit attention in a study of the idea of the progress of knowledge. Rabelais was, in fact, one of the early writers in whom scholarship and artisanship were already joined. Not only did he advocate education in the mechanical arts, but as a doctor he did not disdain dissection, though, according to Zilsel's thesis, his scholarly work on ancient medical texts might have precluded such manual work. The barrier between the intellectual and the manual was, surely, already weak in Rabelais' case.

Jean Bodin, France's most learned political writer in the sixteenth century, and author of the *Methodus ad facilem historiarum cognitionem* (1566) and *Les six livres de la République* (1576), is best known, where the idea of progress is concerned, for his broad and effective attack on the theories of degeneration and the golden age. Whether he believed in progress in a positive sense is a question complicated by his adherence to the famous theory of cycles. But on the progress of knowledge—and that by accumulation—there can be little doubt. He says, for example,

Some one will say that the ancients were inventors of the arts and to them the glory ought to go. They certainly did discover many things—especially the power of the celestial bodies, the calculated courses of many stars—but yet not all—the wonderful trajections of fixed stars and of those called 'planets.' Then they noted carefully the obscurities of nature and explained many things accurately, and yet

[5] An excellent sketch of the idea of progress in Renaissance thought, citing Leroy and Bodin among others, may be found in H. Weisinger, "Ideas of History during the Renaissance," *JHI*, VI (1945), 415–35. As Weisinger says, Bury's and Delvaille's books (*The Idea of Progress*, London, 1924; *L'ideé du progrès*, Paris, 1914) are both weak on the Renaissance, and much work remains to be done.

[6] *Gargantua and Pantagruel*, Urquart-Motteux trans.

they left incomplete many of these things which have been. completed and handed
down to posterity by men of our time.   No one, looking closely into this matter,
can doubt that the discoveries of our men ought to be compared with the discoveries
of our elders; many ought to be placed first.   Although nothing is more remarkable
in the whole nature of things than the magnet, yet the ancients were not aware of
its use. . . . Nature has countless treasures of knowledge which cannot be exhausted
in any age.[7]

More than this, Bodin lists some of the lines along which progress has
occurred—discovery, exploration, commerce, geography, medicine, warfare,
weaving, handicrafts—"with which the life of man has been aided in a remarkable way"; so that, making social utility an aim of learning, Bodin
shows much the same concern as the artisans cited by Zilsel.

The third notable case is that of Loys Leroy (or Regius), whose *De la
vicissitude des choses en l'univers* appeared in 1577.   As early as 1540,
exhibiting an irreverent spirit toward the writers of antiquity, Leroy held
that much learning had been accumulated since the days of Aristotle.   In
his *G. Budaei Vita* (1540) he asserted that nature is not so exhausted that
she cannot produce as great works now as in times gone by,[8] the very idea
which Zilsel finds in a work by Peter Apian written in the same period.   On
the gradual building up of knowledge, Leroy spoke as follows:

Arts and sciences receive their perfection, not by relying upon the sayings and
opinions of men of former ages, of how great authority soever they were, but by
correcting of the same, and changing in them whatsoever is found not to be good.
. . . I have collected [historical and political data] to the intent to add the same
to the governments of Plato and Aristotle, as a thing most necessary for the understanding of their books, and for the knowledge of the faculty of government, which
is not all so manifest in their observations, how learned and elegant soever they be,
but there doth and will remain many precepts and observations behind for learned
men to join thereunto, and that without losing their labour.   Truth sheweth herself to all such as will seek for her, and are of capacity to receive her.   She is
not yet all taken up and engrossed, great things come slackly forward, and shew
not themselves manifestly together at one instant, but are from time to time augmented or brought to better order and elegance.   And so it may fall out in this science politics, after the help that we receive by the observations of the ancients, after
so many examples wherewith we are instructed by them that have been before us,
after so long experience and practice of two thousand years or thereabouts, which
have passed since the time wherein our authors wrote till this present.[9]

Beginning, in the *Vicissitude*—as the title implies—with the idea of
cycles or ups-and-downs, Leroy was carried away in the course of his study
by the gradual ascent of humanity, and his final chapter is a veritable

[7] *Methodus*, ch. 7.   (Eng. trans. by Beatrice Reynolds, New York, 1945.)

[8] Edition of 1542, p. 4.

[9] *Les Politiques d'Aristote* (Paris, 1568), argument to Bk.   II.   (Eng. trans.,
London, 1598.)

paean to progress. Indeed, it would be difficult to find a more complete statement of the idea of progress anywhere in the sixteenth century. The following sentences indicate the tenor of the whole last book:

So almost all the arts were found by use and experience, then systematized by observation and reason, consequently reduced to better and surer form . . . not by stopping at what the first men had done, said, and written: but by later generations adding their own, so that things were discovered and made clear as time went on— the honor usually going to the last as most accurate and accomplished. . . . If the ancients had proposed to write or say nothing but what had been written or said before them, no art would have been invented and all would have remained in their first stages without being increased. . . . It is therefore reasonable to apply industry and research to the truth, as they did, and to try to augment the knowledge of those who went before. . . . Nothing prevents this age from producing in philosophy men as eminent as Plato and Aristotle, or in medicine as Hippocrates and Galen, or in mathematics as Euclid, Archimedes and Ptolemy, after the help which we get from their books, after so many observations and inventions made since them, after such a long experience in all things: so that, when we consider well, there was never a century more happily placed for the advancement of letters than the present one.

There is no substantial difference between these statements of Rabelais, Bodin, and Leroy on the one hand, and those of the progressive artisans quoted by Zilsel on the other—e.g., the following from the surgeon Ambroise Paré:

The arts are not yet so perfected that one cannot make any addition: they are perfected and polished in the course of time. It is sloth deserving blame to stop with the inventions of the first discoverers, only imitating them in the manner of lazy people without adding anything and without increasing the legacy left to us. . . . More things are left to be sought after than have been found. . . .[10]

Zilsel's erudition undoubtedly embraced the works of Rabelais, Bodin, and Leroy. That he failed to give proper emphasis to their statements of progress must be attributed partly to the fact that his studies inevitably focused more on Italy than on France, and partly to his enthusiasm for the more continuous "progressive" work of the artisans. But in the long run Zilsel would not have allowed himself to adopt what is almost the same kind of scorn for the scholars as some of the early scholars had for the artisans. What is more, Zilsel would surely have found that the men discussed here, and others like them, had been strongly affected by technological innovations and discussions, and he would have integrated them in the larger presentation which he planned. It is with a view to establishing such

[10] Malgaigne ed. (3 vols., Paris, 1840), I, 8. Quoted by Zilsel.

a balance, and not for the purpose of criticizing an important and original student of the Renaissance, that this note has been written. The *idea* of progress in the Renaissance, was an expression of *real* progress, and scholarship had as much ground on which to base its view of cumulative advance as had technology. Renaissance scholars cannot seriously be thought of as unaffected by the world about them; humanists like Rabelais, Bodin, and Leroy were not unaffected by technological progress, which, joined with the enthusiasm for the progress of scholarship, produced well before 1600 the general statements of the progress of knowledge cited above.

THE RAMUS-RHETICUS CORRESPONDENCE

The emergence of modern science was attended by a vigorous debate about the proper function of hypothesis in scientific method. Peter Ramus (Pierre de la Ramée, 1515–1572), the celebrated adversary of Aristotle, persistently called for the general abandonment of hypotheses. In a letter addressed in 1563 to George Joachim Rheticus (1514–1576), Ramus urged the friend and disciple of Copernicus to "... convince us by cogent proof ... that astronomy, resting only on the elements and principles of arithmetic and geometry, can stand very well without any hypotheses;" and to "... undertake the task ... of freeing astronomy from the fictions of hypotheses."[1]

I wish to direct particular attention to the following sentence in Ramus's letter, because it involves a hitherto neglected aspect of the reception of the Copernican theory:

At hypotheses epicyclorum et eccentricorum commenta falsa et absurda esse, epistola tua, ni fallor, Copernico praeposita, manifeste ex epicyclo Veneris ostendit. [But the letter (written by you, unless I am mistaken) that was placed at the beginning of Copernicus's book shows clearly, by reference to the epicycle of Venus, that the hypotheses which employ epicycles and eccentrics are false and absurd fictions.]

Marie Delcourt translates *epistola tua, ni fallor, Copernico praeposita:* "ta lettre adressée, si je ne me trompe, à Copernic"[2] [your letter, sent, if I am not mistaken, to Copernicus].

Surely *praeposita* seldom, if ever, described a letter as "sent." If the word was employed in the usual way, *epistola ... Copernico praeposita* means "the letter that was placed at the beginning of [the book by] Copernicus," not "the letter that was sent to [the person] Copernicus." *Praeposita* was used with precisely the same force by a pupil of Ramus,

---

[1] The earliest biography of Ramus (*Petri Rami vita* by John Thomas Freigius in *Petri Rami praelectiones in Ciceronis orationes octo consulares,* Basel, 1574; Basel, 1575) contained a plea for the publication of his letter to Rheticus. It was apparently first printed in *Petri Rami ... collectaneae praefationes, epistolae, orationes* (Marburg, 1599), pp. 213–18. It was reprinted at least twice thereafter: Charles Desmaze, *P. Ramus, sa vie, ses écrits, sa mort* (Paris, 1864), pp. 68–78; Ludwik Antoni Birkenmajer, *Mikołaj Kopernik* (Cracow, 1900), pp. 603–6.

[2] The Latin text of the letter was reproduced by Marie Delcourt, who provided also a translation into French (*Bulletin de l'Association Guillaume Budé,* No. 44, July, 1934, p. 12).

John Pena,[3] in the title: Εὐκλείδου Ὀπτικὰ καὶ Κατοπτρικά. *Euclidis Optica et Catoptrica, numquam antehac graece aedita. Eadem latine reddita per Ioannem Penam Regium Mathematicum. His praeposita est eiusdem Ioannis Penae de usu Optices praefatio* . . . (Paris, 1557). It will be observed that Pena's Preface was placed at the beginning (*praeposita*) of his Greek text and Latin translation of Euclid's *Optics* and *Catoptrics*. But since it is the usage of Ramus that is under examination, some examples of *praeponere* in the positional sense should be adduced from his writings. The first occurs in a letter which he sent in 1564 to Jean de Monluc, bishop of Valence; insisting upon a proper order of studies, he says: *si vel Ptolemaeus ipse initio mathematicae disciplinae praeponeretur,*[4] "even if Ptolemy were placed at the beginning of instruction in mathematics." Another instance appears in the Preface to one of his books; discussing the arrangement of the subject matter, he declares: such and such topics I have put at the beginning (*praeposui*), such and such others at the end (*postposui*).[5] There can be little question, then, that by *praeposita* Ramus meant "placed at the beginning."

But it may perhaps be urged as an objection to the proposed interpretation of *epistola . . . Copernico praeposita* that Copernicus is the name of a man, not a book. There are, however, abundant examples of the metonymical use of an author's name for the book he wrote. An instance occurs in the clause quoted, just above, from the letter to Monluc. A second example may be chosen at random from Ramus's works: *Physica materia de rebus caelestibus solida est in Ptolemaeo et Copernico,*[6] "the physical material on astronomical topics in Ptolemy and Copernicus is sound." Hence there is no difficulty in accepting "the book written by Copernicus" as the proper rendering of *Copernico*.

This philological analysis is decisively confirmed by an examination of the historical context. For Delcourt's interpretation would make Rheticus the author of a letter to Copernicus in which epicycles and eccentrics were declared to be false and absurd fictions. There is, in the first place, no evidence that there was any correspondence between Rheticus and Copernicus. Rheticus, in 1543, held no such view about epicycles and eccentrics. In the *Narratio prima* (1540) he sharply dissociated himself from Averroes,

---

[3] On the question of the relationship between Ramus and Pena, see C. Waddington-Kastus, *De Petri Rami vita, scriptis, philosophia* (Paris, 1848), p. 56 and p. 70, n. 5; and Charles Waddington, *Ramus, sa vie, ses écrits et ses opinions* (Paris, 1855), pp. 21, 110–11, 290. In the closing paragraph of his Preface (*De usu optices praefatio*) to the Greek text Pena calls Ramus "my teacher" (*praeceptor meus*).

[4] *P. Rami . . . collectaneae praefationes* . . . (Marburg, 1599), p. 170.

[5] *Ibid.,* p. 34.

[6] *Ibid.,* p. 69.

who denied their existence in nature.[7]   In fact, he used them throughout his book and nowhere exhibited any doubt about their existence.[8]   Indeed, Rheticus was so deeply convinced of their reality that he attributed to one of them effective control over the rise and fall of political empires.[9]   And he continued to adhere to these beliefs, as can be seen in papers published by him in 1550[10] and 1557.[11]   Later, we shall see, he adopted Ramus's views.

We may, then, confidently set Delcourt's interpretation aside on the grounds that it misunderstands the meaning of *Copernico praeposita*, that it requires the existence of a letter from Rheticus to Copernicus, and that it attributes to Rheticus a view concerning epicycles and eccentrics which is contradictory to the one he actually held.

Let us now turn to an examination of the document which, if the previous argument is sound, was described by Ramus as *epistola . . . Copernico praeposita*.   It was printed on the first two pages of Copernicus's *De revolutionibus orbium caelestium* (1543)[12] and would, therefore, naturally be described as placed at the beginning of Copernicus's book (*Copernico praeposita*).   Moreover, it was entitled *To the Reader, Concerning the Hypotheses of this Work*, and hence might appropriately be designated a letter (*epistola*).   These external considerations are buttressed by a study of the document's contents.[13]   It asserts that the astronomer cannot discover the

[7] See my recent book, *Three Copernican Treatises* (New York: Columbia University Press, 1939), p. 194.   In another passage (*ibid.*, p. 140) where Rheticus spoke of men who deserved to be pitied rather than hated, the marginal comment by Michael Mästlin, teacher of Kepler and editor of the fourth (1596) and fifth (1621) editions of the *Narratio prima*, reads: "He means those who reject epicycles and eccentrics" (Mästlin's edition of Kepler's *Mysterium cosmographicum* and Rheticus's *Narratio prima*, Tübingen, 1596, p. 114; Frankfurt, 1621, p. 110).

[8] In his acceptance of this basic principle Rheticus agreed completely with his master, Copernicus, whose view is strikingly revealed by the following passage in the *De revolutionibus*: "From all these considerations it is clear that the same apparent inequality is produced, whether by an epicycle on a homocentric deferent or by an eccentric equal to the homocentric; and that the two arrangements do not differ from each other at all, provided that the distance from the center of the eccentric to the center of the homocentric is equal to the radius of the epicycle. It is, therefore, not easy to determine which of these arrangements exists in the heavens."   (Thorn edition, 1873, p. 207, lines 2–10.)   It will be observed that Copernicus is uncertain whether it is the epicycle or the eccentric that exists, but he is entirely certain that either the epicycle or the eccentric exists in the heavens (*existat in caelo*).

[9] *Three Copernican Treatises*, pp. 121–22.

[10] See Leopold Prowe, *Nicolaus Coppernicus* (Berlin, 1883–84), II, 395–96.

[11] See *Abhandlungen zur Geschichte der math. Wiss.*, XXIV, Pt. I (1907), fol. a 5 r–v.

[12] The first edition was reproduced in facsimile (M. J. Hermann, 1927).

[13] A translation into English will be found in *Three Copernican Treatises*, pp. 24–25.

true causes, or true hypotheses, of the heavenly motions;[14] the causes are unknown to astronomy,[15] which is not expected and is unable to furnish true hypotheses.[16] When the astronomer devises hypotheses, he does not seek to convince anyone of their truth;[17] these hypotheses need not be true nor even probable.[18] And they give rise to absurdities;[19] the epicycle of Venus is offered in illustration. The only hypotheses with which the document deals are epicycles and eccentrics. Can there be any doubt, then, that these propositions formed the basis of Ramus's remark about the contents of the *epistola . . . Copernico praeposita*: ". . . by reference to the epicycle of Venus, it shows clearly that the hypotheses which employ epicycles and eccentrics are false and absurd fictions"?

The foregoing philological, historical and doctrinal analyses have converged to establish that when Ramus wrote *epistola tua, ni fallor, Copernico praeposita*, he had in mind the document which is now called the *Praefatiuncula* (little preface) to the *De revolutionibus*. As the words *tua, ni fallor* show, he believed that its author was Rheticus, although he was not entirely certain.[20] The reason for his hesitation is that it was unsigned.

The anonymous *Praefatiuncula* appeared in 1543, and more than sixty years passed before its author was first identified in a printed work[21] as the Lutheran theologian, Andreas Osiander. Not until eighty years ago was it realized that Osiander had disagreed with Copernicus regarding the nature of astronomical hypotheses[22] and, in consequence, during Copernicus's last

[14] *Deinde causas earundem, seu hypotheses, cum veras assequi nulla ratione possit* [*astronomus*] . . .

[15] *Satis enim patet, apparentium inaequalium, motuum causas, hanc artem penitus et simpliciter ignorare.*

[16] *Neque quisquam, quod ad hypotheses attinet, quicquam certi ab astronomia expectet, cum ipsa nihil tale praestare queat, ne si in alium usum conficta pro veris arripiat, stultior ab hac disciplina discedat, quam accesserit.*

[17] *Et si quas fingendo excogitat, ut certe quamplurimas excogitat, nequaquam tamen in hoc excogitat, ut ita esse cuiquam persuadeat* . . .

[18] *Neque enim necesse est, eas hypotheses esse veras, imo ne verisimiles quidem* . . .

[19] *Sunt et alia in hac disciplina non minus absurda* . . .

[20] Delcourt's translation contains a further error, for it attaches the uncertainty expressed by *ni fallor* to the recipient of the letter, instead of to its author. The position of the words argues against this interpretation; *ni fallor* qualifies *tua* rather than *Copernico*.

[21] Kepler's *Astronomia nova . . . de motibus stellae Martis* (Prague, 1609), on the verso of the title page.

[22] Excerpts from Osiander's letters to Copernicus and Rheticus, and an indication of Copernicus's attitude, were included in Kepler's *Apologia Tychonis contra Ursum*. But this work was not printed until 1858 (*Joannis Kepleri astronomi opera omnia*, ed. Christian Frisch, Frankfurt am Main, 1858–71, I, 245–46).

illness, suppressed the Introduction written by the great astronomer[23] and replaced it by the *Praefatiuncula,* from which he withheld his signature.

The resultant question of authorship, so long as it remained unsolved, exerted a powerful influence upon the reception of Copernicanism and upon the interpretation of astronomical theory and scientific method. For the brief document contained an uncompromising statement of the view that astronomy cannot deal with reality or come to know the truth, and that astronomical hypotheses (or theories) are devised only to support calculations in agreement with the observational data. As an excellent expression of the fictionalist philosophy, according to which truth is unattainable in the natural sciences and by the scientific method, it stood diametrically opposed to the fundamental principles of Copernicus's book, in which the motion of the earth, to use the single most important example, was regarded as real, and truth as attainable.[24]

If, on the one hand, Copernicus was the author of the *Praefatiuncula,* as was widely believed,[25] surely the sting was drawn out of Copernicanism. For then, in the Copernican system, the earth's motion is not real; it is merely a fiction, introduced to simplify astronomical computations. But if, on the other hand, Copernicus was not the author, because the *Praefatiuncula* spoke of him in the third person and eulogized him in a manner which ordinary modesty would not permit in a self-appraisal, then who wrote it? It has never been noticed before, so far as I am aware, that so well-informed a person as Ramus, an intellectual leader of his generation, and a scholar who followed closely the progress of mathematical studies, was misled by Osiander's maneuver and believed that Rheticus was the author of the *Praefatiuncula.*

Ramus would have been attracted to its author in any case, because its fictionalist views approached his heart's desire of an astronomy without hypotheses. But he had already conceived a high admiration for the published work of Rheticus.[26] Therefore, upon being informed that Rheticus "has some desire to visit France," he writes at one point in the letter: "This news has given me the opportunity to declare my affection for you and to promise you all the kindness and courtesy of the most solicitous host

[23] It was, however, preserved in Copernicus's autograph (Quido Vetter, "Sur les destins du manuscrit pragois du Kopernik," in *Mémoires de la société royale de Bohême,* classe des sciences, Prague, 1931) and was printed for the first time in the fourth edition of the *De revolutionibus* (ed. Jan Baranowski; Warsaw, 1854), pp. 10–12.

[24] For a delineation of the opposing views of Copernicus and Osiander, see Pierre Duhem, ΣΩΖΕΙΝ ΤΑ ΦΑΙΝΟΜΕΝΑ, *Essai sur la notion de théorie physique de Platon à Galilée* (Paris, 1908), pp. 71–81.

[25] In lieu of the many who might be cited, I choose the highly significant case of J. B. J. Delambre, *Histoire de l'astronomie moderne* (Paris, 1821), I, 139–40.

[26] *Bulletin . . . Budé,* No. 44, pp. 5, 7.

if you come to Paris.''[27]   He was eager to secure for Rheticus an appointment to teach mathematics at the University of Paris.[28]   It was probably
with this information in mind that in 1564 Rheticus confided to a friend:
"France also invites me.   What shall I do?   I have not yet decided.''[29]   In
any case, he was not appointed to the vacant chair.   However, a reply which
he sent to Ramus in 1568 has been in part preserved.[30]   In the course of an
enumeration of books written or projected, Rheticus states: "In the fourth
place, I shall now for the first time undertake the work, which has been
present in your mind also, of freeing astronomy from hypotheses, by re-
stricting myself to the observations alone.''   And he closes the list with the
remark: "So many and so important are the subjects which I treat, and for
these undertakings the practice of medicine has, as my Maecenas, hitherto
supplied the expenses.''

This reply of Rheticus's found an echo in Ramus's publication of the
following year: "[Urged] by my letter to undertake the task of freeing
astronomy from hypotheses, Rheticus had also given hope of adorning the
University of Paris; and had he not been compelled to master medicine and
make the practice of it a sort of Maecenas, mathematics would now for a
long time be proclaiming a second Copernicus.''[31]

---

[27] *Ibid.*, p. 7.

[28] Letter from Jacob Calonius Portanus to Rheticus, written from Paris on
August 17, 1563 (Latin text in L. A. Birkenmajer, *Mikolaj Kopernik*, p. 603).

[29] Letter to Paul Eber, dated Cracow, April 12, 1564.   Published from the
original by L. A. Birkenmajer, *Stromata Copernicana* (Cracow, 1924), p. 376.

[30] In the Preface to Adrian Romanus, *Ideae mathematicae pars prima, sive
methodus polygonorum* (Antwerp, 1593), fol. ** ii r–v.   The excerpt is reprinted
in L. A. Birkenmajer, *Mikołaj Kopernik*, pp. 611–12.   The reply must have been
written before August 8, 1568, since it is mentioned in a letter bearing that date
(see Theodor Wotschke, *Der Briefwechsel der Schweizer mit den Polen* [= *Archiv für
Reformationsgeschichte*, ed. W. Friedensburg, Ergängzungsband III, Leipzig, 1908],
p. 302, no. 389; reprinted in L. A. Birkenmajer, *Stromata Copernicana*, pp. 377–78).

[31] *Scholarum mathematicarum libri unus et triginta* (Basel, 1569), p. 66.

3 THE SCIENTIFIC REVOLUTION

The Scientific Revolution

THE RENAISSANCE PERIOD is often regarded as ending in 1600, with the burning of Giordano Bruno, the heretic who opposed Aristotle's finite world by poetically conceiving nature as infinite, "with its center everywhere and its circumference nowhere." This idea, when it is made scientifically precise, implies that neither the earth nor the sun need serve as the center of the universe—and leads to the relativistic view in astronomy.

The seventeenth century has so vast a galaxy of scientific thinkers of the first magnitude in every field—logic, mathematics, physics, biology, and psychology—that we can select for discussion only a few exemplary figures in each of these sciences. A brief examination of their main accomplishments, however, will provide illustrations of the background against which the relevance of the essays in this part of our collection becomes clear.

LOGIC

Francis Bacon, though trained in law and achieving fame as the Lord Chancellor of Queen Elizabeth, had early in life stated his intentions of making all knowledge his province. This ambitious scope was typical of the *uomo universale* of the late Renaissance. The discovery and exploration of the New World not only increased commerce and adventurous emigration but also encouraged intellectual adventures in search of new truths and a new logic of discovery based on experimental methods of investigating nature.

Bacon made no scientific discoveries and practiced none of the natural sciences, but he had a philosophical journalist's sense of what was brewing in the thought of his time, and there was no doubt in his own mind that the key to future progress lay in the hands of experimental science. His *Novum Organum,* or new instrument of science, was the inductive method of the experimental sciences as distinct from the syllogism which was useful only for *demonstrating* what was already known.

After showing that certain Idols of the mind served to obstruct the course of scientific investigation and preserve preconceived notions, Bacon proceeded to formulate a set of canons or rules for scientific method. These Idols are famous in textbooks of logic and schools of education even today, and a brief exposition of them will indicate the modernity of Bacon's views.

There are four classes of Idols: Idols of the Tribe, of the Cave, of the Market Place, and of the Theatre. Although Bacon's language is grand, the meaning of each Idol is clear. By "the Tribe," Bacon means nothing less than the whole human race, whose tendency to self-centredness leads to the fallacious notions that everything in nature was made or exists for the benefit of man and that whatever appeals to the human mind's desire for simplicity must be true of Nature. When Voltaire satirically explained that man had one nose and two eyes because such an arrangement was best suited to support eyeglasses, he was illustrating Bacon's Idol of the Tribe as well as the spuriousness of *ad hoc* final causes. Bacon even regarded the desire for simplicity in one's explanations as dangerous when it led to oversimplified, hasty, and false generalizations about nature. That the circle is the most perfect type of path for a heavenly body to follow actually kept astronomers until Kepler's time from considering any paths other than circular ones. The attractiveness of the circle was an Idol of the Tribe when it took to astronomy.

The Idols of the Cave are those one-sided dispositions of the individual mind due to peculiarities of heredity or education which distort one's conceptions of the external world. Here we may turn the tables on Bacon. Bacon's own training in law led him to formulate rules of scientific method as if they were legal statutes: Tables of Presence, Tables of Absence, Tables of Variation. The great physiologist Harvey, discoverer of the circulation of the blood, said of Bacon's tables that they were composed by a man who wrote about science as a Lord Chancellor.

The Idols of the Market Place are what we call today semantic fallacies due to the misuse of language. Words are the medium for the exchange of ideas as coins are in the market place. Such words as "humor" in Bacon's time meant either a quality of one's temperament—*e.g.,* one of the four humors (bilious, choleric, sanguine, phlegmatic)—or simply humidity. Similarly, in the seventeenth century physicists argued about the "force" of motion without distinguishing momentum (mass times velocity) from energy (mass times the square of the velocity). Another example may be seen in eighteenth-century physics: "caloric" designated heat and temperature indiscriminately, even in the work of the great Sadi Carnot, discoverer of the second law of thermodynamics.

Finally, we have the Idols of the Theatre, or those dogmatic systems of ideas that parade as the Truth with a show of finality. Such were the scholastic dogmas that blocked free inquiry, and such were the panaceas of quacks. Bishop Berkeley was a keen psychologist and epistemologist, but he believed that tar-water held the virtues of all medicines.

Bacon himself did not accept the Copernican astronomy because he thought that the motion of the earth around the sun was not supported by experience. He formulated a general theory of heat as a form of motion, but his method of verification lacked precise instruments of measurement. But what Bacon does represent is the modern sense of the practical importance of experimental method for discovering new truth.

"Knowledge is Power" is one of Bacon's many aphorisms that have set the tone for certain public attitudes toward science, especially with the rise of modern technology. Wishing to employ science "for the relief of man's estate," Bacon regarded the research scientist as a "merchant of light." His remarkable utopia, *The New Atlantis,* strikingly anticipates our modern industrial research laboratory, and the problems of ethics and politics discussed by him deal with the impact of the new sciences on society.

MATHEMATICS AND PHYSICS

The rise of commerce and the rivalry of European nations after the discovery of the New World was accompanied by an equally stirring outbreak of thought in the mathematical and physical sciences. New horizons called for broader concepts. The sixteenth-century Italian mathematicians, such as Scipio del Ferro, Tartaglia, Bombelli, and Cardan, had solved algebraic problems like the general solution of cubic equations, but it required the more universal genius of a Descartes to show how to combine algebra with geometry and facilitate the solution of problems in conic sections dating back to Pappus and Apollonius of Alexandria about the third century B.C. Pappus, for example, had proposed the problem of "contacts"—that is, of constructing a circle touching three given circles. So long as one employs only geometrical relations, the solution is very intricate. What Descartes did in his analytic geometry was to show how to represent the circles in algebraic form and then to reduce Pappus' problem to that of solving three simultaneous equations.

Although Francis Bacon had sought the unity of the sciences through the experimental search for the Forms of nature, he gave no valuable indications of how to demonstrate such a unity. Descartes and Leibniz looked to the new mathematical developments for the generalizing principles that would provide the broad concepts needed for the unity of science. Because of its symbolism, no science is more general than mathematics. Descartes did not discover analytic geometry (the application of algebra to geometry was already begun by Oresme and Fermat), but he devised a new symbolism and had the philosophic insight to see the potentialities of the new mathematics. He improved the symbolism of algebra by introducing exponents, so that the cube of x, hitherto expressed as $x·x·x$ or Cube x, became x^3. Such inventions as Napier's logarithms (which, according to Kepler, "tripled the life of the astronomer") not only save time but economize thought and facilitate the perception of abstract relations.

For Descartes, all deduction was a running series of intuitions of clear and distinct ideas, and mathematics was the most valuable form of deduction, since it rose to generalizations about equations and curves of any degree of complexity. Hence, Descartes wrote, in *Rules for the Direction of the Mind,* "A proof that it far surpasses in facility and importance the sciences which depend upon it is that it embraces at once all the objects to which these are devoted and a great many others besides."

Leibniz continued to advance Descartes' quest for certainty and unity in the sciences. Leibniz, too, made important contributions to perfecting the symbolism of mathematics. He invented the notation of determinants in solving simultaneous equations, and the "dy/dx" symbol of the calculus. Although Newton is regarded as the independent discoverer of the calculus, mathematicians prefer Leibniz's notation to Newton's.

The idea that economy of symbols is helpful to scientific thought may be traced back to the fourteenth-century medieval logician William of Occam, who enunciated the principle known as "Occam's Razor": "Do not multiply hypotheses more than is necessary"—necessary, that is, to explain phenomena or to carry out the calculations required in scientific work. We have already seen that the main intellectual purpose served by the systems of atsronomy in ancient times was "to save the appearances"—that is, to construct a scheme of geometric symbols that would comprehend the observed recurrences of celestial phenomena and make predictions possible. Copernicus's chief improvement on Aristotle's and Ptolemy's geocentric systems was to show the greater simplicity of the heliocentric scheme once offered by the Pythagoreans in a cruder form.

It would be a historical mistake to say that this practical economy of symbols and thought was the *sole* aim of Copernicus, Descartes, or Leibniz. There is no doubt that they regarded their scientific theories as *true* and necessary representations of a simplicity and logical order in the natural phenomena. We know that the Preface to Copernicus' work, which claimed that the new astronomy was simply a convenient mathematical scheme "to save the appearances," was written not by Copernicus but by the theologian Osiander, who wished to preserve the authority of scriptural revelation against the moving of the earth to a planetary position. Copernicus and Galileo had a more elevated conception of the relation of science to religious faith than such apologists as Osiander, for in the minds of these dedicated scientists the discovery of new scientific knowledge was a greater service to the wisdom and glory of man and God than the defense of dogmatic theological authorities who wished to reduce science to merely practical devices.

Another aspect of the seventeenth-century faith in the simplicity and regularity of nature appears in the identity that was assumed between mathematical order and physical laws; the laws of nature were regarded as written in the language of Euclid's geometry. The logical assumption was that since Euclid had, with his genius for order, established once and for all time the nature of space, all that physicists had to do was to find illustrations of Euclidean geometry in the external world of levers, planes, circular motion, and mechanical forces. The Newtonian law of universal gravitation—which maintains that the gravitational attraction between two bodies varies inversely with the square of the distance between them—is based upon a property of the square—namely, that the surface is proportional to the square of the radius. The other part of this law (gravitational force is directly proportional to the product of the masses) is less clear, because it assumes arbitrarily that each body has in it some absolute mass regardless of its motion or relations to other bodies— an assumption abandoned in Einstein's theory of the relativity of mass and motion. So also, Descartes identified space or extension with matter, and for several centuries textbooks in physics defined matter as "that which occupies space" and (after Newton) "has weight." The fact that Leibniz had criticized Newton's view of absolute space, time, and mass did not impress the writers of textbooks or even research workers in physics until Einstein's work appeared in 1905.

Yet, if we consider the great scientific achievements of the continuators of "Newton's mathematical way," there is no denying the great historical value of the false identification of Euclidean geometry with physics. Laplace and Kant, applying the Newtonian laws of motion and gravitations to the problem of explaining the evolution of the solar system and stars, came forth independently with the nebular hypothesis. Coulomb applied the inverse-square law to Franklin's experimental observations of electrical charges. Ampère applied the same inverse-square law to induced currents of electricity. Oersted made use of the same property of the surface of a sphere to measure the force of electro-magnetism. Before long it was clear to physicists that the intensity of gravitation, electricity, magnetism, and light conformed to the same inverse-square law. But it was not realized that the root of this unification was the assumption of a Euclidean space—an assumption continuously maintained for more than two thousand years.

BIOLOGY AND PSYCHOLOGY

Like the physical sciences, the sciences of life and mind had to break away from the authority of Aristotle as interpreted by his scholastic commentators. One of the transition figures during the Renaissance period was the Swiss physician and astrologer Theophrastus Philippus Bombastus von Hohenheim (1493–1541), better known by his Latin name, Paracelsus. He defied the traditional lecture method used in medical faculty of the universities, where the professor stood on a high dais with the authoritative texts of Aristotle, Galen, and commentaries before him, while below in the amphitheater a barber (known as the barber-surgeon) handled the parts of a cadaver whenever the professor of medicine wished him to point to some organ of the body. Going back to Hippocrates, the father of Greek medicine, Paracelsus explained disease in terms of an imbalance among the elements of which the body was composed. Instead of the four chemical elements of the Aristotelians (Earth, Air, Fire, and Water), Paracelsus hypothesized three elements—salt, sulphur, and mercury—and advocated the experimental study of the waste products of the body, horrifying his academic audiences by bringing into the lecture room the feces of patients. He thus founded the school of iatrochemistry, which applied chemistry to medicine and therapy—as in the use of mercury in treating syphilis.

A prominent medical contemporary of Paracelsus, Fracastoro of Verona (1483–1553), laid the foundations for the experimental study of contagion and epidemics in his work *De contagione* (1546). In his work on syphilis—the Gallic, or French, disease (as the Italians called it)—he anticipated the germ theory of disease.

The outstanding Renaissance anatomist was the Belgian Vesalius (1514–1564), whose major work was *De humani corporis fabrica*. The mathematician and physician Cardano (1501–1576), contemporary of Leonardo (d. 1519) and Vesalius (b. 1514), remarked that a painter is also a student of natural science (or "philosophy" as this term was then used), adding, "for proof there is that remarkable imitation of the human body which [I saw] many years ago, by Leonardo da Vinci of Florence, which was almost complete; but the task required a great master and investigator of nature such as Vesalius." Vesalius, who practiced the dissection of the human body, held the chair of surgery in Padua, where Copernicus studied medicine, and where later Harvey studied and Galileo carried out his famous experiments on falling bodies. Padua was under the governance of Venice, which in its defiance of the Papal authority, enabled the University of Padua to pursue scientific and logical studies in freedom from Rome.

Harvey's great work, *On the Motion of the Blood,* was published in 1628, about twenty-five years after his medical studies at the University of Padua, where he became familiar with the work of Vesalius and absorbed the experimental spirit of that university. Harvey successfully disposed of the vague theory of the spontaneous generation of life by maintaining that all living creatures are generated from certain "egges." Francesco Redi in 1668 supported Harvey's conclusion by means of experiments on maggots and plant grubs.

Robert Hooke (1635–1703) at Oxford had made elaborate microscopic studies of the common house fly, the body louse, and thin sections of plant tissues in which he discerned "cells." In Holland, the simple, self-taught shoemaker Leeuwenhoeck made a plain microscope and observed the human spermatozoon (which he called "homunculus" or little man, because he interpreted what he saw as a pre-formed miniature adult). The idea that the embryo contained the form of the adult was none other than a version of Aristotle's view that the adult was pre-formed in male sperm. This theory was glorified in the metaphysical system of Leibniz's monads. Leibniz thought that the spiritual development of each monad was like the metamorphosis of insects described by Jan Swammerdam in his *Historia Insectorum Generalis* (1669).

Malpighi and Grew, in the seventeenth century, discovered the cellular structure of plants and animals and prepared the way for the more detailed cytological and histological studies by Schwann and Schleiden in the nineteenth century.

Thus, the Greek concepts of the elements and the atomic constitution of nature found their way into biology, aided by the seventeenth-century use of the microscope. And just as Copernicus' astronomy and the mechanics of impetus were first conceived wihtout the use of instruments but advanced later with the aid of the telescope and accurate clocks, so the search for the unitary components of life progressed rapidly through the invention of the microscope. Behind these two major extensions of man's visual range were the ideas of the infinitely large and infinitely small, before whose vast distances Pascal pictured man standing in fright.

The atomism, which Galileo, Boyle, and Newton accepted as the theoretical basis for their experimental work in mechanics and chemistry, also was transposed to psychology. In Locke's *Essay*

Concerning Human Understanding, the contents of the mind were analyzed into "simple ideas" of sensation and reflection; "reflection" was conceived on the analogy of light corpuscles bounding off mirror surfaces.

In the articles that follow, some of the major figures and trends of seventeenth-century scientific thought are examined and discussed in detail.

Nicolson's discussion of "Kepler's *Somnium* and John Donne" indicates the reflections of astronomical discoveries in the works of two of the major literary figures of the period.

In "Gresham College: Precursor of the Royal Society," Johnson illustrates the role of scientific societies in this period and traces the origins of the Royal Society to a group of Boyle's associates at Gresham College.

Houghton's "History of Trades" reveals how the practical interests and techniques of craftsmen led to the mechanical arts being given the central place in the Baconian "reconstruction of the sciences" by the Royal Society.

Prior's essay on "Bacon's Man of Science" depicts the moral and social interests of Bacon's ideal scientist, an ideal persisting in later conceptions of the cultural role of scientists.

McRae, "The Unity of the Sciences in Bacon, Descartes, and Leibniz," traces the quest for a unifying conception of nature and man—a quest characteristic of the seventeenth-century predilection for simplicity.

In "Newton's Mathematical Way," Strong analyzes Newton's conception of the relation of mathematical analysis to experiment in physical theory.

Evans' "Aristotle, Newton, and the Theory of Continuous Magnitude," traces the linkage between Newton's infinitesimal calculus and Aristotle's concept of continuity.

In "Newness and Novelty in Seventeenth-century Science and Medicine," Thorndike takes note of the frequent recurrence of the word "new" in the titles of scientific works as documentary evidence of what we have called "the scientific revolution."

Boas' discussion "Bacon and Gilbert" points out that Bacon understood the differences between the experimental work on magnetism and the more speculative cosmology of Gilbert.

Wiener's account of Leibniz' project illustrates further the role of scientific societies in the promotion and diffusion of science in the seventeenth century. The interested reader might consult Volume VI of the Prussian Academy edition of Leibniz's collected works. As Professor Paul O. Kristeller has pointed out, this edition contains another version of the Leibniz fragment which alters in some points the edited translation included here.

⤳ξ Marjorie Nicolson

KEPLER, THE *SOMNIUM*, AND JOHN DONNE

It is one of the curious ironies of history that the *Somnium* of Johann Kepler should have been almost completely neglected by historians both of science and of literature. Yet it was, in its final form, the last work of a great scientist; it is in itself no negligible item in the history of lunar theory; its notes include Kepler's last pronouncements on matters of great importance in both physics and astronomy. As a work of literature, it is important as the first modern scientific moon-voyage, and a chief source of many of the later "cosmic voyages"[1] of the seventeenth and eighteenth centuries. It is also of unusual biographical significance, since it throws light upon certain hitherto obscure matters in Kepler's life. In addition, the *Somnium* had an immediate effect upon English astronomy, and also a curious effect upon the work of at least one important English poet. I propose at the present time to discuss it from various points of view, considering first its biographical bearings, then indicating a probable relation between the *Somnium* and one of John Donne's works, finally suggesting briefly its importance to students of English literature.[2]

I

In the form in which it was posthumously published in 1634, the *Somnium*[3] included, in addition to the brief tale from which the

[1] In its original form this paper was read before the Philological Association of the Johns Hopkins University, on the same day on which I gave as the Tudor Stuart lecture a paper on "Cosmic Voyages," to be published in the forthcoming number of *ELH*. The other paper offers the background for the *Somnium* as a cosmic voyage; I have attempted to avoid duplication by leaving out of this paper various matters treated in the other.

[2] I am not attempting to treat the many important scientific conceptions which Kepler promulgated in this, the last of his works.

[3] *Joh. Keppleri mathematici olim imperatorii Somnium sive Opus posthumum de astronomia lunari. Divulgatum a M. Ludovico Kepplero Filio, Medicinae Candidato. . . .* (Francofurti, 1634). No English translation of the *Somnium* has been published; I shall discuss later the modern German translation. I have used a copy of the 1634 edition of the *Somnium*, which the Smith College Library fortunately possesses. The text may be found also in *Joannis Kepleri Astronom. Opera Omnia edidit* Dr. Ch. Frisch (Francofurti, 1870) Vol. VIII. I am greatly

volume takes its name, a long series of *"notae in Somnium Astronomicum,"* an appendix containing notes upon these notes, the first Latin translation of Plutarch's *De Orbe in Facie Lunae,* and a series of notes upon that work. I am concerned, however, only with the original tale.[4] Like so many imaginary voyages, before and after, this is cast into the form of a dream. Kepler relates that in the year 1608, when discord was raging between the brothers Prince Rudolf and Archduke Matthias, the author became interested in reading Bohemian legends, particularly those concerning the Libyan virago, most celebrated in the art of magic. One night, after a period of reading and of contemplation of the heavenly bodies, he fell into a deep slumber, and seemed to be reading another book of which he tells the general intent.

The tale within a tale has to do with the fortunes of a young man, named Duracotus, a native of Islandia, "which the ancients call Thule." He was the son of remarkable parents; his father he did not remember, but, according to the account given him by his mother, he had been a fisherman, who died at the ripe age of 150 years, when his son was still an infant. The mother, Fiolxhilda, was a "wise woman," who supported herself by selling to mariners little bags of herbs in which were contained mysterious charms. Unfortunately Fiolxhilda was a woman of ungovernable temper; upon one occasion when her young son curiously examined the contents of one of the bags, she became inflamed with anger, and impulsively pledged the boy as the property of the captain in place of the little sack which he had destroyed, in order that she might retain the money.

For a time the mother disappears from the tale, and we follow the fortunes of the son, whom Kepler portrays with much sympathy. We accompany him on a voyage between Norway and England, and see him arrive at last in Denmark. Violently ill from the rough sea, he is of little value to the captain, who is glad to rid himself of an incubus. Since the captain is carrying letters to the Danish astronomer, Tycho Brahe, on the Island of Wena, he dismisses the boy as messenger, promising to return for him in time. For some years Duracotus remained with the great astronomer, who saw promise in him, since, when the captain returned, Tycho refused to send the youth home. So he remained, learning the lore

---

ndebted to my colleague Miss Eleanor Duckett for assistance in the Latin text of the *Somnium,* and to Margaret Grierson for assistance in many ways.

⁴ The account which follows is based upon the *Somnium,* ed. 1634, pp. 1–5.

of astronomy, "the most divine of sciences."   He was particularly
interested in the fact that Tycho and his students "studied the
stars and moon for whole nights with wonderful machines, a fact
which reminded me of my mother, since she was also accustomed
to hold assiduous colloquy with the moon."

After five years Duracotus returned home, happy to find his
mother still alive, often repenting the fit of temper in which she
had sent away her son.   To his surprise, he came to realize that
the "wise woman" was as wise as Tycho Brahe in lore of the skies.
In some way his mother had learned by experience all that Tycho
knew only in theory, and, after a long period of hesitation, she was
finally persuaded to confide in her son the source of her knowledge.
Thus Duracotus learned that his mother was in league with the
"daemons of Levania"—the spirits of the moon—whom she could
summon upon occasion, and with whom mortals voyage to the distant land.   Upon a certain evening, Duracotus achieved his desire:
the time was spring, the moon was crescent and joined with the
planet Saturn in the sign of Taurus; the omens were auspicious.
"My mother, withdrawing from me into the nearest cross-roads,
and uttering a few words loudly . . . returned, and, commanding
silence with the palm of her right hand outstretched, sat down near
me.   Scarcely had we covered our heads with a cloth (as is the
custom) when behold, there arose the sound of a voice. . . ."

So ends the first section of the *Somnium*.   In spite of the language of legend and superstition, the first part of the tale is clearly
based upon Kepler's own life, and the allusions are so thinly veiled
that they can be readily recognized—as Kepler was to learn to his
sorrow.   The parallel does not, indeed, hold good throughout.   The
father is a fictional character; Kepler's own father, "ignoble scion
of the noble family of Kepler . . . a mercenary of the notorious
Duke of Alva,"[5] lived only too long after his son's birth.   More
than once he deserted wife and children, so that the boy Kepler
grew up in a poverty not far different from that which he describes
in his tale.   Kepler's mother, however, is truly depicted in the tale.
Almost illiterate, far below her husband in birth, she was nevertheless a woman of remarkable attainments, a "wise woman" in the
true sense of the term.   She was also a woman of ungovernable
temper, which was finally responsible for the great tragedy of

[5] *Johann Kepler: a Tercentenary Commemoration of His Life and Work.*
Published by the *History of Science Society* (Baltimore, 1931) p. 2.

Kepler's life. The early life of Duracotus differed from that of his creator in that Kepler finally managed to secure an education, including training in theology at the University of Tübingen, where he came under the influence of Michael Maestlin, and for the first time came into contact with the revolutionary theories of Copernicus, from which he never departed. Duracotus, as a youth, was apprenticed for five years to Tycho Brahe on the island on which the Danish astronomer established his castle of the heavens, Uraniborg; Kepler himself became Tycho's assistant at a somewhat later age and for a shorter time, when Tycho, having lost his patron, settled in Prague. But as in the tale, so in reality, the older Tycho and the younger Kepler worked together for several years, and at Tycho's death in 1601, Kepler fell heir to the rich collection of papers and notes in which Tycho left many of his findings to posterity. Kepler's first monumental work, the *Astronomia Nova,* in which he propounded the first two of his eternal laws, was the result of long work with Tycho on the problem of the planet Mars.

So far the parallelisms, while purposely not exact, are clearly intentional. For my present purposes, only one other biographical fact is necessary. In 1615, largely as a result of her constant quarrels, Kepler's mother was charged with sorcery, and came near to condemnation.[6] Kepler worked heroically to free her from the charges, and was finally successful after a law suit which lasted five years, during part of which his mother was in prison under ignominious conditions. Shortly after her release, she died.

So much for the similarities between the tale and Kepler's own life. But before indicating what seem to me the important implications in those suggestions, it is necessary to consider the date of composition of the first part of the *Somnium.* The date of its publication offers no assistance, for Kepler left the manuscript unfinished when he died.[7] The only section which is dated by Kepler himself is the series of notes, which were written between 1620 and 1623. Hence Charles Frisch, the editor of the *Opera Omnia* of

[6] The most complete account of the trial is given by Ludwig Gunther, *Ein Hexenprocess: Ein Kapitel aus der Geschichte des dunkelsten Aberglaubens* (Giessen, 1906).

[7] His son-in-law, whom he named as literary executor, endeavored to prepare it for the press, but he too died during his work upon the manuscript. Kepler's son finally acted as editor.

Kepler, inclines to that period as the time of composition,[8] though he reminds us of Kepler's interest in the astronomy of the moon which appears as early as his student days at Tübingen, when he defended certain theses in regard to the moon.   The other important German editor, who has made the only modern translation of the *Somnium*, Ludwig Gunther,[9] takes for granted without question that the work was written in 1609, because of a sentence in Kepler's *Dissertatio cum Nuncio Sidereo*, published in 1610.   Here Kepler states that during the previous summer he had applied himself to fundamental problems concerning the moon, though he does not definitely say what he was writing on the subject.   While it is entirely possible that much of the *Somnium* might have been written in the summer of 1609, it could not then have been written in its present form.   For Gunther does not see clearly that the moon-world of the *Somnium*, influenced though it was by Plutarch, Lucian, and a host of other early writers, is not the moon-world of the classics, but the moon-world of Galileo's telescope.   There are details which could not possibly have been known to Kepler before the spring of 1610, when the "optick tube" of the Tuscan artist disclosed a new heavens, and Galileo in the *Sidereus Nuncius*[10] announced excitedly to an amazed world that the moon was a world,

[8] Frisch in his "Proemium Editoris" has collected all references to the *Somnium* in Kepler's other works. He does not actually commit himself as to the date of composition.

[9] *Keplers Traum von Mond* von Ludwig Gunther (Leipzig, 1898), p. x. Gunther follows closely Frisch's evidence, but inclines to date the original composition in 1609 because of the sentence in the *Dissertatio*, which Frisch had quoted. He does not discuss the matter in any detail.

[10] I have already pointed out, in a number of published works, the great importance of Galileo's *Sidereus Nuncius* in the history of literature. Kepler certainly indicates in the passage referred to above, that in 1609 he had anticipated many of Galileo's discoveries concerning the moon, thanks to his reading of Plutarch, Lucian, Cicero's *Somnium Scipionis* and various other works in which the possibility of life on the moon had been postulated. I have no reason to doubt the statement that much of the *Somnium* as it exists today, might have been written in 1609. However, Kepler's enthusiastic reception of the *Sidereus Nuncius* has been recognized by all his commentators; Galileo offered him empirical proof of logical theories. Kepler himself procured a telescope in August, 1610, and made his own observations. His conclusions differ from Galileo's ultimate conclusions only in one important particular: in the *Somnium* Kepler posits the possibility of water on the moon; Galileo implies such a belief in the *Sidereus Nuncius*, but later denies it. The fact that Kepler persisted in his belief is indicated by the fact that he left these sections of the *Somnium* untouched when he returned to them in later life.

like our world in geography, with irregularities of all sorts which could not be detected by the naked eye.

It is a remarkable thing that no one of the commentators on the *Somnium* seems to have considered Kepler's own evidence on the subject, presented in one of the notes[11] to the *Somnium,* nor has anyone considered the remarkable implications in that note concerning the part played by the *Somnium* in Kepler's own life.[12] To be sure, it is a mysterious note, purposely cryptic in language, intended to be understood only by those of Kepler's contemporaries who had intimate knowledge of his own life. Yet it is entirely clear to anyone who knows the circumstances under which

[11] Note 8, edition 1634, p. 32; Frisch, *Opera Omnia,* pp. 41–2: "Fallor an author [*sic*] Satyrae procacis, cui nomen Conclave Ignatianum, exemplar nactus erat hujus opusculi; pungit enim me nominatim etiam in ipso principio. Nam in progressu miserum Copernicum adducit ad Plutonis tribunal, ad quod, ni fallor, aditus est per Heclae voragines. Vos amici, qui notitiam habetis rerum mearum, & quae mihi causa fuerit peregrinationis proximae in Sueviam, praesertim, si qui vestrum antehac manuscriptum nacti fuerunt, libellum istum, ominosa ista mihi meisq[ue] fuisse censebitis. Nec ego dissentio. Magnum equidem est mortis omen in vulnere lethali inflicto, in veneno epoto; nec minus fuisse videtur cladis domesticae, in propalatione hujus scripti. Credideris scintillam delapsam in materiam aridam; hoc est, exceptas voces istas ab animis intus furvis, furva omnia suspicantibus. Primum quidem exemplar Praga Lipsiam, inde Tubingam perlatum est anno 1611 a Barone a Volckerstorff, ejusque morum & studiorum Magistris. Quantum abest, ut credatis, in Tonstrinis, (praesertim si quibus est ab occupatione Fiolxhildis meae nomen ominosum) in his igitur, confabulatum fuisse de hac mea fabula? Certe equidem ex illa ipsa urbe & domo enati sunt sermones de me ipso calumniosi proxime succede[n]tibus annis: qui excepti ab animis insensis, tandem exarserunt in famam, imperitia & superstitione sufflantibus. Nisi fallor, sic censebitis potuisse & domum meam carere vexatione sexennali, & me peregrinatione annali proxima, nisi somniata praecepta Fiolxhildis hujus violassem. Placuit igitur mihi, somnium hoc meum ulcisci de negocio exhibito, vulgatione libelli: adversariis aliud mercedis erit."

[12] There is no indication that any commentator upon the *Somnium* has ever considered this note, with the single exception of Ludwig Gunther. He translated it in part, *op cit.,* pp. 27–28, but shows no awareness of its significance. He omits entirely the sentences referring to the *Conclave Ignatii* which I discuss below, evidently considering them either unintelligible or not significant. He translates only a part of the note, and varies the order of Kepler's sentences, so that the final impression is quite different from that which Kepler intended. He evidently takes for granted that Kepler was referring to some manuscript which was never published—in spite of Kepler's last sentence, declaring that he intends to publish the manuscript. Neither in the *Traum von Mond* nor in the *Hexenprocess* does Gunther show any awareness of Kepler's own suggestion that this work was in part responsible for his mother's trial for withcraft.

Kepler's mother was tried for witchcraft. In the note, Kepler is referring to some work of his own which he calls at one time "libellum," at another "manuscriptum." After two sentences which I shall consider later, he says: "You, my friends, who are familiar with my affairs and understand the reason for my late journey into Swabia[13] (especially if any of you had had a look at the manuscript previously), you will understand that that little book, that those happenings, were of evil omen to me and mine. I think so, too. There is indeed a deep foreboding of death in the infliction of a deadly wound, in the drinking of poison; and there seems to have been no less of private tragedy in the circulation of this work. It was really a spark dropped on kindling wood—by which I mean those reports, caught by hearts black to the core, filled with dark suspicion." In the next sentence Kepler offers a specific date for the circulation of the manuscript. "The first draft was carried from Prague to Leipzig, and thence to Tubingen in 1611 by Baron Volkerstorff[14] and his tutors." He suggests the result: "Now is it not only too probable that in the barbers' shops—especially those where my name is in bad repute because of the occupation of my Fioxhilda—there was gossip about this story of mine? No doubt at all that from that same city and house lying tittle-tattle came forth about me, me myself, in the years that followed, and that these whispers, harboured by stupid minds, and fanned by ignorance and superstition, blazed out at last into a real story."

Clearly, then, some work of Kepler's, written about 1610, was circulated in manuscript, and, carried into the "*tonstrinae*"—those early predecessors of the coffee-house—fanned a spark already burning, which then blazed up into the fire which almost con-

[13] Katherine Kepler, though technically under arrest after 1615, was actually imprisoned only in 1620, when she was taken to the prison in Leonberg. [Gunther, *Ein Hexenprocess*, p. 41.] She was transferred to Gueglingen on August 25 of that year, and kept in the tower in solitary confinement, under unhealthy conditions, in heavy iron chains. [*Ibid.*, p. 47.] Kepler demanded that she be lodged in more humane quarters; from that time on she was kept in the house of the town's gate-keeper, though again chained and guarded by two men. Kepler made a journey to protest against her treatment.

[14] I can find no information about Baron Volkerstorff; Ludwig Gunther is equally at a loss, and mentions [*op. cit.*, p. 27 n.] that this is the only word printed in black-letter in the original edition. Volkerstorff may well have been a former pupil of Kepler's, to whom, in good faith, Kepler had given the manuscript Kepler was living in Prague at this time.

sumed Kepler and his mother. Reasons for popular distrust of Kepler in 1611 were already legion. As early as 1597 he had become a religious exile. Archduke Ferdinand was an ardent Catholic, who had sworn that he would extinguish heresy—and Kepler was an ardent Protestant. At that time he had fled to Hungary, from which he was permitted to return, only to be banished again. It was at this period that he came into contact with Tycho Brahe. In addition to religious difficulties, the Kepler family was in constant trouble in every community in which they lived, largely because of the ungovernable temper of ''Fiolxhilda,'' though Johann Kepler seems to have inherited his mother's remarkable inability to live in peace with her neighbors. Most of all, Kepler was an avowed ''Copernican'' in a period in which Copernicanism was suspect. His Copernicanism had been clearly shown in the *Astronomia Nova,* which, although it is considered one of the great scientific classics today, had no such reputation in its own day. In 1606 he had defended the ''absurd'' and ''impious'' theories of Galileo concerning the ''new star'' of 1604 against the Aristotelians, and championed those theories with such vigor and mastery of logic that to this day the star of 1604 has been universally called ''Kepler's *nova.*'' In 1610 he published his *Dissertatio* on the same subject. Thus in 1610 Kepler was in disrepute with his neighbors, and was looked upon with grave suspicion both by Catholics and by Aristotelians. In addition to all these, Kepler in 1610 had written a ''manuscriptum'' in which he himself had apparently not only described his own mother as a ''wise woman,'' but had declared to the world the fact that she was in frequent communion with the ''daemons'' of the moon! For the ''libellum'' which Baron Volkerstorff carried into the barbershops was none other than the *Somnium* itself.[15] In the

---

[15] This seems to me the only possible interpretation of Kepler's note. To him and to his friends there was no mystery; but he carefully couched his note in such terms that others, who did not know the tragic circumstances, would not necessarily recognize his realization of the irony of the words written long before. I am at a loss to understand how Ludwig Gunther, who spent many years upon his study of Kepler, could have failed to realize the significance of this note. The fact that he has omitted some sentences in his translation, and transposed others, leads me to conclude that he failed to understand the note. Since he followed his study of Kepler with a careful account of the trial of Kepler's mother, it seems doubly strange that he should have missed Kepler's implication that his interpretation of his mother as Fiolxhilda added fuel to the flames. It is curious also that Gunther

little fantasy in which he had described his own life, his own experience with Tycho, and particularly the character of his own mother, Kepler unwittingly put into the hands of his enemy the most potent of all charges against his mother, the evidence of her own son. "Caught by hearts black to the core, filled with dark suspicion," this was in truth "a spark dropped upon kindling wood."

If we consider for a moment the context at the point at which this note is appended, it will be clear that Kepler is speaking of the *Somnium*. It must be remembered that this particular note was written after the death of Kepler's mother, a fact of which Kepler was only too poignantly aware when thirteen years later he annotated his original text. Duracotus is speaking in the text: "My mother was Fiolxhilda, who having lately died, furnished to me freedom for writing, for which I had been yearning. . . . She often said that there were many ruinous haters of the arts who accuse what they fail to understand because of dullness of mind, and hence make laws injurious to the human race; and, condemned by those laws, doubtless not a few have been swallowed up by the pits of Hecla." These words, with unconscious prophecy, Kepler had evidently written many years before, when his mother was not only alive, but when she was as yet known only as a "wise woman" in the least dangerous sense of that term. Had he heeded her warning and restrained from writing at that particular time, who can tell how different the fortune of the whole Kepler family might have been? Kepler's mother may have been illiterate; but she was truly wise, and from her own limited experience she realized that calumny would befall the person who dared to think otherwise than did his neighbors. In her limited circle she was to suffer persecution; and her son, in his broad circle— or perhaps in an ellipse such as that of the planet whose course he was the first to determine—was to suffer also for different heretical opinions. Kepler's Fiolxhilda indeed came close to the gates of Hecla. Her son concluded this most personal of all his notes: "So I decided to take revenge for this dream of mine, for the trouble it gave me, by publishing this little book; there will be some other reward for my enemies."

---

makes practically no comment upon the similarities between the life of Kepler's hero Duracotus and Kepler's own life.

II

I have thus far purposely omitted discussion of the two first sentences in Kepler's remarkable note, since they have nothing to do with the biographical facts, and lead us from Germany to England. Nevertheless, to students of English literature they are the most interesting sentences in the note, since they seem to offer evidence for some relationship between Kepler's *Somnium* and an important work of an English satirist and poet. Kepler wrote: "I suspect that the author of that impudent satire, the *Conclave of Ignatius,* had got hold of a copy of this little work, for he pricks me by name in the very beginning. Further on, he brings up poor Copernicus to the judgment seat of Pluto—if I don't mistake, the approach to that is through the yawning chasms of Hecla." On January 24, 1611,[16] the Latin edition of John Donne's *Conclave Ignatii* was entered in the Stationer's Register; on May 18, 1611, an English translation was entered under the title, *Ignatius his Conclave.* Elsewhere I have suggested the immediate effect of Galileo's *Sidereus Nuncius* upon Donne.[17] Profoundly moved by the implications of the "new astronomy" in the *Anatomy of the World,* written a year later, Donne in the *Conclave Ignatii* is merely pleasantly amused. In this, the most brilliant of his satires, he makes use of the Galilean idea that the moon may be a world, to propose an immediate translation to that world of all the Jesuits who infest this one. The main satire of the *Conclave Ignatii* is concerned with the Jesuits. But into an "impudent satire" Donne has introduced important passages concerning the "new astronomy," several of which indicate his recent reading of Galileo and of Kepler.

The similarities between Kepler's brief description and John Donne's finished work are so close as to make it seem inevitable that Kepler in his note was referring to Donne. Within the first few lines of *Ignatius his Conclave* we find a reference to Galileo, "who of late hath summoned the other worlds, the Stars to come nearer to him, and give him an account of themselves."[18] This is

[16] Another edition in Latin appeared in 1611 on the continent; *cf.* Geoffrey Keynes, *Bibliography of John Donne* (Cambridge, 1932).

[17] *Cf.* "The 'New Astronomy' and English Literary Imagination," *Studies in Philology,* XXXII (1935), pp. 428 ff. A much more important treatment of the same subject will be found in Charles Monroe Coffin, *John Donne and the New Philosophy* (New York, 1937).

closely followed by a reference to "Keppler, who (as himselfe testifies of himselfe) ever since Tycho Brache's death hath received it into his care, that no new thing should be done in heaven without his knowledge."[19] Later there appears in the satire "a certain Mathematitian, which till then had been busied to finde, to deride, to detrude Ptolomey." By his first speech we recognize him: "Are these [doors] shut against me, to whom all the Heavens were ever open, who was a Soule to the Earth, and gave it motion?" With the author we conclude: "By this I knew it was Copernicus."[20]

The similarities are such that it seems practically inevitable that Kepler was referring to Donne's work. But how could Donne, who published his *Conclave Ignatii* early in 1611, have known of Kepler's manuscript, which, written in 1609 or 1610, was circulating in Germany at this same time? To be sure, if we are to follow the earlier date of 1609, there is not much difficulty; if, however, Kepler completed his manuscript, as I believe, after Galileo's publication of the *Sidereus Nuncius* in March, 1610—or even after his own telescopic observations in August 1610—the problem is more difficult. Since no actual evidence seems to be in existence in Donne's published letters, I must for the present limit myself to hypotheses. Certainly John Donne was in touch with various sources through which he rapidly received news of developments in astronomy, for he was well acquainted with the *Sidereus Nuncius* shortly after its publication. So far as Galileo is concerned, the link may well have been Sir Henry Wotton, Donne's close friend and correspondent. Wotton it was who on the very day of the publication of the *Sidereus Nuncius* sent a copy of the work, together with a telescope, intended for James I, to the Earl of Salisbury. In the accompanying letter[21] Wotton described the excitement in Italy aroused by the book "come abroad this very day." Although no letter on the subject has been published, Wotton may well have sent another copy of the work to Donne, of whose insatiable curiosity he was well aware. It is conceivable, also, that Kepler's work, circulating as it was in manuscript, may have been sent or

---

[18] *Ignatius his Conclave* in *Complete Poems and Selected Prose,* edited by John Bloomsbury, 1929, pp. 358–9.

[19] *Ibid.,* p. 359.

[20] *Ibid.,* p. 363.

[21] *The Life and Letters of Sir Henry Wotton,* edited by Logan Pearsall Smith (Oxford, 1907), I, 486.

brought to Wotton in Italy.   While Wotton seems to have met Kepler only much later, in 1620, when he visited the astronomer at Linz, he knew of Kepler's work in this earlier period.   However, we may well ask whether there was any more direct way in which a copy of the *Somnium* might have reached John Donne in England, since if Kepler completed the manuscript only in 1610, the time element is of importance.

Kepler's most exalted acquaintance in England was James I himself,[22] to whom Kepler sent a copy of his *De Nova Stella* in 1606, with a flattering inscription.   That James continued his interest in the astronomer is shown from Kepler's dedication to him in 1619 of the *Harmonice Mundi* and from James's invitation to Kepler in 1620 to come to England as Astronomer Royal.   Donne, of course, had many friends at court, from whom he might have heard of the *Somnium* if Kepler sent a copy of the manuscript to His Majesty, as he occasionally sent his published works.   Another source, however, seems to me the most likely one.   Among Kepler's correspondents in England was the most important English astronomer, Thomas Hariot.   While only a few of the letters they interchanged have been published,[23] those few indicate that the two astronomers were in close touch at the period under consideration.   Kepler began the correspondence in October 1606, saying that he had heard of Hariot's accomplishments in natural philosophy from his friend John Ericksen.   The other letters show that the two men sent papers of observations on matters of common interest and kept each other informed of the progress of science in the two countries.   In 1608 John Ericksen who had been for some time with Hariot in England, returned to Germany, bearing messages to Kepler.   In September 1609, Kepler indicates that Ericksen has again been in England with Hariot and is again returning to Prague.   Ericksen, therefore, was with Kepler in Prague in the

[22] It seems likely that James's interest in Kepler came about through Tycho Brahe, whom His Majesty had visited at his observatory when James went to Denmark for his bride, in 1589–90.   Kepler in his dedication of the *Harmonices* to James I, refers to the fact that James, while yet a boy, thought the astronomy of Tycho Brahe worthy of the ornaments of his genius.

[23] Five letters which passed between Kepler and Hariot have been published in *Joannis Keppleri Aliorumque Epistolae Mutuae* (Francofurti, 1718).   Brief digests of the ones to which I refer below are given by Henry Stevens, *Thomas Hariot, the Philosopher, the Mathematician and the Scholar* (London, 1900), pp. 178–180.

autumn of 1609 at the period when Kepler was working seriously upon problems of the moon.   What more natural than that, upon his return to Hariot in England, Ericksen should have discussed in detail Kepler's theories about the moon, and that later, when the manuscript was complete, Kepler should have sent a copy either to Ericksen in England—or if Ericksen had again returned to Prague as he seems to have done annually—by Ericksen to Hariot in England?   Although no letters between the two are extant for 1610, letters which passed between Hariot and his disciple Lower show how closely Kepler was being studied by the English astronomers.   On February 6, 1610,[24] Lower wrote to Hariot: "Kepler I read diligentlie, but therein I find what it is to be so far from you.   For as himself, he hath almost put me out of my wits. . . . "   Lower included in this letter a long and technical discussion of many of Kepler's conclusions drawn from the *Astronomia Nova* published in the preceding year.

On June 21, 1610,[25] Lower writes excitedly about the new discoveries of Galileo which Hariot has just communicated to him. Evidently Hariot knew of these discoveries before he saw a copy of the *Sidereus Nuncius,* for Lower adds: "Send me also one of Galileus' bookes if anie yet be come over and you can get them." In the same letter he mentions that, just at the time of the arrival of Hariot's letter, "wee Traventane Philosophere were a consideringe of Kepler's reasons by which he indeavors to overthrow Nolanus and Gilberts opinion concerninge the immensitie of the Sphaere of the starres and that opinion particularlie of Nolanus by which he affirmed that the eye beinge placed in anie parte of the Univers the apparance would be still all one as unto us here."— Not only had Kepler challenged that conclusion of Bruno's in *De Nova Stella,* but this is the central doctrine of the *Somnium,* upon which much of its originality depends.   In view of the great interest of both Lower and Hariot in this new theory, what more natural than that Ericksen should have brought back or sent to England a copy of Kepler's manuscript with his latest conclusions on the subject?

It is impossible to tell, from the published correspondence of John Donne, whether he knew Hariot or not.   Yet certainly there were many bonds between them.   I shall consider for the moment

[24] Quoted in Stevens, *op. cit.,* p. 121.   The letter is given in full.
[25] *Ibid.,* p. 118.

only one of the many men in England closely associated with both, who had reason to be much interested in such works as the *Somnium.* Henry Percy, ninth Earl of Northumberland, was known everywhere as a man greatly interested in science and in semiscience. With Raleigh and Hariot, he was one of the original members of the ill-fated "School of Night," which Shakespeare may have satirized in *Love's Labor's Lost,* in which recent critics have found traces of Shakespeare's criticism of both Raleigh and Hariot.[26] "Deep-searching Northumberland," as Chapman called him—the "Wizard Earl" as he appears to a modern commentator—here was a man who seized avidly upon all that was new under the sun. Northumberland had been closely associated with Donne at the time of Donne's furtive marriage to Anne More in 1610. When it became clear that someone must break the news to the father of the bride, Percy was chosen. Early in February, Northumberland proceeded upon his mission, armed with a letter from Donne.[27]

In 1610, Northumberland, with Raleigh, was imprisoned in the Tower. Such commitment, however, did not mean that either was inaccessible. Indeed, during a long part of their detention, both Northumberland and Raleigh continued to carry on their active interest in science, each of them having his laboratory, both of them keeping in close touch with the outside world. While Raleigh's bonds were tightened for a short time in 1610, there is no evidence that the limitation continued for long, nor was a like limitation imposed upon Northumberland. During the whole period of the imprisonment, Hariot was a constant and frequent visitor to both men. That his interest was not confined to Raleigh alone is to be seen from Hariot's will,[28] in which he bequeathed to Northumberland his most important telescopes, and in which he gave instructions that his papers were to be sent to the Earl.

Here, then, is exactly the sort of connection which could explain how John Donne in England might have seen the manuscript of the *Somnium,* sent or brought to Hariot from Kepler. And the *Somnium* was the sort of work in which men like Northumberland and Raleigh and Donne would have been even more interested than

[26] See Frances Yates, *A Study of Love's Labour's Lost* (Cambridge, 1936), Chapter VII and *passim.*

[27] See Edmund Gosse, *Life and Letters of John Donne* (London, 1899), pp. 99 ff.

[28] The will is given in Henry Stevens, *Thomas Hariot,* pp. 192–203.

they would have been in Kepler's technical published works.   For
the combination of mystery and mysticism in the *Somnium* was
the sort of thing which had always fascinated members of the
"School of Night," and both Raleigh and Northumberland would
have reason to know that it would have been equally interesting to
John Donne, who must have visited his friend in the Tower as
Hariot visited Raleigh and Northumberland.

One final point remains: why did Kepler "suspect" that the
impudent English satirist had read the manuscript of the *Somnium?*   Certainly there is nothing in Donne's straightforward
statement in the *Conclave Ignatii* to lead Kepler to that suspicion
Donne merely said: "Keppler, who (as himselfe testifies of himselfe) ever since Tycho Brahe's death hath received it into his
care, that no new thing should be done in heaven without his knowledge."   But Kepler, of all men, understood that reference, and
knew that Donne was referring in that sentence, not to the
Somnium but to Kepler's dissertation on the new star—for the
main part of the sentence is merely a translation of Kepler's published words.[29]   Why, then, the "suspicion"?   The answer to that
question is very important, and not only brings together into a
complete pattern the labyrinthine threads which have been followed
above, but also explains something which has long puzzled critics—
the peculiar structure of the *Conclave Ignatii*.

The main body of Donne's work consists of a series of scenes
in Hell, with an inquisition upon a number of men famous because
of theological disputes.   The introduction of the "new astronomy"
seems almost irrelevant: references to Galileo and Kepler appear
at the very beginning, and to Galileo again close to the end.
Neither one of them is made a character in the story, as is
Copernicus.   Even more curious is the fact that Donne's work
begins with a suggestion that he is intending something very different from the work he actually published.   Donne's first words
clearly suggest that he is writing a cosmic voyage, and that the
device which he is using is that of trance.   "I was in an Exstasie,'
he says,

> My little wandering sportful Soule,
> Ghest, and Companion of my body,

[29] This fact was first pointed out by Evelyn Simpson, *A Study of the Prose
Works of John Donne* (Oxford, 1924), p. 184 n.

1ad liberty to wander through all places, and to survey and reckon
1ll the roomes, and all the volumes of the heavens, and to compre-
1end the situation, the dimensions, the nature, the people, and the
policy, both of the swimming Islands, the Planets, and of all those
which are fixed in the firmament.''[30]   Surely this is a complete outline of a cosmic voyage; yet the device is entirely neglected in the
work itself.   Only in his brief suggestion that the Jesuits are to
be transferred to the world in the moon does Donne suggest it
again, and even there, there is no real use of the device implied at
the beginning, for the moon-world is to be drawn to earth through
Galileo's improved optic glasses.   One sentence alone in this section carries out the idea of a cosmic voyage: ''And with the same
ease as you passe from the earth to the Moone, you may passe
from the Moone to the other starrs, which are also thought to be
worlds.''[31]   The theme of the ecstatic trance, too, completely disappears from the *Conclave*, and is remembered by Donne only in
one of the concluding sentences: ''And I returned to my body.''

    The *Conclave Ignatii,* let us remember, was entered in the Sta-
tioner's Register in January, 1611.   Presumably it was written
therefore late in 1610.   Let us suppose for the moment that Donne
originally wrote it—as in the main it is—merely as a series of
dialogues in Hell, a satire on the Jesuits.   Its structure is perfectly
consistent if we omit the brief introduction and the final reference
to the return of the soul to the body.   But when the work was ready
for the press, let us suppose again that Donne, through Northumberland or Raleigh or Hariot himself—or any other source—saw
the manuscript of the *Somnium,* and realized the rhetorical value
of its introduction, with its dream-vision of a cosmic voyage.
Time—or perhaps the printer—would not permit the fundamental
changes necessary to recast the whole work into the form of a
cosmic voyage.   Donne therefore contented himself with the mere
addition of a new introduction and conclusion in which he deliberately adopted the double device of dream and cosmic voyage used
by Kepler in the *Somnium,* with the result that the *Conclave of
Ignatius* has continued to puzzle critics who have recognized the
inconsistency of the two different forms employed by Donne, but
who have found no satisfactory explanation for the lack of artistic
unity in the finished work.[32]

[30] *Ignatius his Conclave,* ed. cit., p. 359.
[31] *Ibid.,* p. 399.

This, it seems to me, is the explanation of Kepler's "suspicion" that the impudent satirist had "obtained a copy" of his manuscript.   Certainly Kepler was in a position to know whether or not it was possible for the English poet to have done so; if Kepler had not known it to be possible, he could hardly have entertained the suspicion.   And this explanation seems to me perfectly consistent not only with Kepler's note and with the structure of the *Conclave Ignatii,* but also with the hypotheses I have attempted to establish as to the date of composition and the circulation of Kepler's manuscript both in Germany and in England.   Intent upon his lunar ideas in 1609, Kepler communicated his interest to Ericksen, who in turn brought the word to Hariot and his group in England.   But no matter how much of the *Somnium* was written in 1609, Kepler must inevitably have revised it after the publication of the *Sidereus Nuncius,* which offered proof for his theories and gave him certain details which he could not have known in 1609.   Sometime in 1610 the manuscript was complete.   Circulated on the continent in 1611, it brought tragedy to Kepler and his family.   Circulated in England, in 1610, it brought new light to Hariot and to Lower, and helps to explain the close similarity of certain astronomical conclusions reached in England and on the Continent.   Falling into the hands of the English poet and satirist, the first modern scientific cosmic voyage, written on the Continent, caught the imagination of the English poet, who at least suggested, if he did not finally produce, the first modern cosmic voyage in England.

III

It is impossible to discuss in detail at this time the remarkable moon-voyage of the *Somnium* and to trace its effect upon English literature.[33]   For the present I must content myself with very general statements.   The *Somnium,* as I have suggested, is the first modern scientific moon-voyage.   Behind it lies a long literary tradition, his debt to which Kepler was quick to realize.   In his notes, he discusses at length the many works on the subject which had stimulated his imagination, most of all Lucian's *True History*

[32] Mr. Coffin, *John Donne and the New Philosophy,* discusses at some length, pp. 204 ff., the curious inconsistency in the structure of the work, and can find no really satisfying explanation, though he suggests various hypotheses.

[33] I have discussed the classical, medieval and Renaissance background of the cosmic voyage in the paper referred to above.

and Plutarch's *De Facie in Orbe Lunae.* Yet with all its debt to
the past, the *Somnium* belongs to the modern world. True, Kepler's device for flight to the moon still looks back to the world of
the supernatural, not forward to the development of the flying-
machine, as do many of the English cosmic voyages written in the
seventeenth century. For Duracotus learns from the *"Daemon ex
Levania"* who came from the moon at Fiolxhilda's summons, that
mortals may reach the moon only by the assistance of the "daemons." Yet even this section shows the scientific temper of
Kepler, for he discusses, both in text and notes, the effect of gravity upon the human body and the "orb of attractive power" of the
earth. Like the later writers of modern cosmic voyages, Kepler's
imagination plays, too, with the question of the intervening space,
the "dark Illimitable ocean, without bound, without dimension"
which Milton's Satan faced as he looked out from hell-gates upon
the chaos of the new space. As a scientist rather than as a writer
of romance, he considers the effect of the rarefied air upon human
beings, and his daemons take great care to guard against "pro-
hibited respiration . . . by sponges moistened and applied to the
nostrils." Once the "attractive orb" of earth is passed, "convey-
ance becomes easier"; force is no longer necessary. For more
than a century this pattern is followed in English cosmic voyages;
voyager after voyager enjoys the strange experience of resting
upon his wings, or dismounting from his "flying-chariot," to find
himself travelling more swiftly than before, without effort, without
hunger, thirst, weariness—all ills resulting from the effect of
gravity.

But when Kepler's travellers reach the moon, fantasy drops
away, and we find ourselves in the "new world in the moon," not
with a writer of romance such as Godwin, a satirist such as Cyrano
de Bergerac, nor yet with a poet; our guide is a true scientist. In
this respect Kepler's work is almost unique among modern cosmic
voyages. Non-scientific writers spent their originality chiefly on
ingenious methods of travelling to the moon, and on descriptions of
the voyage. Their moon-worlds are, as a rule, conventional utopias, or mere convenient vehicles for satire concerning social and
political customs in this world. Kepler, on the other hand, develops in the most exact detail the geography of the moon, as the
science of Plutarch had presupposed it, as the telescope had shown
it. It is a world as strange to us as the new world seemed to

Galileo.   Seasons, length of day and night, climate, all these are peculiar to Levania.   It is divided into two zones, Subvolva and Privola, the first of which enjoys its "Volva" in place of our moon, the second of which is completely devoid of light.   In Privolva "night is 15 or 16 of our days long, and dreadful with uninterrupted shadow."   On one zone the sun never shines; all things are rigid with cold and frost.   In the other the "parching air burns frore."   In Subvolva, the climate is somewhat less intolerable, thanks to the Volva.   But throughout the whole of Levania, we find extremes to which ours are as nothing, cold more intense, heat more parching.   Geographically, the world of the moon is much like our own, save that everything is on an exaggerated scale, the mountains much higher, the fissures and valleys more profound.   The life which exists on the moon—and Kepler continues to posit the existence of life in spite of Galileo's denial that water exists on the moon—bears no relation to our life, for Kepler was too good a scientist not to realize the effect of climate and environment upon life.   In Subvolva whatever is born is of monstrous size; the life-span of all creatures and plants is brief, since they are often born to die in a single day, springing up to prodigious size while they exist.   Here we find no men and women, but creatures who share alike a "serpentine nature," though some of them are winged, some crawl, some swim in water.   Civilization, as we understand it, does not exist; they build no towns, they establish no governments. Nomadic creatures, they appear for a short time in the heat of the sun, like lizards basking in tremendous warmth, then disappear either into the seas or into the caverns and fissures which nature has designed for their protection.   A gigantic race of living creatures, they seem to the modern reader reminiscent of a prehistoric world, lunar pterodactyls or ichthyosauri, as, for a moment basking in heat, then creeping into darkness or flying upon prehistoric wing, they disappear forever from the light of Volva, creatures of only a day.   The *Somnium* is a dream; but it is a dream with nightmare touches.   From this vision of monstrous and grotesque creatures which man is glad he may forget, we gladly wake, to find with the author that the strange book is only part of a dream. Duracotus, Fiolxhilda, daemons and lunar monsters left behind, the author woke "to find my head covered with a cushion, and my body tangled with a rug."   The *Somnium* is over.

It is not strange that the moon-world of the *Somnium* should have continued to haunt its readers.   It would be difficult to over-estimate its effect in England upon the long tradition of cosmic voyages in which the seventeenth and eighteenth centuries de-lighted.[34]   John Wilkins, in his *Discovery of a New World,* pub-lished four years after the *Somnium,* did much to popularize it for English readers, delighting in its combination of imagination and science.   It was known by nearly all the English writers on cosmic voyages—and, indeed, its indirect influence still lies behind such modern writers as Jules Verne and H. G. Wells.   In its own cen-tury it is quoted again and again, sometimes seriously, sometimes with amusement.   Henry More, in whose serious philosophical works the influence of Kepler is found more than once, uses the moon-world of the *Somnium* as the basis of his minor poem "In-somnium Philosophicum," in which he, too, beholds a vision of another world of light and darkness.   Samuel Butler, who de-lighted to satirize the popular interest in a world in the moon, chooses the moon-world of the *Somnium* for his description in "The Elephant in the Moon":

> Quoth he—Th' Inhabitants of the Moon,
> Who when the Sun shines hot at Noon,
> Do live in Cellars underground
> Of eight Miles deep and eighty around
> (In which at once they fortify
> Against the Sun and th' Enemy)
> Because their People's civiler
> Than those rude Peasants, that are found
> To live upon the upper Ground,
> Call'd Privolvans, with whom they are
> Perpetually at open War.

Perhaps, in a study which contains so much of conjecture and hypothesis, one more may be permitted.   Kepler's is the last im-portant moon-voyage to use the old supernatural means of flight to another world; but the last great supernatural flight through space was really written by a poet.   The flight of Milton's Satan through Chaos draws clearly from the long tradition of cosmic voy-ages established by Lucian and Plutarch, newly interpreted by Kepler, Godwin, Wilkins, and many others.   May there not also be a momentary reminiscence of the *Somnium* in that voyage

[34] I shall discuss the influence of the *Somnium* in more detail in a forthcoming book.

through space? For the most part in the first two books of *Paradise Lost* Satan is a majestic figure; yet as he forces his way into the chaos of the new interplanetary space, he takes on temporarily something of the grotesqueness of Kepler's lunar creatures, as eagerly the Fiend

> O'er bog, or steep, through strait, rough, dense, or rare,
> With head, hands, wings, or feet, pursues his way,
> And sinks, or swims, or wades, or creeps, or flies.

In another, earlier scene in *Paradise Lost,* I believe that there are definite reminiscences of Kepler's moon-world—in Milton's third Hell. The smaller Hell surrounding Pandemonium had its sources, as I have suggested elsewhere.[35] Pandemonium, the second Hell, has also been shown to have had its original. But what of that vaster Hell, stretching out indefinitely, which is explored in Book II by bands of adventurous fallen spirits,—more than a continent, for it contains both continents and seas—almost an unknown new world? Certainly only Milton has expressed in poetry anything of the strange grandeur and grotesque picturesqueness of Kepler's world in the moon. Milton's Hell, like Kepler's moon, is a place of "fierce extremes, extremes by change more fierce"; its cold is colder than anything on earth, its heat more torrid; "the parching air burns frore, and heat performs the effect of fire." As Kepler briefly suggests, so Milton describes the frozen world:

> a frozen continent
> Lies dark and wild, beat with perpetual storms
> Of whirlwind and dire hail, which on firm land
> Thaws not, but gathers heap, and ruin seems
> Of ancient pile; all else deep snow and ice.

Kepler's lunar mountains tower to heights more ghastly than even the Caucasus; his caverns and fissures are

> a gulf profound as that Serbonian bog
> Betwixt Damiata and Mount Casius old
> Where armies whole have sunk.

Visitors to Kepler's moon, in short, would have found themselves in just such a world as was experienced by the wandering fallen angels in Milton's Hell:

[35] "Milton's Hell and the Phlegraean Fields," *University of Toronto Quarterly,* VII (1938), pp. 500–513.

Thus roving on
In confused march forlorn, the adventurous bands
With shuddering horror pale, and eyes aghast,
Viewed first their lamentable lot, and found
No rest. Through many a dark and dreary vale
They past, and many a region dolorous,
O'er many a frozen, many a fiery Alp,
Rocks, caves, lakes, fens, bogs, dens and shades of death—
A universe of death which God by curse,
Created evil, for evil only good,
Where all life dies, death lives, and Nature breeds,
Perverse, all monstrous, all prodigious things,
Abominable, unutterable, and worse
Than fables yet have feigned, or fear conceived,
Gorgons, and Hydras, and Chimaeras dire.

༈ *Francis R. Johnson*

GRESHAM COLLEGE: PRECURSOR OF THE ROYAL SOCIETY

Of paramount interest to all students of the history of ideas is the development, in the seventeenth century, of formally organized scientific societies from the informal gatherings of devotees of science that preceded them.   Today we can see clearly that one of the causes for the relative stagnation of science in Western Europe during the Middle Ages is that new findings—and there were many new facts of nature brought to light during this period[1]—too often perished with their discoverers or were buried in manuscripts which, being available to few other investigators, gave little impetus to further progress.   We likewise recognize that the remarkably accelerated advance of science from the seventeenth century onward was due in no small measure to the increased rapidity with which scientific information came to be transmitted not only among the scientists of separate localities and nations, but among investigators dispersed throughout the Western World.   The importance of the first permanent scientific societies in this dissemination and interchange of scientific ideas and discoveries is universally conceded, and many valuable histories have been devoted to the careers of those organizations that survived.   Insufficiently explored, however, either in the initial chapters of these histories or elsewhere, are the earlier attempts at co-operative endeavor[2]—the groups

[1] For numerous illustrations of important scientific discoveries from the tenth to the sixteenth centuries, see Lynn Thorndike, *A History of Magic and Experimental Science,* Vols. I & II (New York, 1923), Vols. III & IV (New York, 1934); *Science and Thought in the Fifteenth Century* (New York, 1929).

[2] A third edition has recently appeared of the invaluable pioneering survey of the contributions of the scientific societies in the seventeenth century: Martha Ornstein's *The Rôle of Scientific Societies in the Seventeenth Century* (Chicago, 1938; the first edition was published posthumously in 1913).   A new edition at this time is a witness to the soundness of Miss Ornstein's work within the scope that it set for itself, and a recognition of the intrinsic importance of the subject.   On the other hand, it proclaims how few works, in the interval of twenty-five years, have sought to delve more deeply into the subject that she explored.   Several of the French groups devoted to scientific inquiry have been admirably dealt with by Harcourt Brown in *Scientific Organizations in Seventeenth-Century France, 1620–1680* (Baltimore, 1934).   Dorothy Stimson's article, "Dr. Wilkins and the Royal Society," *Journal of Modern History,* III (1931), 539–63, has analyzed and discussed the accounts of the

which met together without formal organization or royal charter, and thus sowed the seed and nurtured the immature plant of scientific association until it became firmly rooted.

Our concern here is with England, and the evolution there of groups promoting the association and co-operation of men sharing an active interest in science. Historians of the Royal Society recognize that its formal establishment in 1660 and the granting to it of a royal charter in 1663 was but the culmination of a series of regular gatherings of scientifically-minded men in London and in Oxford. The familiar accounts of the origin of the Society trace these antecedent gatherings back as far as the year 1645, when a group which included several of the Society's later founders were meeting regularly in London after the astronomy lecture at Gresham College, and usually in the rooms of the Gresham Professor of Astronomy.[3] The purpose of this article is to present evidence indicating that these meetings of English scientists went back to a period much earlier than 1645, and that by long tradition gatherings of this sort for the interchange of information and the witnessing of experiments had centered about Gresham College and its professors of astronomy and geometry.

The intimate connection between Gresham College and the Royal Society during the first fifty years of the latter's existence is familiar to all who have had occasion to investigate the history, the science, or the literature of England during the late seventeenth century. Except for a period of seven years following the great fire of London in 1666, which destroyed the Royal Exchange and resulted in the temporary housing of the former tenants of the Exchange in the Gresham College buildings, Sir Thomas Gresham's foundation provided a meeting-place for the Royal Society and quarters for its library and scientific collections from the beginning until the year 1710, when the society purchased a building of its own. In the literary works of the day, the early fellows of the Royal Society were colloquially known as "Greshamites" or "Men

---

origin of the Royal Society of London. But, for England in the early seventeenth century, we need a comprehensive and detailed study similar to Harcourt Brown's for France. The present article's modest aim is to make one small contribution to this end and to indicate profitable lines of further investigation which can be followed out whenever research in English archives again becomes possible.

[3] The best accounts of the origin of the Royal Society are in C. R. Weld, *A History of the Royal Society* (2 vols.; London, 1848), I, chaps. i–iv, and in *The Record of the Royal Society of London* (3d ed.; London, 1912), pp. 1–22.

of Gresham.'' The Gresham College professors—not only those holding the three scientific chairs of Astronomy, Geometry, and Physic, but several others as well—were among the most active of the Royal Society's early members. Thus the two organizations were linked together by both membership and locality, and finally (and in consequence) by popular imagination.

The younger of these organizations, the Royal Society, was formally established in 1660. The elder, Gresham College, began its active career in 1598, with the distinguished mathematician Henry Briggs as its first professor of geometry. From this time on, Gresham College, with an unbroken line of enthusiastic mathematical scientists among its professors, and with its central location in London, offered an ideal rendezvous where those engaged in scientific pursuits could meet with others who shared their interests, exchange news concerning the latest investigations and discoveries, and gain the stimulus that comes from association with eager fellow-workers. That English scientists should wait until 1645 before taking advantage of such opportunities seems inconceivable. We should expect that the natural course of events, as each decade passed, would make Gresham College increasingly important as a gathering-place for scientists, so that by the 1640's Englishmen interested in the ''new philosophy'' would have been long enough in the habit of assembling informally there to make the custom a well-established tradition. A group having so secure an anchor as Gresham College would not require the stabilizing force of formal organization to maintain a continued existence through all the fluctuations in membership that the passage of time would bring about. Suppose, then, that in 1645 or thereabouts, a few energetic and enthusiastic young men were admitted to the group, and this generation among the membership was the only one which survived to become the leaders in the founding of the Royal Society. These young recruits of 1645, looking back late in life, would naturally tend to date the origin of the meetings which grew into the Royal Society from the time of their first participation in them.

The hypothesis that I have just sketched postulates the gradual and uninterrupted evolution of an informal club, if we may so call it, composed of Englishmen interested in science—a club which constantly had as its nucleus one or more Gresham professors and his friends, and which had Gresham College as its usual meeting place. This hypothesis is contrary to the generally accepted account, which implies that the group which Robert Boyle described as the "Invisible College" came suddenly into being about 1645, the result of the enthusiasm of a few young men for scientific investigation, combined with their desire to escape, occasionally, from the political and religious turmoils of the day. Let us see what evidence can be offered in favor of this newly proposed hypothesis.

We may begin by examining the evidence upon which the accepted theory is based, to see whether the known facts will bear the new interpretation that is proposed. The first official account of the Royal Society, Thomas Sprat's *The History of the Royal-Society of London* (1667), states that the foundation of the Society was laid, not in London in 1645, but in the Warden's (John Wilkins's) lodgings at Wadham College, Oxford, in 1649.[4] Since Sprat's *History* was written under the supervision of Wilkins, then secretary of the Society, this version has his authority and represents his point of view. John Wallis, on the other hand, traces the origin of the Society to meetings at Gresham College in London about 1645. Although the existence of such meetings is confirmed by references in Robert Boyle's letters of October 22, 1646, and January 20, 1646/7,[5] Wallis remains our only first-hand witness for the date, the place, and the membership of the group.[6] As Miss Stimson has shown,[7] the accounts of Wilkins and Wallis may easily be reconciled by assuming that Wilkins considered the meetings at Oxford to have a superior claim to recognition because there the group was formally organized and kept minutes, and thus provided a precedent for the organization of a society in London after most of the Oxford contingent had returned to the capital.

It is to Wallis's statements, therefore, that we must turn. In 1678 Wallis, in a pamphlet entitled *A Defence of the Royal Society:*

[4] *Op. cit.,* p. 53.

[5] Robert Boyle, *Works,* ed. T. Birch (London, 1744), I, 20. It seems certain that Boyle refers to the same group that Wallis describes.

[6] Anthony Wood, in his enlarged English translation of his *Historia et Antiquitates Universitatis Oxoniensis* (1674), *History and Antiquities of Oxford,* ed. J. Gutch (Oxford, 1786), II, Part ii, 632–33, apparently derives his information from Wallis's *Defence* (1678). The original Latin edition of 1674 does not contain the reference asserting the prior claims of the 1645 meetings against the version given in Sprat's *History.*

[7] "Dr. Wilkins and the Royal Society," *JMH,* III, 544–47.

An Answer to the Cavils of Doctor William Holder,[8] gave an account of the circumstances surrounding these early meetings:

I take its [the Royal Society's] first Ground and Foundation to have been in London about the year 1645 (if not sooner) when the same Dr. Wilkins (then Chaplain to the Prince Elector Palatine, in London), Dr. Jonathan Goddard, Dr. Ent (now Sir George Ent), Dr. Glisson, Dr. Scarbrough (now Sir Charles Scarbrough), Dr. Merrit, with myself and some others, met weekly (sometimes at Dr. Goddard's Lodgings, sometimes at the Mitre in Wood-street hard by) at a certain day and hour, under a certain Penalty, and a weekly Contribution for the Charge of Experiments, with certain Rules agreed upon amongst us. Where (to avoid diversion to other discourses, and for some other reasons) we barred all Discourses of Divinity, of State-Affairs, and of News (other than what concern'd our business of Philosophy) confining our selves to Philosophical Inquiries, and such as related there-unto; as Physick, Anatomy, Geometry, Astronomy, Navigation, Staticks, Mechanicks, and Natural Experiments. . . .

These meetings we removed, soon after, to the Bull-head in Cheapside and (in Term-time) to Gresham Colledge, where we met weekly at Mr. Foster's Lecture (the Astronomy-Professor there) and after the Lecture ended, repaired sometimes to Mr. Foster's Lodgings, sometimes to some other place not far distant, where we continued such Inquiries; and our Numbers encreased.[9]

But a more detailed account of these early meetings was given by Wallis in 1697, when, at the age of eighty, in an "account of some passages in his own life," he set forth in these words his own recollection of the circumstances leading to the Society's establishment:

About the year 1645, while I lived in *London* (at a time when, by our Civil Wars, Academical Studies were much interrupted in both our Universities:) beside the Conversation of divers eminent Divines, as to matters Theological; I had the opportunity of being acquainted with divers worthy Persons, inquisitive into Natural Philosophy, and other parts of Humane Learning; And particularly of what hath been called the *New Philosophy* or *Experimental Philosophy*.

We did by agreement, divers of us, meet weekly in *London* on a certain day, to treat and discourse of such affairs. Of which number were *Dr. John Wilkins* (afterward *Bp. of Chester*), *Dr. Jonathan Goddard, Dr. George*

---

[8] Dr. Holder had stated that "the first ground and foundation of the Royal Society" had been laid at Oxford in 1649. See J. F. Scott, *The Mathematical Work of John Wallis* (London, 1938), p. 9.

[9] Pp. 7–8.

Ent, Dr. Glisson, Dr. Merret, (Drs. in Physick), Mr. *Samuel Foster* then Professor of Astronomy at *Gresham College*, Mr. *Theodore Hank* [Haak] (a German of the *Palatinate*, and then Resident in London, who, I think, gave the first occasion, and first suggested those meetings) and many others.

These meetings were held sometimes at *Dr. Goddard's* lodgings in *Woodstreet* (or some convenient place near) on occasion of his keeping an Operator in his house for grinding Glasses for Telescopes and Microscopes; and sometime at a convenient place in *Cheap-side;* sometime at Gresham College or some place near adjoyning. . . .

About the year 1648, 1649, some of our company being removed to *Oxford* (first *Dr. Wilkins,* then I, and soon after *Dr. Goddard*) our company divided. Those in *London* continued to meet there as before (and we with them, when we had occasion to be there;) and those of us at *Oxford;* with *Dr. Ward* (since *Bp. of Salisbury*) *Dr. Ralph Bathurst* (now *President of Trinity College in Oxford*) *Dr. Petty* (since *Sr. William Petty*) *Dr. Willis* (then an eminent Physician in *Oxford*) and divers others, continued such meetings in *Oxford;* and brought those studies into fashion there; meeting first at *Dr. Pettie's* Lodgings, (in an Apothecarie's house) because of the convenience of inspecting Drugs, and the like, as there was occasion: and after his remove to *Ireland* (tho' not so constantly) at the Lodgings of *Dr. Wilkins,* then Warden of *Wadham Coll.* And after his removal to *Trinity College in Cambridge,* at the Lodgings of *the Honorable Mr. Robert Boyle,* then resident for divers years in *Oxford.*

Those meetings in *London* continued, and (after the King's Return in 1660) were increased with the accession of divers worthy and Honorable Persons: and were afterwards incorporated by the name of the *Royal Society.*[10]

For the years immediately preceding 1660, Wallis's account needs supplementing from Sprat's narrative, which gives further particulars and adds the names of those who in 1658 were active members of the London group. Sprat says that the meetings at Oxford continued until about 1658, but in that year,

those [at Oxford] being called away to several parts of the nation, and the greatest number of them coming to London, they usually met at Gresham College at the Wednesday's and Thursday's lectures of Dr. Wren and Mr. Rooke; where there joyn'd with them several eminent persons of their common acquaintance: The Lord Viscount Brouncker, the now Lord Brereton,

[10] From a letter by Wallis addressed to Dr. Thomas Smith, dated January 29, 1697; published by Thomas Hearne in his edition of *Peter Langtoft's Chronicle* (2 vols.; Oxford, 1725), "The Publisher's Appendix to His Preface," I, clxi–clxiv.

Sir Paul Neil, Mr. John Evelyn, Mr. Henshaw, Mr. Slingsby, Dr. Timothy Clark, Dr. Ent, Mr. Hall, Mr. Hill, Dr. Crone, and diverse other gentlemen, whose inclinations lay the same way. This custom was observed once, if not twice a week, in term-time; till they were scattered by the miserable distractions of that fatal year; till the continuance of their meetings there might have made them run the hazard of the fate of *Archimedes:* for then the place of their meeting was made a *quarter for soldiers.*[11]

To this evidence we must add one more document, the memorandum of the meeting of this group held on November 28, 1660, at which steps were taken to organize it as a scientific society. This memorandum reads:

These persons following, according to the usual custom of most of them, mett together at Gresham Colledge to heare Mr. Wren's lecture, viz. The Lord Brouncker, Mr. Boyle, Mr. Bruce, Sir Robert Moray, Sir Paul Neile, Dr. Wilkins, Dr. Goddard, Dr. Petty, Mr. Ball, Mr. Rooke, Mr. Wren, Mr. Hill. And after the lecture was ended, they did, according to the usual manner, withdrawe for mutuall converse. Where amongst other matters that were discoursed of, something was offered about a designe of founding a Colledge for the promoting of Physico-Mathematicall Experimentall Learning. And because they had these frequent occasions of meeting with one another, it was proposed that some course might be thought of, to improve this meeting to a more regular way of debating things, and according to the manner in other countryes, where there were voluntary associations of men in academies, for the advancement of various parts of learning, so they might doe something answerable here for the promoting of experimentall philosophy.

In order to which, it was agreed that this Company would continue their weekly meeting on Wednesday, at 3 of the clock in the tearme time, at Mr. Rooke's chamber at Gresham Colledge; in the vacation, at Mr. Ball's chamber in the Temple.[12]

Upon the accounts that I have just quoted at some length rests the case for the inception of the Royal Society at the informal gatherings of the year 1645, and also for the tracing of the Society's development from the time of those gatherings until its founding in 1660. Are these accounts inconsistent with the hypothesis that the meetings taking place in 1645 were not a new venture—that the date merely marked the accession of a few new and youthful members to a long-established coterie of scientifically-minded Englishmen? If we analyze Wallis's statements we observe that in both accounts he is not precise about the date—it was "1645, if not

[11] *History of the Royal-Society of London* (1667), p. 57.

[12] Quoted from the Journal-book, I, 1, in *The Record of the Royal Society of London,* pp. 7–8.

sooner.'' This is not surprising, since one report was written more than thirty years after the event, and the other more than fifty years afterward, when Wallis was over eighty years old. In 1645 he was a young man of twenty-nine who, after receiving his M.A. in 1640 at Emmanuel College, Cambridge, had come to London late in 1641 as chaplain to Lady Vere. Certainly Wallis nowhere claims to have had a share in launching the meetings of scientists that followed the weekly astronomy lecture at Gresham College. Instead, he apparently found the group already well established before he joined their circle, since he reports, at second hand, the conjecture that Theodore Haak, who came to England in 1625, had been the first to suggest these assemblies.[13] Naturally enough, the members of this group that Wallis, many years later, recalled and included in his partial list were those who lived on to become members of the Royal Society and take a prominent part in the activities of its early years. This, under the circumstances, was only natural. Natural enough, also, was the fact that his list, in consequence, included men who, like himself, were in 1645 still young enough to be just reaching their prime in the 1660's. Of the men he mentions, both of the London and the later Oxford group, all except Samuel

[13] The notion that Theodore Haak was the one who had originally inspired the meetings of this group has, so far as I can discover, Wallis's statement in 1697 as its only source, and Wallis there does not assert it as a fact, but merely throws it out as a supposition of his own. It may have been Haak that first introduced Wallis to the group, for Wallis at the time (1644–46) was secretary to the Westminster Assembly of Divines, and Haak was engaged in translating the Dutch annotations to the Bible for this Assembly. That Haak, for some years, had been associated with a group of English scientists and served as a link with scientists on the continent seems certain, but that he was the prime mover in the meetings at Gresham College awaits proof. See Harcourt Brown, *Scientific Organizations in Seventeenth-Century France*, chap. iii, for an account of Haak's correspondence with Mersenne, which indicates that as early as 1639–40 Haak was acting as corresponding secretary for an informal group of English scientists which definitely included John Pell and Gabriel Plattes. What the relations of these men were to the Gresham College circle could probably be determined by a detailed study of the Haak-Mersenne correspondence from this point of view, together with an examination of the Pell manuscripts in the British Museum. I have not had the opportunity to make such a study, but these points in Mr. Brown's description of the Haak material are worth noting for the clues they may give to some other investigator: 1. Haak sent Mersenne Gellibrand's book, *The Variation of the Magneticall Needle* (see pp. 348–49). 2. There is a reference in the correspondence to a Mr. Harrison and his method of making catalogues and indices. This may be the same person as the unidentified Harrison who assisted at Gellibrand's magneticall experiments described on p. 348. 3. There are references to John Greaves, who at that time was Gresham Professor of Geometry, but who was absent much of the time in foreign travel in the Near East pursuing Oriental studies.

Foster lived to become fellows of the Royal Society. Of these, all except George Ent (b. 1604) and Francis Glisson (b. 1597) were young men who were under thirty or had just reached their thirty-first year.[14]

Wallis had a special reason for including Samuel Foster while omitting all others who failed to live on into the Restoration period. Foster, a generation older than Wallis, was in 1645 professor of astronomy at Gresham College, and it was in his lodgings, after his Wednesday lecture, that the meetings of this group were customarily held.

Foster died in 1652, but the later accounts prove that the established time and place of meeting of the club, if we may call it so, were not altered. The group continued to gather each Wednesday afternoon in term-time at the astronomy lecture of Foster's successor, Lawrence Rooke, and to repair afterwards to Rooke's lodgings for their meeting. When, in 1657, Rooke transferred from the astronomy professorship to that of geometry, and was succeeded as Gresham Professor of Astronomy by the brilliant young Christopher Wren, then only twenty-five, the group met often twice a week, both after Wren's lecture, on Wednesday, and Rooke's Thursday lecture. And it was at a regular Wednesday meeting, following Wren's lecture, that the resolution was taken to establish an organized society to replace their regular, but hitherto informal gatherings.

Clearly, then, for the fifteen years from 1645 to 1660, the assembling of this group of persons interested in science centered, as if by long tradition, about Gresham College and its Professors of Astronomy, regardless of the incumbent at the moment. Moreover, a careful analysis of these basic accounts of the Royal Society's origin impels one to ask when the real inception of these

[14] For biographical discussions concerning the relations between the men cited by Wallis as members of the group in 1645, see the excellent articles by Dorothy Stimson: "Dr. Wilkins and the Royal Society," cited above; "Puritanism and the New Philosophy in 17th Century England," *Bulletin of the Institute of the History of Medicine*, III (1935), 321–34; "Comenius and the Invisible College," *Isis*, XXIII (1935), 373–88. In these articles Miss Stimson shows that most of the young men mentioned had come from colleges at Oxford and Cambridge which were strongholds of Puritanism, and that in the religious and political struggles of the times their sympathies were with the moderates among the Puritans who supported Parliament against the King but did not succumb to the violent hatreds of the period of the civil war. Her most recent article, appearing after this study was written, is "Amateurs

scientific meetings at Gresham College took place. To this question I do not pretend to be able to give a definite answer, with a specific date. Indeed, so gradual and so natural was the growth of an informal scientific group about the successive Gresham College professors that, even if we could call back the participants for questioning, they would probably disagree in their choice of the specific action that marked the beginning of their continued association. We may, however, attempt to chart a few landmarks in the evolution of collaborative scientific study in England, well aware of the multitude of details that will be lacking, leaving the resulting map tantalizingly inadequate and incomplete. But such a chart will be a rough guide for the thorough history of the antecedents of the Royal Society that may be written when English archives can again be peacefully studied by scholars. In preparing this rather crude chart, we may best turn back to the founding of Gresham College,[15] and from there proceed forward.

Sir Thomas Gresham, the famous financial adviser to Queen Elizabeth and the founder of the Royal Exchange, died in 1579. In his will, dated four years earlier, he bequeathed all the revenues from the land and buildings comprising the Royal Exchange, and also his great mansion house in Bishopsgate Street, jointly to the City of London and the Company of Mercers. In return, they were charged with supporting from the revenues of the Royal Exchange seven professors, who were to be lodged in his mansion house and there to read public lectures in their respective faculties of Law, Rhetoric, Divinity, Music, Physic, Geometry, and Astronomy. The will reserved to his wife, for so long as she should live, the use of the mansion house and all the revenues from the Exchange. Since Lady Gresham did not die until December of 1596, the City of

---

of Science in 17th Century England," *Isis*, XXXI (November, 1939), 32–47. In this article she sums up much of the material presented in the others cited above, and accepts the thesis here advanced: that the meetings mentioned by Wallis as the precursor of the Royal Society may be traced back to a period much earlier than 1645 (see pp. 36 and 40 ff.). Miss Stimson, however, does not attempt to present evidence for earlier gatherings of scientists at Gresham College, since that is not the subject of her article.

[15] The account of the founding of Gresham College is based primarily upon John Ward's preface to his *Lives of the Professors of Gresham College* (London, 1740). Ward was a professor of rhetoric at Gresham and had full access to the records of the college in producing this work, which had the official approval of Gresham College.

London and the Mercers' Company did not come into possession until 1597, and it was not until Michaelmas term of 1598 that the seven professors were installed in full possession of Gresham's mansion house, now become Gresham College, and commenced the reading of their lectures.

The opening of Gresham College was the culmination of a long effort in Elizabethan England to bring about the establishment of a permanent, endowed foundation which would offer instruction and further research in the mathematical sciences and provide a convenient rallying point for all who were concerned with promoting progress in the practical application of these sciences to useful works.   Lectureships in medicine had, early in the sixteenth century, been founded at Cambridge and Oxford,[16] and a lectureship in surgery in connection with the Royal College of Physicians had been founded by John, Baron Lumley, in 1583.   But for astronomy and geometry, the first enduring recognition came with the creation of professorships in those subjects in Sir Thomas Gresham's foundation.   Not until 1619 were the Savilian Professorships of Astronomy and Geometry established at Oxford, and the early incumbents of these Savilian Professorships were chosen from men then holding chairs at Gresham College.   For example, the first two Gresham Professors of Geometry, Henry Briggs and Peter Turner, became in turn the first two Savilian Professors of that subject, and John Greaves, the third Gresham professor, became the second Savilian Professor of Astronomy.

Since in the Gresham professorships of astronomy and geometry England received the first enduring institution dedicated to the mathematical sciences, and one which served as a rallying point for all who were interested in those subjects, it will not be out of place, before proceeding, to consider and dismiss briefly the other organizations which have been proposed as precursors of the Royal Society.   Weld mentions only three English precursors.[17]   The first is the Society of Antiquaries supposedly founded in 1572 by Archbishop Parker and dissolved by James I in 1604.   Its interests were antiquarian and philological, and its aims, though allied to the scientific movement, were not identical with it.   The second of

[16] In 1518 Thomas Linacre founded lectureships in medicine at Merton College, Oxford, and St. John's College, Cambridge.

[17] *Op. cit.,* I, 15–23.

Weld's societies was the abortive scheme of Edmund Bolton for founding a Royal Academy in England, first broached in 1617 to please the vanity of James I. As the plan developed—it was never completed, and was dropped after the death of King James—membership in the academy was to be limited to the nobility and wealthy gentry—a group composed entirely of dilettantes rather than of serious scientific workers. The third organization mentioned by Weld is worthy of more consideration than Bolton's scheme. This is Sir Francis Kynaston's *Musaeum Minervae,* a college to be erected in Covent Garden for the education of the youth of noble families. Kynaston received in 1635 a royal license for its founding, and this license names the men who were to hold its six professorships of Medicine, Languages, Astronomy, Geometry, Music, and Fencing. *The Constitutions of the Musaeum Minervae,* a rare pamphlet giving further details concerning this academy, was published in 1636. But, being designed solely for the education of noble youth adhering to the Royalist party, it died an early death amid the turmoil of the times, and left no discernible mark of its influence.

As precursors of the Royal Society none of these, except perhaps the first, can claim any real significance. The two latter contributed nothing to the advancement of science, and their real interest lies solely in their being examples of attempts to secure royal patronage for an educational institution in which scientific instruction was ostensibly to be given some place. Compared with Gresham College, which was a center of scientific activity in London from the beginning of the seventeenth century, these societies are not deserving of a moment's consideration.[18]

Of far greater import, however, was the success of John Dee, in the period beginning with the accession of Elizabeth and continuing until Dee's departure for the continent in 1583, in gathering about him a group of friends and pupils which, in effect, constituted a sort of scientific academy. Courtiers like Sir Philip Sidney and Sir Edward Dyer came to Dee's house at Mortlake to receive in-

---

[18] Another early proposal for an educational institution allotting an important place to science was Sir Humphrey Gilbert's plan, drawn up in 1572, for an *Academy* for the education of the sons of nobles and gentlemen; see MS Lansdowne 98 (1), printed in Early English Text Society, Extra Series, VIII (London, 1869), 1–12. This is not mentioned by Weld.

struction in science.[19] Lord Burghley and the Queen herself visited and consulted him. Thomas Digges, the first modern astronomer to portray an infinite, heliocentric universe with the stars scattered at varying distances throughout infinite space, was successively a ward, pupil, and intimate friend and co-worker of Dee's. Among the others who were associated with Dee and received scientific instruction and advice from him were almost all the names famous in Elizabethan exploration and discovery—Richard Chancellor, William and Stephen Borough, Martin Frobisher, Sir Humphrey Gilbert, John Davis, and Sir Walter Raleigh. Dee, through his acquaintance and correspondence with the most eminent scientists on the continent, such as Gemma Phrysius, Mercator, Ortelius, and Orontius Finaeus, kept the English group in constant touch with new ideas and discoveries originating abroad. His own library of scientific books and manuscripts, consisting in 1583 of over 4,000 volumes, was always at the disposal of Dee's fellow-scientists. Nor must one forget the great collection of scientific instruments that Dee possessed, including the huge *radius astronomicus* that he had designed in collaboration with Richard Chancellor and which Thomas Digges had doubtless used in making a set of observations on the new star of 1572 which were far more accurate than any others save Tycho Brahe's.

As a coterie of scientific workers maintaining active co-operation among themselves, providing instruction for others, and keeping in close touch with scientific activity abroad, the group centering about John Dee must be ranked as the earliest ancestor of the Royal Society to contribute significantly to its patrimony. Less important than Dee's group, yet of greater moment than the societies, actual and proposed, mentioned by Weld, is the Mathematical Lecture established in London in 1588, the year of the Spanish Armada. Whereas earlier efforts to obtain public endowment for a lecture had been unavailing, the national crisis stirred a slothful government to sudden, energetic action. On the plea that some mathematical instruction was urgently needed for the untrained officers of the militia mustered for the defense of London, the wealthy merchants of the city, inspired by Thomas Smith, later the first governor of the East India Company, were persuaded to contribute to the

[19] For a further account of the group centering about John Dee and its importance to science in sixteenth-century England, see Francis R. Johnson, *Astronomical Thought in Renaissance England* (Baltimore, 1937), pp. 134–40 and *passim*.

sum necessary to support such a lecture for two years. Thomas Hood, a Londoner and a graduate of Cambridge, was chosen as lecturer. When the two-year term expired, however, the crisis was over, and, although funds were finally raised to continue the lectures for another two years, they were abandoned thereafter.[20]

These early institutions and informal societies for the advancement of scientific learning have been described at this length because they deserve a place which they have not hitherto received in the accounts of the forerunners of the Royal Society. We now return to the Royal Society's immediate ancestry, and to the institution which contributed, far more than any other, to its ultimate development—Gresham College.

In his will, Sir Thomas Gresham had provided that the professors of his foundation should be unmarried, should occupy his mansion house and have free use of its gardens and all other appurtenances, and that each professor should receive an annual stipend of fifty pounds, a handsome salary in those days.[21] The Mercers' Company was charged with the original selection and the payment of the professors of law, physic, and rhetoric, and the Mayor and Aldermen of the City of London with the selection and payment of the professors of divinity, music, geometry, and astronomy.

Soon after the death of Lady Gresham brought this benefaction under their control, the City of London and the Mercers' Company sent out letters to Oxford and Cambridge Universities asking for the recommendation of suitable candidates for the posts that had been placed in their charge.

In the final choice of the seven original professors, the two universities were equally represented (John Bull, the first music professor, was a graduate of both). The first professor of astronomy was Edward Brerewood, an Oxford man. The first geometry professor was Henry Briggs, a graduate of St. John's College, Cambridge, and one of the ablest mathematicians of the day. His contribution to the development of logarithms is familiar to all, for it was he who saw the great practical advantage of using the number ten as a base, and devoted his energies to computing the Briggsian tables of logarithms, and to popularizing the use of logarithms throughout the scientific world.

[20] For a detailed account of Hood's Mathematical Lectureship, see Johnson, *op. cit.*, pp. 198–205.

[21] Ward, *op. cit.*, preface.

To Briggs, more than to anyone else, was due the immediate establishment of Gresham College as a meeting place of scientists and a clearing-house for scientific information. The comfortable and spacious quarters of the Gresham professors, the central location of the college in London, and the eminence of Briggs himself all contributed toward this end. Briggs was the friend and the collaborator of most of the noted scientists of his day. Thomas Blundeville, Sir Thomas Chaloner, William Barlowe, Marke Ridley, Edward Wright, and William Gilbert were among the leading English scientists with whom Briggs was associated. The relations of this group may be traced in the scientific publications of the day, and in other contemporary records.

Gilbert acknowledges help from Barlowe in the research on magnetism that was set forth in his *De Magnete*.[22] Edward Wright, whose great work was the reform of the theory of navigation and the correction of Mercator's projection,[23] contributed an important preface to Gilbert's work. Blundeville, in a work of his own published in 1602,[24] included an appendix by Gilbert, describing two magnets he had invented, and Briggs, to this appendix, contributed a table which he had calculated for the use of these magnets. Both Wright and Briggs co-operated in making Napier's invention of logarithms known to English mathematicians. Wright translated Napier's book on logarithms into English immediately,[25] and Briggs added a special preface to the work, together with a short treatise of his own on the methods of interpolation when using the tables. In this preface, Briggs mentions his teaching "the meaning and the use of this booke at Gresham house."[26]

[22] See William Barlowe, *Magneticall Aduertisements* (London, 1616), sigs N4r–N4v.

[23] *Certaine Errors in Nauigation* (London, 1599).

[24] *The Theoriques of the seuen Planets* (London, 1602). Blundeville had also, in his *Exercises* (London, 1594), published an advance notice of Wright's correction of Mercator's projection, which Wright first published in *Certaine Errors of Nauigation* (1599).

[25] *A Description of the Admirable Table of Logarithmes* (London, 1616) Napier's work first appeared in 1614.

[26] *A Description of the Admirable Table of Logarithmes,* sig. A6r. Briggs also prepared tables which were appended to Edward Wright's *Certaine Errors* in the second edition (London, 1610).

Another noted member of this group was William Bedwell, one of the most learned men of his day, the father of Arabic studies in England, and one of the Westminster Company of translators who prepared the King James version of the Bible. Bedwell was also a mathematical scholar, and published a number of mathematical works and translations, chief among these being a translation of Peter Ramus's geometry, greatly enlarged by Bedwell himself.[27] In 1601 Bedwell became rector of St. Ethelburga's in Bishopsgate Street, close by Gresham College. Thus a friendship with Briggs born of common interests, which probably had begun at Cambridge —for the two were contemporaries there[28]—was cemented and continued throughout both their lives. In 1606 Briggs sent to Mr. Clerke of Gravesend a description of a special type of ruler invented by Bedwell.[29] His correspondence was probably with the John Clerke who, in 1636, after the death of both Briggs and Bedwell, published his friend Bedwell's book, dedicating it to John Greaves, who had become professor of geometry at Gresham College in 1631, just a year before Bedwell's death. This preface indicated that Greaves's short but happy friendship with Bedwell dated from the time Greaves came from Oxford to London in 1630 to assume his duties at Gresham College.[30] Bedwell, in his own preface, mentions his friendship with Briggs, and states that Briggs had examined the work and had repeatedly urged him to publish it.[31]

Still another distinguished member of the Gresham College circle in Briggs's time, and later, was the famous mathematician William Oughtred, who made important contributions to mathematical notation and invented the rectilinear and circular slide rules. By his private teaching Oughtred greatly furthered the progress of mathematical knowledge in England, and he numbered among his pupils Seth Ward and John Wallis. Oughtred, from 1610 to his death in 1660, was rector of Albury, near Guildford in Surrey, and on each of his journeys to London visited his friends at Gresham College. In a pamphlet published in 1633, he describes a visit made in 1618:

[27] *Via Regia ad Geometriam* (London, 1636).

[28] Briggs took his B.A. in 1581 and his M.A. in 1585 at St. John's and remained as a Fellow of his college. Bedwell proceeded B.A. in 1585, M.A. 1588 at Trinity.

[29] Ward, *op. cit.*, p. 129.

[30] *Via Regia ad Geometrium,* sigs. A3^r–A4^r.

[31] *Ibid.*, author's preface.

In the Spring 1618 I being at London went to see my honoured friend Master *Henry Briggs* at Gresham Colledge: who then brought me acquainted with Master *Gunter* lately chosen Astronomie reader there, and was at that time in Doctour *Brooks* his chamber.   With whom falling into speech about his quadrant, I shewed him my Horizontall Instrument: He viewed it very heedfully: and questioned about the projecture and use thereof, often saying these words, it is a very good one.   And not long after he delivered to Master *Briggs* to be sent to me mine owne Instrument printed off from one cut in brasse: which afterwards I understood he presented to the right Honourable the Earle of Bridgewater, and in his booke of the Sector printed sixe yeares after, among other projections he setteth down this.[32]

Oughtred is writing nearly fifteen years after his visit, and gives the erroneous impression that in 1618 Gunter was already Gresham Professor of Astronomy.   It is worth noting, therefore, that Oughtred found Gunter, who was not elected professor until the following March, occupying rooms in Gresham College.

From the early years of the seventeenth century there is evidence of a close association, in scientific investigations, of the Gresham College professors and the sea captains, the shipbuilders, and the administrative officials of the English Navy.   Briggs, in 1609, served with Sir Thomas Chaloner in judging a controversy between two factions among the shipwrights over some innovations in design which Phineas Pett had introduced.[33]   John Clerke, whom we have seen as the friend and correspondent of Bedwell and Briggs, is probably the John Clerke who, in 1628, is found sharing with one John Cowper the grant of the office of Surveyor and Keeper of His Majesty's Armoury in the Tower and at East Greenwich.[34]

In 1619, just before Briggs left Gresham College to become the first Savilian Professor of Geometry at Oxford, Edmund Gunter was chosen Gresham Professor of Astronomy.   Gunter must have begun, at Brigg's instigation, the work of calculating the logarithms of the trigonometric functions even before his election, for his

[32] *The just Apologie of Wil: Oughtred, against the slaunderous insimulations of Richard Delamain, in a Pamphlet called Grammelogia, or the Mathematicall Ring* (London, 1633), sigs. B3ᵛ–B4ʳ.

[33] *The Autobiography of Phineas Pett*, ed. W. G. Perrin, Navy Records Society Publications, Vol. 51 (London, 1918), pp. lxxxii and 59 ff.

[34] *Calendar of State Papers, Domestic, Charles I*, Vol. CXIX, No. 33 (October 27, 1628).

Canon Triangulorum was published early in 1620.   After Briggs's departure for Oxford, Gunter became the central figure of the Gresham College scientific circle, and continued so until his death in December, 1626.   With Gunter, the association of Gresham College and its circle with a group of navy officials stationed at the naval base across the Thames at Deptford continued.

The key figure uniting the two groups was an able mathematician and scientist, John Wells, who, from 1606 until his death late in the year 1635, held the important office of Keeper of His Majesty's Naval Stores at Deptford.   He was a friend and fellow-worker successively of Briggs, Gunter, and, finally, Henry Gellibrand, who, in 1626, succeeded Gunter as professor of astronomy at Gresham College.   The only scientific work that Wells published was an excellent book on the construction of all sorts of dials, which was issued in 1635, shortly before Wells's death.   In his preface Wells states:

This tract of Dyalling was written for mine owne private delight and exercise, above thirteene yeeres since, as divers of my friends know: wherein I have beene the more curious, to handle every kind of Plane; not with any thought, or purpose, ever to print the same, but to keepe it by me, for satis-faction to my selfe, and friends whensoever there should be cause to use it. Yet shortly after the Worke was finished, occasion to make use of it, drew on occasion for my friends to take notice thereof: amongst the rest, my two late worthy friends, Master *Henry Briggs,* (iustly stiled by a Reverend Divine our *English Archimedes*) and Master *Edmund Gunter, Astronomie Lecturer of Gresham Colledge,* desired to peruse it; and finding that the Arithmeticall part was performed by Logarithmes of both kinds, and therefore might serve instead of uses for the Chiliads and Canon, compiled by them, did earnestly sollicite mee to print the same: but they both dying, this motion of theirs died with them.

Of late it hath beene againe revived, by the request of other Friends; but especially by the encouragement of my much respected, and learned Friend Master *Henry Gellibrand,* who hath annexed his approbation of that, which in my owne opinion I never thought worthy of so much esteeme.   I have therefore at length (yeelding to the importunitie of Friends) consented to let it passe to the publike view.   If any benefit grow from it, let him have the honour, that is the Authour of all good gifts, and let my Friends share in the thankes, that have in a manner extorted it out of my hands.[35]

[35] *Sciographia* (London, 1635), sigs. ¶5ᵛ–¶6ᵛ.

It was in tracking down John Wells, the friend and collaborator of three successive Gresham College professors, that most of the evidence concerning the activities of the Gresham College circle during the quarter-century preceding 1645 was unearthed. It will therefore be profitable to trace Wells's career briefly. Though he does not appear in the *Dictionary of National Biography,* and there is no record of his having attended either university, he was a man of considerable importance in the seventeenth century. The information concerning his career that I have been able to collect comes from the Calendar of State Papers, the histories of the British Navy, the county histories of Kent, and the references to him in the works of Gresham professors. Whether or not he came from a family long connected with naval affairs I do not know. Certain it is that his wife, Catherine Wallinger, whom he married in 1610[36] belonged to the same family as Benjamin Gonson, Sr., who was Treasurer of the English Navy from 1549 to his death in 1577, when he was succeeded by Sir John Hawkins.[37] Our first record of Wells, however, consists in the grant, on May 10, 1606, to him and Antony Lewis, jointly, of the office of Keeper of the Naval Stores at Deptford Strand, Chatham, and Portsmouth for life.[38]

In 1615 a new grant of this office was issued, this time to John Wells alone.[39] As Keeper of His Majesties Stores at the Navy

[36] See the registers for St. Nicholas Parish, Deptford, in *Hasted's History of Kent, corrected and enlarged by Henry H. Drake,* Pt. I: The Hundred of Blackheath (London, 1886), p. 40.

[37] Anthony Wood, *Athenae Oxonienses,* ed. Philip Bliss (London, 1813–17), III, 1155, under "Benjamin Wells" (the son of John Wells), gives an account of Benjamin's father, "the famous mathematician of Deptford." Wood states that John Wells married Catherine Wallinger, daughter of Thomas Wallinger, Esq., by Benedicta Gonson, his wife. Benjamin Gonson, Sr.'s mother was named Benedicta, and one of his daughters, Catherine, married Sir John Hawkins. Catherine Wallinger's mother may have been a daughter of Benjamin Gonson, Jr., the brother of Lady Hawkins. Benjamin Gonson, Jr. was twenty-six when his father died in 1577 (*Hasted's History of Kent,* p. xix). Of his other sisters, Anne married Abraham Fleming, an important writer of scientific treatises in Elizabeth's reign, and Thomazine, after the death of her first husband, Captain Edward Fenton, married Christopher Browne of Sayes Court, Deptford, and was therefore the grandmother of the wife of John Evelyn. Evelyn, who was a member of the Royal Society group at the time of the Society's founding, was from 1652 on settled at Sayes Court.

[38] *State Papers, Domestic, James I,* Vol. XXI, No. 21 (May 10, 1606).

[39] *Ibid.,* Vol. LXXX, No. 5 (January 17, 1615).

Yard at Deptford, often called East Greenwich, Wells had the use there of a fine house with a spacious garden second in size and value only to the adjacent house reserved for his immediate superior, the Treasurer of the Navy.[40] Here at Deptford Wells's associates were the high naval officers, the mariners who constantly brought back from distant lands data that would be scientifically valuable to anyone who could elicit and make use of it, and finally the naval architects from the adjacent shipyards. Among these master shipwrights would be Phineas Pett, Edward Stevens, Hugh Lydiard, and Henry Goddard, the father of the Jonathan Goddard who was one of the group mentioned by Wallis as meeting at Gresham College in 1645. Nearby, also (after 1622, at least), would be John Clerke, who has already been mentioned in connection with Briggs and Bedwell, and was Keeper of the Armoury at Greenwich.[41]

Most important, however, was the association of Wells and his naval friends with Briggs, Gunter, and Gellibrand, in turn. The State Papers carry no record of his association with Briggs, so here we must rely upon Wells's own statements. But certainly through such a man as Briggs's friend, Edward Wright, who was the foremost authority of the day on navigation, the Gresham professors would quickly be made acquainted with the navy group.[42]

In Gunter's case, however, the State Papers give ample evidence of intimate association and collaboration with Wells and his shipwright friends. Gunter, Wells, Phineas Pett, Hugh Lydiard and Edward Stevens worked out together a more accurate method of calculating the tonnage of ships, and the State Papers for the years 1626 to 1628 are filled with records of their proofs of its

[40] There is a plan of Deptford made in 1623, to which additional remarks by John Evelyn have been joined, printed in *Hasted's History of Kent,* facing p. 18. It shows the Storekeeper's house and garden in the lower left (northwest) corner, next to the Treasurer's house. Sayes Court Manor House, then owned by Evelyn's father-in-law, and later the residence of Evelyn, was diagonally across the lane from the Storekeeper's house. After John Wells's death in 1636 his son, John Wells, Jr., who had taken his B.A. at St. Alban's Hall, Oxford, in 1632, succeeded him in the office, and apparently retained the post until 1663 (see *State Papers, Domestic, Charles II,* Vol. LXXXII, No. 100 [Oct., 1663]).

[41] *State Papers, Domestic, James I,* Vol. CXXXI, No. 10 (June 4, 1622).

[42] Edward Wright died in 1615, and Briggs moved to Oxford as Savilian professor in 1619, so that the association between Gresham College and the naval authorities at Deptford was established in the early years of the seventeenth century.

superiority and of the campaign to secure its adoption.[43]

After Gunter's death in December, 1626, an equal intimacy sprang up between Wells and Gunter's successor at Gresham College, Henry Gellibrand. Gellibrand's most notable contribution to science was the proof of the secular variation of the magnetic needle—the "variation of the variation." Gellibrand, with Wells and several others, made the observations which led to the discovery of the secular variation in the garden of Wells's house at Deptford. There they repeated the observations that Wells and Gunter had made in the same place twelve years earlier, in 1622. Finding a difference of more than two degrees between his and Gunter's determination of the variation, and a difference of seven degrees between his determination and that made by William Borough in 1580, Gellibrand demonstrated that the variation near London had been gradually decreasing. But let us turn to Gellibrand's own report of his experiment, published in his pamphlet *The Variation of the Magneticall Needle* in 1635:

> Thus hitherto (according to the Tenents of all our *Magneticall* Philosophers) we have supposed the variation of all particular places to continue one and the same: So that when a Seaman shall happily returne to a place where formerly he found the same variation, he may hence conclude, he is in the same former *Longitude*. For it is the Assertion of *Mr. Dr. Gilberts. Variatio vnicuiusq; Loci constans est,* that is to say, the same place doth alwayes retaine the same variation. Neither hath this Assertion (for ought I ever heard) been questioned by any man. But most diligent magneticall observations have plainely offred violence to the same, and proved the contrary, namely that the variation is accompanied with a variation. For whereas in the year 1580 *Mr. Burrows* (a man of unquestionable abilities in the *Mathematiques*) found the variation at *Limhouse* neere *London* to be 11 gr. 15 min. or neere one point of the Compasse; In the yeare 1622 *Mr. Gunter* sometimes professor of *Astronomie* in *Gresham Colledge,* found the variation in the same place to be but 6 gr. 13 min. And my selfe this present yeare 1634 with some friends had recourse to *Diepford* (where Mr. *Gunter* had heretofore made the same observations with those of *Limehouse*) and found it not much to exceed 4 degrees.[44]

Gunter's results had been printed in his *The Description and Use of the Crosse-Staffe* (1623).[45] Gellibrand, after giving in detail

[43] *State Papers, Domestic, Charles I;* see XXVII, 67; XXIX, 7 & 10; XXXVIII, 30; XXXIX, 63; LV, 39; LVII, 42, 43, & 45; LIX, 24 & 26; LXXXVIII, 63. See also M. Oppenheim, *A History of the Administration of the Royal Navy, 1509–1660* (London, 1896), pp. 266–67.   [44] Pp. 6–7.   [45] P. 66.

Gunter's experiment to determine variation in 1622, continued:

I deny not the Artifice to be very nice and subtle, and that an error may unawares easily insinuate it selfe, which together with this great discrepance, moved some of us to be overhasty in casting an aspersion of error on *Mr. Burrows* observations, (though since upon noe just grounds) till an acquaintance of ours [marginal note: *Mr. Iohn Marr*], lately applying *Mr. Gunter's* owne Needle to the side of the Cubicall Stone of his Majesties Diall in White Hall garden, could not finde the variation so great as 6 gr. 15 min: formerly found; whereupon resolving with some friends to make an experiment hereof, we went to Diepford the last yeare 1633 the day of the Sunnes entrance into the summer Solstice, to the very same place where Mr. Gunter heretofore had made observation, and found it much lesse then five degrees; And afterwards calling into Question the Insufficiency of our Instruments, that all scruple might be quite taken away, we had recourse this presente yeare 1634 Iun. 12, stilo vet: to the same Garden of our learned and ingenuous friend *Mr. John Welles,* with a Quadrant of six foote Radius for solar Altitudes, continually rectified with great care, and a Horizontall Quadrant of two foote Radius, for the determining of the *Magneticall* Azimuthes, exactly set to the Magneticall meridian, and in paralellisme to the Horizon; (otherwise great error might ensue) with two Needles of twelue inches in length, well touch't with good Magnetts; And for the better satisfaction, took with us also the very same Needle wherewith *Mr. Gunter* made the foresaid observations, in length ten Inches; all three most accurately respecting the same Magneticall Meridian as we then proved.   And least there might arise some diversity in the variation through the touches of severall stones, I caused the one Needle first touch't by a very good Magnet, to be retouch't by another as good if not better, and the same wherewith most of our sea compasses are touch't, and yet found no difference betweene them.[46]

Gellibrand then proceeds to record and tabulate his data.   In the margin, opposite his table of "Observations made at Diepford An. 1634 Iunij 12 before Noone," Gellibrand has: *"Testibus ab sociis* D[omin]is Wells, Harrison, Marr, Butler, Hopton, Hocknell."

Who were the other men in this group participating in this experiment?   So far I have been able to discover very little about them.   John Marr was a gentleman of Greenwich, who died in 1652 or shortly before, since his will was probated in that year.[47]   He was a student of magnetism, for we find other contemporary refer-

---

[46] *The Variation of the Magneticall Needle,* p. 16.

[47] *Hasted's History of Kent,* p. 113.

ences to his expert knowledge of that subject. Captain Thomas
James, in his book recounting his voyage in 1631 in search of the
Northwest Passage, mentions, among the instruments taken on the
voyage, Gunter's Crosse-Staffe, tables calculated according to
directions given in Gunter's book *The Description and Use of the
Crosse-Staffe* (1623), a log line divided according to the method of
Snellius and approved by Gunter, and "four speciall *Needles,*
(which my good friends Master *Allen* and Master *Marre* gave mee)
of sixe inches diameter: and toucht curiously, with the best *Loade-
stone* in England."[48]

The Butler in the group was probably the Robert Butler who
in 1633 published a mathematical work entitled *The Scale of Interest, or Proportional Tables.* Hopton I am unable to identify
satisfactorily. There was a family of that name prominent in the
navy in the sixteenth century, and also there was an able mathematical writer, Arthur Hopton, who died about 1614. Wells's
friend may have been related to one of these. The other two
names have so far eluded identification.

The noted sea-captain and explorer Thomas James, whom we
have already mentioned, should be added to this group of Gellibrand's friends and collaborators. Before James left on his
famous voyage seeking the Northwest Passage, Gellibrand arranged with him to take simultaneous observations of the eclipse of
the moon on October 29, 1631, Gellibrand at Gresham College and
James wherever he might be in the northern regions of the New
World. Gellibrand added "An Appendix touching Longitude"
to James's *Strange Voyage,* in which he compared the two sets of
observations and from them calculated by a more exact mathematical method than would have otherwise been possible the precise
longitude of James's position near Hudson's Bay.

The meetings and scientific investigations of Gellibrand and
his associates at Gresham College and Deptford in the early 1630's
contributed notably to the advancement of science. Could it be
that Anthony Wood's statement[49] that Gellibrand "suffer'd con-
venticles (being himself a puritan) to be kept in his lodgings" at
Gresham was based upon a report that confused these scientific
gatherings with clandestine Puritan meetings? In view of the pre-

[48] Thomas James, *The Strange and Dangerous Voyage of Captaine Thomas
James* (London, 1633), sigs. Q1^r–Q1^v.

[49] *Athenae Oxonienses,* ed. Bliss, II, 622.

ponderantly Puritan sympathies of the members of the succeeding Gresham College group of the next decade,[50] the supposition is at least plausible. An unostentatious assembly of a small group of men known to be of the Puritan party might well be suspected of having religion rather than scientific inquiry as its aim.[51]

Wells died in 1635,[52] and Gellibrand less than two years later.[53] The State Papers contain a document dated May 22, 1636, referring a petition of one Capt. Marmaduke Neilson to a commission composed of Sir James Galloway, John Selden, Henry Gellibrand and William Oughtred, "to consider and certify whether they hold the petitioner able to perform the particulars mentioned in his petition."[54] We have already observed the long standing association of Oughtred with the professors of Gresham College and their group. The commission with Oughtred is the last record we have of Gellibrand's activities.

Wells was succeeded as Storekeeper of the Navy at Deptford by his son, John Wells, who was then twenty-four years of age.[55] The younger Wells held this office throughout the Commonwealth period,[56] although for a time he was forced to share the post with John Davies and had great difficulty collecting his salary during the troubled years.[57]

[50] See the articles by Dorothy Stimson cited above, note 14.

[51] Joseph Foster, *Alumni Oxonienses, 1500–1714* (Oxford, 1891), II, 556, notes that Gellibrand's father, Henry Gellibrand of St. Paul's Cray, Kent, proceeded B.A. from Magdalen Hall, Oxford, in 1584 and later established himself as a physician in London. An Edward Gellibrand, probably the uncle of the mathematician, proceeded B.A. at Magdalen College, Oxford, in 1573, and later became the minister of the English Church at Middleburgh, Holland, where he died in 1601.

[52] See the petition of his son, dated December 14, 1635 for the grant of the patent for his late father's post, *State Papers, Domestic, Charles I*, Vol. CCCIV, No. 10. Drake, in *Hasted's History of Kent*, notes that Wells's will is to be found in P.C.C., 68 Pile, 1636. Anthony Wood is certainly in error in stating, *Athenae Oxonienses*, ed. Bliss, III, 1155, that Wells relinquished his office to his son and retired to Bembridge in Hampshire.

[53] Gellibrand died February 9, 1636/7. See Ward, *op. cit.*, p. 83.

[54] *State Papers, Domestic, Charles I*, Vol. CCXXI, No. 75.

[55] The younger John Wells was born December 1, 1611 (see *Hasted's History of Kent*, p. 39). His petition to succeed his father in his office as Storekeeper of the Navy was granted April 5, 1636 (*State Papers, Domestic, Charles I*, Vol. CCCXVIII, No. 24.

[56] See note 40 above.

[57] See *State Papers, Domestic, Charles I*, Vol. DVII, No. 86 (May 24, 1645); Vol. DXVIII, No. 8 (February 8, 1648).

Gellibrand's successor as Gresham Professor of Astronomy was Samuel Foster, in whose rooms Wallis first became acquainted with the group which he credits with being the "first begetters" of the Royal Society. One member of this group was young Jonathan Goddard, one year junior to Wallis. Born in 1617 at East Greenwich in Kent, the son of Henry Goddard, John Wells's associate and close neighbor, Jonathan Goddard, after completing his studies at Cambridge, returned to London in 1640 to take up the practice of medicine. It is not surprising to find him, five years later, meeting with a group at Gresham College. When, in 1660, the Royal Society was established, Goddard had for five years been Gresham Professor of Physic.[58]

Foster, in 1652, was succeeded by Lawrence Rooke, and it was in Rooke's, or Wren's rooms that the group was meeting in 1658 to 1660. But Rooke, also, was from Deptford, where he was born in 1622, the year in which Gunter and Wells took observations on the magnetic variation in Wells's garden. His biographer states that after receiving his M.A. at Cambridge in 1647, he retired to his estate in Kent, but in 1650 he went to Oxford and settled in Wadham College, for the sake of Dr. Wilkins, who was then warden.[59] But Wilkins did not go from London to Oxford until 1648, so that it is entirely possible that association with Wilkins in London, at the Gresham College gatherings, may have inspired Rooke to follow him to Oxford.

With this we bring to a close our narrative of the circle of scientific enthusiasts who gravitated about the successive Gresham professors during the half-century preceding the establishing of the Royal Society. In spite of the many obvious gaps in the evidence —gaps which research in English archives should some day remove

[58] An eminent mathematician and scientist of the day who may well have met with the group at Gresham College in the 30's and 40's, was Edmund Wingate, whom Samuel Foster appointed his literary and scientific executor, and who saw many of Foster's works through the press after the latter's death in 1652.

In the 20's Wingate had been in France, as English tutor to Henrietta Maria, and had been responsible for making his friend Gunter's work, especially his slide rule, as improved by Oughtred, known to the French mathematicians. He is mentioned as the friend of many who were definitely in the Gresham College circle, including Briggs, Gunter, and Oughtred. Since he died in 1656, he would not be one whom Wallis would remember as among those who became original members of the Royal Society.

[59] Ward, *op. cit.*, p. 90.

—the outlines of the story stand out in clear relief. They picture a steady growth, from the very beginning of the seventeenth century, of association and collaboration among English scientists under the sponsorship of the Gresham professors of geometry and astronomy, and a close liaison throughout this period between the Gresham circle and prominent officials, captains, and shipbuilders of the English navy. Without formal organization, but with the stability that only a secure and permanent foundation like that of Sir Thomas Gresham could supply, this circle, ever recruiting new members as the older ones passed on, entitles the Gresham College professors and their associates to the distinction of being named the true precursors of the Royal Society.

≈§ Walter E. Houghton, Jr.

THE HISTORY OF TRADES: ITS RELATION TO SEVENTEENTH-CENTURY THOUGHT

The History of Trades has remained unexplored, and in fact forgotten, but there can be no question of its major importance in the minds of such distinguished men as Bacon and Boyle, Petty and Evelyn; and no adequate account of English science or education in the seventeenth century can afford to neglect it. The project was first sketched in *The Advancement of Learning* and then expanded in the *Parasceve* appended to the *Novum Organum;* but in this, as in other cases, there are anticipations of Bacon's thought in the previous century.

In the 1530's we notice a modification of earlier humanist education. Although virtuous action continues to be the primary end of learning, the strain of practical wisdom and the appeal to reason and experience, both implicit in the humanist position, are given greater emphasis. As a result, the observation of man and nature takes its place in a curriculum hitherto limited mainly to classical reading. This is evident in Rabelais and Vives, and makes possible the inclusion of trades as a branch of study. On rainy days, Gargantua and his tutor

went likewise to see the drawing of metals, or the casting of great ordnance; how the lapidaries did work; as also the goldsmiths and cutters of precious stones. Nor did they omit to visit the alchemists, money-coiners, upholsters, weavers, velvet-workers, watchmakers, looking-glass framers, printers, organists, and other such kind of artificers, and . . . did learn and consider the industry and invention of the trades.[1]

Two years earlier Vives had formulated a similar program in his *De Tradendis Disciplinis* (1531), where, among higher studies, he recommends the arts of cooking, clothing, building, agriculture, and navigation, "wherefore and how they were invented, pursued, developed, preserved, and how they can be applied to our use and profit."[2] In this connection, Vives recognizes an

[1] *Master Francis Rabelais, Five Books of the Lives, Heroic Deeds and Sayings of Gargantua and his Son Pantagruel,* translated into English by Sir Thomas Urquhart . . . and Peter Antony Motteux (1904), I, 73 (in bk. i, ch. 24).

[2] *Vives: On Education. A Translation of the "De Tradendis Disciplinis" by Juan Luis Vives . . .* by Foster Watson (1913), p. 208.

obstacle we shall meet again—the traditional disdain for vulgar knowledge; but learned men, he insists, must "not be ashamed to enter into shops and factories, and to ask questions from craftsmen, and to get to know about the details of their work." (*Ibid.*, 209.) And then follows a passage (*ibid.*, 210) which carries us to the threshold of the History of Trades:

How much wealth of human wisdom is brought to mankind by those who commit to writing what they have gathered on the subjects of each art from the most experienced therein! . . . By such observation in every walk of life, practical wisdom is increased to an almost incredible degree; those who make such observations should hand them down and let them serve posterity, for whom we ought to care as we do for our own sons.

This sentence shows how the study of trades "applied to use and profit" leads naturally to the description of industrial processes; but the conception of the History of Trades as an organic and systematic work is not in Vives' mind. That appears first in Bacon, and it does so because the study of mechanical arts held a central place in his program for the "reconstruction of the sciences."[3]

I

So much stress has been laid on his inductive method that we sometimes forget Bacon's reiterated claim that "the foundation of this reconstruction must be laid in natural history," though it is to be a natural history "of a new kind and gathered on a new principle."[4] As early as 1605, the outline of the subject in *The Advancement of Learning* reveals his major innovation.[5] In the past, he says, natural history has scarcely gone beyond "nature in course" or the "history of Creatures." "Nature erring or varying" and "nature altered or wrought"—the history of Marvels and the history of Arts—have been "handled so weakly and unprofit-

[3] This article makes no attempt to deal with histories of trades, except in so far as certain histories, like those of Evelyn and Petty, were written as contributions to a History of Trades. It is only that concept as an idea which the article explores.

[4] Preface to the *Magna Instauratio*, in *The Works of Francis Bacon*, ed. J. Spedding, R. L. Ellis, and D. D. Heath (1857–1859), IV, 28. *Cf.* IV, 28–29, 127, 251, 252; V, 211, 507–509. R. F. Jones, *Ancients and Moderns; a Study in the Background of the "Battle of the Books"* (1936), pp. 56–59, places the right emphasis on natural history in Bacon's thought.

[5] *Works*, III, 330–333. *Cf.* also the expanded passage in the *De Augmentis Scientiarum* (1623), in *Works*, IV, 294–299.

ably, as I am moved to note them as deficient.'' Of the latter, there have been ''some collections made of agriculture, and likewise of manual arts; but commonly with a rejection of experiments familiar and vulgar. For it is esteemed a kind of dishonour unto learning to descend to inquiry or meditation upon matters mechanical.''[6] Bacon's protest against such social fastidiousness is all the more vigorous because, of the three, the History of Nature Wrought or Mechanical is by far the most important. The paragraph which makes this claim is the central text,[7] and must be quoted in full:

> But if my judgment be of any weight, the use of History Mechanical is of all others the most radical and fundamental towards natural philosophy; such natural philosophy as shall not vanish in the fume of subtle, sublime, or delectable speculation, but such as shall be operative to the endowment and benefit of man's life: for it will not only minister and suggest for the present many ingenious practices in all trades, by a connexion and transferring of the observations of one art to the use of another, when the experiences of several mysteries shall fall under the consideration of one man's mind; but further it will give a more true and real illumination concerning causes and axioms than is hitherto attained. For like as a man's disposition is never well known till he be crossed, nor Proteus ever changed shapes till he was straitened and held fast; so the passages and variations of nature cannot appear so fully in the liberty of nature, as in the trials and vexations of art.

If we follow the implications of this passage we see how closely the History of Trades is related to Bacon's whole cast of thought. It is, for one thing, a particular instance of knowledge directed to the ''benefit of man's life'' in contrast to scholastic speculation, ''cobwebs of learning . . . of no substance or profit.''[8] And as the failure of the Schoolmen is laid to their neglect of nature and of the observations of experience (*ibid.*, III, 292), so, we may assume, the success of the mechanical arts is due to the contrary method. This is explicit in the *Novum Organum*, where the vigorous growth of these arts is contrasted with the static or degenerate state of the intellectual sciences. It is because doctrines have been torn up from their proper roots in nature that ''the sciences stand where they did'' centuries ago; ''whereas in the mechanical arts, which are founded on nature and the light of experience, we see the contrary happen, for these . . . are con-

[6] *Cf. Novum Organum*, bk. i, aphorism 120, in *Works*, IV, 106–107, where he calls such fastidiousness "childish and effeminate."

[7] *Works*, III, 332–333.

[8] *The Advancement of Learning*, in *Works*, III, 286.

tinually thriving and growing.'"[9] Elsewhere, the same contrast is used to illustrate another and related axiom of the advancement of learning, the rejection of authority. "The overmuch credit that hath been given unto authors in sciences, in making them dictators" to be followed and annotated, means that "the first author goeth furthest, and time leeseth and corrupteth." But in the "arts mechanical the first deviser comes shortest, and time addeth and perfecteth," as, for example, in artillery, sailing, and printing.[10] Finally, in the paragraph quoted above, we see that a history of these arts would be the perfect expression of Bacon's twofold desire for immediate and for future benefits—for experiments of fruit and experiments of light, production of works and discovery of laws.[11] The first of these purposes extends Vives's scheme of separate histories to a single organic project of one man's mind, since only then can the successful technique in one trade be applied to the improvement of another. The second purpose, new in Bacon,[12] and for him the more important, now seems a curious motive for a History of Trades. We, of course, associate the discovery of causes and axioms with hypothesis and laboratory experiment, but when Bacon failed to grasp the short-cut method of hypothesis and found no laboratories at hand for the collection of experimental data, he naturally turned to factories and workshops. For in his time they alone could supply conditions later reproduced in a laboratory, namely, when nature "by art and the hand of man . . . is forced out of her natural state, and squeezed and moulded." (*Ibid.*, IV, 29.) Indeed, as we shall see, even when Bacon plans a scientific college of research, some of his laboratories are workshops built on the grounds.

So important was the History of Trades in Bacon's mind that in 1608 he determined if possible to get it started himself. In July of that year we find a memorandum in his diary[13] which incidentally

[9] Part i, aphorism 74, in *Works,* IV, 74-75.

[10] *The Advancement of Learning,* in *Works,* III, 289-290.

[11] See *Works,* III, 165; IV, 17, 105.

[12] He says so himself in the *Parasceve,* in *Works,* IV, 254: "Natural History, which in its subject (as I said) is threefold, is in its use twofold. For it is used either for the sake of the knowledge of the particular things which it contains, or as the primary material of philosophy and the stuff and subject-matter of true induction. And it is this latter which is now in hand; now, I say for the first time."

[13] James Spedding, *The Letters and the Life of Francis Bacon, including all his Occasional Works* (1861-74), IV, 65-66, in the *Commentarius Solutus.*

gives a more detailed description of the scheme:

To procure an History mechanique to be compiled wth care and diligence (and to profess it that is of the experim^{ts} and observations of all Mechanicall Arts). The places or thinges to be inquyred are; first the materialls, and their quantites and proportions; Next the Instrum^{ts} and Engins requesite; then the use and adoperation of every Instrum^{t}; then the woork it self and all the processe thereof wth the tymes and seasons of doing every part thereof. Then the Errors wch may be comytted, and agayn those things wch conduce to make the woorke in more perfection. Then all observacions, Axiomes, directions. Lastly all things collaterall incid^{t} or intervenient.

But how was such a vast history to be written? The very next entry reads: "Layeng for a place to comand wytts and pennes. Westminster, Eton, Wynchester, Spec. Trinity College in Cambridg, St Jhons in Camb. Maudlin College in Oxford and bespeaking this betymes, wth ye K. my L. Archb. my L. Treasorer."[14]   If he could get himself appointed to some commanding office in one of these schools or colleges, the scheme might be set on foot. "Qu. of young schollars in ye Universities," he continues; "*It must be the postnati.*" In the meanwhile, perhaps he could start by hiring some research workers to collect materials. And at once that purpose and that notion of cooperation stir his imagination to the conception of Solomon's House: "Foundac. of a college for Inventors" with a "Library and an Inginary . . . Vaults, fornaces, Tarraces for Insolacion; woork houses of all sorts." In a word, the collocation of entries shows Bacon's mind moving from the History of Trades to a scientific college where the plan could best be realized.[15] It is therefore hardly surprising that when he wrote the *New Atlantis* in 1624, he included, along with gardens and furnaces and observatories, "brew-houses, bake-houses, and kitchens," together with shops of "divers mechanical arts . . . papers, linen, silks, tissues; dainty works of feathers of wonderful lustre; excellent dyes, and many others."[16] These are the chief laboratories of the three "mystery-men," appointed to "collect the experiments of all mechanical arts." (*Ibid.*, 164.)

Before this, however, Bacon had published his principal account of the History of Trades—in the *Parasceve,* or *Preparative*

[14] That is, Bancroft and Salisbury, the chancellors, respectively, of Oxford and Cambridge.

[15] For this interpretation I am partly indebted to Spedding's introductory remarks on p. 25.

[16] *Works,* III, 159, 161.

towards a Natural and Experimental History, affixed to the *Novum Organum* (1620). Logically, this belonged to a later section of the *Magna Instauratio,* but as he explains, it is printed now because the indispensable natural history on which all scientific progress depends is a thing of great size, requiring vast labor and expense, and the help of many people. It must therefore be started at once, and on the method herein laid down.[17] The aphorisms that follow expand the passage on natural history in *The Advancement of Learning,* insisting again that of the three kinds, "the history of Arts is of most use, because it exhibits things in motion, and leads more directly to practice"; and again protesting against ".all fineness and daintiness" which considers such work too mechanical and illiberal for gentlemen to stoop to. (*Ibid.,* 257.) After the aphorisms, Bacon prints a "Catalogue of Particular Histories by Titles," those of trades running from numbers 81 to 128, and including all those which later were written or planned during the century. And as we shall see, the later work was probably guided by Bacon's own selection of the most important (*ibid.,* 257–258):

Among the particular arts those are to be preferred which exhibit, alter, and prepare natural bodies and materials of things; such as agriculture, cookery, chemistry, dyeing; the manufacture of glass, enamel, sugar, gunpowder, artificial fires, paper, and the like. Those which consist principally in the subtle motion of the hands or instruments are of less use; such as weaving, carpentry, architecture, manufacture of mills, clocks, and the like; although these too are by no means to be neglected.

At this point we can summarize our conclusions as follows. Bacon reached his original conception of a History of Trades from two related premises: in general, from the first principle of his thought, the inductive study of nature for the use and benefit of man; and in particular, from the groundwork for such a study in a new natural history that would include and emphasize the mechanical arts. Once achieved, such a history would benefit mankind by the discovery not only of many ingenious practices in trades, but also, and primarily, of scientific causes and axioms. The project was thus bound up tightly with the Baconian program for the advancement of learning. That is why we hear no more of a History of Trades until, in the 1640's, Bacon's thought began to bear fruit.

[17] *Works,* IV, 251, 252.

II

Broadly speaking, we can see Bacon's influence, after 1640, working in two directions, each corresponding roughly with a particular group of men. On the one hand, it stimulated the growth of experimental philosophy and the formation of a cooperative group of scientists. This group was first organized as the "Invisible College" in 1645, was continued at Oxford in the 1650's, and was given formal embodiment in 1663 as the Royal Society. Because their various interests were centered in the common goal of a Baconian natural history, these men were inevitably concerned with the manual arts; and, as we shall see, one of their leaders, Robert Boyle, was already thinking in 1647 of the great History of Trades which was later undertaken by the Royal Society.

At the same time the broader implications of Bacon's thought were affecting another set of men who were primarily reformers rather than scientists in the strict sense. This group, typified and largely led by Samuel Hartlib, and including John Dury, William Petty, and John Evelyn, was thinking less about "experiments" than "improvements," less about scientific laws than the amelioration of society.[18] To some extent they found in Bacon practical suggestions for what they called "the reformation of the whole world,"[19] but their main debt is less concrete and more potent— the inspiration to apply knowledge to the immediate and practical needs of middle-class society. We have, for example, the testimony of Hartlib's friend, John Dury, in 1649, that "the advancement of learning hath been oftener and in a more public way at least mentioned in this nation of late than in former times, partly by the publication of those excellent works of the Lord Verulam."[20] And more significant, we find that the master of Hartlib's Office of Address is "to put in Practice the Lord *Verulams* Designations,

[18] It is true that Petty and Evelyn were both members of the Royal Society, and that Petty in particular worked with Boyle at Oxford on experimental anatomy. But since both thought of the History of Trades as primarily a contribution to social and commercial improvement, I place them here. The two categories are not to be taken too rigidly.

[19] *The Works of the Honourable Robert Boyle*, ed. T. Birch (1772), VI, 132, in a letter from Hartlib to Boyle, Nov. 15, 1659. *Cf.* Petty's remark, p. 363.

[20] *A Seasonable Discourse Written by Mr. J. Dury* (1649), quoted in Foster Watson, *The Beginnings of the Teaching of Modern Subjects in England* (1909), p. 230.

De Augmentis Scientiarum, amongst the Learned.''[21]

As we shall see in a moment, the designation uppermost in Hartlib's mind was the History of Trades, but not as part of a natural and experimental history. It is Bacon's secondary motive that appeals to Hartlib and his group. This general shift in emphasis from philosophy to practice, with special reference to the practice of trades, can be seen at once when we compare *Macaria* (1641) with the *New Atlantis* on which it was modelled. In Hartlib's utopia we find that Solomon's House is dedicated not to ''the knowledge of Causes, and secret motions of things,'' but to the immediate and commercial improvement of middle-class society:

> They have an house, or College of Experience, where they deliver out, yearly, such medicines as they find out by experience; and all such as shall be able to demonstrate any experiment, for the health or wealth of other men, are honourably rewarded at the publick charge.[22]

Moreover, the college is a minor element. Most of the tract is devoted to the councils of husbandry, fishing, trade by land, trade by sea, and new plantations, organized to the end that men may ''live in great plenty, prosperity, health, peace, and happiness.'' (*Ibid.*, 381.)

The same frame of mind, sympathetic to a History of Trades, can be seen also in John Dury. In *The Purpose and Platform of my Journey into Germany* (1631),[23] the main purpose is to find a basis of union among all Protestants. But in the course of his travels, Dury also planned, he says, to observe ''all Inventions, and Feats of Practise in all Sciences'':

> For Inventions and Industries, I will seeke for such chiefly as may advance learning and good manners in the Universities, Schooles, and Commonweales; next for such as may bee profitable to the health of the body, to the Preservation and Encrease of wealth by trades and mechanicall Industries, either by sea or Land; either in Peace or Warre.

That quotation shows how commercial motives combined with the influence of Bacon and Comenius to foster a reform of education

[21] *Considerations Tending to the Happy Accomplishment of Englands Reformation* (1647), p. 47; and cf. pp. 50–51.

[22] *A Description of the Famous Kingdome of Macaria* (1641), reprinted in *The Harleian Miscellany* (8vo. ed., 1808–11), IV, 382.

[23] Printed by G. H. Turnbull, *Samuel Hartlib* (1920), pp. 10–13, from Sloane MSS. (British Museum) 654, ff. 247–249. The quotation below is on p. 11.

based on the study of "things" and the introduction of scientific
and vocational training.   This is the educational theory we find
in the two works directly inspired by Hartlib—Dury's *The Reformed School* (about 1649) and Petty's *The Advice of W. P. to
Mr. S. Hartlib for the Advancement of Some Particular Parts of
Learning* (1648).   Indeed, in Petty's program we find that the
principal text-book is the History of Trades.

In this respect, the immediate background of Petty's *Advice* is
important.   Late in 1647, the year in which Hartlib spoke of his
Office of Address putting "in Practice the Lord Verulams Designations," he sent to Boyle a "design of the History of Trades,"
assuring him that it was the "meat or banquet to which I desire
to invite mainly all ingenious spirits and discerning palates at this
time"; and he appeals to Boyle for financial support, certain that
"to your sense it will be a delicacy, and the best venison that ever
I could have hunted out for you in this populous wilderness."[24]
As the final remark implies, Hartlib knew that he was turning to
a sympathetic mind, and through Boyle to his associates in the
Invisible College, who would welcome so necessary a contribution
to Bacon's natural history.   In this way, I suggest, Hartlib was
counting on the alliance of the two groups.   And by a lucky chance,
he had found a man for the job who combined both points of view.

For the actual design, the outline of the scheme sent to Boyle,
was not Hartlib's.   "The author . . . is one *Petty,* of twenty-four
years of age . . . a most rare and exact anatomist, and excelling
in all mathematical and mechanical learning"; and it is Petty who
is to write the history if and when "at least a hundred and twenty
pounds *per ann.*" can be guaranteed.   To help raise these funds
Hartlib has asked him to write out a specimen "in one trade (which
also is near done) and set down all the terms and conditions upon
which he desires that annual assistance."[25]

Petty was ideally suited for the work.   The son of a clothier
who "also did dye his owne clothes," his greatest delight as a boy
"was to be looking on the artificers,—e.g. smyths, the watchmakers,
carpenters, joyners, &c.—And at twelve yeares old could have

---

[24] *The Works of Boyle* (1772), VI, 76, 77.

[25] *Ibid.*   The actual design is quite possibly the papers for Petty's History
of Trades, Sloane MSS. (British Museum), 2903, 63 ff, which I have been unable
to see.

worked at any of these trades.'"[26]   At fifteen he went to France, "and began to play the merchant, and had so good successe that he maintained himselfe, and also educated himselfe." (*Ibid.*, 482.) Besides Latin, Greek, and French, he learned, as he says himself, "the whole body of common Arithmetick, the practicall Geometry and Astronomy conducing to Navigation, Dialing, &c. with the knowledge of severall Mathematicall Trades.'"[27]   Back in England in 1646, he took up his father's trade of clothier, and "devoted himself to the study of mechanical improvements in textile processes.'"[28]   This was the person of "admirable inventive head, and practicall parts"[29] whom Hartlib, with his keen eye for genius, discovered in 1647, and at once determined to make the historian of trades.

But at that time it was not easy to raise £120 a year.   Meanwhile, Petty might begin work on another of Hartlib's favorite schemes, the reform of education.   Already Hartlib had publicized the theories of Comenius and persuaded Milton to write his tractate; and here was a man who had actually had the very type of education desiderated by the reformers—the broad encyclopedic range, the scientific subjects, the stress on "real" as opposed to verbal learning.   Petty, however, was not an educationalist.   He was a business man, fascinated by the possibilities of applied science.   As Hartlib talked with his protégé, they must suddenly have hit on a brilliant idea.   Within the framework of a Comenian essay, why not propose a scientific college on the model of Solomon's House, with a faculty of tradesmen engaged mainly on industrial experiments—and on the writing of a History of Trades for the common benefit of scientists and artificers?   In fact, wouldn't such a history have so many values even for laymen that it would in itself be the principal text-book of the new education?   Once we gain this perspective, we see how misleading is the common notion that Petty's *Advice* is simply another contribution to Comenian

[26] John Aubrey, *Letters Written by Eminent Persons in the Seventeenth and Eighteenth Centuries* (1813), II, 481.

[27] From his will, reprinted in Lord Edmund Fitzmaurice, *The Life of Sir William Petty, 1623–1687* (1895), pp. 318–319.

[28] Lord Edmund Fitzmaurice, in the *D.N.B.* article on Petty. This makes it highly probably that the specimen of one trade which Hartlib says Petty had nearly completed in 1647 was a history of clothing. Years later he read a history of clothing to the Royal Society. See below, p. 52.

[29] Aubrey, *op. cit.*, II, 486.

education. Its main inspiration is not Comenius but Bacon—Bacon of the *New Atlantis* and of the history of mechanical arts, as his thought was modified by the more utilitarian and commercial spirit of Hartlib and Petty. But its immediate provocation, the spark that set pen to paper, was the letter to Boyle; and its primary purpose, I believe, is to persuade a wide audience to support the scheme for a History of Trades.

After two pages on the education of children in literary workhouses which should combine practical studies with the learning of a trade, we come to the heart of the essay, the erection of "a *gymnasium mechanicum* or a college of tradesmen," "for the advancement of all mechanical arts and manufactures":[30]

> From this institution we may clearly hope . . . that all trades will miraculously prosper, and new inventions would be more frequent, than new fashions of cloaths and household-stuff. Here would be the best and most effectual opportunities and means, for writing a history of trades, in pérfection and exactness; and what experiments and stuff would all those shops and operations afford to active and philosophical heads, out of which, to extract that interpretation of nature, whereof there is so little, and that so bad, as yet extant in the world?

The appeal at once to London tradesmen and Gresham College philosophers is skilfully handled; and the appeal is quite definite, for Petty is not talking utopias. "For more expedition, until such a place could be built, . . . the most convenient houses, for such a purpose, may be either bought or hired." (*Ibid.*, 146.) Beyond that there will be no further expense, since in lieu of salary, the tradesmen-fellows will have a ready market for goods produced by such famous workmen.

After the outline of institutions, that is, the literary workhouses and the new college, "we now come to speak of such books, as, being well studied and expounded in those schools, would lay a very firm foundation of learning in the scholars."

> We recommend therefore in the first place . . . the compiling of a work, whose title might justly be *Vellus Aureum sive Facultatum Lucriferarum Descriptio magna*, wherein all the practised ways of getting a subsistence, and whereby men raise their fortunes, may be at large declared. And, among these, we wish that the history of arts or manufactures might

[30] *The Advice of W. P. to Mr. Samuel Hartlib for the Advancement of Some Particular Parts of Learning* (1648), reprinted in *The Harleian Miscellany* (8vo. ed., 1808–11), VI, 146.

first be undertaken as the most pleasant and profitable of all the rest, wherein should be described the whole process of manual operations and applications of one natural thing, (which we call the elements of artificials) to another, with the necessary instruments and machines, whereby every piece of work is elaborated, and made to be what it is; unto which work bare words being not sufficient, all instruments and tools must be pictured, and colours added, when the descriptions cannot be made intelligible without them. (*Ibid.*, 152–153.)

We need not linger on Petty's exposition of "the nature, manner, and means of writing the history of trades," beyond noticing the personal reference when he says that the compiler must be a young man if he is to finish the work (Petty was twenty-five at the time). But the long list that follows of "profits and commodities" redounding to society from such a book—inserted, significantly enough, "for the better encouragement of the undertakers" (*ibid.*, 155)—is of the first importance. A few selections (*ibid.*, 155–157) will indicate the range of utility which justifies the claim he later made that the History of Trades was one of "the great pillars of the reformation of the world."[31]

All men whatsoever may hereby so look into all professions, as not to be too grossly cozened and abused in them.

Scholars, and such as love to ratiocinate, will have more and better matter to exercise their wits upon, whereas they now puzzle and tire themselves, about mere words and chimerical notions.

All men in general that have wherewithal will be venturing at our *vellus aureum,* by making of experiments: and whether thereby they thrive or no, the directions in the preface being followed, they shall nevertheless more and more discover nature.

All ingenious men, and lovers of real knowledge, have a long time begged this work, wherefore it can be no small honour to him that shall satisfy them.

A vast increase of honourable, profitable, and pleasant inventions must needs spring from the work, when one man (as the compiler thereof) may, *uno intuitu,* see and comprehend all the labour and wit of our ancestors, and be thereby able to supply the defects of one trade with the perfections of another.

There would not then be so many fustian and unworthy preachers in divinity, so many petty-foggers in the law, so many quack-salvers in physick, so many grammaticasters in country schools, and so many lazy

[31] *The Works of Boyle,* VI, 113, quoted in a letter from Hartlib to Boyle, Aug. 10, 1658.

serving-men in gentlemen's houses, when every man might learn to live otherwise in more plenty and honour; for all men, desirous to take pains, might, by this book, survey all the ways of subsistence, and chuse out of them all one that best suits with his own genius and abilities.

Boys, instead of reading hard Hebrew words in the bible (where they either trample on, or play with mysteries) or parrot-like repeating hetero-clitous nouns and verbs, might read and hear the history of faculties expounded . . . It would be more profitable to boys to spend ten or twelve years in the study of things, and of this book of faculties, than in a rabble of words.[32]

This work will be an help to eloquence, when men, by their great acquaintance with things, might find out similitudes, metaphors, allusions, and other graces of discourse in abundance.

To arithmeticians and geometricians, supplying them with matter, whereon to exercise those most excellent sciences. . . . The number of mixt mathematical arts would hereby be increased.

Divines, having so large a book of God's works, added to that of his word, may, the more clearly from them both, deduce the wisdom, power, and goodness of the Almighty.

Lastly, This history, with the comments thereupon, and the indexes, preface, and supplements thereunto belonging, would make us able, if it be at all possible, to demonstrate axioms in philosophy, the value and dignity whereof cannot be valued or computed.

Anyone familiar with the period will see in this list an extra-ordinary reflection of the 'climate of opinion'—the new philosophy, the rejection of Scholasticism, the commercial drive, the attack on grammar with the demand for a practical study of things, the sop to rhetoric in the promise of new materials for tropes,[33] the growth of applied mathematics, the apology for science as the study of God's second book, and over all, the full spirit of utilitarianism. Is it too much to say that in Bacon's conception of the History of Trades, Petty has condensed and focussed the ideals of the scientific middle-class society which was born in the Interregnum and grew up in the Restoration? And it is literally Bacon's conception, for after the last "profit," Petty concludes the essay:

[32] In *The Petty Papers,* edited by the Marquis of Lansdowne (1927), II, 45, is a document called "Three Sorts of Education, 1686." In the first curriculum, which the editor suggests is for "a successful man of the world," we find the History of Trades as a subject of study.

[33] *Cf.* Sprat in 1667, *The History of the Royal Society* (ed. 1734), pp. 413-417. Since "the *Wit* of the *Fables* and *Religions* of the *antient World* is well-nigh consumed," the new science will supply fresh imagery drawn from "a vast Number of *Natural* and *Mechanical* Things."

The next book, which we recommend, is the history of nature free; for indeed the history of trades is also an history of nature, but of nature vexed and disturbed. What we mean by this history, may be known by the Lord Verulam's most excellent specimen thereof; and, as for the particulars that it should treat on, we refer to his exact and judicious catalogue of them, at the end of his advancement of learning.[34]

III

It was at his own house in 1656, and probably on April 12th in the company of Wilkins and Jeremy Taylor, that Evelyn first met Boyle.[35] They were at once attracted to each other, and Evelyn has described how the acquaintance ripened quickly into friendship.[36] After a polite exchange of "divers letters . . . in civilities, . . . we became perfectly acquainted and had discovered our inclination of cultivating the same studies and designes, especially in ye search of natural and usefull things"; and of one thing in particular, for Evelyn continues:

my selfe then intent on collections of notes in order to an History of Trades and other mechanical furniture, which he earnestly incouraged me to proceed with: so that our intercourse of letter was now only upon y^t account, and were rather so many receipts and processes, than letters.

We are, of course, prepared for Boyle's enthusiastic support of the scheme which had been abandoned in 1648; but what had led Evelyn just at that time and independently of Boyle, to undertake the same work? On November 27, 1655, he paid a visit to "honest and learned Mr. Hartlib, a public spirited and ingenious person, who had propagated many usefull things and arts."[37] In Evelyn's notes on the conversation, there is mention only of various mechanical inventions, and the conclusion, "This gentleman was a master of innumerable curiosities and very cummunicative." Five months later Evelyn is "intent on collections of notes in order to an History of Trades." One can scarcely imagine that the loqua-

---

[34] *Ibid.*, Page 157. He means, of course, at the end of the *Novum Organum*.

[35] In 1696, Evelyn speaks [in the *Diary of John Evelyn, Esq., F.R.S.,* to which are added a Selection from his Familiar Letters, edited by Henry B. Wheatley (1879), III, 481] of meeting Boyle "almost fourty yeares since;" and (IV, 34) at his own house at Deptford. The entry for April 12, 1656 (II, 83) is the first mention of Boyle.

[36] In a letter to William Wotton, Sept. 12, 1703 (*ibid.*, IV, 35–36).

[37] *Ibid.*, II, 80.

cious Hartlib, finding Evelyn concerned at once with mechanical arts and public improvements, and possessed of a good-sized income, could have failed to mention the project of 1648 and its manifest advantages to society.   It is true, no doubt, that a work which "all ingenious men and lovers of real knowledge, have a long time begged" was already in Evelyn's mind, and would, in any case, have appealed to a man so devoted to public service and the new philosophy; but the collocation of dates makes it highly probable that some remark of Hartlib's set Evelyn going.   At any rate, Hartlib had a share in the new venture, for it is to him that Evelyn sent, in 1659, a specimen of a history of the trade of gardening, which Hartlib in turn was to send on to Boyle for further criticism.[38]

About a year after their first meeting, Evelyn reports to Boyle on his progress, in a letter so important that most of it must be quoted.[39]   Of the "trifles" which Boyle was pleased to command, he encloses only a receipt for making varnish;[40] as for the other trades,

I have omitted those of brasse, &c. because they properly belong to Etching and Ingraving: which treatise, together with five other (viz. Paynting in Oyle, in Miniature, Anealing in Glasse, Enamiling, and Marble Paper), I was once minded to publish (as a specimen of what might be further done in the rest) for the benefit of the ingenious: but I have since ben put off from that designe, not knowing whether I should do well to gratifie so barbarous an age (as I feare is approaching) with curiosities of that nature, delivered with so much integrity as I intended them: and least by it I should also disoblige some, who made those professions their living: or, at least, debase much of their esteeme by prostituting them to the vulgar.   Rather, I conceived that a true and ingenious discovery of these and the like arts, would, to better purpose, be compiled for the use of that Mathematico-Chymico-Mechanical Schoole designed by our noble friend Dʳ Wilkinson, where they might (not without an oath of secresy) be taught to those that either affected or desired any of them: and from thence, as from another Solomons house, so much of them onely made publique, as should from tyme to tyme be judged convenient by the superintendent of that Schoole, for the reputation of learning and benefit of the nation.   And upon this score, there would be a most willing contribution of what ingenious persons know of this kind, & to which I should most freely dedicate what I have."

[38] *Ibid.*, III, 261, in a letter, dated Aug. 9, 1659.

[39] *Ibid.*, III, 235, dated May 9, 1657.

[40] This was probably used by Boyle for his own history of varnish.   See p. 373.

In the first place, this letter marks the difference between Evelyn and his associates.   The superior tone of the gentleman scholar, condemned by Vives and Bacon, never appears in Hartlib or Petty, and was scorned by Boyle.[41]   In the next place, this attitude, as it combines with the aesthetic side of his nature, determines the kinds of trades which we see Evelyn willing to examine, those which are not so much manual arts as fine arts.   Finally, the letter prophesies what later became a fact, that the scheme might best be undertaken in such a scientific foundation as Dr. Wilkins was planning, that is to say, in the Royal Society, and that to such an academy, Evelyn would, as we shall see that he did, freely dedicate his own histories.[42]

After this letter we half expect the confession two years later that "in the History of Trades, I am not advanced a step"; nor are we surprised at his excuse, that he cannot support "the many subjections . . . of conversing with mechanical capricious persons."   And so the design is abandoned, with the acknowledgment of his fault "if from any expression of mine there was any room to hope for such a production, farther than by a short collection of some heads & materials, & a continual propensity of endeavouring in some particular, to encourage so noble a work, as far as I am able."[43]

But even as he was writing, circumstances were forming to give ample room for such a hope, and in less than two years his own collection of heads and materials was the basis of a fresh attempt. For in 1658 many of the Oxford virtuosi came up to London, and here we find the weekly meetings at Gresham College which were to lead directly to the Royal Society; and there, with other "eminent Persons of their common Acquaintance," they were joined by "Mr. *John Evelyn*."[44]

[41] See p. 371.

[42] "Dr. Wilkinson" is an error for "Dr. Wilkins." Obviously referring to his letter, William Wotton, at work on his life of Boyle, wrote to Evelyn in 1703 *Diary*, IV, 32): "In one of your l^res to Mr. B. you mention a Chymico-Mathematico-Mechanical Schole designed by Dr. Wilkins: what farther do you know bout it?"   To which Evelyn answered (p. 34), that at Oxford in the 1650's there was "a famous assemblage of virtuosi," where Boyle, Christopher Wren, Seth Ward, "and especially Dr. Wilkins (since Bishop of Chester): the head of Wadam Coll: . . . used to meete to promote the study of the new philosophy, which as since obtained.   It was in that Colledge where I think there was an elaboratory, and other instruments mathematical, mechanical, &c. which perhaps might e that you speake of as a schole"—that is to say, which I spoke of in that letter.

[43] *Diary*, III, 260–261, in a letter to Boyle, Aug. 9, 1659.

[44] Sprat, *History of the Royal Society*, p. 57.

IV

Both in aims and methods, as in size and range of membership, the Royal Society was nicely constituted to attack the History of Trades. Their purpose, wrote Sprat (*ibid.*, 61), is "to make faithful *Records* of all the Works of *Nature*, or *Art*"; their method is "to heap up a mixt Mass of *Experiments*," registered "as bare unfinish'd Histories." (*Ibid.*, 115.) In this Baconian way, the society would avoid the barren fruits of the old philosophers, busy with speculative opinions instead of the solid groundwork of natural history (*ibid.*, 118). It is significant that Sprat finds the sterility of ancient thought obstructing trade quite as much as natural philosophy. What help, he asks, did it ever bring to the vulgar? "What visible Benefit to any City or Country in the World? Their *Mechanicks,* and *Artificers* (for whom the true natural Philosophy should be principally intended), were so far from being assisted by those abstruse Doctrines," that learning made no contribution to "Professions and Trades." (*Ibid.*, 117–118.) All this, of course, is straight Bacon—all except the highly significant clause in the parentheses. For Bacon had said, "I care little about the mechanical arts themselves: only about those things which they contribute to the equipment of philosophy."[45] The notion that natural philosophy was principally intended for mechanics and artificers would have shocked him profoundly. That Sprat could adopt such a position so casually, and in the face of his claim that the Royal Society was the child of Bacon's thought,[46] is largely explained, I think, by a passage like the following:

Of our chief and most wealthy *Merchants* and *Citizens,* very many have assisted it with their Presence; and thereby have added the industrious punctual, and active *Genius* of Men of *Traffick,* to the quiet, sedentary, and reserv'd Temper of Men of *Learning.* They have contributed their *Labours,* they have help'd their *Correspondence;* they have employ'd their *Factors* abroad to answer their *Inquiries;* they have laid out in all Countries for *Observations;* they have bestow'd many considerable Gifts on their *Treasury* and Repository.

And he goes on to praise the recent establishment by Sir John Cutter of a lectureship in mechanics, to be read "where the *Royal Society* shall meet," the first lecture of its kind, and "the most necessary of all others."

[45] *Works,* IV, 271, at the end of the *Parasceve.*
[46] *History,* pp. 35, 144.

For this has chiefly caus'd the slow Progress of *manual Arts;* that the *Trades* themselves have never serv'd *Apprentiships,* as well as the *Tradesmen;* that they have never had any *Masters* set over them, to direct and guide their Works, or to vary and enlarge their Operations.[47]

Late in the volume a long and glowing section is devoted to "the Purpose of the *Royal Society,* and the probable Effects of *Experiments,* in respect of all the *Manual Trades."* (*Ibid.,* 378–403.)

The fact is, of course, that the Royal Society was riddled with a utilitarian and commercial spirit far beyond anything in Bacon. He was writing for the Stuart court and the learned scholars of Europe, appealing for the advancement of natural philosophy. Sprat is writing quite as much for the city and the country, giving the advancement of trade and industry an equal place with the advancement of pure science. The difference is seen with significant clarity in the famous passage on style, where the society goes on record as preferring "the Language of Artizans, Countrymen, and Merchants, before that of Wits, or Scholars." (*Ibid.,* 113.) Or, with greater relevance to our purpose, the shift in emphasis comes out in Hooke's remark that "they [the members of the Royal Society] do not wholly reject Experiments of meer *light* and *theory;* but they principally aim at such, whose Applications will *improve* and *facilitate* the present way of *Manual Arts."*[48] In short, it was primarily the acquisitive temper of the middle-class, building on the heritage of Bacon and the social reformers, that directed the virtuosi to the History of Trades.

The project was at once brought to their notice by two members already prepared with plans and methods. In the minutes for the meeting of January 16, 1661, we find the following entries:[49]

The catalogue of trades brought in by Mr. Evelyn, and that of Dr. Petty, were referred to them and Dr. Merret, to be compared, methodised, and returned to the society. . . .

Dr. Merret was requested to bring in writing that account of refining, which he had delivered in discourse this day. . . .

Mr. Evelyn was desired to bring in an history of engraving and etching: And

Dr. Petty to communicate the history of some trade at his own choice.

[47] *Ibid.,* 129–130. *Cf.* other salutes to the *"noble* and *inquisitive Genius of our Merchants"* on pp. 67, 88, 121, 407.

[48] Robert Hooke, *Micrographia* (1665), preface, quoted in Jones, *Ancients and Moderns,* p. 206.

[49] Thomas Birch, *The History of the Royal Society of London for Improving of Natural Knowledge* (1755–1757), I, 12.

Petty's catalogue, which must have been drawn up originally for Hartlib in 1647, is very likely the list of histories, modelled on Bacon, which still exists among his *mss.*[50] And I assume that Evelyn's paper, which he calls "my Circle of Mechanical Trades,"[51] is the "short collection of some heads & materials" that he mentioned to Boyle in 1659. The actual document is preserved in the Archives of the Royal Society. It consists of four pages, in Evelyn's own hand, with the title, *History of Arts Illiberal and Mechanical.* The arts are divided into eight groups, the last of which is headed "Exotick and very rare Seacrets."[52] Five months later, when Evelyn drew up a design for the library of the Royal Society, he included, of course, a section of "Books of Arts Illiberal and purely Mechanick," the working bibliography for the history, divided into sections which must correspond roughly with the grouping mentioned above: "Usefull & Vulgar, Meane, Servile, Rusticall, Female, Polite, More Liberall, Curious, Exotick, Modells & Engines belonging to them."[53]

Quickened by this initial meeting, interest in the History of Trades steadily increased. A few weeks later Petty talked to the King for "half an hour before the forty Lords, upon the philosophy of shipping, loadstones, guns, &c., feathering of arrows, vegetation of plants, the history of trades, &c., about all of which I discussed *intrépide* and I hope not contemptibly."[54] Later in the year, Cowley's *Proposition for the Advancement of Learning* outlined a philosophical college in which men were to learn "the Mysteries of all Trades, and Improvement of them; the Facture of all Merchandizes, . . . and briefly all things contained in the Catalogue of Natural Histories annexed to My Lord *Bacon's Organon.*"[55] Within the Royal Society itself the subject was constantly

[50] Printed in *The Petty Papers,* I, 203–205.

[51] *Diary,* II, 122, under Jan. 16, 1661.

[52] Since I have been unable to see the *ms.,* I have taken these facts from A. H. Church, *Evelyn's Sculptura, with the Unpublished Second Part,* ed. C. F. Bell (1906), part II, pp. i–ii; and Geoffrey Keynes, *John Evelyn; a Study in Bibliography & a Bibliography of his Writings* (1937), p. 112.

[53] Keynes, p. 18. The *ms.* is dated May 22, 1661.

[54] Quoted by Fitzmaurice, *The Life of Petty,* p. 104, from a letter to his brother John, Feb. 5, 1661.

[55] In *Abraham Cowley; the Essays and Other Prose Writings,* ed. A. B. Gough (1915), p. 34.

under discussion. In March, "Dr. Merret was to be asked for the catalogue of trades, which he took, of Mr. Evelyn's and Dr. Petty's." (Birch, *loc. cit.*, I, 19). On May 22nd, "the business of the history of trades was appointed to be discoursed of at the next meeting" (I, 24), though no discussion appears in the minutes for May 28th. A similar promise occurs in an entry for October 23rd: "Dr. Merret and Dr. Clarke were desired to bring in their account of trades at the next meeting." (I, 50.) Finally, the matter was apparently turned back to Petty, who promised on February 26, 1662, "to produce on that day fortnight his paper concerning trades." (I, 77.)

In the meanwhile various particular histories had been pianned or written. Drawing on his first-hand experience, Petty had read papers on the history of clothing, the history of dyeing, and "propositions concerning shipping."[56] Boyle had been asked "for what he knew relating to varnish," and Oldenburg was to write on "making steel and lattin plates."[57] I find no notice of Christopher Merret's account of refining, but in 1662 he translated the Italian work of Antonio Neri, *De Arte Vitraria* (1612), a book which Boyle was later to cite as a model of mechanical history.[58] Finally, Evelyn had contributed an *"Account of the making of marbled paper,"*[59] and then elaborated another of the treatises written in association with Boyle, that on etching and engraving,[60] which he published in 1662: *Sculptura; or, The History and Art of Chalcography and Engraving in Copper.*

The dedication to Boyle, at whose "reiterated instances," Evelyn says, the work was prepared, is only natural. But this is followed, unexpectedly, by "An Account of Signor Giacomo Favi,"

[56] The paper on clothing, read on Nov. 27, 1661, is reprinted by Birch, I, 55–65; that on dyeing, read on May 7, 1662 (Birch, I, 83), was published in 1667 by Sprat in *The History of the Royal Society* (ed. 1734), pp. 284–301. The material on shipping (Birch, I, 65) was presented on Nov. 27, 1661.

[57] Birch, I, 52, dated Oct. 30, 1661. It will be recalled (see p. 369) that Evelyn sent a history of varnish to Boyle in 1657. See also p. 380.

[58] *The Art of Glass wherein are shown the wayes to make and colour glass, pastes, enamels, lakes, and other curiosities, . . . translated into English, with some observations on the author,* London, 1662. For Boyle's mention of this work, see p. 380.

[59] Birch, I, 69, dated Jan. 8, 1662.

[60] See the letter quoted on p. 371.

which has nothing to do with engraving, and which seems, from Evelyn's description, to be utterly irrelevant. It is taken, he says, from a discourse of M. Sorbière's "concerning the utility of great travel and forreign voyages";[61] and translated here "because it approaches so neer to the idea which I have propos'd, and may serve as an encouragement and example to the gentlemen of our nation, who for the most part wander, and spend their time abroad, in the pursuit of those vain and lower pleasures, fruitless, and altogether intollerable."[62]   The example which Favi gives is not, however, related to the usual precepts for the *grand tour*.   On the contrary, Favi went from country to country "collecting with a most insuperable diligence all that the mechanics had invented for Agriculture, Architecture, and the fabric of all sorts of works, belonging to sports, and to cloathes, for use and for magnificence." (*Ibid.*, 248.)   Then, at the close of the sketch (p. 250), Evelyn himself draws the moral:

His intention was, as I have been credibly inform'd by one that did often converse with him (though Monsieur Sorbière is silent of it) after he had travelled over all the world (for his designe was no lesse ample) at returne into his native country, to compile, and publish a compleat Cycle and History of Trades, with whatsoever else he should judge of use and benefit to mankind: but this had been a charity and a blessing too great for the world, because it do's not depart from its vices and impertinences, and cherish such persons, and the virtues which should render it worthy of them.

This explains why Favi's life approached the idea which Evelyn had proposed, and why it is prefixed to the *Sculptura*. For the published volume is plainly intended to call the "gentlemen of our nation" to similar contributions toward a complete cycle of trades. And not merely gentlemen. At the end of the book, Evelyn inserted an important note. He had intended, he says, to add a translation of M. du Bosse's treatise on the rolling press, but had desisted when he heard that William Faithorn, the engraver, was planning to translate the same work. Given this occasion, Evelyn concludes:

[61] Samuel de Sorbière (1615–1670), *Lettres et Discours sur Diverses Matières Curieuses* (Paris, 1660), lettre lxxxiii, p. 644.

[62] The dedication, in *The Miscellaneous Writings of John Evelyn,* ed. William Upcott (1825), p. 246.

could wish, with all my heart, that more of our workmen would (in imitation of his laudable example) impart to us what they know of their several trades and manufactures. . . . For what could so much conduce to their profit and emolument? when their several mysteries being subjected to the most accurate inspection and examen of the more polite and enquiring spirits, they should return to their Authors again so greatly refin'd and improved,[63] and when (through this means also) Philosophy her self might hope to attain so considerable a progress towards her ultimate perfection.[64]

One feels here, and still more in the previous passage, that Evelyn is somewhat discouraged. Neither gentlemen nor workmen had apparently backed the History of Trades with the vigor he desired. The activity cited above was largely confined, we notice, to the old guard—that is, to Petty, Boyle, and Evelyn himself. The project had not yet caught on, as it did later after 1664. This accounts for Evelyn's discouragement in 1662, and provides a further explanation of his earnest appeal to gentlemen and workmen.[64a]

He himself continued his efforts, developing the early specimen sent to Hartlib on the trade of gardening[65] into his largest work, published in 1664:

Sylva, or a Discourse of Forest-Trees, and the Propagation of Timber in his Majesties Dominions. By J. E. Esq. As it was deliver'd in the Royal Society the XVth of October, MDCLXII; . . . to which is annexed Pomona, or an Appendix concerning Fruit Trees in relation to Cider, the making and severall wayes of ordering it. Published by express order of the Royal Society. Also Kalendarium Hortense, or the Gard'ners Almanac, directing what he is to do monethly throughout the year.

[63] *Cf.* Sprat's remark quoted on p. 370.

[64] *Miscellaneous Writings*, pp. 335–336. We notice that Evelyn, in contrast to Bacon, and in harmony with the Royal Society, sees the scientific value of mechanical history as subordinate to its commercial value. His translation of du Bosse was published as part II in C. F. Bell's edition of *Sculptura* (1906).

[64a] In this connection we have the evidence of the anonymous translator of Guido Pancirollus, *The History of Many Memorable Things Lost* (1715), appendix, p. 431, where he finds that the attempts of the virtuosi "to look into our Manufactures, Country-Business, and common Shop-Trades" to make them "more easy and gainful" were "met at first with no small Discouragements, even from the Mechanicks themselves."

[65] See p. 368.

If this hardly seems part of the History of Trades, we need only refer back to Bacon's catalogue, "History of Agriculture, Pasturage, Culture of Woods, &c.; History of Gardening."[66] And in any case Evelyn himself wrote to Wotton in 1703 that "what I gathered of this nature [the collections made with Boyle toward "a History of Trades"], and especially for the improvement of planting and gardening; my *Sylva* and what else I published on that subject, being but part of that work, . . . would astonish you, did you see the bundles and packets."[67] Among these bundles and packets were certainly the four treatises mentioned earlier on "Paynting in Oyle, in Miniature, Anealing in Glasse, Enamiling," as well as his *Panificium, or the Several Manners of Making Bread in France,* read to the society on March 1, 1665.[68] Nor does this exhaust Evelyn's contribution, for we must add also, I think, another of his principal works, *A Parallel of the Ancient Architecture with the Modern,* translated from the French of Roland Fréart (1664). This is primarily a critical essay on architecture as a fine art, but the title-page insists that it was "made English for the benefit of builders"—a purpose emphasized by Evelyn's glossary of technical terms which he says is intended even for "the capacities of the most vulgar understandings."[69] Moreover, he connects the *Parallel* directly with *Sylva:* "After I had (by the commands of the Royal Society) endeavour'd the Improvement of Timber and the Planting of Trees, I have advanced to that of Building, as its proper and natural consequent." (*Ibid.,* 339.)

As long ago as 1755, an anonymous biographer claimed that Evelyn's "great work was to have been intitled, 'A general History of all Trades'."[70] No proof was given, and none exists today to warrant the remark as a statement of fact. And yet, when we look back over all the evidence assembled and remember in particular the eulogy of Favi, we see that as a piece of criticism the remark is penetrating. For it indicates the neglected truth that

[66] *Works,* IV, 270.

[67] *Diary,* IV, 34. This follows the quotation given on p. 368.

[68] Birch, II, 19. It was published in John Houghton, *A Collection of Letters for the Improvement of Husbandry and Trade,* no. xii, Jan. 16, 1683. This would come under Bacon's entry in the catalogue of trades (*Works,* IV, 269) for a "History of Baking, and the Making of Bread."

[69] In *The Miscellaneous Writings,* p. 353.

[70] In the second edition of *Sculptura,* p. xxxi.

much of Evelyn's endless and apparently random virtuosity was directed towards a single goal.

We have now seen, as prophesied, that Evelyn's choice of trades falls under the "polite" or "more Liberall" categories.[71] After 1664, however, when the formation of a committee for "Histories of Trade" stimulated fresh interest, the trend was more and more toward the "Usefull & Vulgar." A catalogue was finally drawn up, and in December the members were invited to choose such trades "as they would give the history of."[72] By 1667, when Sprat reviewed the progress, plans of vast scope had been formed and considerable work accomplished:

> They have propounded the composing a *Catalogue* of all *Trades, Works,* and *Manufactures,* wherein Men are employ'd; in order to the collecting each of their Histories, by taking notice of all the physical Receipts or Secrets, the Instruments, Tools, and Engines, the manual Operations or Slights, the Cheats and ill Practices, the Goodness, Baseness, and different *Value* of Materials, and whatever else belongs to the Operations of all *Trades.*[73]

The following paragraphs refer to plans already under way for the *"Manufacture of Tapestry;* the improving of *Silk-making:* the propagating of *Saffron:* the melting of *Lead-Oar* with Pitcoal"; the study of soils and clays "for the better making of *Bricks* and *Tiles"*; and the culture of potatoes. And this list is later expanded by another which includes the histories of iron-making, tinneries and tin-working, lead, saltpeter, brass, varnish, cloth, leather, marble paper, hats, bread, and a host of others. (*Ibid.,* 258.) After sample specimens, one of which is Petty's *Apparatus to the History of the Common Practices of Dying* (*ibid.,* 284–301), Sprat closes with a glowing prophecy (*ibid.,* 310):

They have assured grounds of *confidence,* that when this attempt shall be compleated, it will be found to bring innumerable benefits to all practical *Arts:* When all the secrets of *Manufactures* shall be discover'd, their *Materials* describ'd, their *Instruments* figur'd, their *Products* represented: It will soon be determin'd, how far they themselves may be promoted, and

[71] In his design for a library, p. 372.

[72] Birch, I, 407, for the creation of the committee on March 30, 1664. It included Boyle, Evelyn, Merret, and Petty. On June 8th, Merret was made chairman (I, 439) and fortnightly meetings were arranged. At the Dec. 7th meeting (I, 502, where the quotation appears), Seth Ward said he had seen a printed catalogue of trades, but if this is not Bacon's, I have found no trace of it.

[73] Sprat, *History of the Royal Society,* p. 190.

what new consequences may thence be educ'd. . . . In short, by this help the worst *Artificers* will be well instructed, by considering the *Methods,* and *Tools* of the best: And the greatest *Inventors* will be exceedingly inlighten'd; because they will have in their view the labours of many men, many places, and many times, wherewith to compare their own.

V

Ever since 1647 Robert Boyle had been offering encouragement and suggestions to others; in 1671 he spoke out himself. The quickened interest of the years from 1664 to 1667 had again died down; the scattered and desultory work of the virtuosi needed more concentration, firmer conviction, fresh stimulus. Ignoring catalogues and specific plans, Boyle wrote the finest apology we have for the History of Trades as an idea, gathering up into a rounded essay the full range of its meaning for his time. Because he was a scientist, and Bacon's greatest disciple, he reaffirmed its highest function, long subordinated, even in the Royal Society, to considerations of trade and industry:

For I look upon a good history of trades, as one of the best means to give experimental learning both growth and fertility, and like to prove to natural philosophy what a rich compost is to trees, which it mightily helps, both to grow fair and strong, and to bear much fruit.[74]

But because he was defending science in an age of commercial expansion, Boyle looked also to its immediate practical application:

I have often wished, that some ingenious friends to experimental philosophy would take the pains to enquire into the mysteries, and other practices of trades, and give us an account, some of one trade, and some of another, . . . towards the melioration of the professions they write of.   (*Ibid.*)

Balancing these values in complementary sections, he composed his essay, *That the Goods of Mankind may be much increased by the Naturalist's Insight into Trades.*[75]

As we might expect, the first section on the contribution of trades to a natural history, is little more than an elaboration of Bacon's pregnant suggestions. Quite possibly with Evelyn in mind, Boyle reproves the childish disdain of learned men to converse with "illiterate mechanicks" in their workhouses and

---

[74] *Works,* III, 449.   I give the title of the tract just below in the text.

[75] Essay IV in *Some Considerations Touching the Usefulness of Experimental Natural Philosophy* . . . *The Second Tome* (1671), in *Works,* III, 442–456.

shops.[76] For it is there that we find "nature in motion, and that, too, when she is (as it were) put out of her course"—Bacon's "nature wrought or altered"—and consequently most instructive. (*Ibid.*, 443.) Because by 1670 such conditions could often be reproduced in laboratories, largely non-existent in Bacon's time, Boyle does not argue that factories alone could supply mechanical data. Instead, by contrasting tradesmen in their shops with the virtuosi in their laboratories, he brings out the continued importance of the former for the advancement of science. For one thing, they are more diligent than other "experimenters" since their livelihood is at stake; and if their observations are less accurate than those of learned men, "that defect is recompensed by their being more frequently repeated, and more assiduously made, than most of the experiments, wherein men of letters have furnished natural history." Or again, want of tools and accommodation will often force a craftsman to discover "new uses and applications of things," otherwise hardly found out by "even a knowing man." And finally, workshops contain many things "unknown to classical writers"—Boyle himself has learned more about stones from "two or three masons, and stone-cutters, than ever I did from *Pliny,* or *Aristotle* and his commentators." In fact, their very ignorance of books and the theories of the schools, makes tradesmen examine "the things they deal with, by mechanical ways,"—ways that seem extravagant to a "bookman," but prove true and useful to the scientist.[77]

In these last remarks we notice an attitude familiar enough today, but one which was just emerging in the middle of the seventeenth century, the disdain of the scientist for the "bookman." It is the extreme form of a general tendency of thought. The attack on pedantry in Montaigne and such English disciples as Feltham, Osborne, and Locke, leads to the subordination of reading to observation of the social world. In Comenius and his followers, the study of things, the phenomena of nature and crafts, is opposed to the long discipline in grammar and rhetoric. But the extreme position is found among the Baconians, with their passion for empirical knowledge. Petty boasted to Aubrey that he had read little since he was twenty-five, for "had he read much, as some men have, he had not known so much as he does, nor should he have

---

[76] *Ibid.*, 442, 443. For Evelyn's attitude, see p. 368f.
[77] All quotations are on pp. 443–444, *op. cit.*

made such discoveries and improvements.''[78] It is this conviction which makes him claim, in the *Advice to Hartlib*, that a man educated in the Gymnasium Mechanicum ''would certainly prove a greater scholar than the walking libraries so called, although he could neither write nor read.''[79] It is a kind of scientific primitivism. And Boyle shares this view to an unexpected extent. Speaking of his studies in anatomy with Petty, ''I have seen,'' he says, ''especially in the dissections of fishes, more of the variety and contrivances of nature . . . than all the books I ever read in my life could give me convincing notions of.''[80] Or, in another field, the writing of meditations, he finds a great difference between ''him that but takes up instructions in books of morality and devotion, and him that by occasional reflections derives them from the book of nature.''[81] It is not surprising that Evelyn found Boyle's library to be small, ''as learning more from men, real experiments, & in his laboratory (which was ample and well furnished), than from books.''[82] And sometimes, as we have just seen, the men were workmen, and the laboratory, their shops. In short, to people like Petty and Boyle, strongly suspicious of traditional knowledge, even to the point of actual distaste for reading, the direct study of manual arts took on special validity and special appeal.

We need not pause on Boyle's arguments in section two. Starting again from Bacon, he illustrates how practices in one trade may be applied by analogy to the improvement of another—if and when a group of scientists will set themselves methodically to a collection of mechanical histories. By way of example, he refers the reader to a specimen of his own, a history of the trade of varnish; mentions Italian accounts of particular professions which, like Merret's translation of *De Arte Vetraria*, should be made English; and begs all the virtuosi of our country ''not to disdain to contribute their observations to the history of trades.''[83] And

[78] *Letters Written by Eminent Persons* (1813), II, 486.

[79] In *The Harleian Miscellany*, VI, 146–147.

[80] *Works*, VI, 55, in an undated letter to Clodius, Hartlib's son-in-law.

[81] *Occasional Reflections upon Several Subjects* (1665), in *Works*, II, 340.

[82] *Diary*, III, 485, in a letter to Wotton, Mar. 30, 1696.

[83] *Works*, III, 449. See p. 373 and p. 358 for Boyle's earlier interest in the history of varnish. He promises to give this specimen ''at the close of this essay,'' but I cannot find it there or anywhere else.

then, to emphasize its importance, Boyle inserts a sentence of auto-biography (*ibid.*, 450) which throws further light on his activities before the Restoration:

I once designed, if the publick calamities of my country had not hindered, to bind several ingenious lads apprentices to several trades, that I might the better, by their means, both have such observations made as I should direct, and receive the better historical accounts of their professions, when they should be masters of them.

And so, like Bacon's and Petty's and Evelyn's, Boyle's design was never achieved, and the History of Trades remains unwritten. Its scope was too vast; its promoters were virtuosi, men of a thousand interests, unfitted for the prolonged concentration demanded; its contribution to science was no longer needed when laboratories increased in number and efficiency, and when the method of hypothesis supplanted the mere collection of experimental data. It remains, however, of real historical importance. For almost a hundred years the History of Trades was an idea closely associated with the progress of science, education, and society. And without recognizing its influence, we cannot fully appreciate the work of Bacon and the Royal Society, of Petty, Evelyn, and Boyle.[84]

[84] Since this paper was written, Francis R. Johnson's "Gresham College: Precursor of the Royal Society," pp. 328–352 (originally published in *Journal of the History of Ideas*), definitely shows that long before the "Invisible College" of 1645, a cooperative group of scientists was centered at Gresham College. My statement, therefore, on p. 368, needs qualification; but my claim that Bacon's influence first became active about that time is unaffected by Mr. Johnson's evidence, since the men he discusses were apparently indifferent to Bacon's work.

BACON'S MAN OF SCIENCE

The dominating motive of Bacon's intellectual life was the complete reformation of learning, and he labored under the conviction that he was, almost single-handed, promoting a revolution in knowledge to the end that man might win a new empire over things. In those of his writings which he regarded as the parts of his grandiose plan, he gave frequent expression to his new conception of the proper goals of human knowledge and proposed new methods by which they were to be attained. And clearly implicit in this new approach to learning was an alteration in the conception of the learned man. Since the new aim and the method were to make unprecedented demands on the knower, it became necessary for Bacon to conceive a new scientist as well as a new science. This is not immediately apparent because it was to the development of his aims and methods that Bacon gave primary attention in his writings. Incomplete as his system remains, the outlines of his plan are clear and explicit, and portions are developed in detail; but the details of his picture of the new man of science are scattered, and the image has to be pieced together. From the writings of such later men as the early members of the Royal Society, for whom Bacon was a patron saint, the common elements of an image of the new scientist are clearly discernible; but though it was largely from Bacon that they caught the lineaments of the ideal which inspired them, the later portrait appears generalized and simplified when compared to the original. Every detail of the character of Bacon's new scientist is rooted in the goals which he set up and the methods he proposed. All of Bacon's objection to the learning of the past, all his hopes for the future, and all his philosophical aims are reflected in the image which he seems to have clearly visualized of the new scientist who was to be the instrument of the new learning as well as its product.

The intellectual, psychological and ethical qualities which Bacon demanded of his new scientist form an organic concept, but it is possible to distinguish certain qualities which are associated very closely with the requirements of the method and certain others which are necessarily bound up with the proper aims of learning and the rôle which they impose on the scientist. The immediate purpose of Bacon's methodological principles was nothing less than truth and certainty, and the goal he proposed was nothing less than the profound improvement of man's lot. The spirit and tone of his writings is therefore strongly optimistic. But Bacon did not ground his hopes on any extravagant estimate of man's powers. The hard realism of his mind, so clearly manifested in his comments on worldly affairs, is also revealed in his adoption of a very critical attitude toward the limited capacities by means of which man perceives and comes to a knowledge of his universe. Bacon's method, therefore, is founded on a review not only of the errors and defects in learning but of the deficiencies of the knower. If the past was to be swept aside, the mind wiped clear, and a new way charted, the positive program could begin only after all established illusions about man himself had been anatomized and taken into account.

For a rigorous critique of the failings in man which stood in the way of attaining certainty Bacon had not far to seek. The Sceptics of antiquity had systematically analyzed the defects in man's capacity to perceive and judge of reality, and had concluded on the basis of this analysis that nothing can be known. Strengthened by new illustrations and revitalized by literary embellishment, notably in the writings of Montaigne, this ancient school enjoyed a vigorous revival during the sixteenth century. But neither in motives nor conclusions were the ancient Sceptics or the new essentially akin to Bacon. Bacon—like others among the philosophers of the new developments in natural science—found the sceptical critique of man powerfully stimulating; moreover, he recognized it as something to be acknowledged and met before a way to truth could be recommended. Bacon's awareness of the force of the sceptical arguments is everywhere apparent, but it is in the famous discussion of the Idols in *Novum Organum* (I, xxxviii–lxviii) that the influence is most direct. Incorporated into a novel analysis and surrounded by many important original extensions can be discovered all of the sceptical "modes." The sceptical deductions and conclusions are, however, missing. Bacon simultaneously accepted scepticism as a critique and rejected it as a philosophy of knowledge: he represented himself as one who maintained not that nothing can be known, but that nothing can be known except in a certain way.

This way—the new method—was thus to provide correctives for the limitations of the knower. The critique of the Sceptics Bacon acknowledged, but despair in consequence of it he regarded as merely the result of neglecting the aid available: " The doctrine of those who have denied that certainty could be attained at all, has some agreement with my way of proceeding at the first setting out; but they end in being infinitely separated and opposed. For the holders of that doctrine assert simply that nothing can be known; I also assert that not much can be known in nature by the way which is now in use. But then they go on to destroy the authority of the senses and understanding; whereas I proceed to devise and supply helps for the same." [1] Scepticism becomes therefore not a philosophy of knowledge but a principle of method: "that which I meditate and propound is not *Acatalepsia* but *Eucatalepsia;* not the denial of the capacity to understand, but provision for understanding truly." [2]

For the defects of the senses Bacon proposed as correctives the use of instruments and, most important of all, experiments. The correction of the defects of the understanding, however, demanded more subtle forms of control. Scepticism as a method called for calmness of spirit equal to the demands of systematic doubt—of unwillingness to assent or deny prematurely. But this was an attitude very different from the *ataraxia* and *epoche* of the ancient Sceptics, which it resembles superficially, just as it had little in common with the ultimate triumph over passion of the Stoics.[3] And it was necessarily opposed to the dogmatism of the system-builders and to the agitation encouraged by the disputatious methods of the schools. Bacon described it as an attitude that mediated between the extremes of dogmatism and scepticism, "between the presumption of pronouncing on everything and the despair of comprehending anything." [4] And its ultimate destination was truth: "Another error is an impatience of doubt, and haste to assertion without due and mature suspension of judgment . . . if a man will begin with certainties, he shall end in doubts; but if he will be content to begin with doubts, he shall end in certainties." [5]

This restraint of the intellect—the chronic doubt and suspension of mind which were the necessary temperamental consequences of scepticism used as method—failed to meet the sceptical argument that certainty was unattainable because life was short and art was long, the depth of nature profound and infinite, and the span of man's life finite and subject to the cycles of time. Bacon understood the discouraging potency of these arguments: "But by far the greatest obstacle to the progress of science and to the undertaking of new tasks and provinces therein, is found in this—that men despair and think things impossible. For wise and serious men are wont in these matters to be altogether distrustful; considering with themselves the obscurity of nature, the shortness of life, the deceitfulness of the senses, the

---

[1] *Novum Organum*, I, xxxvii, in *The Works of Francis Bacon*, edited by Ellis, Spedding, and Heath (Boston, 1860–1864), Vol. VIII. All references to Bacon's writings will be to this edition.   [2] *Novum Organum*, I, cxxvi.

[3] On Bacon's attitude toward the ancient philosophic sects see F. H. Anderson, *The Philosophy of Francis Bacon* (Chicago, 1948), especially chapters X, XI, XII.

[4] Preface to *Novum Organum, Works*, VIII, 59.

[5] *Advancement of Learning, Works*, VI, 133.

weakness of the judgment, the difficulty of experiment and the like; and so supposing that in the revolution of time and of the ages of the world the sciences have ebbs and flows; that at one season they grow and flourish, at another wither and decay, yet in such sort that when they have reached a certain point and condition they can advance no further."[6] Bacon's answer to this melancholy wisdom of the ages was to substitute for it a radical, progressive attitude toward truth and knowledge. One error in the old sceptical view lay in approaching the problem of knowledge in terms of the limits of a single life and to despair because the goal was so clearly out of reach. Bacon was indifferent to this despair because he placed certainty as the limit toward which a properly organized search for knowledge continuously moved. " I propose," he wrote in the Preface to *Novum Organum,* " to establish progressive stages of certainty." The fullness of knowledge lay in the fullness of time, and time was generative in a progressive way: " let great authors have their due, as time which is the author of authors be not deprived of his due, which is further and further to discover truth."[7] For Bacon, " truth is the daughter of time."[8] Truth will therefore appear impossible only when viewed from the conventional perspective as something to be encompassed by individual men through the exercise of their powers of understanding: " touching impossibility, I take those things are to be held possible which may be done by some persons, though not by everyone; and which may be done by many, though not by any one; and which may be done in succession of ages, though not within the hourglass of one man's life; and which may be done by public designation, though not by private endeavour."[9] Thus while granting a premise that traditionally led to despair, Bacon's progressive view of knowledge encouraged an optimistic outlook in the scientist, not only because the new method promised accelerating results but because fulfilment was continuous. Bacon sometimes seems naïve in his hopes that through collaborative effort on the right principles a complete history of nature might be a finite task whose end could be foreseen, but it is difficult to determine at times whether the source of his enthusiasm lies there or in the possibility of continuous progress: " There is therefore much

---

[6] *Novum Organum,* I, xcii. Also *Advancement, Works,* VI, 93 and *Valerius Terminus of the interpretation of nature, Works,* VI, 41, 47.

[7] *Advancement, Works,* VI, 129.

[8] *Novum Organum,* I, lxxxiv. Bacon said of his own contributions to knowledge, " I am wont for my own part to regard this work as a child of time rather than of wit." (*Magna Instauratio, Works,* VIII, 25. See also *Novum Organum,* I, lxxviii.)

[9] *Advancement, Works,* VI, 182. See also *Valerius Terminus, Works,* VI, 47.

ground for hoping that there are still laid up in the womb of nature many secrets of excellent use, having no affinity or parallelism with anything that is now known, but lying entirely out of the beat of the imagination, which have not yet been found. They too no doubt will some time or other, in the course and revolution of many ages, come to light of themselves, just as the others did; only by the method which we are now treating they can be speedily and suddenly and simultaneously presented and anticipated." [10]

In this progressive view of the problem of knowledge and certainty there was, moreover, a further consequence for the character of the Baconian scientist more profound than chronic optimism. For him there could never be the gratification of bringing all truth into a single order through the strength of the intellect. This, Bacon insisted, was an illusion of the dogmatist, who, out of arrogant pride in the operation of his intellect, substituted the patterns of his mind mistakenly for the complexities of the universe. [11] Real confidence and hope lay only in the realization that the true goal was distant and that it required not one man but many, not one lifetime but generations of men working with a common purpose. [12] In the optimism which grew out of a progressive and collective view of knowledge and truth the Baconian scientist buried his pride.

This subduing of the pride of intellect has a direct bearing on Bacon's views concerning the proper end of knowledge. The failure of learning, Bacon maintained, had resulted from "the mistaking or misplacing of the last or furthest end of knowledge," [13] and the hope for the future of learning lay in the realization of its proper goal: "It is not possible to run a course aright when the goal itself has not been rightly placed. Now the true and lawful goal of the sciences is none other than this: that human life be endowed with new discoveries and powers." [14] If knowledge was to dedicate itself to "the

[10] *Novum Organum*, I, cix; see also cxxix. This progressive aspect of Bacon's view of knowledge seems particularly to have fascinated the English writers on science of a later generation. Their enthusiasm seems often to arise not so much from the expectation, also voiced by Bacon, that the new science would bring in a speedy harvest, as that it gave promise of infinite progress in the effective exploration of an infinite complexity. Glanvill wrote in *Plus ultra* (1668), 7: "They [the Royal Society] believe, there is an inexhaustible variety of treasure which Providence hath lodged in things, that to the world's end will afford fresh discoveries, and suffice to reward the ingenious industry and researches of those that look into the works of God, and go down to see his wonders in the deep."

[11] *Advancement, Works*, VI, 132. See also *Novum Organum*, I, x, xxiv, cxii.

[12] *Novum Organum*, I, cxiii.

[13] *Advancement, Works*, VI, 134. See also *Valerius Terminus, Works*, VI, 34.

[14] *Novum Organum*, I, lxxxi.

glory of the Creator and the relief of man's estate," [15] it must be directed toward a deep understanding of the behavior of nature and the application of this knowledge to the systematic development and improvement of the arts. The difference between civilization and barbarism, Bacon maintained—replying at the same time to various old and current theories—" comes not from the soil, not from climate, not from race, but from the arts." And " the empire of man over things depends wholly on the arts and sciences. For we cannot command nature except by obeying her." [16]

In the light of this aim, many conventional and apparently normal motives to study lose their importance for Bacon and in effect become base or misleading: " For men have entered into a desire of learning and knowledge, sometimes upon a natural curiosity and inquisitive appetite; sometimes to entertain their minds with variety and delight; sometimes for ornament and reputation; and sometimes to enable them to victory of wit and contradiction; and most times for lucre and profession; and seldom sincerely to give a true account of their gift of reason, to the benefit and use of men." [17] Some of these common and traditionally admired motives may be, Bacon conceded, " more worthy than others "; they are nevertheless " all inferior and degenerate." [18] Moreover, their setting aside involves a radical departure from traditional standards for the character and conduct of a learned man. The traditional ideal of contemplation as the perfect activity and final good of rational man is abandoned—and so apparently must be its modern analogue, disinterested curiosity. Bacon's scientist is disinterested only in preferring the common good to private good, and Bacon finds it necessary to reject the Aristotelian and scholastic ideal of the contemplative life: " It [the common good] decides the question touching the preferment of the contemplative or active life and decides it against Aristotle. For all the reasons which he brings for the contemplative respect private good, and the pleasure and dignity of a man's self; in which respects no question the contemplative life has the pre-eminence . . . . But men must know that in this theatre of man's life it is reserved only for God and the Angels to be lookers on." [19] The contemplative ideal, by exalting the " pleas-

---

[15] *Advancement, Works*, VI, 134.

[16] *Novum Organum*, I, cxxix. This idea is aphoristically stated in the special vocabulary of Bacon's philosophy of nature in *Novum Organum*, II, i.

[17] *Advancement, Works*, VI, 134.   [18] *Valerius Terminus, Works*, VI, 34.

[19] *De Augmentis Scientiarum* (Bk. VII, ch. I), *Works*, IX, 197–98. See also *Novum Organum*, I, cxxiv.

ure and dignity of a man's self," perverts the end of learning by depriving it of its power.   Only a change in emphasis can restore to learning its true character: " this is that which will indeed dignify and exalt knowledge, if contemplation and action may be more nearly and straitly conjoined and united together than they have been." [20]

The inspiration for true learning was for Bacon not the pleasure of study and the excitement of discovery, but the needs of mankind. Though many assertions made during his divided life by this remarkable man have been looked at with suspicion, it is impossible to question the sincerity of his expressed compassion for the lot of man.   In his celebrated letter to Burghley, which contains the first recorded statement of his intellectual ambitions, he concludes: " This, whether it be curiosity, or vain glory, or nature, or (if one take it favourably) *philanthropia,* is so fixed in my mind as it cannot be removed." [21] Bacon may have listed the inferior motives because he did not wish to expose his earnestness and sincerity too clearly before the worldly minister, but later expressions of this theme appear with no concessions.   The superior ethical motive became inseparable from the intellectually superior end, as though Bacon had realized that no motive other than " philanthropia " could ever guarantee that science would hold to the proper end of learning and consequently employ correct methods.   If learning was to become the mastery of nature for the uses of life, it could be guided only by men who were continually inspired by compassion for the lot of man.   At the conclusion of the " Proemium " to the *Magna Instauratio* Bacon thus explains his haste in publishing: " The cause of which haste was not ambition for himself, but solicitude for the work; that in case of his death there might remain some outline and project of that which he had conceived, and some evidence likewise of his honest mind and inclination towards the benefit of the human race.   Certain it is that all other ambition whatsoever seemed poor in his eyes compared with the work which he had in hand, seeing that the matter at issue is either nothing, or a thing so great that it may well be content with its own merit, without seeking other recompence."   Even in his most worldly practical discourses, Bacon discredited as inferior the actions that stem from self-love (" Of Wisdom for a Man's Self "), and proclaimed " philanthropia " as the noblest of man's capacities ("Of Goodness and Goodness of Nature "). Philanthropia was the seed from which the new science must grow, and so the new man of learning must of necessity be touched by the

[20] *Advancement, Works,* VI, 143–35.

[21] James Spedding, *The Letters and the Life of Francis Bacon* (London, 1868–90), I, 109.

needs of others.   How deeply Bacon's own feelings ran can be seen by
the following lines from the Preface to *The Great Instauration:*

Wherefore, seeing that these things do not depend upon myself, at the outset
of the work I most humbly and fervently pray to God the Father, God the
Son, and God the Holy Ghost, that remembering the sorrows of mankind
and the pilgrimage of this our life wherein we wear out our days few and
evil, they will vouchsafe through my hands to endow the human family with
new mercies.[22]

Compassion is the invariable mark of Bacon's true scientist.   Of the
personage who addresses the gathering of learned men in *Redargutio
Philosophiarum* he writes: " aspectus . . . admodum placidi et sereni;
nisi quod oris compositio erat tanquam miserantis." [23]   And in the
description of one of the Fathers of Salomon's House in *New Atlantis,*
almost the first detail has to do with compassion: " The day being
come, he made his entry.   He was a man of middle stature and age,
comely of person, and had an aspect as if he pitied men." [24]

The identification of scientific truth with use and therefore with
charity, with power and therefore with pity, is fundamental to Bacon's
conception of true learning.

*   *   *

[22] *Works,* VIII, 34–5. This also appeared, with slight variations, among his
prayers and meditations with the heading " The Student's Prayer." *Works,* XIV, 101.

[23] *Redargutio Philosophiarum, Works,* VII, 59.

[24] *Works,* V, 395. " He detested self-revelations, but whenever he painted the
portrait of his ideal philosopher, pity for mankind is the dominant trait." (Benjamin
Farrington, *Francis Bacon, Philosopher of Industrial Science* [New York, 1949], 70.)

⚭ℰ *Robert McRae*

THE UNITY OF THE SCIENCES: BACON, DESCARTES, LEIBNIZ

The seventeenth and eighteenth centuries saw numerous schemes for the systematic organization of knowledge in dictionaries and encyclopaedias. It was a period in which the unity of the sciences acquired a special significance in relation to the ideals of the Enlightenment, for the unity of the sciences opened up the possibility of the universality of all knowledge. At the beginning of the seventeenth century the efforts of Bacon and Descartes to bring about a radical reform of the sciences had been accompanied in each case by an insistence on the unity of the sciences as an essential element in the reform. Their conceptions of the nature of this unity were, however, markedly different. Yet certain conceptions of both Bacon and Descartes were brought together by Leibniz, the third of the great philosophical contributors of that century to the idea of the unity of the sciences.

In one of the earliest of his projects for the regeneration of the sciences, Bacon gave expression to the ideal of a universal wisdom based on the unification of all science and learning. He noted that " the professors of wisdom in Greece did pretend to teach a universal *Sapience* .... And it is a matter of common discourse of the chain of the sciences how they are linked together, insomuch that the Grecians, who had terms at will, have fitted it of a name of *Circle Learning*." With one aspect of the Greek conception Bacon was in agreement: " the particular arts and sciences " must not be " disincorporated from general knowledge." But as to the mode of their integration he intended something new and much more profound than the " note and conceit of the Grecians." [1]

The unity of science is conceived by Bacon at the cost of severe limitations and exclusions. The limits are not fixed, however, by theory of knowledge but by religion, which sharply separates itself from science and, having done so, declares what is to be reserved to its own jurisdiction. The absolute line of division laid down between the realm of the divine and the world of nature leaves to science only the world of nature or matter, and hence all sciences must be natural sciences. This has important consequences for metaphysics, logic, ethics, and politics.

To begin with metaphysics, it implies that a radical transformation of traditional conceptions of that science is required if it is to be retained as a science. As Bacon plainly puts it, metaphysics is to be

---

[1] *Valerius Terminus*, ch. I [*The Works of Francis Bacon*, edited by Spedding, Ellis, and Heath (New York, 1869), VI, 43].

regarded as " a part of Physic, or of the doctrine concerning Nature." [2] The separation means also the exclusion from science of all theory about man's rational soul, for the words of Scripture declare this soul to be divine. It is through Scripture that we know that man is made in the image of God, and that " He hath made man of the dust of the earth, and breathed into his nostrils the breath of life." [3] Only that part of man which is the dust of the earth, i.e., material, can be the subject-matter of science, but knowledge of the breath of life or the rational soul "must be drawn from the same divine inspiration from which that substance first proceeded." This excludes many traditional questions which have had their place in philosophy, questions "whether [the rational soul] be native or adventive, separable or inseparable, mortal or immortal, how far it is tied to the laws of matter, how far exempted from them; and the like." [4]

The religious limitation determines also the scope of logic and ethics. Since the faculties of the rational soul, though not part of nature, have their employment in nature, science can inquire into " the use and objects " of these faculties and it is this which makes it possible for logic and ethics to have a legitimate, and, however important, nevertheless a restricted, place among the sciences. " Logic discourses of the Understanding and Reason; Ethic of the Will, Appetite, and Affections: the one produces determinations, the other actions." [5] This permissible logic will, however, since it is limited to the *use* of the faculties of understanding and reason, be concerned only to direct and strengthen that use. The new organon is a technical device applied *ab extra* to the mind, so that " the business be done as if by machinery." [6] This logic is not theory about the nature of logical thinking, nor is it theory of knowledge.

The case with ethics is somewhat similar. The severe limitations imposed by religion relegate it, in so far as it is science, to the status of a technique for controlling the appetites and the affections and suborning action. More ambitious claims for a science of ethics are just those claims which led originally to man's fall from grace. It was not the desire for the knowledge of nature which was the occasion of Adam's default. " It was the ambitious and proud desire of moral knowledge to judge of good and evil, to the end that man may revolt from God and give laws to himself, which was the form and manner of the temptation." [7] Adam's supposition was that good and evil did

[2] *De Augmentis Scientiarum*, Bk. IV, ch. iii, *Works*, IX, 59.
[3] *Ibid., Works*, IX, 48. [4] *Ibid., Works*, IX, 49f.
[5] *Ibid.*, Bk. V, ch. i, *Works*, IX, 61.
[6] *Novum Organum*, Preface, *Works*, VIII, 61.
[7] *The Great Instauration*, Preface, *Works*, VIII, 35f.

not have their origin in the commands of God but had other foundations, and that if these could be discovered man could depend wholly
on himself. The moral law belongs with the sacred mysteries to
Sacred Theology. The greater part of it " is higher than the light of
nature can aspire to." [8]   It has its source not in the dictates of reason
but in divine will as revealed in Scripture. As for all questions about
the *summum bonum,* over which the heathen philosophers infinitely
disputed and speculated, they " are by the Christian faith removed." [9]

The more modest task which remains for a scientific ethics is that of
determining " how to frame and subdue the will of man " to conform
with the requirements of the moral law. This ethics as a " Georgics
or Culture of the Mind " for subduing, applying and accommodating the will of man rests on a knowledge of characters and dispositions and on a science of the affections and passions. The material
for such knowledge is derived from history. The particular utility of
history for morals and politics is that it shows how the passions can
be controlled by the use of one passion against another. This technical knowledge for controlling action is not derived from theory of the
good or the right but from fact alone. Bacon conceives it to be the
great merit of Machiavelli and other writers like him that they
" openly and unfeignedly declare or describe what men do, and not
what they ought to do." [10]   The strongest approbation is given by
Bacon to Machiavelli's political discourses based directly on history.
It is civil history which provides the inductive basis for this knowledge necessary in ethics or politics for the ruling of action.

The science of politics, although traditionally associated with
ethics, suffers none of the restrictions imposed on ethics by religion,
for Bacon simply dissociates politics altogether from ethics. Bacon's
politics becomes that of *raison d'état,* the art or technique of exercising power, and therefore it appropriately comes within the sphere
of natural inquiry. The state is not, as in earlier conceptions, related
to the life of man to give politics an authoritative rôle in the ordering
of all human pursuits. Its object is not " the good for man," for no
science can legitimately claim to encompass that aspect of man which
is outside the natural order and which belongs to the divine.

It is, then, religion which is responsible for the first limiting condition of the unity of the sciences. It determines that all rational
knowledge shall be confined to nature, and that all sciences be natural sciences. But another condition of their unity derives from nature
itself. Nature is a unity, self-sufficient and self-subsistent, and science is but a reflection or imaging of nature. In Bacon's interpretation of the fable of Pan, in the *Wisdom of the Ancients,* Pan is taken

[8] *De Aug.,* Bk. IX, ch. i, *Works,* IX, 348.   [9] *Ibid.,* Bk. VII, ch. i, *Works,* IX, 194.

to represent " the Universe or the All of Things." It is noted that in this fable no loves are attributed to Pan except his love with Echo. This is intended to signify that the world enjoys itself or is self-suffi-cient. It wants nothing outside itself, for love is a desire of some-thing lacking. And that Pan, or the world, has no offspring is taken by Bacon as another allusion to its sufficiency or perfection. " Genera-tion goes on among the parts of the world; but how can the whole generate, when no body exists out of itself? " The marriage of Pan with Echo was a marriage, not with something substantial, but with a voice, that voice being *discourse* or science. " But it is well devised that of all words and voices Echo alone should be chosen for the world's wife; for that is the true philosophy which echoes most faith-fully the voices of the world itself, and is written as it were at the world's own dictation; being nothing else but the image and reflection thereof, to which it adds nothing of its own, but only iterates and gives it back." [11]

Primary matter from which all things are derived is self-subsistent. There is nothing in nature more original than it. It belongs to no genus. " Wherefore," says Bacon, " whatsoever this matter and its power be, it is a thing positive and inexplicable, and must be taken absolutely as it is found, and not be judged by any previous concep-tion." [12] It cannot be known by a cause, for as the cause of all natu-ral phenomena it is itself without a cause. Though revelation informs us that God created the world, God himself lies completely outside nature, and there can be no argument within the chain of causes to God as First Cause. The knowledge of nature cannot supply the basis for the knowledge of anything else, nor does it depend on the knowl-edge of anything else.

Within this one self-sufficient nature all diversity is ultimately explicable by a single principle, which Bacon calls the Summary Law of Nature; it is " that impulse of desire originally impressed by God upon the primary particles of matter, which makes them come to-gether, and which by repetition and multiplication produces all the variety of nature." [13] This aspect of the unity of nature, the identity underlying all the diversity, is expressed in the *Wisdom of the Ancients* by Pan's horns. " Horns are attributed to the Universe, broad at the base and pointed at the top. For all nature rises to a point like a pyramid. Individuals, which lie at the base of nature, are infinite in

---

[10] *Ibid.*, Bk. VII, ch. ii, *Works*, IX, 211.   [11] *Ibid.*, Bk. II, ch. xiii, *Works*, VIII, 456.

[12] *De Principiis atque Originibus, Works*, V, 291.

[13] *De Sapientia Veterum*, XVII, *Works*, XIII, 123.

number; these are collected into Species, which are themselves manifold; the Species rise again into Genera; which also by continual gradations are contracted into more universal generalities, so that at last nature sems to end as it were in unity; as is signified by the pyramidal form of the horns of Pan." [14]   Science, again, is merely the imaging of this ordered ascent from the multiplicity and diversity of individuals to the unity of the Summary Law. Beginning with natural history, it aspires to reach through axioms of increasing generality that one law which includes all the rest.

All particular sciences are parts of one science of nature. Natural philosophy is designated by Bacon as " the great mother of all the sciences. For all arts and sciences, if torn from their root, though they be polished and shaped and made fit for use, yet they will hardly grow." [15]   The sciences have a common basis in " one universal science," which Bacon calls *Philosophia Prima,* and which is compared to the trunk-stem of a tree, of which the particular sciences are branches, " which stem grows for some distance entire and continuous before it divides itself into arms and boughs." This universal science is " a receptacle for all such axioms as are not peculiar to any of the particular sciences, but belong to several of them in common." It is also a doctrine of transcendentals like " Much, Little; Like, Unlike; Possible, Impossible; likewise Being and Not-Being and the like." These, however, must be treated physically " as they have efficacy in nature and not logically." [16]   The common axioms are not to be regarded as mere "similitudes"; they are " the same footsteps of nature, treading or printing upon several subjects or matters." The body of these axioms is described as " displaying the unity of nature " and it is the showing of this unity which is the true office of *Philosophia Prima.*

It is principally upon this *Philosophia Prima* that Bacon relies for restoring the ancient ideal of a universal wisdom. The unity of the sciences manifests itself, however, in other ways than that of their possession of a common basis in *Philosophia Prima.* In one very significant respect Bacon explicitly opposes himself to the divisive character of Aristotle's organization of the sciences. According to Aristotle each of the sciences marks off some genus with which it is concerned. It is impossible in demonstration to pass from one genus to another. It is furthermore impossible to prove the basic truths of the several sciences. Each science stands on its own indemonstrable

[14] *De Aug.,* Bk. II, ch. xiii, *Works,* VIII, 449.
[15] *Nov. Org.,* I, lxxix, *Works,* VIII, 110.
[16] *De Aug.,* Bk. III, ch. i, *Works,* VIII, 471–475.

premises. There is no supreme or sovereign science from which its basic truths are derived.

A repudiation of this doctrine is already implicit in Bacon's conception of *Philosophia Prima,* for the importance to him of this universal science arises from the necessity of "intercourse" between the particular sciences, and from the fact that "the particulars and instances of one science" supply information for the "framing or correcting of the axioms of another science in their very truth and notion." [17]   But further, in commenting on the doctrine that the principles of each science must be taken from the science itself, and that they are indemonstrable, Bacon argues that "true logic ought to enter the several provinces of science armed with a higher authority than belongs to the principles of those sciences themselves, and ought to call those putative principles to account until they are fully established." [18]   This authority logic exercises by establishing all axioms by induction from the particulars of history, and by proceeding in unbroken ascent from less general axioms to higher and more general axioms.   As a result knowledge is organized as a pyramid, and the sciences in this pyramid are related to one another in the order of their generality.   At the base of the pyramid is Natural History.   On that is built Physics, which has two parts, one less general and one more general.   On Physics is built Metaphysics, which subsumes the axioms of Physics under axioms of still greater generality.   At the vertical point, if it should ever be reached, there is the Summary Law of Nature, a single law of the maximum generality embracing everything.[19]   The distinction between these sciences is simply one between levels of generality in the knowledge of nature.

Another aspect of the unity of science arises in connection with the relation between theory and practice, speculation and action.   All Baconian science is subordinated to action.   The end of knowledge is "to establish and extend the power and dominion of the human race itself over the universe," [20] or to produce "a line and race of inventions that may in some degree subdue and overcome the necessities and miseries of humanity." [21]   This goal, the conquest of nature, which Bacon sets before the sciences, is not determined by his materialism, nor is the humanitarian project for the relief of misery an aspect of the hedonism which has generally appeared in history as the

[17] *Val. Term.,* ch. I, *Works,* VI, 43f.
[18] *Great Instauration,* Plan, *Works,* VIII, 43.
[19] *De Aug.,* Bk. III, ch. iv, *Works,* VIII, 507.
[20] *Nov. Org.,* I, cxxix, *Works,* VIII, 162.
[21] *Great Instauration,* Plan, *Works,* VIII, 46.

moral counterpart of materialism or naturalism. The conquest of nature is dictated by religion, for all questions of moral ends belong to religion and the end of science is a moral one—the fulfilling of the Christian obligation of charity. "It is an excellent thing to speak with the tongues of men and angels, but . . . if it be severed from charity, and not referred to the good of men and mankind, it hath rather a sounding and unworthy glory than a meriting and substantial virtue." [22]

The contemplative or theoretical life has reference "to private good and the pleasure or dignity of a man's self." It is therefore forbidden. The ultimate superiority of the contemplative life is not disputed by Bacon, "but men must know that in this theatre of man's life it is reserved only for God and angels to be lookers on." The obligation of charity prohibits in this world a "mere contemplation which should be finished in itself without casting beams of heat and light upon society." [23]

The consequence of this requirement imposed upon science by religion is that all science is productive science. Bacon does indeed distinguish between a "Speculative" part of natural science and an "Operative" part. But they are not distinguished as two kinds of knowledge, but as two kinds of activity in a division of labor within a single project, the one activity being the acquisition of knowledge by an inquiry into causes, the other being the use of the same knowledge in the production of effects. What theoretical inquirer and active producer know is the same. Thus in making a division of natural philosophy into a speculative and an operative part Bacon does so on the basis of "two professions or occupations of natural philosophers," but not on the basis of the kind of knowledge possessed by each.[24]

Even ethics and politics are absorbed by Bacon into productive science. A scientific ethics is not concerned with determining what the moral good is, for this is the prerogative of religion, but in accommodating men's wills and desires to the good. Bacon conceives of the science which shows how this may be effected to be analogous to the science of medicine, and the analogy is carefully elaborated. Both medicine and ethics are sciences for the control of nature, or of man in so far as he is a part of nature. Politics too presents itself in the same guise in Bacon's interpretation of the fable of the Sphinx. "Now of the Sphinx's riddles there are in all two kinds; one concern-

---

[22] *Advancement of Learning*, Bk. I, *Works*, VI, 94.
[23] *De Aug.*, Bk. VII, ch. i, *Works*, IX, 198f.
[24] *Ibid.*, Bk. III, ch. iii, *Works*, VIII, 480f.

ing the nature of things, another concerning the nature of man; and in like manner there are two kingdoms offered as the reward of solving them; one over nature, and the other over man. For the command over things natural,—over bodies, medicine, mechanical powers, and infinite other of the kind—is the one proper and ultimate end of true natural philosophy . . . . But the riddle proposed to Oedipus . . . related to the nature of man; for whoever has a thorough insight into the nature of man may shape his fortune almost as he will, and is born for empire . . . ." [25] Ethics and politics are, then, productive sciences in the same sense as medicine, mechanics, and agriculture.

II

Bacon's conception of the unity of the sciences in a "universal Sapience" is presented in one of the earliest of his writings, the *Valerius Terminus* (*circa* 1603). Descartes also in one of the earliest of his works, the *Regulae* (1628), presents the ideal of a "universal Wisdom" identified with "the sciences taken all together." [26] But the contrast between the two conceptions is striking. For Bacon the basis of this unity is nature, for Descartes it is the mind.

In the opening passage of the *Regulae* Descartes opposes himself immediately to the Aristotelian tradition which teaches that the sciences are distinguished from one another by the nature of their subject-matters, and which assigns to each science a method appropriate to its subject-matter. This teaching is based on a false analogy between the arts which depend upon "an exercise and disposition of the body" and the sciences "which entirely consist in the cognitive exercise of the mind." The arts are always specialized skills and it is their dependence upon the body which compels them to be specialized. A training in one art not only does not help in the exercise of another art but can be a positive hindrance to it. A hand adapted to agriculture, for example, is rendered thereby so much the less adaptable to harp-playing. Consequently, all the arts cannot be acquired by the same man. It has been supposed that the same is the case with the sciences. "Whenever men notice some similarity between two things," says Descartes, "they are wont to ascribe to each, even in those respects in which the two differ, what they have found to be true of the other." [27] Science in contrast with the arts always remains identical, whatever the nature of its objects. It no more suffers differentiation from these than the sun does from the variety of things it illuminates. Hence the pursuit of one science is not an impediment to the

---

[25] *De Sap.*, XXVIII, *Works*, XIII, 161f.

[26] *Regulae*, I, *The Philosophical Works of Descartes*, tr. E. S. Haldane and G. R. T. Ross (Cambridge, I, 1931; II, 1934), I, 1f. [27] *Ibid.*

pursuit of another but can be an aid to it, for it is exactly the same cognitive exercise of the mind which is required in both. For the mind to learn to exercise its cognitive powers upon one kind of object is to render itself all the more fit for other and different kinds of objects.

This conception of science as always the same, whatever its objects, determines the rôle which Descartes assigns to mathematics in the acquisition of right method. The mathematical sciences enjoy a special advantage from the simplicity of their subject-matter. They " alone deal with an object so pure and uncomplicated, that they need make no assumptions at all which experience renders uncertain." This makes them " the easiest and clearest " of all the sciences.[28] Descartes himself has, he tells us, studied them with no other practical end in view but that his mind should become " accustomed to the nourishment of truth and would not content itself with false reasoning." [29]   Here Descartes is merely following the principle laid down in the first of the *Regulae,* that since it is the same cognitive exercise of the mind which is required in all science the pursuit of one science may be of aid in the pursuit of another. Skill is acquired by exercising it first in the simplest subjects. Once acquired there, it may be applied to more difficult subjects. Method resides in a habit or skill in directing the attention to what is capable of being known. Since it is, as Descartes puts it, " very dependent on custom," its rules must be practised " for a long time on easy and simple questions such as those of mathematics." In commenting to Burman on the passage in the *Discourse* in which it is said that " mathematics would accustom the mind to the nourishment of truth," Descartes says, " Mathematics accustoms us to the recognition of truth, because in mathematics we discover correct reasoning such as cannot be found elsewhere. Consequently, anyone who has once accustomed his mind to mathematical reasoning will keep it apt for the inquiry into other truths, for *reasoning is everywhere identical.*" [30]

While Descartes carefully distinguishes science from the mechanical arts, he makes no distinction between science as concerned with theoretical matters and science as applied to conduct. The productive arts involve the use of bodily skills, and therefore are differentiated according to the nature of their objects. But moral decisions are determined wholly in the natural light of reason—the same natural light which illuminates in theoretical matters. Error and moral evil are treated under an identical rubric by Descartes.[31]   In both theory

[28] *Reg.* II, H.R. I, 5.   [29] *Discourse on Method,* Part II, H.R. I, 93.
[30] *Entretien avec Burman, Oeuvres de Descartes,* ed. Adam and Tannery, V, 176 (italics not in text).   [31] See *Meditation* IV.

and moral conduct the same components are involved: (a) a clear rational perception, and (b) a determination of the will in the light of this perception. In theoretical matters this determination of the will consists in an act of assent to what is seen to be true, for all judgment is an act of free will. In the case of conduct there is a similar free adherence of the will to what is seen to be good. Nor is it possible to distinguish a practical reason from a theoretical reason on the basis of their objects—the good in the one case, truth in the other, for the good belongs to the order of truth as much as mathematical or metaphysical matters.[32] Because all knowledge exists for a determination of the will, no ultimate distinction is possible between theoretical and practical sciences. The aim of all science is the same, that the understanding may light the will to its proper choice in all the contingencies of life.[33]

The first aspect of the unity of the sciences consists, then, in the unity of the human mind which is identical with itself whatever it knows. A second aspect of this unity, which Descartes relates to the first, concerns the logical connections between the sciences. " All the sciences are conjoined and interdependent," and for that reason should be studied together rather than in isolation from one another.[34]

The model for the unity of the sciences taken as a whole is found in mathematics. "Those long chains of reasoning, simple and easy as they are, of which geometricians make use in order to arrive at the most difficult demonstrations, had caused me to imagine that all those things which fall under the cognizance of man might very likely be mutually related in the same fashion . . . . " [35] It is possible for Descartes to imagine this since he has asserted that the nature of science as revealed in any one of its subject-matters is the same universally. Hence he conceives of the totality of the sciences as comprising a single deductive system. This system must begin with principles to which two conditions attach: first, they must be so clear and evident that the attentive mind cannot doubt them; and secondly, since it is on them that knowledge of all other things depend, they must be known independently of all other things. "We must accordingly try to so deduce from these Principles the knowledge of things that depend on them, that there shall be nothing in the whole series of the deductions made from them which shall not be perfectly manifest." [36]

---

[32] The reason for the goodness of things is that God wished to create them. " Nor is it worthwhile asking in what class of cause fall that goodness or those other truths, mathematical as well as metaphysical, which depend on God. . . ." *Reply to Objections* VI, H.R. II, 250.

[33] *Reg.* I, H.R. I, 2.   [34] *Ibid.*   [35] *Discourse*, Part II, H.R. I, 92.

[36] *Principles of Philosophy*, Author's Letter, H.R. I, 204.

In presenting this conception of the total system of the sciences Descartes, like Bacon, employs the metaphor of the tree. " Thus philosophy as a whole is like a tree whose roots are metaphysics, whose trunk is physics, and whose branches, which issue from this trunk, are all the other sciences. They reduce themselves to three principal ones, viz. medicine, mechanics and morals—I mean the highest and most perfect moral science which, presupposing a complete knowledge of the other sciences, is the last degree of wisdom." [37]

Just as science is not differentiated by the nature of its objects, so also the ordered relation of the sciences to one another in that systematic whole which comprises philosophy is not determined by the nature of the objects of the sciences. Descartes' tree of knowledge in which one proceeds from metaphysics to physics has been considered to represent a very significant reversal of the Aristotelian and scholastic order in which an ascent is made from physics to metaphysics. But one can only significantly speak of a reversal here if Descartes, like Aristotle, were concerned with the nature and dignity of the *objects* of these two sciences when he ordered them in relation to one another. Descartes explicitly denies, however, that the nature of the objects has anything to do with the ordering of knowledge:

It is to be observed in everything I write that I do not follow the order of subject matters, but only that of reasons, that is to say, I do not undertake to say in one and the same place everything which belongs to a subject, because it would be impossible for me to prove it satisfactorily, there being some reasons which have to be drawn from much remoter sources than others; but in reasoning by order, *a facilioribus ad difficiliora*, I deduce thereby what I can, sometimes for one matter, sometimes for another, which is in my view the true way of finding and explaining the truth; and as for the ordering of subject matters, it is good only for those for whom all reasons are detached, and who can say as much about one difficulty as about another.[38]

Order is described by Descartes as the chief secret of method. " Method consists entirely in the order and disposition of the objects towards which our mental vision must be directed if we would find out any truth . . . . " We attain the right order " if we reduce involved and obscure propositions step by step to those that are simpler, and then starting with the intuitive apprehension of all those that are absolutely simple, attempt to ascend to the knowledge of all others by precisely similar steps." [39] This order, Descartes insists several times, is not an order of things as they exist in nature, but as they exist relatively to our knowledge of them. " Relatively to our knowledge single things should be taken in an order different from that in which

[37] *Ibid.,* H.R. I, 211.   [38] Letter to Mersenne, 24 Dec., 1640

we should regard them when considered in their more real nature;
... We shall treat of things only in relation to our understanding's
awareness of them." [40]   Hence if the sciences form a unified system
this unity does not derive from the nature of the subject-matter of
the sciences but only from the relation which they have to our understanding.   The Cartesian unity of the sciences is unaffected by the
radical bifurcation of reality into spiritual and material substances,
each of which can exist in entire independence of the other.

The true logic, the science of order, applicable indifferently to all
subject-matters, is the basis of that universal wisdom which, Descartes
maintains, should be the object of all our study in the sciences.   The
peculiar status attributed to it is best revealed in his account in *Rule
IV* of his search for a universal mathematics.   The different sciences,
such as arithmetic, geometry, astronomy, music, optics, mechanics
and several others were, he found, regarded as parts of mathematics
because they all involved an investigation of order and measurement,
and it made no difference whether these were sought in numbers, figures, stars, sounds or any other object.   He concluded that " there
must be some general science to explain that element as a whole which
gives rise to problems about order and measurement, restricted as
these are to no special subject matter.   This, I perceived, was called
' Universal Mathematics ' . . . because in this science is contained
everything on account of which the others are called parts of Mathematics.   We can see how much it excels in utility and simplicity the
sciences subordinate to it, by the fact that it can deal with all the
objects of which they have cognizance and many more besides . . . . " [41]

In continuing the discussion of universal mathematics in *Rule XIV*
Descartes points out that " order " has reference particularly to numerical assemblages (*multitudines*) and "measure" to continuous
magnitudes.   Relations of continuous magnitudes can, however, be
reduced, at least in part, to relations between numbers by means of
an assumed or imputed unity.   The assemblage of units can then be
arranged " in such an order that the problem which was previously
one requiring the solution of a question in measurement, is now a
matter merely involving an inspection of order." [42]   This transformation of universal mathematics into a science of order with respect to
numerical quantities and magnitudes has, Descartes says, been effected
by the use of his method or logic.   At the same time it serves to exhibit the character of his logic conceived as a completely universal
science of order, not restricted to any subject matter, but having
reference to all subjects.   Thus universal mathematics becomes the

[39] *Reg.* V, H.R. I, 14.   [40] *Reg.* XII, H.R. I, 40.
[41] *Reg.* IV, H.R. I, 13.   [42] *Reg.* XIV, H.R. I, 64.

model of a science still more universal than itself; that is to say, logic is related to all the particular sciences in the same way that universal mathematics is related to arithmetic, geometry, astronomy, music, optics, mechanics, etc. Just as these are referred to mathematics in so far as in them order and measurement are investigated, so all particular sciences of any kind are referred to the logic of science as such in so far as in them order is investigated. And just as there is one general mathematical science to explain that element as a whole which gives rise to problems of order and measurement, restricted as these are to no particular mathematical subject-matters, so also there is one absolutely general science having a corresponding relation to all problems of order without restriction to special subject-matter of any kind. And finally, since universal mathematics contains everything on account of which arithmetic, geometry, astronomy, music, etc. are called parts of mathematics, so Descartes' method or logic is a universal science containing everything on account of which all particular sciences can be called parts of science.

This conception of logic as a general science, bearing the same relation to the particular sciences as universal mathematics to the particular mathematical sciences, and the conception of this logic as the foundation of the unity of the sciences, are taken up by Leibniz and worked out with a wealth of detail in his schemes for a demonstrative encyclopaedia of human knowledge, far surpassing anything attempted by Descartes.

III

Leibniz's schemes for his encyclopaedia, which was to be the great instrument for bringing civilization to its highest powers, occupied him through his whole life.[43] Lying behind the ideal of encyclopaedia is the conception of a wisdom identified with universality of knowledge. " Wisdom," says Leibniz, " is a perfect knowledge of the principles of all the sciences and of the art of applying them." [44] In some respects his conception of this universal wisdom is closer to Bacon's than to Descartes'. With Descartes it is not knowledge which is valued, but the capacity to form a sound judgment. The wise man is not the polymath, but one whose mind has been so formed that he can

[43] In his study of the logic of Leibniz Couturat has brought into view the decisive rôle of the encyclopaedic ideal throughout Leibniz's career. The encyclopaedia was to be his great philosophic and scientific work. After having worked tirelessly in the midst of innumerable distractions for fifty years of his life, seeking first to persuade the international community of the learned, " the republic of letters," to give him the collaboration which was required, and then finally turning to princes Leibniz died without having realized his dream. His project was plainly what Couturat labels it, gigantic. *La logique de Leibniz* (Paris, 1901).

[44] *Leibniz, Selections,* ed. Philip P. Wiener (New York, 1951), 77.

judge correctly whatever the subject-matter with which he is confronted. It is in this that the universality characterizing his wisdom consists. The Cartesian wisdom directly opposes itself to the Renaissance ideal of a wisdom identified with learning. The learned man is replaced by the "man of good sense," applying his native reason to whatever is required in accordance with precepts of right method. If universality is sought it is as an attribute of the mind's powers, not of what is known by the mind. Indeed, the desire to achieve universal knowledge is condemned by Descartes as "folly."[45] It is a point of view closely resembling that of Montaigne and Charron. It is reflected again in the Port Royal logicians, and it is given the most emphatic expression of all by Malebranche. It underlies Locke's theory of education. To be universally knowing is not necessary to a gentleman.[46] Locke allows "a universal taste of the sciences" some place in the direction of the young, but he at once insists that its value is not in the *knowing* of things. "I do not propose it [universality] as a variety and stock of knowledge, but as a variety and freedom of thinking; as an increase in the powers and activities of the mind, not as an enlargement of its possessions."[47]

[45] *The Search after Truth*, H.R. I, 309.
[46] John Locke, *Some Thoughts concerning Reading and Study*.
[47] Locke, *Conduct of the Understanding*, sec. 19. Montaigne identifies knowledge with erudition. It is something acquired or learned, a possession lodged in memory. It is by relegating knowledge to the faculty of memory that he can oppose it to understanding or judgment, and therefore to wisdom. "In truth," he says, "the care and expense which our fathers devote to our education have no other aim but to furnish our heads with knowledge; of judgment and virtue not a word! ... We labour but to cram our memory and leave the understanding and the conscience empty." *The Essays of Montaigne,* tr. Trechmann (Oxford, n. d.) I, 133f. His disciple, Charron, likewise assimilating knowledge to memory, makes a sharp distinction between science and wisdom. "Science is a great heap, or accumulation and provision of the good of another; that is, a collection of all that a man hath seen, heard, and read in books . . .; now the garner or storehouse where this great provision remaineth and is kept . . . is the Memory. ... wisdome is the rule of the soul; and that which manageth this rule is the judgment, which seeth, judgeth, esteemeth all things, rangeth them as they ought, giving to every thing that which belongs unto it." *Of Wisdome,* tr. Samson Lennard (London, 1670), 446. Descartes, the authors of the Port Royal logic, and Malebranche do not, of course, identify science with erudition, but in so far as science is taken as a mere possession of the mind, it is placed in the same inferior position in relation to judgment. "Thus, the main object of our attention should be," say the Port Royal logicians, "to form our judgment, and render it as exact as possible; and to this end, the greater part of our studies ought to tend. We apply reason as an instrument for acquiring the sciences; whereas, on the contrary, we ought to avail ourselves of the sciences, as an instrument for perfecting our reason—justness of mind being infinitely more important than all the speculative knowledges which we can obtain, by means of sciences the most solid and well-established. This ought to lead wise

Since the Cartesian wisdom dissociates itself from the accumulation of knowledge, it regards history as valueless and ignores it. Here Descartes can be viewed in contrast with Bacon, Pascal, and Leibniz, who have a marked sense of the temporal development of knowledge, not only as the promise of an indefinite advance into the future, but also as an accumulation out of the past.[48] For Leibniz civilization rests on a long history of scientific acquisitions.   " The arts and sciences are the true treasure of mankind; they show the superiority of art over nature and distinguish civilized people from barbarians." [49] It has taken the whole history of the human race to attain them. Science did not spring up overnight as the Cartesians tend to think. " We have known how long it took for mankind to acquire an interest in learning to know nature and to establish the laws of space and mo-

---

men to engage in these only so far as they contribute to that end, and to make them the exercise only, and not the occupation, of their mental powers. If we have not this end in view, the study of the speculative sciences, such as geometry, astronomy, and physics, will be little less than a vain amusement, and scarcely better than the ignorance of these things. . . ." *Logic, or the Art of Thinking*, tr. Baynes (Edinburgh, 1850), 1f. " For when a man gets it into his head," says Malebranche, " to become learned, and the spirit of polymathy begins to agitate him, he scarcely considers what sciences are most necessary to him, either for conducting himself as a gentleman or for perfecting his reason." *Recherche de la vérité*, Bk. IV, c. vii. " It is true that the knowledge of all these things and similar ones is called science, erudition, doctrine, usage has so ordained; but there is a science which is only folly and stupidity, according to Scripture: *Doctrina stultorum fatuitas.*" *Ibid.* The emphasis on judgment as opposed to knowledge leads to the elimination with these authors, as well as with Descartes, of any distinction between the spheres of the theoretical and the practical. The nature of judgment is the same whatever its objects may be, and universal wisdom consists of the perfecting of this judgment so that it can judge of all things.

[48] The emphasis on the historical development of science arises in the case of Bacon and Pascal from their conception of sensible experience as the basis of natural science. " The secrets of nature," says Pascal, " are hidden; although she is continually acting, her effects are not always discovered: time reveals them from age to age, and, although always equal in herself, nature is not always equally known. The experiences which give us intelligence of her multiply continually; and as they are the sole principles of physics, the consequences multiply proportionately." *Fragment d'un traité du vide*. ". . . not only does each man make an advance from day to day in the sciences, but all men taken together make a continual progress in them as the universe grows old, because the same thing takes place in the succession of men as in the different ages of an individual man. So that the whole continued series of men during the course of so many centuries ought to be considered as if it were the same man always subsisting and continually learning." " Time," says Bacon, is " the author of authors, nay rather of all authority. For rightly is truth called the daughter of time," and time must not be denied her rights. *Nov. Org.* I. lxxxiv, *Works*, VIII, 117.

[49] Wiener, *op. cit.*, 596.   [50] *Ibid.*, 61.   [51] *Ibid.*, 30

ion through which our powers are enhanced." [50] If this accumulated knowledge were lost, or if men should become indifferent to it, there would be a reversion to barbarism. The very preservation of civilization, no less than its advancement, requires the organization of all our intellectual possessions into a unified system. If learning is allowed to accumulate in haphazard fashion "in the end the disorder will become nearly insurmountable; the indefinite multitude of authors will shortly expose them all to the danger of general oblivion; the hope of glory animating many people at work in studies will suddenly cease; it will perhaps be as disgraceful to be an author as it was formerly honorable." [51] The possibility of the growth of indifference to learning, and with it of ignorance and the abandonment of the treasure of mankind continually haunted Leibniz. The unified system of the arts and sciences in an encyclopaedia would serve to preserve this treasure against such a possibility.[52] But for Leibniz as for Bacon the encyclopaedic organization of knowledge was not merely the elaboration of an ordered inventory of man's intellectual possessions. It was absolutely essential for the radical reform and advancement of the sciences.[53]

There were two ways in which, according to both Bacon and Leibniz, the unified ordering of the sciences would be productive of progress and would facilitate new discoveries. In the first place it would indicate at once where the gaps in human knowledge existed, and in what directions work remained to be done.[54] In the second place, the organization of the sciences in their hierarchic relations of logical dependence would generate discoveries by the deductions which were thus made possible. Here Bacon only suggested—". . . after the distribution of particular arts and sciences, men have abandoned universality, or *philosophia prima*; which cannot but cease and stop all progression. For no perfect discovery can be made upon a flat or level: neither is it possible to discover the more remote and deeper parts of any science, if you stand but upon the level of the same science, and ascend not to a higher science "[55]—but Leibniz worked out this principle with the utmost rigor.

[52] See *Precepts for Advancing the Sciences and Arts*, and *Essay on a New Plan of a Certain Science* in Wiener.

[53] One of Leibniz's several projections of his encyclopaedia contained within its title the significantly Baconian phrase, "*de instauratione et augmentis scientiarum.*" The full title is *Plus Ultra, sive initia et specimina Scientiae generalis, de instauratione et augmentis scientiarum, ac de perficienda mente, rerumque inventionibus ad publicam felicitatem.* Ger. VII, 49.

[54] Bacon, *Great Instauration*, Plan, *Works*, VIII, 38–40, 405; Leibniz, Ger. VII, 58, 58.

[55] *Advancement of Learning*, Bk. I, *Works*, VI, 131f.

The logically ordered system of the sciences would constitute a "demonstrative Encyclopaedia." Each science in the encyclopaedia having been reduced to its primary propositions and related appropriately to any other science to which it was subordinate, it would be possible then from its elements alone taken together with the rules of the "art of discovery" to extract at will the science in its entirety out of the encyclopaedia. "If this Encyclopaedia were made in the way I wish, we could furnish the means of finding always the consequences of fundamental truths or of given facts through a manner of calculation as exact and as simple as that of Arithmetic and Algebra." Given the primary propositions of any science, "they would suffice to recover the discovery if it were lost and to learn it without a teacher if one wished to apply himself enough, by combining those few propositions in the usual way with the precepts of a higher science assumed to be already known, namely, either the general science of art of discovery, or another science to which the science is subordinate." [56]

Thus it will be seen that for Leibniz logic (the art of discovery) and the encyclopaedia are two aspects of a single project for the instauration of the sciences. This had been the case with Bacon also. The first two parts of Bacon's plan for the Great Instauration were (1) the divisions of the sciences, and (2) the new organon, or the "doctrine concerning the better and more perfect use of human reason in the inquisition of things." [57] But for Bacon the employment of the new logic takes place *after* the completion of the organization of the sciences. With Leibniz, on the other hand, the connection be-

---

[56] Wiener, 40f. "For example, there are several sciences subordinate to Geometry in which it is enough to be a geometer and to be informed of a few leading facts or principles of discovery to which geometry may be applied, so that it is not necessary in addition to discover for one's self the principal laws of these sciences. For example, in the theory of perspective we have only to consider that an object may be outlined exactly on a given surface by marking the points of intersection of visual rays, that is to say, of straight lines going from the eye through the objective point and prolonged to meet or intersect the surface. That is why the position of the eye the shape and location of the surface . . . , and finally, the geometric properties of the object (that is, its position and shape) being given, a geometer can always determine the point of projection on the surface corresponding to the objective point projected. . . . The theory of the sun-dial is only a corollary of a combination of Astronomy and perspective. . . . Music is subordinate to Arithmetic and when we know a few fundamental experiments with harmonies and dissonances, all the remaining general precepts depend on numbers. . . . Besides, we can show a man who does not know anything about music, the way to compose without mistakes. Leibniz adds, however, that in order to compose beautiful music, a man would also require "practice as well as a genius and vivid imagination in things of the ear. *Ibid.*, 41f.

[57] *Great Instauration*, Plan, *Works*, VIII, 40.

ween his new logic and the organization of knowledge is, as Couturat has pointed out, such that they can only develop *pari passu,* for each implies the other.[58] The Universal Characteristic, which was Leibniz's new organon, required the elaboration of the encyclopaedia as the condition of its own development, and the encyclopaedia in its turn could only be developed in its structure as well as in its content by means of the new art of discovery. The Universal Characteristic required the analysis of all knowledge into its ultimate constituents, to those primitive concepts which for Leibniz comprised an " alphabet of human thoughts." It would give characters to these and devise signs for expressing their combinations and relations. But the attainment of the alphabet would by its very nature be the elaboration of an inventory or encyclopaedia of human knowledge, and, since it would consist in carrying all truths back to logically primary principles, it would moreover be a " demonstrative Encyclopaedia." At the same time, to reduce all knowledge to a system, placing the sciences in their appropriate relations of dependence, would be to devise even unwittingly the alphabet in question. " The Characteristic which I envision," says Leibniz, " requires only a new kind of Encyclopaedia. The *Encyclopaedia* is a body in which the most important of human knowledges are arranged in order. This Encyclopaedia being composed according to the order which I have in mind, the Characteristic would be as it were ready made, nevertheless those who were working at it would not know its design, believing themselves to be working only on an Encyclopaedia." [59]

If the aims animating Leibniz's projects for the encyclopaedia have some resemblance to Bacon's, nevertheless his conception of the basis of the systematic unity of the sciences is a development of that of Descartes'. Things knowable are ordered, as with Descartes, in terms of their relation to the mind's awareness of them. If things are taken " in so far as they are objects of the understanding," then, says Descartes, from this point of view they are divisible into " those things whose nature is of the extremest simplicity and those which are complex and composite." [60] The simple elements, which are known *per se*—Descartes' simple natures, or Leibniz's simple concepts—can in their various combinations give rise to all knowledge. ' No knowledge," says Descartes, " is at any time possible of anything beyond those simple natures and what may be called their intermixture or combination with each other." [61] The art of discovering these

[58] Louis Couturat, *La Logique de Leibniz,* 79f.

[59] *Phil.,* VII, B III, 11, quoted by Couturat, *op. cit.,* 80 n.

[60] *Reg.* VIII, H.R. I, 27.   [61] *Reg.* XII, H.R. I, 43.

simple components is the work of analysis, the art of combining them that of synthesis. " The fruit of several analyses of different particular matters," Leibniz says, " will be the catalogue of simple thoughts, or those which are not very far from being simple. Having the catalogue of simple thoughts, we shall be ready to begin again *a priori* to explain the origin of things starting from their source in a perfect order and from a combination or synthesis which is absolutely complete. And that is all our soul can do in its present state." [62]

Leibniz now, however, takes an important step beyond Descartes. The " catalogue of simple thoughts " is to be transformed into an "alphabet of human thoughts" by substituting sensible signs for thoughts. When this is done all the sciences will enjoy the advantages which the mathematical sciences already enjoy through their use of symbols. Descartes had described the usefulness of symbols in mathematics in *Rule XVI*: " When we come across matters which do not require our present attention, it is better, even though they are necessary to our conclusion, to represent them by highly abbreviated symbols, rather than by complete figures. This guards against error due to defect of memory on the one hand, and, on the other, prevents that distraction of thought which an effort to keep those matters in mind while attending to other inferences would cause." [63] These advantages provided by symbols could, Leibniz maintained, be extended to such subjects as metaphysics and ethics, where the problem of fixing the attention is even more acute than it is in mathematics. " If we had [a Characteristic] such as I conceive it, we should be able to reason in metaphysics and ethics almost as we do in Geometry and Analysis, because the Characters would fix our thoughts which are too vague and too volatile in these matters, since imagination does not aid us here except by means of characters." [64]

To this Cartesian advantage of symbolism Leibniz adds another, namely that a science will then carry its own test with it. This is an advantage already enjoyed by mathematics. In mathematics the falsehood of a theorem can always be determined by " an easy experiment, that is, by a calculation, costing no more than paper and ink, which will show the error no matter how small it is." [65] That is to say, in mathematics tests are made not on things themselves, but on the characters written on paper which we have substituted for these

[62] Wiener, *op. cit.*, 80.   [63] *Reg.* XVI, H.R. I, 66.
[64] *Phil.* VII, 21; " The true method must furnish us with a *filum Ariadnes*, that is to say, a certain sensible and palpable means which will conduct the mind, as do the lines traced in Geometry and the forms of operations prescribed to those learning Arithmetic. Without it our mind cannot traverse a long route without going astray." *Ibid.*, 22.

things.   In physics experiments are difficult and costly, in metaphysics they are impossible, but the obstacle can be surmounted by the use of characters.

. . . if we could find characters or signs appropriate for expressing all our thoughts as definitely and as exactly as arithmetic expresses numbers or geometric analysis expresses lines, we could in all subjects *in so far as they are amenable to reasoning* accomplish what is done in Arithmetic and Geometry.

For all inquiries which depend on reasoning would be performed by the transposition of characters and by a kind of calculus, which would immediately facilitate the discovery of beautiful results.   For we should not have to break our heads as much as is necessary today, and yet we should be sure of accomplishing everything the given facts allow.

Moreover, we should be able to convince the world of what we should have found or concluded, since it would be easy to verify the calculation either by doing it over or by trying tests similar to that of casting out nines in arithmetic.   And if someone would doubt my results, I should say to him: " Let us calculate, Sir," and thus by taking to pen and ink, we should settle the question.[66]

A Universal Characteristic making such calculations possible in any sphere of science would, Leibniz says, be " the highest effort of the human mind, and when the project will be accomplished it will simply be up to men to be happy since they will have an instrument which will exalt reason no less than what the Telescope does to perfect our vision." [67]

Descartes had conceived his logic as a universal science of order. Leibniz's logic is similarly a universal science of order, but it becomes, as Universal Characteristic, a science of " the connection and order of characters " or symbols.[68]   This universal science is, as with Descartes, the basis of the unity of the sciences, that is to say, it bears the same relation to all the particular sciences that universal mathematics does to the particular mathematical sciences.[69]   As with Descartes, this universal mathematics is for Leibniz merely the application of a still more general science.   He finds that this general science has up until now been practised only in mathematics.   Taken in its full generality it is " a thing hitherto quite unknown," and even in mathematics it has been very imperfectly applied.[70]   Nevertheless in mathematics

[65] Wiener, *op. cit.*, 13.   [66] *Ibid.*, 15.   [67] *Ibid.*, 16.
[68] "... the firm foundation of truth consists precisely in the connection and order of characters. . . .   You see that no matter how arbitrarily we choose characters, the results always agree provided we follow a definite order and rule in using the characters." *Ibid.*, 11.   [69] For the relation of universal mathematics to the particular mathematical sciences, see *On the Method of Universality, ibid.*, 3.   [70] *Ibid.*, 12.

we do have directly presented for our inspection an example of its application. "The best advantages of algebra," says Leibniz, "are only samples of the art of characters whose use is not limited to numbers or magnitudes."[71]   It is "as if God, when he bestowed these two sciences [arithmetic and algebra] on mankind, wanted us to realize that our understanding conceals a far deeper secret, foreshadowed by these two sciences."[72]   Hence an examination of the method of mathematics is capable of revealing the nature of the absolutely general science which will be applicable to all subject matters.   The general science as thus extracted from the procedures of mathematics can then be applied to physics, metaphysics, ethics, politics, jurisprudence, and medicine.   They will thereupon become sciences, as mathematics is science:[73]

Now since all human knowledge can be expressed by the letters of the Alphabet, and since we may say that whoever understands the use of the alphabet knows everything, it follows that we can calculate the number of truths which men are able to express, and that we can determine the size of a work which would contain all possible human knowledge, in which there would be everything which could ever be known, written, or discovered; and even more than that, for it would contain not only the true but the false propositions which we can assert, and even expressions which signify nothing.

One of the most fundamental and also most persistent divisions in philosophy throughout its history is that made between theoretical science and practical science.   A third science, logic, has frequently been placed beside these two.   The division of philosophy into logic, physics, and ethics was one accepted in common by almost all schools in the ancient world.   It was employed also, among Leibniz's contemporaries, by Locke, who declared each of these sciences to be "*toto coelo* different"—"they seemed to me to be the three great provinces of the intellectual world wholly separate and distinct from one another."[74]   The rigor of Leibniz's conception of the unity of science requires, however, the complete identity of these three sciences, or as Leibniz expresses it, "each part appears to absorb the whole."[75]   All science is one, and any divisions made in it are entirely arbitrary. "The entire body of the sciences may be regarded as an ocean, continuous everywhere and without a break or division, though men conceive parts in it and give them names according to their convenience."[76]   A single truth can be ordered in a number of different ways depending on the different relations it can have.   Leibniz finds that

---

[71] *Ibid.*, 74.   [72] *Ibid.*, 18.   [73] *Ibid.*, 75
[74] *Essay*, IV, xxi, 5.   [75] *New Essays*, tr. Langley, 3rd ed., 622.   [76] Wiener, *op. cit.*, 73.

there are two principal dispositions with which truths are approached, the one synthetic and theoretical and the other analytic and practical. The former leads to the ranking of truths " according to the order of proofs, as the mathematicians do, so that each proposition would come after those on which it depends." The second disposition begins with " the end of men, i.e. with the goods whose consummation is happiness " and seeks "in order the means available for acquiring these goods or avoiding the contrary evils." Both these approaches, the synthetic and the analytic, can, for example, be used in geometry. From the one point of view geometry can be regarded as a *science,* and its truths ordered synthetically as in Euclid; from the other point of view it can be regarded as an *art,* and the procedure will be analytic.

The difference between theoretical science and practical science arises, then, only from the difference of point of view from which one and the same set of truths are ordered with respect to one another. Logic, which with Leibniz is a doctrine of signs or Universal Characteristic, represents merely a third disposition in the ordering of these truths. It would be an "index" for the systematic arrangement of terms " according to certain predicaments which would be common to all the notions." [77] " Now this index would be necessary in order to find together all the propositions into which the term enters in a sufficiently remarkable manner; for according to the two preceding ways, where truths are arranged according to their origin or use, truths concerning one and the same thing cannot be found together." Logic is thus the ordering of knowledge in an encyclopaedia, facilitating invention in the sciences and relieving the memory and often sparing us the trouble of seeking again that which has already been found. " Now considering these three dispositions, I find it remarkable," says Leibniz, " that they correspond to the ancient division, which you [Locke] have renewed, which divides science or philosophy into theoretic, practical and discursive, or rather into Physics, Ethics, and Logic. For the synthetic disposition corresponds to the theoretic, the analytic to the practical, and that of the index according to terms to logic: so that this ancient division does very well, provided we understand these dispositions as I have just explained, *i.e.* not as distinct sciences, but as different arrangements of the same truths as far as we judge it advisable to repeat them." [78]

[77] *N.E.* 625.   [78] *Ibid.*

✑ E. W. Strong

NEWTON'S "MATHEMATICAL WAY"

The task of this historical essay is to make out the procedure which Newton designates as a " mathematical way "[1] to be followed in physical science—a way of "mathematically determining all kinds of phenomena." This procedure with respect to the rôle of measurement in experimental inquiry can be called mathematical experimentalism, and, with respect to reasoning from principles, mathematical demonstration. Pemberton, the editor of the third edition of the *Principia* and an expositor of Newton's science, reiterates a position taken by Newton when he states, " The proofs in natural philosophy cannot be so absolutely conclusive, as in the mathematics. For the subjects of that science are purely the ideas of our own minds. They may be represented to our senses by material objects, but they are themselves the arbitrary productions of our own thoughts; so that as the mind can have a full and adequate knowledge of its own ideas, the reasoning in geometry can be rendered perfect. But in natural knowledge the subject of our contemplation is without us, and not so completely to be known." Pemberton concludes by saying, " It is only here required to steer a just course between the conjectural method of proceeding . . . and demanding so rigorous a proof, as will reduce all philosophy to mere scepticism, and exclude all prospect of making any progress in the knowledge of nature."[2]

E. A. Burtt[3] and J. H Randall, Jr.,[4] have argued that there is an unreconciled conflict in Newton's thought between his mathematical rationalism, on the one hand, and his empiricism, on the other. Neither critic, however, has done justice to Newton's statements

---

[1] The title of this essay is taken from a passage in Newton's *System of the World*: " . . . our purpose is only to trace out the quantity and properties of this force from the phenomena, and to apply what we discover in some simple cases as principles, by which, in a mathematical way, we may estimate the effects thereof in more involved cases, for it would be endless and impossible to bring every particular to direct and immediate observation. We said, *in a mathematical way*, to avoid all questions about the nature or quality of this force, which we would not be understood to determine by any hypothesis; . . . "

[2] *A View of Sir Isaac Newton's Philosophy* (London, 1728), Introduction, 23.

[3] *The Metaphysical Foundations of Modern Physical Science* (New York, 1927)

[4] " Newton's Natural Philosophy: Its Problems and Consequences," in *Philosophical Essays in Honor of Edgar Arthur Singer, Jr.*, ed. by Clarke and Nahm (Philadelphia, 1942).

about measurement and its rôle in the formulation of principles.[5] Newton's "mathematical way" encompasses both experimental investigation and demonstration from principles, that is, from laws or theorems established through investigation. Measurements and rules of measure are crucial to mechanics and optics, for they provide the quantitative data and formulas upon which mathematical demonstrations in these physical sciences depend. When one sees how "measure" prepares for demonstration, there is good ground for modifying the assertion made by Randall, *viz.*, "Newton's actual mathematical procedure made it necessary for him to assume much that his empiricism could not justify; and in his ideas of 'the real world' his scientific procedure and his empirical theory collide violently."

It is true that there has been an opposition of theories with regard to the status of concepts and principles in physical science as these are mathematically formulated. The opposition is reminiscent of the lines from Gilbert:

> Every man that's born alive
> Is either a little lib-er-al
> Or else a little con-ser-va-tive.

Reworded to fit the clash of theories:

> Every philosopher in his twist
> Is either boldly rational
> Or else a cautious empiricist.

[5] Burtt devotes four pages to "The Mathematical Aspect" of Newton's method (*op. cit.*, 204–207). He refers to the passage in the *Opticks* where Newton speaks of "determining mathematically all kinds of phenomena of colours which could be produced by refractions." From this "determination" and the theorems established, Newton concludes that "the science of colours becomes a speculation as truly mathematical as any other part of optics." Burtt is quite right in saying that the science of colors was esteemed to be "truly mathematical" by Newton "as a result of his precise experimental determination of the qualities of refrangibility and reflexibility." But what, then, is this "precise experimental determination" (measurement) and what do Newton's actual procedures, as well as his statements, reveal as its place and importance methodologically? Burtt does not explore the question but stops short in saying only that "Newton's eagerness thus to reduce another group of phenomena to mathematical formulae illustrates again the fundamental place of mathematics in his work; but as regards the method by which he accomplished that reduction his statements are too brief to be of much aid."

Randall's account of Newton's "mathematical experimentalism" presents no discussion of "measure" as this term is used in Newton, nor makes mention of what might be the significance of statements in Newton about measurement.

Considering the long-standing disputes between rationalists and empiricists concerning the status of mathematical ideas and of how mathematical demonstration holds good for physical phenomena, it is not surprising that discussions of Newton's scientific thought have tried to characterize it by seeking to ascertain to which camp Newton belonged. On the one hand, Newton appears to be a mathematical realist when he asserts that space, time, and motion are to be conceived as "absolute, true, and mathematical." On the other hand, Newton was positivistically-minded in his experimental work and in his statements about method in science. If Newton, then, resists classification under one or the other type of thought but is in both camps at once, what is more natural than to argue that there is a fundamental conflict of two theories within his thinking? Yet since Newton's mathematical-physical science could not, without neglect of essential matters, slight either the need for data provided by experimental analysis or the proofs provided by mathematical demonstration, it is pertinent to ask how, on *methodological* grounds, Newton connects investigation and demonstration. What he has to say about "principles" is of central importance here. Once we have made out Newton's position concerning the mathematical way to be employed in physical science, we will then take up a second question, namely, that of the status of strictly mathematical ideas in Newton's method of analysis as set forth in the *Principia* and in his *Quadrature of Curves.* A. J. Snow [6] asserts that Newton assumes or supposes a one-to-one correspondence between elements and relations of his mathematical analysis and those of a physical analysis of nature. Had Newton maintained this, he would indeed have been a rationalist comparable to Kant who maintained that Euclidean geometry was an *a priori* necessary schematism of spatial extension.

The problem characteristic of rationalistic theory is one of descent from pure mathematics to mathematical demonstration in physical science. The problem characteristic of empirical theory is one of ascent from mechanics in an attempt to account for mathematics *per se* in terms of abstractions from experienced objects and physical operations. Hobbes, for example, sought to mount an empirical ladder in providing a physicalist explanation of geometry, and had the ladder pulled out from under him by Wallis. Bishop Berkeley, in his criti-

---

[6] *Matter and Gravity in Newton's Physical Philosophy* (London, 1926), 233. " Newton, however, employing mathematics as a method of procedure, presupposed . . . that each step in a mathematical demonstration is true of the physical world."

cism of Newton, was not so easily routed. He capitalized upon the defense which British mathematicians had made of Newton's method of fluxions in proclaiming it to be superior to Leibniz's differential calculus. The defenders of Newton maintained that the indivisibles of Leibniz were not to be admitted into mathematics because, they said, "they have no Being either in Geometry or in Nature." They argued the legitimacy of mathematical ideas by resting their case upon what is actually or really generated in the physical world. Berkeley was himself a champion of this argument, but turned it against the Newtonians by challenging the logic of their reasoning by which, for example, a physical division *in infinitum* was asserted by Keill and Halley. Like Ernst Mach after him, Berkeley contended that geometry is an abstracted physical science, and that where the abstracting from experienced things could not be established for a mathematical idea, the mathematicians did not know what they were reasoning about. By 1750, the controversies centering around Leibniz and Berkeley had produced admirable clarifications of disputed questions in the writings of Robins, Simpson, and Maclaurin; but the matters to be clarified in Newton's method of fluxions were not so much confounded by Newton as by his followers.

I. *Newton's Mathematical Way in Physical Science*

"In mathematics," Newton writes, "we are to investigate the quantities of forces with their proportions consequent upon any conditions supposed; then, when we enter upon physics, we compare those proportions with the phenomena of nature, that we may know what conditions of those forces answer to the several kinds of attractive bodies. And this preparation being made, we argue more safely concerning the physical species, causes, and proportions of the forces." [7]

In this statement, Newton may be said to differentiate the work in theory of a mathematical physicist from the work of the experimentalist. The former consists in discoveries and demonstrations "upon any conditions supposed" in an inquiry dealing with "quantities of forces with their proportions." How these quantities are furnished to the calculator involves Newton's general statement of method set forth in his "Rules of Reasoning in Philosophy" and his account of the rôle of measurement in experimental investigation. The rules of reasoning, as Pemberton [8] points out, are the "concessions" of induc-

[7] *Sir Isaac Newton's Mathematical Principles of Natural Philosophy*, tr. by Florian Cajori (Berkeley, 1934), 192.   [8] *Op. cit.*, 24–25.

tion required in natural philosophy but not needed in purely mathematical reasoning.   These concessions are the following:

1. " that more causes are not to be received in philosophy, than are sufficient to explain the appearances of nature; "
2. " that to like effects are to be ascribed the same causes; " and
3. " That those qualities, which in the same body can neither be lessened or increased, and which belong to all bodies that are in our power to make trial upon, ought to be accounted the universal properties of all bodies whatever."

A fourth rule is designed by Pemberton as an " additional precept " by which Newton enforces the " method of induction " in Rule 3, " whereupon all philosophy is founded."   Newton states this general precept in these words: " In experimental philosophy we are to look upon propositions inferred by general induction from phenomena as accurately or very nearly true, notwithstanding any contrary hypotheses that may be imagined, till such time as other phenomena occur, by which they may either be made more accurate, or liable to exceptions.   This rule we must follow, that the argument of induction may not be evaded by hypotheses."   Pemberton remarks, " In this precept is founded that method of arguing by induction, without which no progress could be made in natural philosophy.   For as the qualities of bodies become known to us by experiments only; we have no other way of finding the properties of such bodies, as are out of our reach to experiment upon, but by drawing conclusions from those which fall under our examination."

To follow Newton in his statement of the fourth rule of reasoning in philosophy and in other statements in which the terms " hypothesis," " principle," and " theory " occur we need first to make clear how he uses these terms.   A " natural philosopher " is one who investigates phenomena, for example, the motions and paths of bodies, and engages in theory in the calculation of forces.   Forces are not observed but computed in their actions.   From the composition of forces in accordance with mathematical-physical or " mechanical principles," phenomena of nature are demonstrated.   A supposed force, medium, substance, or structure of nature presented as an unverified causal assumption is called a " physical hypothesis."   A physical hypothesis is also a mechanical hypothesis when assumed properties are conceived to be subject to the same kind of quantitative analysis that holds for measured bodies and motions—what Newton calls their " sensible measures."   Qualities that are not in principle measurable are excluded from "mechanical philosophy." Hypothesis is differentiated not only from principles but also from theory. A theory is inductively inferred and abstracted from the results of observations and experiments. The soundness of theory is regarded as independent of the truth or falsity of "hypotheses," where by this term is meant explanation by an assumed cause not empirically verified. Newton uses "query" or "question" for suppositions that lead to further experiment (*i.e.*, for hypothesis in our modern sense as a supposition which is a candidate for verification). What Newton has to say about not making hypotheses refers only to explanations by assumed causes, and not to leading questions to be decided by experiments. Such queries may be corroborated or corrected, whereas mechanical hypotheses, unless brought to experiment and in this converted into queries, remain unconfirmed explanations.

Newton himself advances a mechanical hypothesis in his supposition that light is composed of corporeal particles, and that it is transmitted through an "etherial medium." He vigorously insists, however, upon the differentiation between the corpuscular hypothesis as a "conjecture" about light and his theory concluded from experiments. A strong empiricistic temper is exhibited throughout in his replies to objections brought against his theory.[9]

Having defined Newton's terms as he employs them, we can now restate the questions pertaining to Newton's scientific thought in the light of his description of his method of inquiry.

As in Mathematicks, so in Natural Philosophy, the investigation of difficult Things by the Method of Analysis, ought ever to precede the Method of Composition. This Analysis consists in making Experiments and Observations, and in drawing general Conclusions from them by Induction, and admitting of no Objections against the Conclusions, but such as are taken from Experiments or other certain Truths. For Hypotheses are not to be regarded in experimental Philosophy. And although the arguing from Experiments and Observations be no Demonstration of general Conclusions, yet it is the best way of arguing which the Nature of Things admits of, and

---

[9] *Phil. Tr.*, Vol. VII, No. 85, pp. 5004–5005. The following quotation is typical. "You know, the proper Method for *inquiring* after the properties of things is, to deduce them from Experiments. . . . Therefore I could wish all objections suspended taken from Hypothesis or any other heads than these two: of shewing the insufficiency of Experiments to determine these Quaeries or prove any other parts of the Theory, by assigning the flaws and defects in my conclusion drawn from them; or of producing other Experiments which directly contradict me, if any such may seem to occur."

may be looked upon as so much the stronger, by how much the Induction is more general. And if no Exception occurs from Phaenomena, the Conclusions may be pronounced generally. But if at any time afterwards any Exception shall occur from Experiments, it may then begin to be pronounced with such Exceptions as occur. By this way of Analysis we may proceed from Compounds to Ingredients, and from Motions to the Forces producing them; and in general, from the Effects to their Causes, and from particular Causes to more General ones, till the Argument end in the most general. This is the method of Analysis: and the Synthesis consists in assuming the Causes discover'd and establish'd as Principles, and by them explaining the Phenomena proceeding from them and proving the Explanations.[10]

The questions to be examined in turn are the following: (1) how is an inductive generalization constituted as a mechanical principle from which a scientist is to proceed mathematically to "estimate effects" and to explain phenomena? (2) What does Newton designate as "analysis" in mathematics and what does the analogy between the terms of this analysis and those of experimental inquiry amount to?

Newton states in the Preface to his *Principia* that the "whole burden of philosophy seems to consist in this—from the phenomena of motions to investigate the forces of nature, and then from these forces to demonstrate the other phenomena." Quantity is only traced out if there are measures, for it is measurement alone which provides quantified data for calculation. A principle in physics is "mathematical" if its enunciation states a ratio or proportion, or, as we would now say, a formula or functional relationship. The rôle of geometry in the science of mechanics is defined by Newton as "that part of universal mechanics which accurately proposes and demonstrates the art of measuring. In this sense," Newton continues, "rational mechanics will be the science of motions resulting from any forces whatsoever, and of the forces required to produce any motions, accurately proposed and demonstrated." There are, then, no laws of mechanics which are supplied solely by reasoning in mathematics. Demonstration, of course, is a procedure of mathematical reasoning, but such reasoning, as Newton states, is from "the laws and *measures* of gravity and other forces."

One example will serve to show how Newton proceeds from the method of experimental analysis to the method of composition. Having discovered invariable refractive indices of a prism for rays of

[10] *Opticks* (London, 1730), 380.

differently colored light and having stated his discoveries as " the Laws of Refraction made out of Glass into Air " and " out of Air into Glass," Newton derives two " Theorems." He comments as follows:

By the first Theorem the Refractions of the Rays of every sort made out of any Medium into Air are known by having the Refraction of the Rays of any one sort. . . . By the latter Theorem the Refraction out of one Medium into another is gathered as often as you have the Refractions out of them both into any third Medium.[11]

The two theorems state laws of refrangibility, and have the status of axioms or principles in the demonstration of optical phenomena. Newton adds the following highly significant comment. " And these Theorems being admitted into Opticks, there would be scope enough of handling that Science voluminously after a new manner; not only by teaching those things which tend to the perfection of Vision [*i.e.*, theory of telescopes], but also by determining mathematically all kinds of Phaenomena of Colours which could be produced by Refractions."[12] Methodologically, there is a "determining mathematically" in observation and experiment in making measurements; but such measurements do not of themselves yield laws. To compute a ratio or proportion of quantified data is to institute a *rule of measure:* and such a rule of measure is the comprehension of the scientist of the relevance of what he has measured. Measurements alone of angles, distances, periodicities, and the like yield quantified data. When correlated in some ratio or proportionality, the numbers which read off the measures are now handled by calculations and computations. In some cases, the arraying of measurements may be intuitively grasped by the scientist as exhibiting a rule of measure. In others, the making of computations may disclose some function which can be formulated as a general theorem. The investigator has then discovered a rule of measure and, with respect to what has been measured, he may now consider that he has discovered a physical law.

How had it happened, Newton asks, that, although previous experimenters had measured refractions, they had not discovered the refrangibility of several rays of light, and hence had not arrived at these new theorems for "determining mathematically all kinds of Phaenomena of Colours which could be produced by refractions?" One must know not only how to measure but what to measure.

[11] *Opticks*, 113, 114.　　　　[12] *Ibid.*, 114.

The late Writers in Opticks teach, that the Sines of Incidence are in a given Proportion to the Sines of Refraction, as was explained in the fifth Axiom; and some by Instruments fitted for measuring of Refractions, or otherwise experimentally examining this Proportion, do acquaint us that they have found it accurate. But whilst they, not understanding the different Refrangibility of several Rays, conceived them all to be refracted according to one and the same Proportion, 'tis to be presumed that they adapted their Measures only to the middle of the refracted Light; so that from their Measures we may conclude only that the Rays which have a mean Degree of Refrangibility (that is, those which when separated from the rest appear green), are refracted according to a given Proportion of their Sines. And therefore we are now to shew, that the like given Proportions obtain in all the rest.[13]

Newton proceeds to a mathematical demonstration of the proposition, concluding, " So, then, if the *ratio* of the Sines of Incidence and Refraction of any sorts of Rays be found in any one case, 'tis given in all cases." Finally, he presents the method used and results obtained experimentally which confirm the conclusion.

In working through Book I of Newton's *Opticks,* I had supplied the expression " rule of measure " suitable to the sense in which Newton uses the word " measure " as meaning a ratio or proportion of numbers supplied by measurements. That this accorded with Newton's reasoning was confirmed in *Opticks,* Book II, Part I. Newton, in this part dealing with " rings of Colour " produced by thin transparent bodies, presents a table of measurements.[14]

" And from these Measures," Newton concludes, " I seem to gather this Rule: That the Thickness of the Air is proportional to the Secant of an Angle, whose sine is a certain mean Proportional between the Sines of Incidence and Refraction."

Newton then states this mean proportional so far as he can determine it from the measures he has made. From the measurements in knowing what to measure, the rule is formulated which is now a principle from which to demonstrate phenomena. Towards the end of

---

[13] *Opticks,* 65.

[14] *Opticks,* 180. " In the first two Columns are express'd the Obliquities of the incident and emergent Rays to the Plate of the Air, that is, their Angles of Incidence and Refraction. In the third Column the Diameter of any colour'd Ring at those Obliquities is expressed in Parts, of which ten constitute the Diameter when the Rays are perpendicular. And in the fourth Column the Thickness of the Air at the Circumference of that Ring is expressed in Parts, of which also ten constitute its Thickness when the Rays are perpendicular."

the *Opticks* Newton remarks upon the method of composition in these words: " Now as all these things follow from the properties of light by a mathematical way of reasoning, so the truth of them may be manifested by experiments." In a communication to Oldenburg, July 11, 1672, Newton makes what is perhaps the best summarization about " principles " to be found anywhere in his writings:

In the last place, I should take notice of a casual expression, which intimates a greater certainty in these things, than I ever promised, *viz, the certainty of Mathematical Demonstrations.* I said, indeed, that the science of colours was mathematical, and as certain as any other part of *Opticks;* but who knows not that Optics, and many other mathematical sciences, depend as well on physical sciences, as on mathematical demonstrations? And the absolute certainty of a science cannot exceed the certainty of its principles. Now the evidence, by which I asserted the propositions of colours, is in the next words expressed to be from experiments, and so but physical: whence the Propositions themselves can be esteemed no more than physical principles of a science. And if those principles be such, that on them a mathematician may determine all the phaenomena of colours, that can be caused by refractions, and by disputing or demonstrating after what manner and how much, those refractions do separate or mingle the rays, in which the several colours are originally inherent; I suppose the science of colours will be granted mathematical, and as certain as any part of Optics. And that this may be done, I have good reason to believe, because ever since I became first acquainted with these principles, I have, with constant success in the events, made use of them for this purpose.

Newton's mathematical way, then, requires measures for the formulation of principles in optics and mechanics—principles that incorporate a rule of measure. Were there not mathematical determination in the experiment, there would be no subsequent determination in the demonstration. The quantities with which rational mechanics are concerned are measures expressed in a rule. This is clear in Newton's definitions of mass and momentum in the *Principia:*

Def. I. The Quantity of matter is the measure of the same, arising from its density and bulk conjointly

Def. II. The quantity of motion is the measure of the same, arising from the velocity and quantity of matter conjointly. The bearing of Definitions I and II upon Newton's idea of *Force* is pointed out by Cajori.

By Newton's second Definition, " quantity of motion " (momentum) arises " from the velocity and quantity of matter conjointly," that is, from mv. By Newton's second Law of Motion, " change of motion," that is, change in the quantity of motion, " is proportional to the motive force impressed." Thus we have " change of motion " as the measure of the force which produces it. Thus arose the measurement of force by the product of mass and acceleration.

In view of Newton's position with regard to principles to be admitted into mathematical-physical science, what is one to make of his definitions of absolute, true, and mathematical time and space and motion? Newton writes that parts of an absolute space, like parts of an absolute time, are not

distinguished from one another by our senses, therefore in their stead we use sensible measures of them. For from the positions and distances of things from any body considered as immovable, we define all places; and then with respect to such places, we estimate all motions, considering bodies as transferred from some of those places into others. And so, instead of absolute places and motions, we use relative ones; and that without any inconvenience in common affairs; but in philosophical disquisitions, we ought to abstract from our senses, and consider things themselves, distinct from what are only sensible measures of them. For it may be that there is no body really at rest, to which the places and motions of others may be referred.

Similarly, Newton states, " It may be, that there is no such thing as an equable motion whereby time may be accurately measured. All motions may be accelerated and retarded, but the flowing of absolute time is not liable to any change."

The abstracting " from the senses " here recommended, in view of Newton's own admission that there may be no equable motion and no body absolutely at rest, strongly suggests that absolute space, time, and motion are being proposed as postulates and hence as a possible or presupposed system. Undoubtedly Newton believed that the " absolutes " he postulated were not conventional constructs but were a real order of nature, yet lack of empirical confirmation restrained him from asserting this as a matter of knowledge. " . . . there may be some body absolutely at rest," Newton writes, " but impossible to know, from the position of bodies to one another in our regions, whether any of these do keep the same position to that remote body." It follows " that absolute rest cannot be determined from the position of bodies in our regions." Newton thought that the matter was not " altogether desperate " empirically with regard to absolute motion if one considered the evidence in determining angular velocity from the rotation of vessels filled with water. The experiment, however, does not provide empirical warrant for absolute rectilinear motion implied in the first Law: "every body continues in its state of rest, or of uniform motion in a right line, unless it is compelled to change that state by forces impressed upon it."

There is no conflict or confusion in Newton's reasoning regarding an absolute, true, and mathematical system provided he does not employ the asserted "absolutes" as more than postulates. Newton does assume absolute coordinates from which to compute sensible measures of bodies and motions, but in so doing the expressions are unexceptionable if asserted not as *physical* but only as *mathematical*. A careful reading of Newton supports the following conclusions concerning abstracting from the senses. In effect, Newton distinguishes three levels. In a first level of abstracting, propositions are said to be inferred or deduced from phenomena. In a second level, the propositions are "rendered general by induction," for example, the two theorems in optics previously discussed. As derived from mathematical experimentation, these principles are *mechanical* principles, or mathematical-physical formulas. When Newton postulates absolute, true, and mathematical space, time, and motion, he introduces principles which are not evinced by experiments. Such principles, so far as Newton believes they express a real order of nature, are thereby metaphysical in the sense of being unverified assumptions. They are constructs introduced on the second level of abstracting, but not themselves inductively derived and thereby empirically grounded. So far as Newton's scientific purpose is concerned in his mechanics, nothing more need be asserted or assumed. Yet a third level appears in Newton's views expressed in the General Scholium at the end of the *Principia* and in the conclusion of the *Opticks* where Newton attributes the order of nature to God as the first Cause.

Where interpreters of Newton have gone astray is in supposing that Newton held that Space and Time constitute the "sensorium of God" in order to preserve empiricism in principle for the atomic ingredients and absolute structure of his system. Yet Newton *added* the General Scholium in the second edition of the *Principia* in 1713, twenty-six years after the first edition; and the theological views expressed in the *Opticks*, Queries 28 and 31, did not appear in the first edition of 1704. Had Newton supposed these discussions to be fundamental to his science, he would hardly have omitted them originally. Newton, of course, believed that his system of the world was not incompatible with a traditional conception of God which he never questioned. He wrote the general scholium at the urging of Cotes, who became alarmed by the criticism of Leibniz to the prejudice of a work in which God had not been employed. Newton, however, did not suppose that his scientific theorems either proved the theological doctrine or needed to assume it. His famous statement, "Hypotheses non fingo," is his judgment upon the pertinence of the theological discussion which immediately precedes it. The philosophers who take this third level to be a subscription on Newton's part to theological foundations of his physical science have not followed Newton in his own disavowal. Science proper is limited, by Newton, to the first two levels of abstracting.

Some main points emerging from the preceding discussion can now be summarized:

1. In mathematical computation and demonstration, Newton introduced mathematical postulates which are not mechanical principles but mathematical only. He believed in the reality of these mathematical absolutes, but does not argue that this reality is known from observation and experiment.

2. Success in demonstration tended to confirm Newton's belief in the reality of an absolute system. In Rule III of his "Rules of Reasoning in Philosophy," Newton held that "since the qualities of bodies are known to us only by experiments, we are to hold for universal all such as universally agree with experiments." By extension of this rule, a system of demonstration which holds for phenomena is likewise to be held for universal, not here because the mathematical postulates introduced are derived from experiments but because predictions are verified. Such verification with no known exceptions is a strong impulsion to believe that non-empirical postulates are to be accepted as real in the nature of things.

3. Mechanical principles established from sensible measures have the status of inductive generalizations, or empirically established laws. Definitions of mass and momentum incorporate rules of measure as the meaning of these concepts.

4. Mechanical principles conjoined with mathematical postulates constitute the premises of Newton's theoretical physics. As stated by Roberts and Thomas,[15] "Given clear notions of the method of measuring time and distance, it is possible to define velocity and acceleration relative to some fixed framework. . . . Add to these a satisfactory definition of 'mass' and you have the foundation of Newtonian science: the laws of nature are uniform throughout space,

[15] *Newton and the Origin of Colours* (London, 1934), 42.

and all observations can be expressed, for scientific purposes, in terms of space, time, and mass."

II. *Mathematical Analysis and Mathematical Ideas*

An assumption of Newton's physical analysis is that "the least particles of all bodies" are "extended and hard and impenetrable and movable, and endowed with their proper inertia." Such particles are ingredients of composite, molar bodies. Newton warns against confusing a mathematical analysis of division of quantity *in infinitum* with an actual, physical separation. ". . . that the divided but contiguous particles of bodies may be separated from one another, is a matter of observation; and in the particles that remain undivided, our *minds* are able to distinguish yet lesser parts, as is *mathematically* demonstrated. But whether the parts *so* distinguished, and not yet divided, may, by the powers of Nature, be *actually* divided and separated from one another, we cannot certainly determine."

What our minds are able to distinguish as mathematically demonstrated with regard to infinitesimals has here no empirical determination. Infinitesimals, nascent and evanescent quantities, and the like are mathematical only. As De Morgan [16] has shown, Newton used infinitesimally small quantities, or fixed infinitesimals in his algebraical calculus up to the year 1704; and, according to Cajori, even later. In the first edition of the *Principia*, Newton warns against looking upon "moments" as finite particles comprising magnitudes by apposition, for this, he says, is "contrary to their continuous increase or decrease." Rather, they are to be regarded as "the just nascent principles of finite magnitudes." In 1704, in his *Quadrature of Curves*, Newton tried to avoid use of infinitely small constants. He designates a fluxion as a velocity or time-derivative of a fluent or flowing quantity, and states that fluxions are "in the *first ratio* of the nascent augments," or "in the *ultimate ratio* of the evanescent part." Cajori [17] remarks that

Unless the fully developed theory of limits is read into these phrases, they will involve either infinitely little parts or other quantities no less mys-

[16] *Philosophical Magazine* (Nov. 1852), 321–330, "On the Early History of Infinitesimals in England." Also, *Essays in the Life and Work of Newton* (Chicago and London, 1914), II, "A Short Account of Some Recent Discoveries Relative to the Controversy on the Invention of Fluxions," 67–101.

[17] *A History of the Conceptions of Limits and Fluxions in Great Britain from Newton to Woodhouse* (Chicago and London, 1919), 36.

terious. At any rate, the history of fluxions shows that these expressions did not meet the demands for clearness and freedom from mysticism. Newton himself knew full well the logical difficulties involved in the words ' prime and ultimate ratios '; for in 1687 he said, ' it is objected, that there is no ultimate proportion of evanescent quantities; because the proportion before the quantities have vanished, is not ultimate; and, when they have vanished, it is none.'

The problem of quadratures (integration) consisted in how to find the total amount of change in a given time, given a formula expressing the rate of change at all moments. The problem of tangents (differentiation) consisted in how to find the rate of change at any moment given a formula which expresses the total of all moments. These problems were " equivalent to finding the area enclosed by a curve of any given form, and finding the slope of the tangent to a given curve at a given point." [18] Newton's analysis in dealing with these problems did involve elements which were difficult to define clearly and rigorously within the method itself. For example, an " ultimate velocity " is said to be that velocity " with which the body is moved, neither before it arrives at its last place and the motion ceases, nor after, but at the very instant it arrives; that is, that velocity with which the body arrives at its last place, and with which the motion ceases." Again, " the ratio of evanescent quantities " is said to be that " with which they vanish " and not the ratio just before or just afterwards. If by " prime and ultimate ratios " a theory of limits is intended, then the language of " nascent augments " and " evanescent decrements " is a circumlocution more apt to bewilder than to clarify the logic of reasoning. Yet Newton quite early is at least flirting with the idea of limits; for in defending the intelligibility of an " ultimate proportion of evanescent quantities " in the *Principia* (39), he writes:

There is a limit which the velocity at the end of the motion may attain, but not exceed. This is the ultimate velocity. And there is the like limit in all quantities and proportions that begin and cease to be. And since such limits are certain and definite, to determine the same is a problem strictly geometrical. But whatever is geometrical we may use in determining and demonstrating any other thing that is also geometrical.

Newton insists throughout that the conception of " quantities as least, or evanescent, or ultimate," is not of quantities of any determinate magnitude, " but such as are conceived as always diminished

[18] *Newton and the Origin of Colours*, 31.

without end." From Newton's own comment about quantities so conceived, it is clear that he regards them as strictly mathematical, and that their assertion in mathematical analysis posits no identity with physical particles and magnitudes.

Newton's use of the term *Analysis* for infinite processes dates, according to H. W. Turnbull,[19] from Newton's comment about the method of series in his *De Analysi* (1669).

Neither do I know anything of this kind to which this method does not extend, and that in various ways. Yea, tangents may be drawn to mechanical curves by it, when it happens that it can be done by no other means. And whatever the common Analysis performs by means of equations of a finite number of terms (provided that can be done) this can always perform the same by means of infinite equations. So I have not made any question of giving this the name Analysis likewise. For the reasonings in this are no less certain than in the other; nor are the equations less exact.

As Turnbull points out, it was the contribution of this modern analysis to show that ideas of number, variable, and functionality were more fundamental than those of geometrical points, curves, and tangents which gave rise to them. It is to be noted that in *The Method of Fluxions* Newton first states the problems to be solved geometrically and then restates them in the terms of his new analysis. Was this done to lend weight to a statement which had disastrous consequences when British mathematicians referred to it in arguing the superiority of Newton's calculus? The statement occurs in the " Introduction " to the *Quadrature of Curves*. In asserting that the mathematical quantities treated in the analysis to follow are described by continuous motion, Newton added, " These geneses really take place in the nature of things and are daily seen in the motion of bodies." By Newton's own differentiation of elements that are strictly mathematical from those that are physical and known by observation, as well as from his assertion that analysis by means of infinite equations is no less certain and exact than that of the common analysis, he would appear to be asserting only that we do see bodies passing from motion to rest and from rest to motion.

Yet the notion that geometrical concepts are fundamental in mathematics because of their close " analogy " to nature had prevailed in Barrow who was Newton's teacher. There is no significant departure from Barrow in Newton's work in mathematics up to 1665, which consisted in working over what he had learned from his teacher

---

[19] *The Mathematical Discoveries of Newton* (London and Glasgow, 1945).

and from Descartes.and Wallis, combined with some original contributions upon methods of infinite series and reversions of series.   In
the plague years of 1665–1667, he left Cambridge and entered upon
a highly fruitful period of mathematical discoveries.   J. M. Child [20]
points out that " Within a few months, by November 13, 1665, he had
so far perfected the method of fluxions that he was able to find the
radius of the curvature of any curve at any point, and within another
year was applying the method to problems on the theory of equations."   The labors formed the groundwork of the *De Analysi* which
he communicated to Barrow in July, 1669.   Child asks, " Where then
does the marvellous development of the later years come from?
I suggest, as the source, Barrow's *Lectiones Geometricae;* as the opportunity, Newton's help in preparing them for press; as the occasion,
the removal of the hampering geometrical influence of Barrow; as
the spur, the problems of gravitation and the preparation of the
Principia."

In the *Quadrature of Curves,* Newton declares that it is the mind
which contributes in the reasoning of his analysis " a method of determining quantities from the velocities of the motions of increments,
with which they are generated, denominating the increments by the
name of *fluxions* and the generated quantities *fluents.*"   The ideas of
space and time are designated as mathematical terms and not as
physical concepts.

Since we have no estimation of time except in so far as it is expounded
and measured by equable spatial motion, and further, since we may compare quantities of the same kind and also the increments and decrements of
their mutual velocities, for that reason I shall not be mindful of time formally in what follows, but from the proposed quantities which are of the
same kind I shall conceive another to be increased by an equable motion,
to which the rest shall be referred to as the time, and so to which the name
of time may be deservedly attributed by analogy.

In conceiving time as a fundamental variable, what's in the name
attributed by analogy?   Is some dependence upon geometry or upon
nature being argued as conferring legitimacy upon the method in its
elements and terms?

After defining *Fluents* and *Fluxions* with their notations, Newton
states the two problems to be solved: Problem I: " The Length of the
Space described being continually (that is, at all Times) given, to find

---

[20] " Newton and the Art of Discovery," in *Isaac Newton, 1642–1727, A Memorial Volume,* ed. by W. J. Greenstreet (London, 1927), 122–124.

the Velocity of the Motion at the Time proposed." Problem II: "The Velocity of the Motion being continually given; to find the Length of the Space described at any Time proposed." Restated, Problem I reads: "The Relation of Flowing quantities to one another being given, to determine the Relation of their Fluxions." And Problem II: "An Equation being proposed, including the Fluxion of Quantities, to find the Relation of the Quantities to one another." The idea of quantity infinitely increased or diminished is a logical tool in the solution of physical problems, and is nowhere considered to be more than that by Newton. Although concern for the use of mathematics as an instrument of investigation and demonstration can legitimately have regard for an analogy with nature, the notion that mathematical ideas must correspond to empirically grounded concepts is not championed by him. In physical science, Newton states, we have to do with "such principles as have been received by mathematicians, and are confirmed by abundance of experiments." Newton's mathematical way in physical science, as I have tried to show, requires mathematical experimentalism in which measurements and rules of measure prepare the mechanical principles from which demonstrative reasoning proceeds. Mathematical analysis *per se* is a logic of reasoning advancing concepts requiring no appeal to geometry or to nature. At the same time, as developed by Newton, it was a tool devised to assist in the solution of physical problems.

What was the source of the difficulties in which British mathematicians were caught in their defense of Newton's method of fluxions, first, against Leibniz, and secondly, against Berkeley? The argument presented in the *Commercium Epistolicum* was trapped in a dilemma. Holding that Newton was the original inventor of the calculus and Leibniz the borrower, it was essential to argue that there was nothing to be found in the Leibnizian method that was not in Newton's. Thus Article IV states that "The differential method is one and the same with the method of fluxions, excepting the name and mode of notation." The same argument appears in Humphry Ditton [21] in the statement that the two methods "agree perfectly in all their Operations as to the Point of Practice." Yet the defenders felt it incumbent upon them to maintain the *superiority* and not merely the priority of the fluxional method. The legitimate arguments would have been, first, that of the simplicity and efficiency of the Newtonian method in respect to principles, notation, and operations, could this have been

[21] *An Institution of Fluxions* (London, 1726; 2nd edition).

made out; and, second, that of the power to solve problems presented, *e.g.,* the problem of the curve of quickest descent proposed by John Bernoulli in 1696.   But Hayes,[22] Raphson,[23] and Keill[24] in putting Leibniz under (and subsequently James Jurin[25] and Colson[26] in reply to Berkeley's attack in *The Analyst*) argued, with Ditton, that " The Fundamental Principles which the *Method of Fluxions* is built upon, and proceeds (in all its Operations) from; appear to be more˙accurate, clear, and convincing, than those of the differential calculus."

In seeking to establish an asserted " great difference " between the two methods, two extra-mathematical arguments were introduced. The first was a theory of knowledge which insisted that mathematical ideas framed in the mind or imagination had legitimacy only so far as abstraction from physical objects and processes, or analogy with them, could be shown.   The second was a metaphysical contention that only that which has a being in geometry and nature is eligible to be asserted as an element in mathematics.   Conceivability upon an empirical basis and reference to physical reality were the two criteria. Both arguments were employed to repudiate the infinitesimals of the Leibnizian calculus.   Newton's rejection of infinitely small quantities in the *Quadrature of Curves* was affirmed by the defenders of Newton, who ignored or tried to rationalize away Newton's use in the *Principia* of moments as infinitely little parts.

A typical argument is one appearing in Volume 29, No. 342 of the *Philosophical Transactions* attributed to Keill.

We have no Ideas of infinitely little Quantities, and therefore Mr. Newton introduced Fluxions into his Method, that it might proceed with finite Quantities as much as possible.   It is more Natural and Geometrical, because founded on the prime ratios of nascent quantities, which have a being in Geometry, while Indivisibles, upon which the Differential Method is founded, have no Being either in Geometry or in Nature.

Having committed themselves to the argument that " the idea of the generation of quantities " is to be admitted into mathematics, but

---

[22] *A Treatise of Fluxions* (London, 1704).

[23] *The History of Fluxions* (London, 1715).

[24] *Phil. Trans.,* Vol. 29, No. 342, pp. 205–206.   " An Account of a Book entitled Commercium Epistolicum . . . ."

[25] *Geometry, No Friend to Infidelity;* or a Defense of Sir Isaac Newton and the British Mathematicians in a Letter Addressed to the Author of the Analyst (London, 1734).   Written under the pseudonym of Philalethes Cantabrigiensis; *The Minute Mathematician* (London, 1735).

[26] *The History of Fluxions* (London, 1736).

not Leibniz's infinitesimals, because the latter are both inconceivable and have no being in nature, the British mathematicians became vulnerable to precisely the objections advanced by Berkeley. If it be held that mathematical ideas must have this double warrant of empirical conceivability and existential reality, where in our knowledge of nature are we entitled to assert, Berkeley asks, " quantities infinitely less than the least discernible Quantity; and other infinitely less than the preceding infinitesimals, and so on without end or limit? " Discernible quantity and assignable number, says Berkeley, are intelligible and proper notions; but the infinites of the modern analysis are such that " we shall discover much Emptiness, Darkness, and confusion; nay, if I mistake not, direct Impossibilities and Contradictions."

Neither Berkeley nor his opponents differentiated the meaning of terms assigned within a mathematical system in its procedures from ideas about existence which are subject to an empirical criterion of meaning.

Now as our Sense is strained and puzzled with the perception of Objects extremely minute, even so the Imagination, which Faculty derives from Sense, is very much strained and puzzled to frame clear Ideas of the least Particles of time, or the least Increments generated therein: and much more so to comprehend the Moments, or those Increments of the flowing Quantities in *statu nascenti*, in their very first origin or beginning to exist, before they become finite Particles. And it seems still more difficult, to conceive the abstracted Velocities of such nascent imperfect Entities. But the Velocities of the Velocities, the second, third, fourth, and fifth Velocities, &c. exceed, if I mistake not, all Humane Understanding. The further the Mind analyseth and pursueth these fugitive Ideas, the more it is lost and bewildered; the Objects, at first fleeting and minute, and soon vanishing out of sight. Certainly in any Sense, a second or a third Fluxion seems an obscure Mystery.[27]

Berkeley had a lot of fun in deriding " shadowy entities " and the " ghosts of departed quantities." If the defenders of Newton had acknowledged that Newton used infinitely small quantities in his calculus up to 1704 but had then changed his system, the contradictions pointed out by Berkeley in comparing the *Quadrature of Curves* with statements about *moments* in the *Principia* would not have proved so embarrassing. In any event, Berkeley prodded Robins[28]

[27] *The Analyst: or a Discourse Addressed to an Infidel Mathematician* (London, 1734), 8–9.

[28] *A Discourse Concerning the Nature and Certainty of Sir Isaac Newton's Methods of Fluxions, and of Prime and Ultimate Ratios* (London, 1735).

and Maclaurin [29] to an examination of the foundations of the calculus. Both responded by rejecting the extra-mathematical arguments which their predecessors had advanced in supporting the superiority of the fluxional method, and each contributed clarification of the idea of limits. Newton himself had a hand in his defense in claims made of priority and superiority, and so cannot be exempted from criticism brought against the arguments of his friends. Yet he does not assert as they did, that the foundations of mathematics are to be sought in correspondence of mathematical terms with physical properties. Such a supposition, either on rationalistic or empiricistic theorizing, is offered to account for the success of mathematical reasoning in solving physical problems. Newton rejects both Descartes' *a priori* rationalism in mathematics and the notion that abstraction from experienced objects needs to be argued in support of mathematical ideas. The mathematical way of proceeding in physical science requires no bond beyond itself to connect physical phenomena with mathematical determinations; for the very procedures of quantifying data by measurement and of instituting rules of measure results in the mathematical-physical principles upon which demonstration depends. The devising of mathematical concepts and instruments for the solution of problems presented is the mind's work. The development of an analytical principle is itself a passage from problems presented in geometry and mechanics to universal methods of expansion, differentiation, and integration.

[29] *A Treatise of Fluxions,* 2 vols. (Edinburgh, 1742).

⊷§ Melbourne G. Evans

ARISTOTLE, NEWTON, AND THE
THEORY OF CONTINUOUS MAGNITUDE

In mathematics, entities such as lines, planes, and solids have generally been regarded either as summations of infinitesimal parts, or else as products generated by the flow of some one entity taken as primary. The one view is static, and essentially arithmetical; the other is dynamic, and essentially geometrical.

The intent of this paper is to trace somewhat the history of this long conflict between the arithmetical and the geometrical viewpoints, and to indicate the position occupied by Aristotle and Newton in common opposition to what has been the dominant current of mathematical thought.

I

"Nothing that is continuous," Aristotle held, "can be composed of indivisibles."[1] Aristotle was clear that time is not composed of instants, nor a line of points.[2] For both time and a line are instances of continua, and a continuum is "that which is divisible into divisibles that are infinitely divisible."[3] More exactly, perhaps, a continuous magnitude is one which admits of being cut into an indefinite number of parts, where each cut is the limit of two contiguous parts.[4] However, the magnitude—a line, for instance—is not divisible *ad infinitum*, and therefore continuous, *because* it is a summation of an infinity of points; rather, the magnitude is divisible *ad infinitum* in that a final division is inconceivable. The line is itself a unity. It presupposes the infinity of points only in the sense that any assigned mid-point may be realized by cutting the line at that point.

It is evident that Aristotle's thought is here geometrical, and not arithmetical, in character. It is further evident that Aristotle has here rested the continuity of the line upon the continuity of motion. It is by motion, he holds, that magnitude is perceived,[5] and it is the cessation of motion that divides a line, and thereby realizes its potential mid-points.[6] What is conceivable, therefore, is a continuous motion between any two points, A and B, without regard to mid-points. What alone is inconceivable is a motion so discontinuous as to realize every potential mid-point between A and B. Furthermore, it is motion, Aristotle implies, which is directly responsible for the generation of continuous magnitude: "A moving line generates a surface and a moving point a line."[7] Or, as Simplicius later paraphrased

[1] *Phys.* 231a 24. Unless otherwise noted, references are to the Oxford edition.
[2] Cf. *ibid.*, 215b 19, 220a 18.   [3] *Ibid.*, 232b 24.
[4] Cf. *Met.* 1069a 5, *Phys.* 227a 10.   [5] *De An.* 425a 16.   [6] *Phys.* 262a 23.
[7] *De An.* 409a 4. The ascription of this position to Aristotle requires justification. Aristotle holds that "all lines are intermediate between points" (*Phys.* 227a 30), and he denies categorically that an indivisible, such as a point, can have motion: "that which is without parts cannot be in motion except accidentally . . .

the Aristotelian doctrine, the line is "the fluxion of the point."[8]

II

The argument of Aristotle was no doubt motivated by opposition to Democritean atomism; nevertheless, it reflected the typical, Greek attitude toward the infinitely small (or, for that matter, toward infinity as such). The infinitesimal has, at best, a precarious existence. It is a magnitude smaller than anything finite, yet greater than zero. It is a fictitious magnitude, such as the distance between consecutive points on a line, or the interval of time during which a thrown ball is at the zenith of its arc. As a fixed magnitude, or indivisible, it is a geometrical atom, or an instant of time. Greek rigor could never sanction such a quantity. Indeed, Zeno had long since issued a general dictum against the infinitesimal: "If when something is taken away that which is left is no less, and if it becomes no greater by receiving additions, evidently that which has been added or taken away is nothing."[9] Certainly Aristotle has ample grounds for rejecting infinitesimal considerations.

However, the authority of the Aristotelian tradition was never absolute. The concept of the infinitesimal had a strong appeal, even for Greek thought. Of interest here is a fragment from Democritus:

If a cone were cut by a plane parallel to the base, what ought one to think of the surfaces resulting from the section: are they equal or unequal? If they are unequal, they will make the cone have many steplike indenta-

---

there can be no motion of a point or of any other indivisible " (*Phys.* 240b 8, 241a 7). However, in his analysis of time, Aristotle draws a significant parallel between the generation of motion, and the generation both of time and of a line (Cf. *Phys.* 219b 9ff). Just as the moving body, by virtue of its successive appearances at successive places, generates motion, so the "now," in so far as it pertains first to one and then to another state of affairs, generates time. Since the "now" is the indivisible element in time, it is evident that Aristotle here regards an indivisible as generating a continuous magnitude. But again, the relation of the body to its motion is analogous to that of the point to the line: "there corresponds to the point the body which is carried along . . . this is an identical *substratum*" (*ibid.*, 219b 17). In short, just as the "now," by its constant flux, generates time, and the moving object traces out movement, so the point, by its motion, generates the line.

[8] Cited in W. D. Ross, *Aristotle's Metaphysics* (Oxford, 1924), I, 206. Aristotle does not, of course, claim credit for this definition. Possibly it originated in the Older Academy. At any rate, it seems to have become a part of the later Pythagorean doctrine (Cf. Nichomachus, *Introduction*, II. 6.3ff.), and Sextus ascribes it to the whole school of Greek Geometers: " For they assert that the line is produced by the flow of the point, the surface by that of the line, and the solid body by that of the surface" (*Adv. Geom.* 19).

[9] Frag. 2, in Milton C. Nahm, *Selections from Early Greek Philosophy* (2d ed., New York, 1940), 122.

tions and unevennesses; but if they are equal, the sections will be equal, and the cone will appear to have the same property as a cylinder, being made up of equal, not unequal, circles; which is most absurd.[10]

How Democritus resolved this difficulty—if, indeed, he did resolve it—is not known. Nevertheless, the reference to the cylinder as " being made up of equal . . . circles " suggests the idea of a solid as the sum of an infinite number of parallel planes, or indefinitely thin laminae. It is probable that Democritus had recourse to some such notion as this in first determining the formulae for the volume of the pyramid and the cone.[11] Furthermore, it is now known that even the great Syracusean, Archimedes, was not adverse to infinitesimal considerations. On the contrary, the key to his method of investigation lay in the assumption that the area of any surface can be regarded as composed of the straight lines within it. However, Archimedes warns that by this method, the results are not proved, but rather conjectured, to be correct.[12]

The late medieval period witnessed a searching examination and criticism of the Aristotelian doctrines. Here it will suffice to consider the work of one man, namely, that of Nicole Oresme (d. 1382).

Aristotle had denied categorically the existence of an instantaneous velocity. " Nothing," he held, " can be in motion in a present." [13] Oresme accepted the proposition that every velocity must persist throughout a temporal interval. But Oresme likewise sought to express the concept of an instantaneous rate of change. Thus he noted that an instantaneous velocity can be given graphic representation as a straight line.[14] Furthermore, and more important, he attempted to define a method whereby to determine the instantaneous value of a varying velocity. He notes, for instance, that the velocity of a falling body at any instant can be measured by the distance which that body would traverse, in unit time, " if the motion were to continue uniformly " (*magis descendit vel descenderet si continuaretur simpliciter*) from the given instant.[15]

[10] Frag. 155, trans. by Kathleen Freeman, *Ancilla to the Pre-Socratic Philosophers* (Oxford, 1948), 106.

[11] In fairness to Democritus, it must be pointed out that we cannot, with any certainty, attribute to him a mathematical, as well as a physical, atomism. However, the doctrine of atomism, which we owe to him, had a decisive influence on mathematical thought. This influence was furthered by the singular fact that the later followers of Democritus were likewise followers, not of Aristotle, but of Pythagoras and Plato. Materialism and mysticism here combined in a fruitful, if nevertheless unholy, alliance.

[12] *Geometrical Solutions Derived from Mechanics* (La Salle, Illinois, 1942), 10: " the triangle . . . consists of the straight lines in the triangle . . . and the segment . . . consists of those straight lines within the segment of the parabola . . ."

[13] *Phys.* 234a 24.

[14] Cf. Carl Boyer, *The Concepts of the Čalculus* (New York, 1949), 82.

[15] Pierre Duhem, *Études sur Léonard de Vinci* (Paris, 1913), III, 390.

However, Oresme's analysis of motion had implications which carry far beyond this point. Aristotle had distinguished between uniform and non-uniform velocities, and certain of the early fourteenth-century schoolmen had distinguished between uniform and nonuniform accelerations.[16] Furthermore, these same schoolmen held that any change in the intensity of a quality is by addition, or subtraction, of parts.[17] Thus the acceleration of a velocity would be by the addition, or subtraction, of increments of velocity per unit time. Oresme gave systematic and rigorous expression to these results by use of a coordinate system.

Consider a system of rectangular coordinates. Oresme observes that the extension of any quality capable of variation can be represented by a distance taken along the abscissa of the system, whereas the intension of the quality, taken at any point in its extension, can be represented by a straight line perpendicular to the abscissa. For the particular case of motion, Oresme identified extension with time or duration, the intension at any instant of time being simply velocity.[18]

In terms of this system of coordinates, a uniform motion would be represented by a straight line parallel to the abscissa. But a uniformly accelerated motion is one to which equal increments of velocity are added in equal intervals of time. Such a motion should therefore be represented by a line broken into a series of steps, but proceeding at a constant angle to the abscissa. However, Oresme saw fit to represent a uniformly accelerated motion by a straight line inclined to the abscissa.

What this signifies is simply this: Oresme has here utilized the concept of an instantaneous rate. As against intervals of time represented by the width of narrow rectangles, he considers only instants of time, represented by the width of geometrical, or ideal, lines. Furthermore, Oresme knew that the area under a velocity-time graph represents distance. He offers no proof for this; nevertheless, he seems to regard the area under such a graph as being made up of lines, the length of each line representing the magnitude of the velocity at a particular instant of time, and the " width " of the line the duration of that instant. The " area " of any line must therefore represent the distance traversed during a given instant, and the sum of an infinity of such lines is the distance traversed during a finite interval of time.

The argument of Oresme was repeated throughout the fifteenth and sixteenth centuries. However, it was the seventeenth century which was to witness a virtual flowering of the method of indivisibles. Thus Kepler regarded the circle as an infinite polygon: *Circuli . . . circumferentia partes habet totidem, quot puncta, puta infinitas;* whence it followed that the area of the circle could be determined as the sum ˙of an infinity of triangles,

[16] Cf. *Phys.* 238a 5; Duhem, *op. cit.*, 309ff.

[17] Richard of Middletown saw in the growth of even a form such as charity, the result of a simple addition of parts. Cf. Duhem, *op. cit.*, 330, 344.   [18] *Ib.*, 377–82.

ach having as its base a point on the circumference of the circle, and with common vertices at the center.[19] In like manner, the Oxford theologian nd mathematician, John Wallis, regarded the area of any plane figure as he sum of an infinite number of parallelograms, each an infinitely small art of the altitude of the figure. Wallis introduced the reciprocal of innity to indicate the magnitude of an indefinitely small quantity, or " nonquanta." The parallelogram whose altitude is infinitely small, he held, s " scarcely anything but a line." Only it is a line that is somehow " extensible," a line that has " such a small thickness that by an infinite multilication a certain altitude or width can be acquired." [20]

Kepler and Wallis had only a practical motive in their work: the development of a usable calculus. However, the history of mathematics in he late sixteenth and early seventeenth centuries had been dignified by at east one attempt to argue, rather than to merely assume, the reality of ndivisibles as the constituents of continuous magnitude. This was the ttempt made by Galileo.

Although Aristotle had held that a line, or other continuous magnitude, s potentially divisible without end, he nonetheless denied that it is possible or a body to be divisible, even potentially, " at all points simultaneusly." [21] Galileo has no quarrel with the first of these assumptions. Ineed, he is at pains to point out that by successive division one proceeds ot toward, but away from, the resolution of any given magnitude into an nfinity of parts. Nevertheless, Galileo denies the second of Aristotle's ssumptions. It is entirely possible, he holds, to divide a line simultaneusly at all points. The trick is simply to bend the line into a circle. To uote Galileo's own remarks:

May I not say . . . that, when I have bent the straight line into a polyon having an infinite number of sides, i.e. into a circle, I have reduced to ctuality that infinite number of parts which you claimed, while it was traight, were contained in it only potentially? Nor can one deny that the ivision into an infinite number of points is just as truly accomplished as he one into four parts when the square is formed or into a thousand parts 'hen the millagon is formed; for in such a division the same conditions are atisfied as in the case of a polygon of a thousand or a hundred thousand ides. Such a polygon laid upon a straight line touches it with one of its ides, i.e., with one of its hundred thousand parts; while the circle which is polygon of an infinite number of sides touches the same straight line with ne of its sides which is a single point different from all its neighbors and herefore separate and distinct in no less degree than is one side of a polyon from the other sides.[22]

[19] Léon Brunschwicg, *Les Étapes de la Philosophie Mathématique* (Paris, 1912), 61; Moritz Cantor, *Vorlesungen Ueber Geschichte der Mathematik* (2d ed.; eipzig, 1900), II, 824.

[20] *De sectionibus conicis*, in Boyer, *op. cit.*, 171.   [21] *De Gen. et Corr.* 316b 22.

[22] *Dialogues Concerning Two New Sciences*, trans. by Henry Crew and Alfonso

Here, certainly, is a complete break with the tradition of Aristotle. Greek rigor had never allowed the overt identification of curvilinear with rectilinear figures. Indeed, Aristotle had even gone so far as to deny that a circular arc can have the same length as any straight line! [23]

III

By the time of Newton, two views of the generation of continuous magnitude had been promulgated: that of flowing quantities, and that of the summation of indivisibles.[24]

In his first systematic account of the calculus, the *De Analysi,* Newton, like his predecessors, worked in terms of the infinitely small, or the indivisible. However, even his first treatment of the subject marked a decisive advance. Whereas previous investigators had treated the area under a curve as an aggregate of parallel lines,[25] Newton inverted the pro-

---

de Salvio (Evanston and Chicago: Northwestern University Press, 1939), p. 47. It is significant that Galileo argues his case not merely with reference to geometry, but also to physics and arithmetic. Just as the line is a continuum, resolvable into points, so too, he holds, a physical substance, such as water or a crystal, is a continuum, resolvable into atoms, and the number system is a continuum, resolvable into integers. In short, whatever is continuous is built out of an infinite number of discrete and indivisible elements. Cf. *ib.* 48.   [23] *Phys.* 248a 13, b 6.

[24] It should be pointed out that certain of Newton's predecessors tended to slur over this distinction. Thus Isaac Barrow, Newton's friend and teacher, pointed out that " time has many analogies with a line." For just as time " can be looked upon as constituted from a simple addition of successive instants or as from a continuous flow of one instant," so too a line " can be looked upon as being made up of an infinite number of points or as the trace of a moving point." Here Barrow was no doubt influenced by the Italian school of mathematicians. Cavalieri, for instance had generated continuous magnitudes by addition of indivisible elements. He had likened the indivisibles of a surface to the threads in a piece of cloth, and those of a solid to the leaves of a book. However, even Cavalieri—who held rigor to be an affair of philosophy and not of geometry—was hard put to explain how points, which have no dimensions, lines, which have no width, and planes, which have no thickness, can add up to finite magnitudes in one, two, or three dimensions. Hence Cavalieri was driven, in the final analysis, to the view of Aristotle. By motion, he concluded, the point generates a line, the line a surface, and the surface a solid. *The Geometrical Lectures of Isaac Barrow,* trans. by J. M. Child (Chicago and London, 1916), 37; Bonaventura Cavalieri, *Exercitationes geometrica sex* (Bologna, 1647), 3, 6–7.

[25] This was of course implicit in the work of Oresme. However, Barrow made it explicit: " If through all points of a line representing time are drawn straight lines so disposed that no one coincides with another (i.e. parallel lines), the plane surface that results as the aggregate of the parallel straight lines, when each represents the degree of velocity corresponding to the point through which it is drawn . . . can most conveniently be adapted to represent the space traversed also. . . . It may be contended that rightly to represent each separate degree of

cedure, and treated the area, not as an aggregate of lines, but as a function of the rate of growth, or momentary increase, at a point. Thus, given the curve, $y = f(x)$, the rate of increase in the area at any point under that curve will be equal to the height, y, of the curve at that point. That is to say, $dA/dx = y$; whence, $A = \int y dx$.

This statement of Newton's method has, of course, employed modern terminology. There is no way to know, exactly, how Newton conceived the rate of growth at a point or instant. However, it seems evident that he employed the notion of an indefinitely narrow rectangle whose length and width gives an element, or " moment," of the area under the curve— the total area, as Newton puts it, " from its Moment being at all times given." [26] In other words, the fundamental concept, for Newton, was that of a rate of change, or growth. Given this rate for the area at any point, and the area itself may then be determined as the indefinite integral of the known function of the ordinate. The process of integration, therefore, is no longer one of summation. Rather, the integral is itself now grounded squarely in the notion of the derivative.

The ideas of Newton were further developed and clarified in subsequent works. In the *Methodus Fluxionum*, Newton introduced his characteristic concepts and notation. Adopting the terminology of the fourteenth-century Scholastic, Richard Swineshead, he referred to any quantity which increases uniformly as a " flowing quantity," or " fluent," while its rate of generation was termed a " fluxion." [27] Since the terminology of Newton is archaic, it may be well to point out that fluxions are here taken to be finite rates of change, and not evanescent quantities. It is only the " moment " of a fluxion that is infinitely small, and which corresponds to the dy or dx of Leibniz.

As an illustration of Newton's mode of procedure, consider the equation, $x^2 + 2y = 0$. In any " indefinitely little interval " of time, the flowing quantities, x and y, must generate " indefinitely little accessions," or moments, the moment of a fluent being " the product of its celerity . . . into an infinitely small quantity o." Thus after any such interval of time, the quantities, x and y, must become $x + \dot{x}o$ and $y + \dot{y}o$, and these new values can then be substituted into the original equation. The result is,

$$x^2 + 2x\dot{x}o + \dot{x}o\dot{x}o + 2y + 2\dot{y}o = 0.$$

---

velocity retained during any timelet, a very narrow rectangle ought to be substituted for the right line and applied to the given interval of time. Quite so, but it comes to the same thing whichever way you take it " (*op. cit.*, 39). It is evident that Barrow felt little need for rigor!

[26] *Sir Isaac Newton's Two Treatises of the Quadrature of Curves, and Analysis By Equations of an Infinite Number of Terms*, trans. by John Stewart (London, 1745), 335.

[27] *The Method of Fluxions and Infinite Series*, trans. by John Colson (London, 1736), 20.   [28] *Ibid.*, 24–25.   [29] *Ibid.*, 20.

But, Newton notes, by the original supposition, $x^2 + 2y$ is equal to zero, and these terms can therefore be " expunged," while the remaining terms can be divided by o. There remains,

$$2x\dot{x} + \dot{x}\dot{x}o + 2\dot{y} = O.$$

But again, the quantity o is by definition infinitely small; and hence, Newton continues, " the terms that are multiplied by it will be nothing in respect of the rest." " Therefore," he adds, " I reject them." The result now will be,[28]

$$2x\dot{x} + 2\dot{y} = O.$$

It is of course evident that here, as in the *De Analysi*, Newton based his method upon the infinitesimal. However, it is equally evident that here—as indeed in that former work—the conception was dynamic rather than static. Although Newton remarks that he has no need to regard time in any formal sense,[29] nevertheless, a fluent or a flowing quantity has the character of time, and a fluxion is itself a velocity. Indeed, even the moment of a fluxion, though infinitely small, has the character of an evanescent motion rather than the static form of an indivisible. In short, the idea of generation, basic to Newton's doctrine in the *Methodus Fluxionum*, is that of the continuous motion of a point, and not the constant addition of discrete elements.

With the *De Quadratura Curvarum*, Newton broke once and for all with the notion of the infinitesimal. The overt rejection of infinitesimal quantities in the final stages of a calculation has no sanction in logic, and Newton himself remarks: " The very smallest errors in mathematical matters are not to be neglected." [30] Hence he has sought to show that the method of fluxions does not require the introduction into geometry of infinitely small quantities, and that this method is, in fact, " consonant to the geometry of the Ancients." [31]

Newton illustrates his new mode of analysis by determining the fluxion of x^n. Let the quantity x flow uniformly, and as x becomes $x + o$, the power x^n becomes $(x + o)^n$. Now expand the latter term, subtract the original from the augmented quantities, and divide through by o to get the ratio of the change in x to the change in x^n, namely,

$$1 \text{ to } nx^{n-1} + \frac{n(n-1)}{2} ox^{n-2} + \ldots$$

" Now," Newton concludes, " let these augments vanish, and their ultimate ratio will be 1 to nx^{n-1}."[32]

The ratio, 1 to nx^{n-1}, Newton refers to variously as " the ultimate ratio of the evanescent parts," or as " the first ratio of the nascent augments." [33]

[30] *Sir Isaac Newton's Two Treaties* . . . , 2.   [31] *Ibid.*, 4.   [32] *Loc. cit.*
[33] *Ibid.*, 2.   [34] *Ibid.*, 1.   [35] Boyer, *op. cit.*, 294.

The terminology is unfortunate. However, it is clear that Newton was here able to regard fluxions as ultimate ratios only in so far as he assumed that fluents are themselves generated by continuous motion, and not by the addition of parts. Thus in the introduction to this work, he remarks:

I consider mathematical quantities in this place not as consisting of very small parts, but as described by a continued motion. Lines are described, and thereby generated not by the apposition of parts, but by the continued motion of points; superficies's by the motion of lines; solids by the motion of superficies's; angles by the rotation of the sides; portions of time by a continual flux: and so in other quantities.[34]

"These geneses," Newton adds, "really take place in the nature of things, and are daily seen in the motion of bodies."

With Newton, as with Aristotle, the generation of continuous magnitude is thus ascribed to the motion of a part.

IV

The intent of this paper has been to exhibit an area of essential agreement between the Aristotelian and the Newtonian theories of continuous magnitude. Aristotle and Newton insist upon the necessity, and the validity, of an appeal to the intuition of motion in any analysis of continuous magnitude. They reject, categorically, the abstract, arithmetical viewpoint. Yet as one writer has bluntly remarked: "The introduction of uniform motion into Newton's method of fluxions was an irrelevant evasion of the question of continuity, disguised as an appeal to intuition."[35] There is little doubt but that this criticism reflects the attitude dominant in mathematics today.

However, it is not entirely certain that even Richard Dedekind, that most uncompromising of all protagonists of the arithmetical viewpoint, has succeeded in the effort to ground the theory of continuity in arithmetic, and to eliminate all reference to the intuition of motion.

The doctrine of Dedekind centers in the notion of a "cut." Although an infinity of rational numbers lie between any two rational numbers, however close, it is a singular fact that the entire set of rational numbers can nevertheless be so cut into two classes that every member of one class is less than every member of the other class, and yet no rational number lies between the two classes.[36] Hence the domain of rational numbers is not a continuum. Hence too, the domain of numbers as such can be made continuous only if this gap between the two classes of rational numbers can itself be given the status of a number.

Here Dedekind appeals to geometry. Let the points on a straight line

---

[36] This will be the case, for instance, if the lower class consists of all rational numbers whose squares are less than 2, and the upper class of all those whose squares are greater than 2. The two classes will then strive, so to speak, to meet. But the lower class will have no greatest member, and the upper class no least member. The gap between the two classes will never close.

fall into two classes, such that every point of the first class lies to the left of every point of the second class. Then by Dedekind's axiom of continuity, there exists on the line one point, and only one point, which produces this division of the line into two classes. But distances measured along a straight line correspond to numbers. If, therefore, the very nature of the line demands that a cut shall always be made at a point, so too the very nature of the number system must be such as to demand that any cut in the domain of rational numbers shall be produced by a number. In the particular case under consideration, the number which produces the cut—and is thereby defined by that cut—is not rational, but irrational. By virtue of this creation of irrational numbers, Dedekind notes, the domain of numbers gains " the same completeness . . . the same continuity, as the straight line." [37]

This, in brief, is the doctrine of Dedekind. Certainly it is undeniable that Dedekind's analysis has rendered more intelligible the nature of continuity. However, it is equally undeniable that Dedekind has assumed, but nowhere proven, the continuity of the straight line. He argues that every cut in the domain of rational numbers must define a real number; otherwise, the straight line will have to be regarded as discontinuous, which is absurd. Yet if it is absurd to regard the straight line as discontinuous, this certainly is not the case because that line is conceived to be an aggregate of points. Rather, this must be the case because the line is conceived to be traced out by the continuous motion of a point.

But not only has Dedekind assumed the continuity of the line, he has likewise explicated the continuity of the system of real numbers by analogy with the proper character of time. For time divides into two classes, the past and the future, and the present moment, which produces this cut, can belong to neither class. Hence the division of time, and the cut in the number system when produced by an irrational number, present analogous situations. And just as time, in the opinion of Aristotle, is both divided by the " now," and made continuous by it,[38] so too the domain of real numbers, in the view of Dedekind, is both divided by the irrational number, and made continuous by it.

In short, even the arithmetic of Dedekind pays tacit homage to the viewpoint of Aristotle and Newton, and abandons, in the last analysis, the age-long struggle to free the theory of continuous magnitude from the intuition of uniform motion.

---

[37] Richard Dedekind, *Essays on the Theory of Numbers*, trans. by Wooster W Beman (La Salle, Illinois, 1948), 9.   [38] *Phys.* 220a 4.

~♂ *Lynn Thorndike*

NEWNESS AND NOVELTY IN SEVENTEENTH-CENTURY SCIENCE AND MEDICINE

A remarkable feature of both scientific and pseudo-scientific works of the seventeenth century is the frequency with which such words as " new " and " unheard-of " appear in their titles. It is true that this nomenclature was not unknown to the middle ages, when in the early thirteenth century we have the *Poetria nova* of Geoffrey of Vinsauf and the *Rethorica novissima* of Boncompagni, at its close the *Vita Nuova* of Dante and *dolce stil nuovo,* or in the early fourteenth century the alchemical *Novum lumen* (New Light) and *Novum Testamentum* attributed to Arnald of Villanova. The classical reaction of the so-called Italian Renaissance preferred the antique to the new, but the realization of a *novus orbis* which resulted from the voyages of Columbus and Vespucci was followed by the bestowal of such place names as New Spain and New France, and later New England, New Hampshire, New York, New Jersey, Nova Scotia, Newfoundland, New Haven and Newport. And already in 1537 Bonaventure des Périers was satirizing the craving for news among his contemporaries.[1]

With the appearance of new stars from 1572 on, a new heaven as well as a new earth began to gain recognition. But the idea of newness was already present in other fields of knowledge than geography and astronomy. Paracelsus tried to introduce a New Medicine at the University of Basel in 1527. A book on new diseases appeared in 1541.[2] In 1554 Gomez Pereira wrote on new medicine,[3] and Petrus de Marchetis on new surgery.[4] Presently Claudius Campensius offered a new interpretation of the Aphorisms of Hippocrates.[5] In 1587 appeared the *New Geometry* of Patrizi, and in 1591 he dedicated his *New Philosophy* to Gregory XIV.[6] David Origanus issued new Brandenburg Ephemerides of the movements of the heavens for the years 1595–1655.[7]

With the next century the employment of such titles became more widespread and numerous, more habitual, repetitious and even stereotyped. This development was no doubt fomented and encouraged by growing opposition

---

[1] Lynn Thorndike, *A History of Magic and Experimental Science,* V (1941), 287.

[2] Johannes Baptista de Cavigliolis, *De morbis novis . . . ,* Poitiers, 1541.

[3] Gometius Pereira, *Novae veraeque medicinae . . . ,* 1554.

[4] Petrus de Marchetis, *Nova observatio et curatio chirurgica,* Padua, 1554.

[5] Claudius Campensis, *Hippocratis Aphorismorum nova interpretatio,* Lyons, 1579.   [6] Thorndike, *op. cit.,* VI, 373–77.   [7] *Ibid.,* VI, 60–61.

to Aristotle and scholasticism and the tendency toward a modern philosophy, by the Paracelsan revival of the later sixteenth century with its three *principia* instead of four elements, by the rise and spread of the quarrel of the ancients and the moderns, by the astronomical discoveries made possible by the telescope and heralded in the *Nuncius Sidereus* of Galileo and elsewhere, and by the increasing interest in the experimental method.

Descartes laid much stress upon the point that he had devised a new method, but he was by no means the first to do so. A New Method of Diagnosing Diseases appeared in the first year of the new century.[8] Steechius in 1606 believed that he was employing a method which was indeed derived from Galen and initiated by some recent famous men, but which had so far not been carried to complete fruition by anyone.[9] Despite the book of Claudius Campensis mentioned above, another author in 1612 observed a method in commenting upon the Aphorisms of Hippocrates which he described as " unheard-of in all past ages." [10] The very next year Rodolphe Le Maistre applied " a new interpretation and method " to the Aphorisms,[11] and only three years later yet another new method of treating the Aphorisms was published by yet a third author.[12] And in the year after that, a new method of treating wounds appeared.[13] The *Decisiones medicales* of Philip Savona, printed at Palermo in 1624 in folio, employed " a new mode of writing now first invented " (*novo scribendi modo primum invento*). The next year a new method of learning and practicing medicine was handed down by brief precepts in the Harmonic System of Medicine of Partlicius.[14] In 1631 a new method on the magnet was defended by a student of Athanasius Kircher's,[15] and in 1632 " a hitherto unexplained method of using

[8] Joh. Jessenius, Σημειωτικη, *seu nova cognoscendi morbos methodus*, 1601.

[9] Gott. Steechius, *Ars medica: tota conscripta methodo divisiva a Galeno diversis locis proposita commendata et exemplis illustrata, a recentioribus quibusdam clarissimis inchoata, sed a nemine hactenus absoluta*, Frankfurt-a-M., 1606, in-fol.

[10] Franciscus Fogerolaeus, *Methodus in septem Aphorismorum libros ab Hippocrate observata omnibus tamen retro saeculis inaudita*, Paris, 1612, in-4.

[11] Rudolphus Magister, *Doctrinam Hippocratis: Eiusdem Aphorismos nova interpretatione ac methodo ornatos* . . . etc., Paris, 1613, in-12.

[12] Emanuel Stupanus, *Hippocratis Aphor. nova methodo eiusmodi in ordinem digesta*, Basel, 1615, in-8 .

[13] Caesar Magatus, *De rara medicatione vulnerum . . . nova traditur methodus*, Venice, 1616.

[14] Simeon Partlicius, *Medici systematis harmonici in quo nova plane et artificiosa discendae et exercendae medicinae methodus per precepta brevia traditur*, Frankfurt-a-M., 1625, in-8.

[15] J. J. Sweigkhard, *Ars magnesia . . . experimentalis physico-mathematica de natura viribus et prodigiosis effectibus magnetis . . . novaque methodo*, Würzburg, 1631.

opium " was suggested.[16]

In the case of general presentations of natural philosophy we may first dismiss two works which appeared in print in the seventeenth century and whose titles asserted novelty but which really belong to the previous century. In 1622 was published at Braga the *Nueva filosofia de la naturalezza del hombre no conocida ni alcançada de los grandes filosofos antiguos,* by Dona Oliva Sabuco de Nantes Barrera, but the original Latin edition, with the title, *Nova philosophia de hominis natura,* dated from 1588. William Gilbert's New Philosophy Concerning Our Sublunar World (*De mundo nostro sublunari philosophia nova*) was printed only in 1651, although he had died in 1603, and the book at the date of its publication might have been supposed to be at least a half century behind the times.[17]

Similar titles were applied to works of more recent authorship. Theorems medical and philosophical were set forth with marvelous variety of learning and a new order of writing by Epiphanius Ferdinandus at Venice in 1611,[18] while at Paris in 1619 was published J. B. Morin's New Anatomy of the Sublunar World.[19] Mersenne's Unheard-of Questions in 1634 [20] were followed the next year by Nieremberg's New and Most Curious Questions in Natural History.[21] Fontana issued New Observations of Things Celestial and Terrestrial in 1646,[22] adding cautiously, " and perhaps not hitherto published." Dobrzensky printed his New Philosophy of Fountains in 1657.[23] The Idea of Synopsis of a New and Experimental Philosophy, and The Synopsis of a New Philosophy and Medicine, both by Travaginus, came out in the years 1666 and 1667 respectively.[24] Richard Browne's volume of

[16] Joh. Freitag, *De opii natura et medicamentis opiatis, hactenusque inexplicata iis utendi methodo,* Groningen, 1631, in-8.

[17] Thorndike, *op. cit.,* VI, 379–82, for some account of it.

[18] Epiph. Ferdinandus, *Theoremata medica et philosophica mira doctrinae varietate novoque scribendi ordine donata . . . ,* Venice, 1611, in-fol.

[19] J. B. Morinus, *Nova mundi sublunaris anatomia,* Paris, 1619, in-8.

[20] Marin Mersenne, *Questions inouyes ou récréation des scavans.*

[21] Juan Eusebio Nieremberg (of Madrid), *Historia naturae maxime peregrinae libris xvi distincta, in quibus rarissima naturae arcana . . . ; novae et curiosissimae quaestiones disputantur . . . ,* Antwerpiae apud Balthasarum Moretum, 1635, in-fol.

[22] F. Fontana, *Novae coelestium terrestriumque rerum observationes, et fortasse hactenus non vulgatae,* Naples, Gaffaro, 1646.

[23] J. J. W. Dobrzensky, *Nova et amaenior* (amoenior ?) *de admirando fontium genio philosophia,* Ferrara, A. & J. B. de Marestis, 1657, in-fol.

[24] Franciscus Travaginus, *Idea seu synopsis novae et experimentalis philosophiae quam tum ad medicamenta chemica tum ad alios usus accuravit.* Extat cum Georgii Aras Enchiridio Hermetico-Medico, Venet. apud Joh. Jac. Hertz, 1666, in-12. *Synopsis novae philosophiae et medicinae cuius fundamenta seu principia salia acidum et salsum ex quibus oritur omne fermentum,* Venice, 1667, in-12.

1678 overthrew the principles of things received by the ancients and set up new principles which actually exist in nature.[25]   Saint Romain's Physics or Natural Science Freed from the Quibbles of Scholasticism was further described in its title as A New Work, with many curious experiments and observations from medicine and chemistry.[26]

If we turn to manuscripts, we find a reformed natural philosophy, condemnation and solid refutation of Peripatetic Physiology, and the introduction of a new and truer one by the brothers, Gerard (1604–50) and Arnold Botius (1606–53) M.D.'s of Holland, in a manuscript of the Bibliothèque Nationale, Paris.[27]   The work was also printed—at Dublin in 1641.[28]

Treatises on the new star of 1604 almost inevitably had the word " new " in their titles.[29] But a similar wording is found in other titles of astronomical works.   Kepler set forth two of his famous laws in *Astronomia nova . . . de motibus stellae Martis*, 1609.   In 1609 at Zurich appeared the first edition of a treatise by Leonhard Zubler on a new astronomical instrument devised by himself.[30]   In 1611 at Florence Santucci issued a *Trattato nuovo*

[25] Richard Browne, περί ἀρχῶν.   In quo recepta veteribus rerum principiis evertuntur et nova ut in natura vere sunt stabiliuntur, Londini apud Thomam Passinger, 1678, in-8.   Here again, as in note 8 above, another favorite seventeenth-century practice, of initiating a title with a word or two of Greek, is illustrated.

[26] G. B. de Saint Romain, *Physica sive scientia naturalis scholasticis tricis liberata. Opus novum. Curiosis plurimis ex medicina et chymia experimentis necnon observationibus . . .* , Leyden, 1684, in-12.   The title of the French version is: *La science naturelle dégagée des chicanes de l'école: ouvrage nouveau, enrichi de plusieurs expériences curieuses tirées de la Médecine et de la Chymie; et de quelques observations utiles à la santé du corps*, Paris, 1679.

[27] Latin MS. 12975, incorrectly catalogued as 16th century: Philosophia Naturalis Reformata sive Physiologiae Peripateticae accurata damnatio et solida confutatio, et novae atque verioris introductio per Girardum ac Arnoldum Botios fratres Hollandos medicinae doctores.   Much is crossed out and much rewritten or inserted.

[28] Copies in the Bibliothèque Nationale: R.4325 and Rés.R.1013.

[29] For example, R. Gualterotti, *Discorso sopra l'apparizione de la nuova stella*, Florence, 1605, 36 pp.; Baldassare Capra, *Considerazioni astronomici sopra la nuova stella del 1604*, Padua, 1605; Johann Kepler, *De stella nova in pede serpentarii et qui sub eius exortum de novo iniit trigono igneo*, Prague, 1606; Elias Molerius, *De sydere novo seu de nova stella quae ab 8 die Octobris anni domini 1604 inter astra Sagittarii videri coepit ac annuae revolutionis 1605 periodo proxima extincta evanuit enarratio apodeictica*, Excudebat Iacobus Stoer, 1606: copy in Columbia University Library, 523.6 Z, vol. 2, tract 3.

According to Filippo Vecchietti, *Biblioteca Picena*, 1790–96, a work on the new star of 1604 by Hilarius Altobellus was printed, but I have not found it.   P. Riccardi, *Biblioteca matematica italiana*, 1893, says that it was not printed.

[30] *Novum instrumentum sciotericum*, Zurich, Jonas Gessner, 1609, in-4, 69 pp.: BM 8562.c.48.   The rest of the title and the text are in German.

delle comete and in the same year at Heidelberg Jacob Christmann published a Theory of the Moon demonstrated from new hypotheses and observations.[31] In 1614 were printed at Ingolstadt Mathematical Disquisitions concerning astronomical controversies and novelties.[32] Fortunatus Licetus wrote on new stars and comets [33] and Ilario Altobelli, in a letter in Italian, set forth a New Doctrine concerning the generation of comets against the opinion of Aristotle.[34] A Planisphere or Planetarium which Jacob Bartsch (1600–33), son-in-law of Kepler, first issued at Strasburg in 1624 bore the title, " Index of Aspects Old and New," [35] given more fully in the later edition of 1661 as " Astronomical Use of the Index for finding aspects old and especially new without calculation." [36]

Albrecht Kurtz, a Jesuit who wrote under the pseudonym Barrettus, published a New System of the Heavens in 1626.[37] Wilkins, *Discovery of a New World in the Moon*, came out in 1638. Even those who opposed the Copernican theory might claim novelty for their views, as when the Jesuit Grandami composed a New Demonstration of the Immobility of the Earth.[38] Another Jesuit, Giovanni Battista Riccioli of Ferrara, professor of astronomy at Bologna, entitled his major work in that field, The New Almagest.[39] Huygens published a New Observation of the Moon of Saturn in 1656.[40]

[31] Iacobus Christmann (1554–1613), *Theoria lunae ex novis hypothesibus et observationibus demonstrata*, Heidelbergiae, Gotthard Voegelin, 1611, in-fol. According to a sales catalogue of E. P. Goldschmidt & Co., " Only two copies of this important book are known."

[32] (Christophorus Scheiner), *Disquisitiones mathematicae de controversiis et novitatibus astronomicis quas publicae disputandas posuit propugnavit Jo. Georgius Locher*, Ingolstadt, ex typographeo Ederiano, 1614, in-4.

[33] Fort. Licetus, *De novis astris et cometis*, Venice, 1623, in-4.

[34] Hilarius Altobellus, *Nova doctrina contra opinionem Aristotelis circa generationem cometarum epistola*, italice, Venice, typis Jacobi Sarzinae, 1627.

[35] *Index aspectuum veterum et novorum cum rotulis vii planetarum*, Strasburg, 1624. The accompanying text of this date seems not to have survived, but the preface to it in the edition of 1661 is dated from Strasburg, 1624.

[36] *Usus astronomicus indicis aspectuum veterum et praecipue novorum . . . sine calcula . . . inveniendorum . . . . Cui adjectae rotulae septem planetarum . . . et planisphaerio stellato . . . in plano delineato*, Nürnberg, P. Fürst, 1661.

[37] *Novum coeli systema:* it does not appear in the printed catalogues of the British Museum and the Bibliothèque Nationale.

[38] Jac. Grandamicus, *Nova demonstratio immobilitatis terrae petita ex virtute magnetica*, 1645. There are copies both in the British Museum and the Bibliothèque Nationale.

[39] Joannes Baptista Ricciolus, *Almagestum novum astronomiam veterem novamque complectens*, Bologna, 1651.

[40] *De Saturni luna observatio nova*, 1656.

Pierre Petit issued another new system of the world in 1660;[41] Cornelio Malvasia (1603–66) got out *Ephemerides novissimae* for the years 1661–66 in 1662 at Modena, and added Ephemerides of the Sun and Tables of Refractions " from the newest hypotheses " of Cassini. Bernouilli attempted a New System of Comets in 1682,[42] in which he held that they were satellites of a planet beyond Saturn which was invisible to us, and that they were visible only in the lower part of their orbit. Yet another new system of the world was published in French in 1679 by Mallemont de Messanges,[43] who advanced the hypothesis that all the planets, including the sun with Mercury as its moon, revolved in a Cartesian vortex and in exact concentric circles about an imaginary fixed point.[44]

Titles laying claim to novelty in the realm of experimental physics hardly become noticeable until after the appearance of Bacon's *Novum organum* in 1620 and Galileo's *Two New Sciences* in 1638.[45] Even then they are fewer than might have been expected. We have Pascal's *Expériences nouvelles touchant le vuide* in 1647; Zucchi's *Exclusio vacui contra nova experimenta* in 1649; Boyle's *New Experiments Touching the Spring of the Air* in 1660; Sinclair's New and Great Art of Gravity and Levity in 1669;[46] Leibniz' *Hypothesis physica nova* in 1671; and Otto von Guericke's (1602–86) New Magdeburg Experiments in 1672.[47] Pierre Varignon (1654–1722) published a Project for a New Mechanics in 1687[48] and New Conjectures on Weight in 1690.[49] William Briggs proposed a New Theory of Vision.[50]

[41] Along with *Observationes eclypsium* .... *De novo systemate mundi*, 1660: BM 52.f.13 and 531.h.12; BN R.3765 and V.7769.

[42] Giacomo Bernouilli (1654–1705), *Conamen novi systematis cometarum*, Amsterdam, 1682.

[43] Mallemont de Messanges, *Nouveau système du monde*, 1679.

[44] Louis Trenchard More, *Isaac Newton*, 1934, pp. 221–22.

[45] Galileo Galilei, *Discorsi e dimonstrazioni matematiche intorno a due nuove scienze, attenenti alla mecanica & i movimenti locali*, Leyden, Elzevir, 1638, in-4.

[46] Geo. Sinclair, *Ars nova et magna gravitatis et levitatis*, 1669.

[47] *Experimenta nova Magdeburgica de vacuo spatio*, 1672.

[48] Pierre Varignon, *Projet d'une nouvelle méchanique*, Paris, 1687. Varignon was professor of mathematics in the Collège Mazarin, then succeeded Du Hamel in philosophy at the Collège royale. He entered the Académie des Sciences as geometer in 1688. His *Nouvelle mécanique ou statique dont le projet fut donné en 1687*, was published posthumously in 1725.

[49] Pierre Varignon, *Nouvelles conjectures sur la pesanteur*, Paris, 1690.

[50] *Acta erudita* (1683), 454; also Wm. Briggs, *Ophthalmo-Graphia sive oculi descriptio anatomica, necnon eiusdem Nova visionis theoria Regiae Societati Londinensi proposita*, Leyden, 1686, in-16.

In the field of alchemy and chemistry the expression, New Light, which we have seen applied much earlier to a work ascribed to Arnald of Villanova, was used in the seventeenth century on several occasions. Sendivogius applied it to his volume of 1604,[51] of which there were numerous subsequent editions.[52] It was commented on by Ortelius in 1624 [53] and earlier was translated into French.[54] Glauber repeated the same title in 1664.[55] E. de Clave employed the phrase in French translation in the title of his *Nouvelle lumière philosophique des vrais principes et élémens de nature*, Paris, 1641. Joachim Polemann altered the Latin title of Sendivogius and Glauber to *Novum lumen medicum*, which was printed in 1647 and subsequently.[56] But his theme was still alchemical, the mystery of the sulphur of the philosophers.

Other assertions of novelty in alchemical titles are found in the *Alchimia nova* of J. B. Birellus, printed at Copenhagen in 1654, and in a work in four books by Weidenfeld on Secrets of the Adepts or use of the Lullian spirit of wine, which appeared at Hamburg in 1685. This subject might seem to be an old story, but it was supposed to be presented by a very novel method.[57] The analysis of Rhine wine by Portzius in 1672 was based upon new principles,[58] while Leibniz saw a new kind of chemical separation in the separation of salt and fresh water.[59] Ettmuller's general manual of

[51] Michael Sendivogius, *Novum lumen chymicum*, Prague, 1604.

[52] Frankfurt, 1606; Paris, 1608 by Beguin; Cologne, 1610; Frankfurt, 1611, under a different title, *De lapide philosophorum;* Cologne, 1614; Geneva, 1628; Venice, 1644.

[53] Reprinted in Zetzner, *Theatrum chemicum*, VI (1661), 397 *et seq.*

[54] *Cosmopolite, ou nouvelle lumière de la physique naturelle, traictant de la constitution générale des élémens simples et des composez.* Traduit nouvellement de latin en françois, par le sieur de Bosnay, Paris, 1609, 1618, 1629.

[55] J. R. Glauber, *Novum lumen chemicum*, 1664.

[56] It is included in Zetzner's *Theatrum chemicum*, VI (Strasburg, 1661), 600–74.

[57] Joh. Segerus Weidenfeld, *De secretis adeptorum sive de usu spiritus vini Lulliani libri IV. Opus practicum per concordantias philosophorum inter se discrepantium tam ex antiquis quam modernis philosophiae adeptae patribus mutuo conciliatis summo studio collectum et novissima concinne methodo ita digestum ut vel tyrones possint discernere vegetabilium animalium mineralium praeparationes supposititias sophisticasve a veris pro re medica sive metallica atque sic cavere sibi a vagabundis deceptoribus, imaginariis processibus et suarum pecuniarum dipalidatione*, Hamburg apud Gottofredum Schultzium, 1685, in-12.

[58] Joh. David Portzius, *Bacchus enucleatus . . . . Examen vini Rheani eiusque tartari spiritus aceti etc. ex novis principiis depromptum ac demonstratum*, Heidelberg, 1672, in-12.

[59] " De separatione salis et aquae dulcis novoque separationum chymicarum genere," *Acta eruditorum* (1682), 386.

chemistry, first published in Latin at Leyden in 1684 under the title, *Chimia rationalis ac experimentalis curiosa*, appeared in French translation at Lyon in 1593 as *Nouvelle chymie raisonée*.

Experiment and novelty were associated in chemical titles even later than in those of works of physics. J. J. Becher's *Experimentum chymicum novum* was published at Frankfurt in 1671. The Specimen of a New Chemical Experiment with the volatile salt of plants by G. W. Wedel appeared first in 1672 and again in 1676 and 1682.[60] Hanhard illustrated his treatment of salts by " new experiments." [61]

Kepler's New Stereometry appeared early in the century,[62] as did the treatise on inks of Caneparius, described in its title as " a work indeed new hitherto published by no one." [63] Glauber wrote on new philosophical furnaces or a description of a new art of distillation.[64]

Indeed, there was no field of scientific or natural interest in which new ideas and discoveries were not suggested by the titles of publications. In mathematics Albert Girard wrote *Invention nouvelle en l'Algèbre* (Amsterdam, 1629); and de la Hire composed *Nouveaux elemens des sections coniques* (1679 in-12). The New History of Mexican plants, animals and minerals which Hernandez had published in Mexico in 1615 was reissued at Rome in 1651.[65] The *Novus orbis* or description of the West Indies by Joannes de Laet of Antwerp, published first in Dutch in 1625, reappeared in Latin form with this title at Leyden in 1633,[66] and was translated into French in 1640. Severinus gave to the press New Experiments as to the nature of the viper; [67] Georgius a Turre enriched the catalogue of the botanical garden at Padua with a new increment; [68] Hannemann composed a

[60] G. W. Wedelius, *Specimen experimenti chimici novi de sale volatili plantarum*, 1672, 1676, 1682.

[61] J. H. Hanhard, *De salibus novis experimentis illus.*, Basel, 1685.

[62] Johann Kepler, *Nova stereometria doliorum vinariorum*, Linz, 1615. On the general subject see Geo. Sarton, *Introduction to the History of Science*, III (1948), 1112, 1318, 1580–81; Lynn Thorndike, " Visierkunst, Ars visorandi, or Stereometry," *Isis* 40 (1949), 106–107; " Stereometry before 1250," *Isis* 41 (1950), 48.

[63] P. M. Caneparius, *De atramentis cuiuscunque generis, opus sane novum hactenus a nemine promulgatum*, Venice, 1619; London, 1660; etc.

[64] J. R. Glauber, *Furni novi philosophici sive descriptio artis destillatoriae novae*, 1651.

[65] Francisco Hernandez, *Nova plantarum animalium et mineralium Mexicanorum historia . . .* , Rome, Deversinus et Masotti, 1651.

[66] *Novus orbis, sive descriptionis Indiae Occidentalis libri xviii, cum iconibus ac tabulis geographicis*, Leydae, 1633, in-fol. The Dutch title was *Nieuwe Wereldt* etc.; the French, *L'histoire du nouveau monde*.

[67] M. A. Severinus, *De viperae natura . . . experimenta nova*, Padua, 1651.

[68] Geo. a Turre, *Catalogus plantarum horti Patavini novo incremento locupletior*, Padua, 1662, in-12.

new and accurate method of knowing vegetable simples,[69] and John Ray, a New Method of Plants.[70] Morison published " A New Distribution " of umbelliferous plants in 1672,[71] and applied the same phrase to herbs in general in 1680.[72] Ruland of Regensburg compiled a new pharmacopeia,[73] and Macsius revised his work on *materia medica* by the addition of "most certain and unheard-of experiments." [74] Edmund Hollyng's *Medicamentorum oeconomia nova* dates back to 1610 and 1615. Becher composed a volume on a new way of measuring time; [75] Grindelius supplemented the *Micrographia* of Robert Hooke by a *Micrographia nova;* [76] and Whiston wrote *A New Theory of the Earth.*[77]

The titles of books on machines almost invariably laid claim to a novelty which their actual contents seldom corroborate. There was the *Novo teatro di machine* of Zonca, printed in 1607, five years after the death of its author; the *Machinae novae* of Verantius in 1615–16; the *Nova de machinis philosophia* of Zucchi, which appeared at Pisa in 1646; the *Theatrum machinarum novum* of G. A. Böckler, 1661; and Denys Papin, *Traité de plusieurs nouvelles machines et inventions extraordinaires sur différents sujets,* Paris, 1698, in-12. Rather oddly, in the case of inventions the word " new " does not occur in the title of the *Century of Inventions* of Edward Somerset, sixth earl and second marquis of Worcester, first published in 1663, nor in that of *A Pleasant and Compendious History of Inventions,* by John Harris in 1686. But it is found in *De novis inventis* of G. Paschius, second edition, Lipsiae, 1700.[78] A Jesuit father, Francesco Lana Terza, published a book written in Italian concerning new inventions in 1670.[79]

[69] Joh. Lud. Hannemann, *Nova et accurata methodus cognoscendi simplicia vegetabilia,* Kiloni, 1677, in-4.

[70] John Ray, *Methodus plantarum nova,* London, 1682.

[71] Robert Morison (1620–83), *Plantarum Umbelliferarum Distributio nova,* Oxford, 1672.

[72] *Plantarum Historiae Universalis Oxoniensis pars secunda, seu Herbarum distributio nova . . . ,* Oxford, 1680.

[73] Joh. David Rulandus, *Pharmacopoea nova,* Norimbergae, 1644, in-12.

[74] Joh. Geo. Macsius, *Promptuarium materiae medicae,* Frankfurt, 1654, in-8; Ulm, 1676, in-4; *Nunc vero accurate revisum variis arcanis atque experimentis certissimis ac inauditis auctum . . . ,* Lipsiae, 1677, in-12.

[75] J. J. Becher, *De nova temporis dimetiendi ratione,* London, 1680.

[76] Printed at Nürnberg, 1687.   [77] First edition, London, 1696.

[78] The title of the first edition placed the emphasis rather on antiquity: *Schediasma de curiosis hujus seculi inventis quorum accuratiori cultui facem praetulit antiquitas,* Kiloni, 1695, in-8.

[79] *Prodromo ouero saggio di alcune inuentioni nuoue premesso all' arte maestra . . . . Per mostrare li piu reconditi principii della naturale filosofia, riconsciuti con accurata teorica nelle piu segnalate inuentioni ed isperienze sin' hora ritrouate da gli scrittori di questra materia & altre nuoue dell'autore medesimo . . . ,* Brescia per li Rizzardi; copy in BN Rés.R.208.

Years later he issued in Latin A Mastery of Nature and Art which likewise professed to include almost all ancient inventions as well as many new ones thought out by the author himself.[80]

The progress of anatomical investigation in the sixteenth century and its continuation in the seventeenth made it natural enough to employ the term "new" in that field. Riolan fils illustrated his *Schola anatomiae*, Paris, 1608, with "new and rare observations." When his anatomical *Opuscula* appeared for the first time in 1649 at London, they were similarly characterized as "new." The *Anatomicae Institutiones* of Caspar Bartholinus, which first came out in 1611—subsequently in 1626, 1632, 1641 and, with additions by his son Thomas, in 1645—were also described as accompanied by "many new observations." Jean Pecquet, the discoverer of the thoracic duct, published *Experimenta nova anatomica* in 1651, while Olaus Rudbeck of Upsala printed a *Nova exercitatio anatomica* in 1653. Meanwhile Jan van Horne's *Novus ductus chyliferus nunc primum delineatus* was issued at Leyden in 1652. Regner de Graef in 1668 published Some New Discoveries about the Genital Parts (*De nonnullis circa partes genitales inventis novis*) and in 1672 his *De mulierum organis generationi inservientibus tractatus novus*, in which he showed that viviparous as well as oviparous animals derived from eggs. *Les nouvelles decouvertes* of Louys Barles in 1675 also dealt with the organs of generation. Diemerbroeck's book on the anatomy of the human body professed to give "many new discoveries."[81] Walter Charleton based his *Exercitationes pathologicae* on "new discoveries of the anatomists,"[82] and his *Exercitationes physicoanatomicae* on "new hypotheses in medicine."[83] Stockhamer adorned his description of the human body "with new discoveries of this age."[84]

[80] *Magisterium naturae et artis opus physico-mathematicum P. Francisci Tertii de Lana . . . in quo occultiora naturalis philosophiae principia manifestantur et multiplici tum experimentorum tum demonstrationum serie comprobantur ac demum tam antiqua pene omnia artis inventa quam multa nova ab ipso authore excogitata in lucem proferuntur.* Briziae per J. M. Ricciardum (Parmae, ex typis H. Rosati), 1684–92, 3 vols. in-fol. Copies: BM 32.k.9; BN R.394–96.

[81] Isbrandus de Diemerbroeck, *Anatomia corporis humani pluribus novis inventis instructa*, Utrecht, 1672, in-4.

[82] Walter Charleton, *Exercitationes pathologicae in quibus morborum pene omnium natura generatio et causae ex novis anatomicorum inventis sedulo inquiruntur*, London, 1661, in-4.

[83] Walter Charleton, *Exercitationes physico-anatomicae . . . novis in medicina hypothesibus superstructa et mechanice explicata*, London and Amsterdam, 1659; Leyden, 1678; the Hague, 1681.

[84] Franciscus Stockhamerus, *Microcosmographia sive partium humani corporis . . . descriptio novis huius seculi inventis exornata*, Vienna, 1682, in-12.

Scientific progress in the seventeenth century has usually been held to have been most marked in the fields of astronomy, physics and mathematics, and the medicine of the period has seldom been represented as very enlightened. Yet assertions of new methods and departures, advances and discoveries, occur more often in the titles of medical works in the seventeenth century than anywhere else. We have already seen that it was they especially which emphasized the importance of a new method before Descartes, and they continued to do so after the appearance of the *Discours de la méthode* in 1637. Gallego de la Serna called his True Method of Healing Correctly and Dogmatically " a new work." [85] De la Chambre advanced a New Method for explaining Hippocrates and Aristotle,[86] and Greulich, a true method of curing dropsy which he had newly deduced from observation and confirmed by experience.[87] Globicz of Buczina put out a New Digest of the Aphorisms of Hippocrates as late as 1681.[88]

The existence of new diseases was recognized and new treatments of disease were proclaimed. Diomedes Amicus published a " new work " on sporadic diseases.[89] Carolus Piso of Paris wrote a book " useful and pleasing by its novelty " on diseases which had hitherto been overlooked.[90] Van Helmont published an " Unheard-of doctrine of fevers " at Antwerp in 1642, and Unheard-of Medical Opuscula at Cologne in 1644, the year of his death.[91] The Secret of Detecting Diseases by Julius Millus was " illuminated by new light." [92] Fanoisius discussed " an epidemic disease hitherto unheard-of " which had prevailed in 1669 in Leyden and its vicinity.[93] Monavius dealt with a new kind of venereal disease.[94] Hermann Grube published a New Analysis of the transplanting of diseases.[95]

[85] Joh. Gallego de la Serna, *Recte ac dogmatice medendi vera methodus. Opus novum* . . . , Paris, 1639, in-fol.

[86] *Novae methodi pro explanandis Hippocratem et Aristotelem* . . . , Paris, 1655.

[87] Joh. Geo. Greulichius, *Curandi hydropsis vera methodus quam ex causis sibi noviter observatis deduxit perque experientiam confirmavit*, Frankfurt-a-M., 1681, in-8.

[88] Joh. Dan. Globicz, *Tripus medicinae seu Hippocratis Aphorismorum* . . . *nova digestio*, Nürnberg, 1681, in-12.

[89] Diomedes Amicus, *De morbis sporadibus opus novum*, Venice, 1605.

[90] Carolus Piso, *Selectae observationes et consilia de praetervisis hactenus morbis . . . praeter naturam. Opus novitate . . . utile . . . ac iucundum*, Pont-à-Mousson, 1618, in-4. [91] *Febrium doctrina inaudita* and *Opuscula medica inaudita*.

[92] Jul. Millus, *Naturae morbos decernentis arcanum . . . nova collustrata lucerna*, Venice, 1654.

[93] Guido Fanoisius, *De morbo epidemio hactenus inaudito praeterita aetate anni 1669 Lugduni Batavorum vicinisque locis grassante*, Leyden, 1671, in-12.

[94] Frid. Monavius, *Crystallina puta luis venereae novae inventae species*, 1665.

[95] Herm. Grube, *De transplantatione morborum analysis nova*, Hamburg, 1674, in-8.

Blood transfusion was another highly prized innovation.   Elsholtz treated of it and infusoria in 1667 under the title, *Clysmatica nova*.   The next year Paul Manfredus spoke of the transfusion of blood from one individual to another as a " new and unheard-of operation." [96]

Prothus Casulanus of Siena published a new argument concerning the tongue as a sign of disease at Florence in 1621,[97] and it was reprinted at Cologne in 1626 and Ulm in 1651.   With his tract on opium Freitag printed another on a new way to cure tuberculosis.[98]   Cattier had new observations concerning rheumatism.[99]   Pechlin contributed a " new exercise " on purgatives.[100]   Wirdig's New Medicine of the Spirits is mentioned in another connection.   To Six Decades of Rare Medical Observations Hochstetter added four others " never seen before." [101]   Jones issued New Dissertations concerning the more abstruse diseases and intermittent fevers.[102]   Martin Lister published " New and Curious Exercises " as to medicated baths.[103] " New and wonderful arcana of nature " were promised by Mark Antony Alaymus of Sicily in his work on medicaments which might be substituted for others.   It was published at Palermo in 1637.[104]   Justus Cortnummius in a work on apoplexy which first came out in 1671 [105] adhered to the " Hippocratic period of blood in the human body," and hoped to lead medical men to read Hippocrates more.   But when the third edition of his book appeared in 1685, it was under the new name of Justus Conradus Michaelis and with the new title, " A New Useful and Curious Method of Curing Apoplexy." [106]   Similarly, when the *Progymnasmata physica* (1663) of Tommaso Cornelio of Cosenza was republished twenty years later,[107]

[96] Paulus Manfredus, *De nova et inaudita operatione sanguinem transfundente de individuo in individuum*, Rome, 1668, in-4.

[97] P. Casulanus, *De lingua quae maximum est morborum acutorum signum opus in re medica novi argumenti.*

[98] *De nova phthisin curandi ratione*, Groningen, 1632, in-8.

[99] Isaac Cattier, *De rheumatismo . . . novisque observationibus*, Paris, 1653, in-8.

[100] J. N. Pechlin, *De purgantium medicamentorum facultatibus exercitatio nova*, 1672.

[101] J. P. Hochstetter, *Rararum medic. observ. decades sex, quibus accessere quatuor decades aliae numquam antea visae*, Frankfurt and Leipzig, 1674, in-8.

[102] John Jones, *Novae dissertationes de morbis abstrusioribus et febribus intermittentibus*, London, 1683.

[103] *Novae et curiosae exercitationes . . . thermarum medicatarum*, London, 1686.

[104] For the full title see *Lindenius renovatus*, ed. G. A. Mercklein, Nürnberg, 1686, p. 774, col. a.

[105] *De morbo attonito*, Lipsiae, 1672 and 1677.

[106] *Nova utilis ac curiosa apoplexiam seu morbum attonitum curandi methodus*, Hildesiae, 1685.

[107] Other editions intervened in 1665 and 1681.

although the contents of the volume remained the same, the title was not merely changed to *Physiologia* but went on to lay claim to "new and hitherto unheard of . . . weighty reasoning."[108] Yet Cornelio turned back to Plato for an explanation of motion to avoid a vacuum.[109]

Astrology as well as astronomy succumbed to the charm of professed novelty. Franciscus Allaeus or Father Yves of Paris composed a New Method of Astrology, and, although the first edition of 1654–55[110] is said to have been burnt by the local executioner, there was another in 1658, both at Rennes.

Other forms of occult science, divination and magic also turned out volumes which professed to offer something new. The work of Albrecht Josuel Hunepaeus on divination from dreams, printed at Dortmund in 1607, is described as a new and wonderful book.[111] The *Magia physica* of Valerius Martinius involves "three most new wisdoms";[112] the *Speculum cabalistico-chymicum* of universal medicine of George Figulus is "new and unheard-of";[113] the New Philosophy and Medicine of Edoard Medeira of Arras concerning occult qualities has never been cultivated by anyone, and is followed by an "unheard-of philosophy" concerning the qualities of the Tree of Life in Paradise, the power of music, tarantulas, and electric and magnetic qualities.[114] Goclenius pens a new defense of weapon ointment.[115]

[108] *Thomae Cornelii Physiologia peculiari studio novis atque hactenus inauditis . . . rationum ponderibus atque momentis illustrata*, Lipsiae et Jenae, 1683, in-12.

[109] He had earlier published *Epistola qua motuum illorum qui vulgo ob fugam vacui fieri dicuntur vera caussa per circumpulsionem ad mentem Platonis explicatur. Tum quaestiones aliquot naturales ex occasione incidente dirimuntur et nova quaedam problemata proferuntur in lucem*, Rome, 1648, in-12.

[110] *Astrologiae nova methodus. Fatum universi observatum.* Anno MDCLIIII. *In librum de fato universi nuper editum Disceptatio P. Ivonis Parisini Capuc.* Rennes, Julian Herbert, 1655, in-fol.

[111] Alb. Josuel Hunepaeus, Ὀνειροκρίσις. *Liber novus mirificus etc.*, Dortmund, 1607.

[112] Valerius Martinius, *Magia physica foecunda coelesti divinoque cultu perfusa trium novissimarum totius substantiae sapientiarum simulque claves reconditissimae adytorum naturae omnium proprietatum divinarumque formarum hucusque occultarum . . . .* Pars I, Venice, 1639, in-4. II and III, Venice, 1641, in-4.

[113] Geo. Figulus, *Novum et inauditum medicinae universalis Speculum Cabalistico-Chymicum*, Brussels, Jo. Mommart, 1660, in-16, 207 pp.

[114] Edoardus Medeira, *Novae philosophiae et medicinae de qualitatibus occultis a nemine umquam excultae pars prima, philosophis et medicis pernecessaria, theologis vero apprime utilis. Accedit inaudita philosophia de arboris vitae Paradisi qualitatibus; de viribus musicae; de tarantula; ac qualitatibus electricis et magneticis*, Lisbon, 1650, in-8.

[115] R. G. Goclenius, *Mirabilium naturae liber . . . Adiecta est in fine brevis et nova defensio magneticae curationis vulnerum*, 1625.

Maxwell composes " a new work, admirable and most useful," on magnetic medicine, in which many most secret miracles of nature are disclosed and workings of the vital spirit hitherto unknown are revealed.[116]   Mohy's New Physical Hypothesis by which the causes of natural phenomena were traced to a unique universal motion, to be spurned by neither the followers of Tycho Brahe nor of Copernicus, appeared in the same volume with his treatise on the sympathetic powder by which wounds are cured.[117]   Sebastian Wirdig's New Medicine of the Spirits similarly included cures by magnetism and sympathy.[118]

Some titles oppose rather than profess novelty.   Mundinus Mundinius refuted the "new dogmas" as to the generation of the foetus, hereditary diseases, and so forth.[119]   Disputations at Groningen under Johann Freitag discussed innate heat according to the old medicine and philosophy against the paradoxes of *neoterici* and *novatores*, whose doctrines as to the origin of forms and as to disease were likewise opposed.[120]   Freitag and J. D. Horst also wrote against the new Sennerto-Paracelsic sect.[121]   Didacus de Soria was another medical opponent of Innovators.[122]   Zucchi denied the

[116] Wm. Maxwell, *De medicina magnetica . . . opus novum admirabile et utilissimum, ubi multa naturae secretissima miracula panduntur, spiritus vitalis operationes hactenus incognitae revelantur*, Frankfurt-a-M., 1679, in-12.

[117] Ericius Mohy, *Pulvis sympatheticus quo vulnera sanantur.   Hypothesis Physica Nova qua phenomenorum naturae causae ab unico universali motu neque Tychonicis neque Copernicanis aspernando repetuntur*, 74 and 34 pp.   In-16, Mainz, 1671.   There had been repeated editions of the *Pulvis sympatheticus* since 1634, but this edition of 1671 seems to be the only one of the *Hypothesis Physica Nova*.

[118] Seb. Wirdig, *Nova medicina spirituum . . . in qua primo spirituum naturalis constitutio, vita, sanitas, temperamenta . . . dehinc spirituum praeternaturalis seu morbosa dispositio causae curationes per . . . magnetismum seu sympatheismum*, Hamburg, 1673, in-12.

[119] M. Mundinius, *De genitura pro Galenicis adversus Peripateticos et nostrae aetatis philosophos et medicos disputatio in qua nova praesertim dogmata spectantia ad foetuum generationem, similitudines, morbos hereditarios, notas corporis, facultatem formatricem, calidi nativi animarumque originem corruptibilem refelluntur. Necnon animatio seminis adversus recentiores omnes defenditur*, Venice, 1622, in-4.

[120] Joh. Freitag, *Disputatio medica calidi innati essentiam juxta veteris medicinae et philosophiae decreta . . . opposita neotericorum et novatorum paradoxis, respondente Conrado Walthero*, Groningen, 1632, in-8. *Disputatio . . . de formarum origine contra Neotericorum doctrinam, respondente Henr. Welman*, Groningen, 1633, in-8. *Disputatio . . . de morbis substantiae . . . contra Novatores et Paradoxologos, respondente Jac. Martini*, Groningen, 1632, in-8.

[121] Joh. Freitag, *Detectio et solida refutatio novae sectae Sennerto-Paracelsicae*, Amsterdam, 1636.   J. D. Horstius, *Ruminatio detectionis novae sectae Sennerto-Paracelsicae*, Marburg, 1640, in-4.

[122] Didacus de Soria, *Certamen medicum . . . contra innovatores*, 1635.

existence of a vacuum despite the new experiments,[123] and despite the fact that he had written three years before a New Philosophy of machinery. Gideon Harvey argued that the modern practice in continuous fevers was barbaric and death-dealing.[124]

The titles of other works indicate an aim to reconcile the old and new. L. Savot called his book a New, or more truly, New-Ancient Explanation of the causes of colors.[125]   Pierre Petit described his treatise on the spontaneous movement of animals as " partly Aristotelian, partly new." [126]   Du Hamel wrote on the agreement of old and new philosophy.[127]   Rolfinck and Schenck sought a norm in medicine between old and new,[128] but Janssonius ab Almeloveen was inclined to emphasize the new discoveries.[129]   In the *Decades* of G. H. Welschius (or Velschius) printed posthumously in 1681 is not only " A Way of Making New Experiments in Medicine," but " A New Dissertation in which the Views of the Ancients as to Theriacs are expounded by a New Method." [130]

In any case, the new was very much in the consciousness of the men of the seventeenth century.

[123] Nicolaus Zucchius, *Exclusio vacui contra nova experimenta*, 1649.

[124] Gedeon Harvey, *De febribus . . . in quo praxin curandarum febrium continuarum modernam esse lethiferam et barbaram abunde patefit*, London, 1672, in-8.

[125] *Nova seu verius nova-antiqua de causis colorum sententia*, Paris, 1609.

[126] Petrus Petitus, *De motu animalium spontaneo . . . partim Arist. . . . partim nova*, Paris, 1660.

[127] J. B. du Hamel, *De consensu veteris et novae philosophiae*, Oxford, 1663, 1669.

[128] Werner Rolfinck, *Ordo et methodus medicinae . . . ad normam veterum et novorum dogmatum adornata*, 1669.   He published a work on anatomy in 1664 with a similar title.   J. T. Schenckius, *Medicinae generalis novo-antiquae synopsis*, Jena, 1672, in-4.

[129] Theod. Janssonius ab Almeloveen, *Inventa nov-antiqua, id est, brevis enarratio ortus et progressus artis medicae ac praecipue de inventis vulgo novis aut nuperrime in ea repertis*, Amsterdam, 1684, in-8.

[130] Georgii Hieronymi Welschii . . . *Decades X, Opus posthumum*, 1681, p. 71.

~ई *Marie Boas*

BACON AND GILBERT

" Another error . . . is, that men have used to infect their meditations, opinions, and doctrines, with some conceits which they have most admired, or some sciences which they have most applied. . . . So have the alchymists made a philosophy out of a few experiments of the furnace; and Gilbertus, our countryman, hath made a philosophy out of the observations of a loadstone." [1] So Francis Bacon seemed derisively to deny to William Gilbert any claim to the title of experimental philosopher; and yet the *De magnete* is now generally considered one of the best examples of the new approach to science which Bacon so staunchly advocated. How Bacon could fail to appreciate the brilliant experimental contributions to electricity and magnetism with which the *De magnete* is filled, has puzzled all readers of Bacon. His manifest prejudice, in classing Gilbert with the purely speculative natural philosophers, has been variously ascribed to a lack of any real understanding of science, to personal dislike, and to a distrust of the Copernicanism which Gilbert appears to support. [2] To gain some insight into Bacon's point of view it is necessary to read, as few do now, Gilbert's posthumously published *De mundo philosophia nova*. [3] This is a non-experimental " philosophia contra Aristotelem," a typically Renaissance treatise which attacked Aristotelian doctrines in perceptibly peripatetic style. Gilbert here extended his concept of the earth as a magnet and expanded the cosmological theories outlined in the sixth book of the *De magnete*. Very interesting is his discussion of gravity, which he believed to be caused by magnetic attraction and hence to diminish with distance from the center of the earth. He also treated, in rather wearisome detail, the question of an interstellar (interplanetary) vacuum; the possible composition of the heavenly bodies; the actions of the tides; and various meteorological phenomena such as winds and fountains.

Bacon had certainly read Gilbert's *Philosophia nova*, and with great attention. The manuscript from which the first and only edition was printed was found in Bacon's papers after his death. [4] The numerous references to

[1] *Advancement of Learning*, Book I; Bacon's *Works*, Ellis, Spedding and Heath edition (Boston, 1861–64), VI, 132. Cf. *Novum organum*, Book I, aphorism lxx, " for it generally happens that men make their trials carelessly, and as it were in play. . . . And even if they apply themselves more seriously and laboriously, still they spend their labor in working out some one experiment, as Gilbert with the magnet, and the chemists with gold." Cf. also *Redargutio philosophiarum; Works* VII, 75, and *Cogitata et visa; Works* VII, 118–19.

[2] For the latter opinion, presented in some detail, see Park Benjamin, *The Intellectual Rise in Electricity* (New York, 1895), 318ff.

[3] *De mundo nostro sublunari philosophia nova* (Elzevir Press, 1657).

[4] Benjamin, 318–19.

Gilbert's theories which are scattered throughout Bacon's works are always to material discussed in the *Philosophia nova*. Most of these references are to Gilbert's cosmological system, his theories on gravity, and his notion of an interstellar vacuum,[5] while the resemblance between Bacon's *History of Winds* and the discussion in the fourth book of Gilbert's *Philosophia nova* is very striking.

Bacon knew something of Gilbert's experimental work, for he praised him as one " who has written upon the magnet most laboriously, and after the experimental method." [6] Yet it is doubtful whether he had ever read the experimental *De magnete*. Most of the references to material discussed in the sixth book of the *De magnete* are more probably to the fuller discussions of the same questions in the *Philosophia nova*. This assumption is supported by the fact that in the *De augmentis scientarum* Bacon several times referred to problems settled by Gilbert, apparently in ignorance of Gilbert's work. Thus he noted, " So again amber and jet when rubbed attract straws; will they do the same when warmed by fire? "—a question exhaustively investigated by numerous experiments in the *De magnete*.[7] Similarly Bacon speculated on the effects of calcination upon the action of the loadstone, and of the interposition of various substances between a piece of iron and the loadstone, questions again experimentally studied by Gilbert.[8]

The above evidence indicates clearly that Bacon had never read the *De magnete* but based his opinion of Gilbrt entirely upon the purely speculative *Philosophia nova*. Bacon deserves some credit for recognizing, as he did, that Gilbert's magnetic philosophy was actually based upon careful experimentation. Bacon's estimate of Gilbert is clearly biased; but it might act as a useful corrective to the modern view of Gilbert as an experimental scientist far in advance of his age. Gilbert clearly attached great importance to his cosmological and physical speculations; they show him to have been a Renaissance figure, balanced between the modern spirit of experimentation and the mediaeval spirit of speculation. In his estimation of Gilbert, Bacon was thus far correct.

[5] There are numerous references in the *De augmentis*, the *Novum organum*, the *Descriptio globis intellectualis*, and in many of the minor treatises. Many, though not all, of these references may be found in the index to the Philosophical Works in the Ellis, Spedding and Heath edition.

[6] *De augmentis*, the fable of Pan; *Works* VIII, 451. Cf. *Cogitata et visa*, *Works* VII, 118–19.

[7] *De augmentis*, Book V, chapter II; *Works* IX, 73. For Gilbert's discussion, see *De magnete*, Book II, chapter 2.

[8] *De augmentis; Works* IX, 75–76, 80; cf. *De magnete*, Book III, chapters 3 and 10. This evidence would seem to contradict the theory of Benjamin, who claims (*op. cit.*, 324) that Bacon's list of " bodies attractive and non-attractive is based upon the *De magnete*, Book II, chapter 3; it is more probably derived from Cardan; see Benjamin, 248.

⨳ Philip P. Wiener

LEIBNIZ'S PROJECT OF A PUBLIC EXHIBITION OF SCIENTIFIC INVENTIONS

The following unfamiliar fragment of Leibniz's[1] illustrates an aspect of his thought often inadequately emphasized in textbooks of the history of philosophy. Along with his recognized interest in pure logic, mathematics, and a *priori* metaphysics and theology, he was, as this text shows, as zealous as any Baconian for the promotion not only of empirical investigations but also of their mechanical applications, and for the diffusion of knowledge of these and enthusiasm for them among the general public. The project here outlined was not, indeed, unrelated to current tendencies of the period. More or less "scientific" museums were in the seventeenth century coming into fashion,[2] and in a number of European cities those maintained either by princely houses or by private naturalists or other *savants* were among the show-places visited by educated travellers. Such were the museum of the Settalas, father and son, in Milan; that of Berend Ten Broeke (Bernardus Paludanus, 1550–1633) at Enkhuizen in Holland; Kircher's famous museum,

[1] "*Drôle de pensée touchant une nouvelle sorte de* REPRESENTATIONS— (*plustot Académie des Sciences, Septembre, 1675*)." Edited by Dr. Ernst Gerland in Abhandlungen zur Geschichte der Mathematischen Wissenschaften mit Einschluss ihrer Anwendungen, begrundet von Moritz Cantor, XXI Heft (Leipzig, Teubner 1906): *Leibnizens' Nachgelassene Schriften physikalischen, mechanischen und technischen Inhalts.*—Technischer Teil, Anhang 134. The French *ms.* of Leibniz is apparently in bad condition, and some of Dr. Gerland's readings may be questionable. Several of the discoveries and discoverers mentioned by Leibniz await identification from historians of science. The translator has indicated his own emendations of Gerland's notes (otherwise marked E. G.) by suffixing his initials (P. W.), and has omitted some of the text and some of Gerland's notes. Professor A. O. Lovejoy has in the introduction briefly indicated the historical background of Leibniz's idea and its distinctive place among similar projects or enterprises, and has added some footnotes.

[2] The history of their development has been told with admirable learning by David Murray, *Museums: Their History and Use*, 3 vols., 1904, especially Vol. I.— There were already being written, by the last quarter of the century, books about museums and their history; D. G. Morhof in his *Polyhistor*, 1688, mentions five such *tractatus, e.g.*, a work entitled *Unvorgreifliches Bedencken von Kunst- und Naturalien-Kammern insgemein* (apparently 1674); *op. cit.*, 1732 ed., II, p. 132. Morhof himself shared the enthusiasm for museums: "as in acquiring knowledge of the sciences we have need of books, so in experimental natural science we have need of this one book [*i.e.*, nature] the epitome of which can be furnished for us by a *Museum rerum naturalium*. In providing these both men of learning and entire societies have been solicitous, and there exist not a few of them in various places which have been brought together with no small labor" (*ibid.*).—A. O. L.

visited by Evelyn in 1644, and bequeathed in 1680 to the Jesuit College in Rome; and the Tradescants' "Ark" in London, "considered to be the most extensive collection in Europe at the time," which, purchased by Elias Ashmole in 1659, became the nucleus of the Ashmolean Museum.[3] Many of these were chiefly or solely collections of "natural" rarities (*rariora naturalia*), rather than of recent inventions and discoveries, but examples of the latter, in some cases, found place in the collections.[4] Leibniz's project, therefore, was not without precedent; but it is distinguished by its special emphasis on the comprehensive exhibition of recent progress in science and the practical arts in all countries, and by the popular appeal at which he aimed. And the text shows, in the originator of the Calculus and the author of the *Monadology*, the talents of a great showman; like the director of a latter-day World's Fair, he shrewdly insists upon the indispensability of amusements and spectacles (including seventeeth-century equivalents of moving pictures), and even gambling rooms, in order both to lure the multitude to the scientific and technological exhibits and to increase the revenues of the enterprise. He hoped, it will be noted, that the exposition would be so successful that it would become permanent, and would develop into a self-supporting "academy" for the encouragement and prosecution of further investigations and inventions. The Paris *Académie des Sciences* (1666) and the Royal Society (1662) had already been established, but not as outgrowths of popular exhibitions. The Berlin *Akademie der Wissenschaften* was founded nearly thirty years later, upon a quite different plan drawn up by Leibniz; but his "odd idea" of 1675 appears to have been the germ of his own conception of such an institution.[5]

[3] For all of these, with citations of contemporary references, see Murray, *op. cit. Cf.* also R. T. Gunther, *Early Science in Oxford,* 1925.—A. O. L.

[4] The Settalas' museum is said also to have included *artificia rariora;* Kircher's is described by Evelyn as containing "several mechanical engines, . . . perpetual motions, catoptrics, magnetical experiments, modells, and a thousand other crotchets and devices"; the Tradescants' appears to have shown some specimens of industrial arts; and the Museum of Paludanus is said by a contemporary to have caused a traveller to compose "this following Epigram *ex tempore:*

> *Orbe novo et veteri rarum et mirabile quicquid*
> *Dat natura parens, artificisque manus,*
> *Una* Paludani *domus exhibet* . . .

> In the old world or new what wondrous thing
> Did art to light or nature lately bring,
> This *Paludanus* house doth show . . ."

(Thomas Powell: *Humane Industry: or, a history of most manual arts, deducing the original, progress, and improvement of them.* London, 1661, p. 188. In the Library of Congress.)—A. O. L.

[5] Francis Bacon's *New Atlantis* (1627) was, as Sprat's *History of the Royal Society* amply proves, the fore-runner of the Royal Society, and, as Dean Marjorie Nicolson suggests, undoubtedly exerted an influence on Leibniz's composition of the following fragment.—P. W.

(Translation)

An Odd Thought Concerning a New Sort of Exhibition (or rather,
an Academy of Sciences; September, 1675).

The Exhibition which took place at Paris on the river Seine, of a Machine
for walking on water,[1] gave birth in me to the following thought. However
odd the idea may appear, it could not fail to be of importance, were it carried
out.

Suppose that some persons of means with an interest in curiosities,
especially in machines, should agree to have public expositions made of
such things.   To this end, it would be necessary for them to raise a fund in
order to meet necessary expenses. . . .[2]   It would be all the better if one

[1] Daniel Schwenter (*Deliciae physico-mathematicae.   Mathematische und phi-*
losophische Erquickstunden, darinnen 663—Kunststücklein, Auffgaben und Fragen
aus der Rechenkunst, Lantmessen, Perspectiv, u.s.w. allen Kunstlieben zu Ehren
Nuss.   Nürnberg, first edition 1636, second 1651) had described and illustrated by
diagrams in a rather quaint and amusing fashion an invention for walking through
water (Die XV Auffgab: Des Frantz Kosslers Lufft-und Wasser harnisch zuzu-
richten, pp. 464–469).   The diagrams show a cross-wise leather harness on a wooden
buoy, and a hunter with an air-inflated bag-pipe affair around his waist (*Wind-*
hosen), winged paddles around his ankles (*Flossfedern*), and gun and grouse on
his shoulder, marching waist-high through water and appearing quite confident.
Schwenter claims (p. 469) that "mit dergleichen Windhosen solle Königliche Ma-
jestat zu Dennemarck mit einen Hofdiener eine ganze Meil über die offenbare See
gegangen seyn."   For other seventeenth century texts which aimed at the diffusion
of the growing sciences as both useful and entertaining concerns, see Leurechon:
Mathematical Recreations; or a Collection of Many PROBLEMS Extracted out of
the Ancient and Modern Philosophers: As, Secrets and Experiments in Arithmetick,
Geometry, Cosmography, Horologiography, Astronomy, Navigation, Musick, Op-
ticks, Architecture, Statick, Mechanicks, Chymistry, Water-Works, Fire Works, etc.
not vulgarly manifest till now.   Written first in Greek and Latin, lately (1627)
compiled in French by Henry Van Etten and now in English, with the examinations
and augmentations of divers Modern Mathematicians. London, 1674. Also Ozanam: *Récréations Mathématiques et Physiques,* Paris, 1692.   It is very likely that
Leibniz was acquainted with at least one of these texts.   Charles Hutton in the
Preface (pp. IV–VI) of his English version (1803) of the Montucla's edition of
Ozanam points to the Greek Anthology for "the first example of these mathematical
amusements," and says that "Bachet de Méziriac, a celebrated algebraist, who wrote
a learned Commentary on Diophantus, was induced to collect a great variety of
questions on numbers, which he published in 1626 under the title of *Problèmes*
plaisans et délectables sur les Nombres. This book, next to the problems of the
Greek Anthology, laid the foundations for all the Mathematical Recreations that
afterwards appeared more or less extensively, and in different languages."   Thus
the history of the idea of science as a form of entertainment apparently remains
to be investigated.—P. W.

[2] Leibniz here names several prominent members of Louis XIV's court who
might be induced to advance the money.—P. W.

could dispense with the great noblemen, even with persons powerful at court; and it would be well to have private individuals able to defray the necessary expenses. For a powerful nobleman would monopolize the business when he found it successful. If things went well, one could always have protectors at court.

Beside the persons capable of defraying the expenses, we should also need persons who could constantly invent new things. But as too many would give rise to disorders, I believe that it would be better to have no more than two or three directors who would employ all others and determine the conditions for certain exhibitions, limiting them to a certain period or to as long a period as the principals desire, or until a certain sum of money supplied by them had been repaid. The persons to be employed should be painters, sculptors, carpenters, watchmakers, and other such folk. We may add gradually mathematicians, engineers, architects, boat-builders, entertainers, musicians, poets, book-binders, typographers, engravers, and others.

The exhibitions would include Magic Lanterns (we might begin with these), flights, artificial meteors, all sorts of optical wonders; a representation of the heavens and stars and of comets; a globe like that of Gottorp at Jena; fire-works, water fountains, strangely shaped boats; Mandragoras and other rare plants. Unusual and rare animals. A Royal Circle. Figures of animals. Royal Machine with races between artificial horses. Prize for Archery. Exhibitions of battle scenes. Fortifications built of wood. On an elevated stage, representations of charity, cruelty,—etc.—all in imitation of the maker of the art,[3]—things that I have seen. An instructor in fortification would explain the use of all war games. Infantry drill of Martinet. Cavalry exercise. Naval combats in miniature on a canal. Extraordinary Concerts. Rare instruments of Music. Speaking trumpets.[4] Counterfeit gems and jewelry.

The Show could always be combined with some story or comedy. Theatre of nature and of art. Swimming. Extraordinary rope-dancer. Perilous leap. Show how a child can raise a heavy weight with a thread. Anatomical theater followed by garden of medicinal herbs, laboratory. . . .[5] For besides public exhibitions there will be private ones such as small adding machines,[5a] in others Pictures, Medals, Library. New experiments on water,

---

[3] The meaning here is obscure.

[4] The speaking-trumpet was apparently, in the 1670's, a much talked-about instrument, its invention being in dispute between Sir Samuel Morland (*An Account of the Speaking-Trumpet,* 1671) and Kircher. See Beckmann, *History of Inventions,* 1877, I, pp. 93–102.—A. O. L.

[5] Text obscure; Prof. Morris R. Cohen has indicated that an anatomical theatre and herbarium had existed in 1550 at the University of Padua.—P. W.

[5a] Leibniz himself had invented a multiplying machine about 1671. *Cf. A Source Book in Mathematics,* edited by D. E. Smith (1929), pp. 173–181. Pascal had constructed the first adding machine (1642), but Leibniz says he did not know of it in 1671 (*ibid.,* p. 174).—P. W.

air, vacuum: for the large exhibitions, one would make use of Mons. Guericke's machine of 24 horses, etc., for the small ones, a strong globe.[6] Many things from Mons. Dalencé's establishment,[7] *item*, the magnet. Mons Denis[8] or Mons. ——————— would explain them. One would even distribute certain rarities,[9] *e.g.*, those pixtriques, etc. Operations of transfusion and infusion would be made.[10] *Item,* for holiday spectators, who would be told the weather for the next day, whether it will rain or not, by means of the little man in the cabinet of Father Kircher.[11] We will bring the man from England who eats fire, etc., if he is still alive. Through a Telescope[11a] we could show the moon at night along with other heavenly bodies. We could send for the water drinker.[12] We could test machines which would

[6] Otto von Guericke (1602–86) was Mayor of Magdeburg, (1646), famous for his public demonstration of two teams of horses which could not pull apart the hemispheres of a small hollow globe voided of air. "Otto von Guericke's globe" refers either to this hollow globe voided of air by the air-pump he invented (imitated by Robert Boyle), or to a sulphur-globe with which he was the first to create static electricity by friction and to make the earliest observations of the conduction of such electricity. (A. Wolf, *History of Science, Technology, and Philosophy in the Eighteenth Century*, 214–215; *cf. Source Book in Physics*, W. F. Magie (1935) p. 80; 393). Guericke had a good deal of correspondence with Leibniz, who denied the existence of the vacuum. *Cf.* Leibniz: *Sämtliche Schriften* 2.[1]—P. W.

[7] Dalencé was the author of *Traité de L'aimant*, 1687; *Traittez des baromètres, thermomètres et notiomètres,* 1688.—E. G. [According to Beckman (*ibid.* p. 95, f.n. 3) D'Alencé was accredited by Duhamel as the discoverer of the speaking trumpet.— P. W.]

[8] Denis Papin: amanuensis of Huygens in experiments on air-pump; author of *Experiences du vuide,* 1674. Denis Papin "had the idea of obtaining power on the air-pump principle, and had tried, or at least suggested, the use of either gunpowder or condensed steam for the purpose; but Hooke, we are told, regarded the whole scheme as impractical." (A. Wolf, *History of Science, Technology, and Philosophy in the Eighteenth Century*, Chapter XXIV, Technology, VII The Steam Engine, pp. 611–612). Papin had, along with Guericke and Boyle, also experimented on the intensity of sound in various densities of the media (*ibid.,* 175).—P. W.

[9] Here Leibniz wrote in the margin: "preferably different rooms like palace shops in the same house where private parties having rented the rooms, would show the rarities."—E. G.

[10] Leibniz appended a note to the effect that the Director's office could serve as a clearing-house for all exhibitions; by charging a fee that would go to the Academy, the latter would be self-supporting.—P. W.

[11] A weather-forecaster invented by Athanasius Kircher (1601–80), German mathematician and Jesuit; his *Polygraphia, seu artificium linguarum quo cum omnibus mundi populis poterit quis respondere* (1663), interested Leibniz in connection with his own attempts to invent a universal language.—P. W.

[11a] *Cf.* A. Favaro, "La invenzione del telescopio secondo gli ultimi studi," *Real istituto veneto Atti,* V, 66, pt. 2, pp. 1–54. Venezia, 1906.—P. W.

[12] Leibniz explains the trick in a note, by indicating the use of concealed tubes in the mouth and alimentary tract of the water-drinker.—P. W.

throw things exactly at a given point. Exhibits of the muscles, nerves, bones: *item,* machine representing the human body. Insects of Mons. Swammerdam, Goedartis . . . ,[13] Myrmeleon. Shop of *Mepitus Galinée* and *des Billets.*[14] Arts of Mons. Thevenot.[15] Amusing and colloquial disputes. Exhibit of *camera obscura.* Paintings which can be seen only with a . . .,[16] from one angle presenting one picture, from another, quite a different one, like that of a certain Mons. a l'isle, v.d.—farms as at Versailles on the edge of a Canal. Public diversions (such as) pictures on oiled paper and burning lamps or lanterns. There could be figures who could walk, with a little illumination inside them, so as to show whatever might be printed on the paper. For magic lanterns, there would be not only simple objects painted on something transparent, but also detachable moving pictures of very unusual and grotesque objects, which it would be possible to make.[17]

Ballets of horses. Races round a ring and Turkish head. Artificial machines, such as I have seen in Germany. Power of a mirror to kindle a fire. Gilgevis de Callinus. Chess game . . . showing men on a stage, as in Haychaffle. Pageant in the German style. Other sorts of elaborate games could be taught and performed.

[13] Since Swammerdam, who lived in Amsterdam 1637–80, and Leeuwenhoek both influenced Leibniz (*cf. Monadology,* 66) by their microscopic discoveries, Dr. Gerland thinks that Goedartis . . . (*ms.* torn) refers to Leeuwenhoek, the Dutch microscopist who lived in Delft 1632–1723. But it is more likely that "Goedartis . . ." refers to the Dutch naturalist and painter Goedaert 1620–68, author of *Metamorphosis et historia naturalis insectorum, cum commentario Jo. de Mey et duplici epist. appendice, una de hemerobiis, altera de natura cometarum.* Middelbourg 1662–67. A Dutch version appeared the same year (1662) called "Description of the origin, species, qualities and metamorphoses of worms, caterpillars, etc." Martin Lister translated the work into English and edited it, York, 1682. *Cf.* Michaud, *Dictionnaire biographique,* art. "Goedart." Also, Favaro (*op. cit. supra,* Note 11a, pp. 21 *ff.*)—P. W.

[14] Unidentified. Dr. George Sarton has suggested that names like these in the *ms.* refer perhaps to instrument-makers in Paris, who as a class were not considered worthy or respectable enough to be recorded by historians of science.—P. W.

[15] Thevenot, author of *Relations de divers voyages curieux,* maker of loud-speaking trumpets.—E. G. (See note 4 *supra.*)

[16] Ms. torn, perhaps "instrument."—E. G.

[17] Here Leibniz wrote in the margin: "I had almost forgotten that we might establish an Academy of games or more generally, Academy of pleasures. But I prefer the first name because it is more fashionable. There would be games of cards and of dice."—(Leibniz adds details of games to be played, admission tickets, etc.) "It would be, at the same time, a respectable [gaming] room as at Blyeme's." . . . "There would be several houses or Academies of this nature through the city. These houses or rooms would be built in such a way that the director of the house could hear and see everything said and done without any one perceiving him, by means of mirrors and openings, something that would be very important for the state and a species of political confessional." . . . (rest torn).—E. G.

Play an entire comedy with the amusing games of all sorts of countries
People would imitate these games at home.   There might be in the building
provision for a game of tennis, and for other games, inventing perhaps new
sorts of useful games.

There might be established some training Academies and Colleges for
youth: perhaps join them to the College of the Four Nations [in Paris]
Comedies of the styles, debates of each country, a Hindu comedy, a Turkish
a Persian, etc.   Comedies of the trades, one for each trade, which would
show their skills, peculiarities, jokes, master-pieces, special and ridiculous
styles.   In other comedies, Italian and French clowns who would perform
their buffooneries.   Flying dragons of fire, *etc.*, could be made of oiled paper
illuminated.   Wind-mills, thin boards that can go against the wind, the
chariot of sails from Holland or rather from China.   Instruments that play
by themselves.   Shells, etc.   Hauz's machine of an artificial cavalry and
infantry in battle.[18]   The experiment of breaking a glass by shouting
Petter[19] should come.   Inventions of Monsieur Weigel.[20]   Show the equality
of the oscillations of pendula.   (Here Leibniz adds: People at the Academy
should be forbidden from swearing and blasphemy, for under that pretext
Academies of the sort we are describing have been put under suspicion. . .
The pretext would be met, were it to become fashionable to admire fine
players or performers.   And those who broke the rules should give something, not to the cards but to the house, for in this matter it would be to the
advantage of those who play to observe the law.   But if a troupe of players
were in a rare case unrestrained, and disobeyed this law, admission to any
house should be denied by simply excluding them. . . .[21]

[18] Leibniz's insert: "Palace and isle of magic.   Theater made of oiled paper
within a dark place."—E. G.

[19] "Petter"—unidentified.   See *supra,* note 14.

[20] Erhard Weigel (1625–99).   Professor at Jena from 1653 on.   Author of a
series of works whose titles aroused curiosity, *e.g., Himmel-Spiegel* (1661), *Zeit-
spiegel* (1664), *Erdspiegel* (1665), *Vorstellung der Kunst und des Handwerks*
(1672), *Neu erfundenen Reiserat* (1672), *Pendulum ex tetracty deductum* (1674),
Wirkliche Probe der Feldkutsche (1674), etc.—E. G.

[21] Rules of playing and gambling follow, ending with the statement: "Gambling
would be the finest occasion in the world for initiating a thing as agreeable and
useful to the public as the present plan.   For we must offer the public some bait
take advantage of its weakness and deceive it in order to cure it.   Is there anything
so just as making use of extravagance in order to establish order?
   Games of "chasse passe" (pass the hunter).   Map games.   These things might
be made part of comedies played by a performer.   At the end the opera will be
added to all this, along with many other things; pantomime in comedies in the
Italian and German style would be of interest.   When the curtain is down it would
not be bad to know what to do in the interim.   Something might be shown in the
dark, and magic lanterns would be appropriate for that.   The actions of these trans-

The use of this enterprise to the public as well as to the individual, would be greater than might be imagined.   As to the public, it would open people's eyes, stimulate inventions, present beautiful sights, instruct people with an endless number of useful or ingenious novelties.   All those who produce a new invention or ingenious design might come and find a medium for getting their inventions known, and obtain some profit from that.   It would be a general clearing house for all inventions, and would become a museum of everything that could be imagined.   A Menagerie.   Simple machines.   Observatory.   Anatomical theater.   Museums of rarities.   All people with curious minds would write to it.   This would be the way to spread these things abroad (*débiter les choses*).   There would be added Academies, colleges, tennis courts and other games, concerts, galleries of paintings.   Conferences and lectures.

The profit for the private individual would apparently be great.   Optical curiosities would hardly cost much and would constitute a large part of these inventions.   All respectable people (*tous les honnêtes gens*) would want to see these curiosities in order to be able to talk about them; and even ladies of fashion would want to be taken there, and more than once.   There would always be an inducement to improve things further, and it would be a good thing if those who undertook it were assured of the project in other large cities[22] such as Rome, Venice, Vienna, Amsterdam, Hamburg, by persons enjoying privileges from kings and republics.   It could even serve to establish everywhere an Assembly of Academies of Sciences, which would be self-supporting, and would not cease producing fine things.   Perhaps some curious Princes and distinguished persons would contribute some of their wealth for the public satisfaction and the growth of the sciences.   In short, everybody would be aroused and, so to speak, awakened; and the enterprise might have consequences as fine and as important as could be imagined, which would some day perhaps be admired by posterity.[23]

---

parent marionettes might be represented by a few words or songs.   Shows might be given of the antiquities of Rome, and others of great men.   In a word, all sorts of things."—E. G.

[22] "Having a fund, there would be a perpetual income from interest and from other sources, such as the formation of companies for new manufactures."—Leibniz's marginal note.—E. G.

[23] At the end Leibniz added the following: "At the close a purchasing office would be added.   A register of catalogs and other useful things.   Bring together the Marionettes du Marmis and the Pygmies.   Shadows might be added to these, either on stage or at the ends near the spectators, where there are lights, and little wooden figures, so agitated that they will throw their shadow against the paper in very startling and magnified proportions.   But in order to prevent this shadow world from appearing all on one plane, resort to perspectives might bring about diminishing sizes of shadows.   They will approach the center from the edge and that will make it appear as if they are coming forward from the rear.   They will

Editorial Comment of Dr. Ernst Gerland (1906)

The foregoing sketch contains so much for the history of the natural sciences "made interesting," that it was included in this collection [of *Leibniz's Unpublished Physical, Mechanical and Technological Writings* although its content belongs to the field of cultural history.   Not a few of Leibniz's projected ideas which he calls "drôle" have been long since realized. . . . Like so many of Leibniz's ideas, those here expressed went far beyond his times, and were realized long after his death, some only in our day.   More important still should we consider his inspired and constant vision of the general welfare, of constantly striving after the reunion of the individual arts, already splitting apart, into one whole in terms of which each distinct art can fully develop its useful work.   This same basic idea kept the discoverer of the Infinitesimal Calculus working also to persuade the rulers of his time to establish Academies of the Sciences, and led him to become founder of the Berlin Academy.[24]

---

increase in size because of their distance from the light, a thing easily managed There will be no end of wonderful metamorphoses, perilous leaps, flights.   Circle of the Magi who transform whoever appear into demons of hell.   Then of a sudden, al would be darkened.   The same trick could be produced by subduing all light except that one alone which is near the movable little wooden figures.   This remaining light with the aid of a Magic Lantern would throw against the wall admirably beautiful and moving figures which obey the same laws of perspective.   All of this would be accompanied by song from below the stage.   The little figures would be moved from below or by their weight, so that whatever is used to move them is invisible.   Song and music would accompany everything."—E. G.

[24] How manifold Leibniz conceived the aims of such academies to be, can be seen by an extract from one of his letters to Prince Eugene, besieger of the Turks (Guhrauer, *Gottfried Wilhelm Freiherr von Leibniz*.   Breslau, 1846.   Bd. II, 288) In this letter, the activities of academies of science extend to historical works and investigations of charts and manuscripts, a library for the newest publications in literature, a museum of coins and antiquities, a theater of nature and art, a chemical laboratory,.an observatory, a shop for models and machines, a botanical garden, a museum of minerals and rocks, schools for anatomy and surgery, an annual physico medical History of the Seasons and Statistics of the Interior, research-expeditions in the fields of art, nature and literature, salaries and encouragement of persons devoted to these tasks of research and discovery, prizes and gratuities to inventors.

4 FROM THE WORLD-MACHINE TO COSMIC EVOLUTION

From the World-Machine
to Cosmic Evolution

PERSISTING THROUGH the eighteenth and nineteenth centuries, the Newtonian idea of the external world as an ingenious mechanical contrivance governed by differential equations of motion and the universal law of attraction prevailed in all the sciences. It was left to the poets to wonder and to the metaphysicians to argue whether the laws of mechanics had been decreed by the Chief Engineer or Architect of the Universe or were inherent in the motions of matter itself. Insofar as the Industrial Revolution shifted people and production from the farms and handicrafts to teeming cities and factories, social and economic changes called for more mathematical and technical skills. As we approach the twentieth century the specialization of scientific research becomes so rapidly accelerated that the main currents of intellectual history are difficult to discern. Until the problem of communication among scientists today is alleviated, the task of the intellectual historian will remain difficult indeed, although it remains a pressing one.

Among the famous post-Newtonian mathematicians of the eighteenth century, we find the Scot Maclaurin, the Swiss Bernouillis and Euler, the French d'Alembert, Clairaut, Laplace, and the Franco-Italian Lagrange; and of a lesser magnitude, in the new republic of the United States, was David Rittenhouse. Lagrange generalized Newton's laws of motion. The others also applied the calculus to astronomical and physical phenomena in

471

which continuous and fairly uniform rates of change are observable.

Laplace used Newton's law of gravitation in his nebular hypothesis of the origin of the solar system; independently, the German philosopher Kant, who also taught astronomy, had likewise worked out a theory of the evolution of the stars and planets along Newtonian principles. French materialism reached its high point in Laplace's belief that, given the initial positions and velocities of physical bodies, one could predict with absolute certainty all future states of these bodies. This has been taken as the classical statement of the mechanical view of nature. To Napoleon's question about God, Laplace's famous reply was "I have no need for that hypothesis." (The Emperor, of course, had the last word by remarking, "But it is indeed a useful hypothesis.")

With all his faith in mechanical determinism, Laplace, like Fermat and Pascal in the preceding century, contributed to the mathematical theory of probability. He offered solutions to some knotty problems involving causes, games of chance, lotteries, population and medical statistics, life-expectation, and insurance. He even calculated the probable duration or stability of the solar system in terms of formulas which assumed the equiprobability of unknown independent causes. This is, of course, the most vulnerable of assumptions and can be shown to be dubious in many cases. But what is significant from the perspective of the intellectual historian is the root of Laplace's idea of equiprobability. If we recall Laplace's firm faith in the idea of complete mechanical determinism, then probability for him—and for all those who followed him, including Maxwell, De Morgan, and even Einstein —had to be simply a measure of our ignorance concerning all the causes. Where a large number of small causes are at work— in determining the sex of a child, for example—they tend to cancel each other and approach a statistical limit through a convergent series of frequency ratios. What Laplace and his followers did not foresee was that the very laws of mechanics would become statistical summaries of the net uniformities of behavior among large numbers of unpredictable individual variations.

The Newtonian faith in the fixed mechanical laws of nature continued to dominate the scientific outlook into the first sixty years of the nineteenth century before it was succeeded by a shift to the evolutionary perspective. Even Maxwell, the greatest British mathematical physicist of the nineteenth century, assumed that atoms were eternally stable in their physical properties—"unchanged as they proceeded from the hand of the Creator." He also assumed that the ideally complete system of physics would be thoroughly deterministic, so that the statistical laws of gases were only temporary expedients due to our ignorance of the mechanically uniform behavior of individual molecules. Einstein was brought up on this classical view and was sympathetic to it despite the revolutionary progress of the new concepts of statistical quantum mechanics.

In the twentieth-century version of statistical laws found in Bohr's theory of complementarity, Schrödinger's psi-function of probability waves, and Heisenberg's principle of indeterminacy, the mechanical determinism of continuous functions received a fundamentally new set of postulates. Discontinuity seems to function as an important feature of the behavior of electrical particles, as continuity does for the field, so that the problem of theoretical physics today is to find the appropriate mathematical symbols and techniques for handling both. We know whole numbers or discrete integers (Moseley's numbers) were found to order the chemical elements better than Mendeleyeff's periodic table. Mendeleyeff's remarkable theory was suggested by Newland's quasi-musical notion of octaves, arranging the chemical properties in families of eight according to their atomic weights.

Again, the tempo of scientific progress was set by a marvelous union of experimental observations and imaginative theoretical construction. When the observations accumulated thick and fast in the workshops and machineshops of industry as well as in the laboratories of research, the scientists' need for unifying theories became acute. In the more observational sciences, such as chemistry, new properties of elements were being discovered. Boyle had already shown in the seventeenth century that the four

Aristotelian elements (Earth, Water, Air, Fire) were not "simple" but could be analyzed further. In the eighteenth century, Priestley had made careful experiments on combustion, collecting one of the gases of combustion present in air, in a trough over water, and even measured the diminution by volume of air when substances were burned in it.

These same experiments repeated by Lavoisier with quantitative precision led to his discovery of oxygen as the element that supported combustion. But from the standpoint of logic, Priestley's defense of phlogiston was not a sheer piece of obstinacy which failed to recognize Lavoisier's experiments as "crucial." Within the framework of the assumptions of phlogiston as the principle of combustion, Priestley's experiments were as conclusive as Lavoisier's. The important point is that it was not experimental observation or accuracy alone that decided in favor of Lavoisier but rather the more comprehensive theory of Lavoisier that rejected the "negative weight" of phlogiston as incompatible with known physical laws. From the standpoint of the history of ideas such theoretical considerations are often more important for the progress of science than the sheer accumulation of isolated "facts."

Another illustration of the importance for empirical science of what at first appeared to be a purely abstract consideration is the discovery of non-Euclidean geometry in the third decade of the nineteenth century (by Bolyai and Lobachevsky, students of Gauss). Apart from the use made much later of non-Euclidean geometry, the very notion that some of the axioms of a long-established science such as geometry could be replaced and lead to an equally consistent deductive system was a logically revolutionary insight. Leibniz and others (Roberval, Pascal) had intimated that axioms were not absolute or irresolvable, but the long-accepted view that certain truths were "self-evident," and hence unquestionable as axioms, kept the theoretical framework of science within arbitrarily fixed bounds. In fact, the history of the discovery of non-Euclidean geometry is a notable illustration of the danger of prematurely setting too rigid a framework on any field of research, the time for setting up systematic limits being *after* inquiry has broken through new territory.

Let us review briefly the discovery of non-Euclidean geometry. Geometers had for many centuries sought to provide a proof of the "parallel-postulate." ("Only one line can be drawn through a given point parallel to a given line" is the usual textbook form of Euclid's axiom, although not Euclid's.) The method of proof was the indirect *reductio ad absurdum* form: assume the contrary proposition that two lines can be drawn through the given point, both parallel to the given line, and show that a contradiction would result. This was Father Saccheri's approach in 1733, but he failed to find a contradiction and gave up, leaving the proof to be provided, as he thought, by some future mathematician. Had he continued to draw theorems from his assumption, it might have dawned on him, as it did on Bolyai and Lobachevsky, that there could not be any contradiction *if the parallel postulate of Euclid were independent of the other postulates*. This is a purely logical question. A proposition is logically independent of other propositions if and only if its truth or falsity does not affect the truth of the other propositions. Hence, assuming the parallel postulate to be false and finding it possible to retain the other postulates without any contradiction only proved that Euclid had had the logical genius to set down intuitively a postulate that was *independent* of the other postulates. What Bolyai and Lobachevsky had done, therefore, in working out a consistent deductive geometry with the denial of Euclid's parallel postulate was to prove rigorously what Euclid had intuitively surmised: the independence of his assumption of parallels.

The application of non-Euclidean geometry to our theories of the extent of space is basic to modern cosmology, in which Einstein's relativity theory makes use of non-Euclidean (Riemannian) geometry. Even without an examination of the technical details, we may characterize the shift from the Newtonian world view as a change from the idea of the universe as a machine which produces motions by contact to the idea of an evolving and growing universe whose laws are not even picturable in any model other than a mathematical one. What strikes the student of modern theoretical physics is the increased distance between theory (of ultimate particles such as neutrons, mesons, neutrinos; of space-time curvature, etc.) and observation. Two kinds of hypotheses are used: first, abstractions from such observations as the tracks of electrons in a Wilson cloud-chamber, and second, postulates required to round out a deductive system—*e.g.*, the constancy of the velocity of light in a vacuum as a maximum velocity, or the use of a Hilbert space in quantum mechanics. Since Gibbs's use in 1877 of a vector-space for analyzing the variables of volume, pressure, and temperature in thermodynamics had led to so many new developments and whole new chemical industries, it is expected similarly that twentieth-century researches in nuclear physics will also transform our industrial life which is threatened by an eventual lack of fuel or power.

The connection between scientific thought and its technological uses can be amply documented from the early part of the nineteenth century (at the opening of the Industrial Revolution), when mathematics and physics reached their zenith in the French Military School of Technology (*École Polytechnique*), with its very high standards of research and examinations. Among its illustrious products were Monge, Poisson, Fourier, Cauchy, Lazare and Sadi Carnot, Poncelet, Coriolis, and the ill-fated youthful genius Galois. These engineering students and teachers were not restrained from pursuing the most theoretical problems in pure as well as in applied mathematics. The results amply justified the policy, for in every branch of modern mathematics and physics today these men laid down fundamental theorems and broke fresh ground: Monge's descriptive geometry; Poisson's statistics and mechanics; Fourier's series in thermodynamics; Cauchy's theory of functions, elasticity, and optics; Carnot's theory of the gas-engine cycle and law of entropy; Poncelet's mechanics of solids, and projective properties of figures; Coriolis' force of relative motion; and Galois' theory of groups for the solution of higher degree equations.

Another break with the traditional or classical idea of fixed conceptions of nature occurred in the field of biology, which made a tremendous advance after Darwin's *Origin of Species* appeared in 1859. Here we wish only to indicate again lines of continuity and discontinuity in the progress of biological thought. Darwin's theory of natural selection shifted the direction of scientific thought in nearly every field and thus led the way to a break with outmoded theological conceptions of life as owing its origin to some supernatural act of "special creation." But, in doing so, Darwin also established the continuity of man with the rest of the natural world of living creatures, and, on a higher level of discussion, his theory is continuous with the naturalistic tradition that since the time of the Greek philosophers sought to find a basis for the life of man in the physical conditions of life and its observable environment.

Certain elements of discontinuity and continuity appear in the main features of Darwin's theory of natural selection: (1) the occurrence in reproduction of chance variations or mutations with characters deviating from those of the rest of the species; (2) the elimination of those variations which did not enable the organism to adopt itself to environmental conditions or to reproduce; (3) the preservation of adaptive variations which form through reproduction and heredity new species over a period of time.

Before Darwin, there were evolutionary theories among such biologists as Buffon and Lamarck and also among geologists from Leibniz to Lyell. Goethe in his amateur speculations on the development of the flower from characters internal to the leaf and of the brain from the spinal cord of vertebrates belongs to this pre-Darwinian group. Chambers' *Vestiges of Creation* was a forerunner of Darwin's *The Origin of Species*. Darwin himself tells us that one of the main sources of his theory was Malthus' account of the disproportion between human population growth and the slower accumulation of the food supply that led to a struggle for economic survival—a struggle which furnished Darwin with the clue to his own close observations of adaptations among flora and fauna in South America during his voyage on *H.M.S. Beagle* and, after his return, in England.

Wallace had independently come to the same conclusion as Darwin about the selective action of environmental changes, but since Darwin had started to describe in detail the evidence he had accumulated from geology, embryology, and paleontology, Wallace unselfishly gave Darwin full credit for the theory.

The American pragmatists were all profoundly affected by the Darwinian theory and extended its implications to the social sciences and philosophy. Charles Peirce, the most original and speculative of American philosophers of science, went so far as to declare that the elements and laws of the universe itself were constantly evolving. Thus, it is not surprising to find scientists today exploring the evolution of the chemical elements from the first half hour of creation, the evolution of the earth's crust, the evolution of the stars, the evolution of life, and the evolution of social institutions. Substance and the mechanical view of the world have been transformed into an evolving and expanding universe.

Kant's philosophy of science showed the impression made on him by the union of theory and observation in physics, culminating in the Newtonian system of mechanics and the nebular theory of the evolution of the heavenly bodies. In the first edition of his *Critique of Pure Reason* (1781), he had denied to chemistry the status of a science because it lacked deductive mathematical system; after the experiments and theories of Stahl, Priestley, and Lavoisier, however, Kant, in the second edition of the *Critique* (1787), included chemistry with physics as illustrating the creative activity of the questioning scientific mind.

In the preface to this second edition, Kant said: "When Galilei let balls of a particular weight, which he had determined himself, roll down an inclined plane, or Torricelli made the air carry a weight, which he had previously determined to be equal to that of a definite volume of water; or when, in later times, Stahl changed metal into calx, and calx again into metal by withdrawing and restoring something, a new light flashed on all students of nature. They comprehended that reason has insight into only that which she herself produces on her own plan, and that she must move forward with the principles of her judgments, according to fixed law, and compel nature to answer her questions, but not let herself be led by nature, as it were in leading strings, because otherwise accidental observations, made on no previously fixed plan, will never converge towards a necessary law, which is the only thing that reason seeks and requires. Reason, holding in one hand its principles, according to which concordant phenomena alone can be admitted as laws of nature, and in the other hand the experiment, which it has devised according to these principles, must approach nature, in order to be taught by it: but not in the character of a pupil, who agrees to everything the master likes, but as an appointed judge, who compels witnesses to answer the questions which he himself proposes.''

More recent philosophies of science (as held by scientists themselves), support Kant's view that the investigator of nature is helped or guided by conceptual structures or models but reject the idea that there is any finality or certainty which the mind may legitimately impose on nature. The growth of the sciences testifies to the flexible and evolutionary character of their leading ideas as well as to the unpredictable effects which new discoveries have on the very forms of thought and types of problems with which scientists approach nature, more often as pupils eager to learn than as self-appointed judges.

In the essays that follow, some of the major intellectual trends and transitions of the period are examined in detail.

Toulmin's essay on ''Crucial Experiments: Priestley and Lavoisier,'' which is based upon a re-examination of Priestley's original papers, throws light on the methodological problem of choice of hypotheses in experiments that lay at the roots of modern chemistry.

Vartanian's discussion of ''Trembley's Polyp'' takes up once again the protoplasm problem—a problem which, as we have seen, concerned the Greeks two thousand years earlier. Here the context is the French materialism of the eighteenth century and the ''man-machine'' concept of La Mettrie.

The antecedents of Darwinian evolution in the eighteenth and nineteenth centuries are examined by Mandelbaum in ''Scientific Background of Evolutionary Theory in Biology.''

Ellegård, in "Darwin's Theory and Nineteenth-century Philosophies of Science" notes the influence of Darwin upon two philosophers of science and upon public opinion through the medium of popular literature.

The contributions of America's leading nineteenth-century mathematician (and the father of the pragmatic philosopher Charles S. Peirce) are expounded by Sven Peterson in "Benjamin Peirce: Mathematician and Philosopher."

In "One Universe or Many?" Munitz traces the intellectual history of recent cosmological theories.

Wiener's evaluation of "Sir James Jeans on Physics and Philosophy" focuses upon Jeans' attempts to interpret recent physical theory and its history in terms of a philosophy of a Berkeleyan cast.

Lalande, in "Henri Poincaré," points out the great French mathematician's chief methodological contributions to the foundations of twentieth-century science.

Cohen's "Recent Works on the History of Science" is a comprehensive and critical review of contemporary research in the history of science. It points out clearly the relationships between the history of science and the history of ideas.

⁓ S. E. Toulmin

CRUCIAL EXPERIMENTS: PRIESTLEY AND LAVOISIER

Any one who begins to study the history of science at all critically soon learns to distrust all second-hand statements, even those which are most confidently and most often repeated. Lessons which have long been learnt in other branches of history have, in the history of science, yet to make their full effect felt, and meanwhile a mass of historical and philosophical preconceptions stands in the way of knowledge. Lately, it is true, we have begun to see something in the way of a revolution in the subject, in which the University of Cambridge is playing a distinguished part; [1] but one cannot afford to have any illusions about the amount that remains to be done to disentangle the issues in even the most familiar and discussed historical episodes. Perhaps, indeed, it is the most discussed episodes which need the most careful attention, since it is around them that the greatest accretion of misconceptions has formed. So one need not apologize for raising again the question, what was really in dispute between Priestley and Lavoisier, and just how mortally the Phlogiston Theory was wounded by Lavoisier's work.

In any case there are philosophical as well as historical motives for disinterring this question. For one of the preconceptions which has done most to cloud our understanding of the science, both of our own and of earlier generations, is a logical one: the idea that a new theory supersedes an old one as a result of a direct, hand-to-hand contest. According to this doctrine, a new theory can prove its merits over an old through a single, 'crucial' experiment, as a result of which the old theory is left dead upon the field and the young contender, as in Fraser's account of primitive societies, reigns in its place in the sacred grove.

This picture of the progress of science has a certain appeal, both to our logical sense of tidiness, and to our historical self-esteem. For it would make the logical analysis of scientific theories a good deal neater if their acceptance or rejection could, in appropriate circumstances, be justified by reference to a single experimental observation —theoretical doctrines could then be comfortably assimilated to those straightforward statements of fact which, we think, we understand so much better. As a matter of history, too, we are happier if we can believe that the abandoned ideas of our predecessors were plain false, if not ridiculous, and that our own ideas stand as firmly as could be asked. So, looking back on the history of earlier science, we find ourselves continually tempted to pick on this experiment or that, this ob-

[1] This paper was originally delivered at a meeting of the Cambridge University Philosophy of Science Club, 21 November, 1955.

servation or the other, as a truly crucial one, in Francis Bacon's original sense—as being the parting of the ways from which only two roads lead, a true one leading up of course to *us,* and a false one leading back into the realm of error and superstition. Even the most honored historians of science sometimes find this temptation too strong for them, as those will know who have read Professor Sarton on the subject of Aristotle and Plato.[2]

Many people realize nowadays how false, in fact and in logic, this picture of the progress of science is. " The more we treat the theories of our predecessors as myths, the more inclined we shall be to treat our own theories as dogmas; "[3] the task is to get both sets of theories into proper focus. But it will take a long time to adjust completely the binoculars through which we survey the history of science in the way in which this new understanding requires, and to correct the proportion and the perspective in which all the chief steps in the development of the sciences are presented. The aim of this paper is to add a further item to the agenda, and to suggest some of the points which will have to be covered in dealing with it.

I

Lavoisier's revolution in chemistry has commonly been presented, like every other major advance in science, as a decisive one. It was forced upon him, writers suggest, by experimental observations which admit of only one interpretation, and which are fatal, in the eyes of all but the perverse and the blind, to all previous theories and notably to the phlogiston theory. The experiment which is most often presented as playing a crucial part is the famous experiment with the red calx of mercury, in which Lavoisier first obtained the calx from mercury by heating, and subsequently reversed the reaction, showing how the volume of gas in a container attached to the vessel in which the reaction took place first decreased by one-sixth as the calx formed, and then returned to its original volume as the mercury appeared again on reduction.[4] There is no need to say how very striking this experiment is if one sees it, and must also have been to Lavoisier himself. As we watch the volume of gas changing, we find it hard to deny that here, before our eyes, is an irresistible proof that the calx is a compound not an element; and that it is converted into a metal not by imbibing anything from outside, but by giving off the extra gas which we see in Lavoisier's container, and whose loss from the calx the balance confirms. Any supporter of the phlogiston theory who saw this experi-

[2] See, for instance, *A History of Science,* Vol. I (Harvard, 1953), Chapters XVI and XIX.

[3] This way of putting the point I owe to Dr. J. B. Thornton of the New South Wales University of Technology.

[4] *Traité Elémentaire de Chimie* (Paris, 1789), Part I, Chapter III.

ment, we feel, would have had to recognize its force. He would find himself in a position like that of the Dutch explorers who first landed in Western Australia and found black swans swimming on the river near the place where the city of Perth now stands: for them it could never again be possible in honesty to declare that whiteness was a universal characteristic of swans; and the Phlogistonian too, we think, must concede the force of Lavoisier's empirical demonstrations and abandon forever his long-held ideas. Dr. Holmyard, indeed, has even made for Imperial Chemical Industries a film called *The Discovery of Oxygen* in which this view of the matter is taken. On the screen we see the mercury experiment re-enacted at the hands of a gentleman in period costume—I say ' the hands ' advisedly as we never see his face —and the commentary implies that, after this, there can no longer be any question of preferring the phlogiston theory of calcination to Lavoisier's explanation in terms of oxygen.

It comes as a momentary surprise to us to recall that this experiment was in fact devised originally, not by Lavoisier, but by Joseph Priestley, and that Priestley himself, though he lived for twenty more years until 1804, was never reconciled to Lavoisier's new system of chemistry. But the surprise does not last long, for the history of science would be dull if it did not contain villains as well as heroes, stupid men as well as geniuses, and we soon hit on the idea of turning Priestley into a kind of Polonius. This allows us the pleasure of patronizing him and saying, ' Of course the poor fellow was too wedded to the old ideas to be open to the manifest correctness of Lavoisier's theory: ' we may even quote against him, as his biographer T. E. Thorpe does, the warning he uttered himself:

We may take a maxim so strongly for granted that the plainest evidence of sense will not entirely change, and often hardly modify, our persuasions; and the more ingenious a man is, the more effectually he is entangled in his errors, his ingenuity only helping him to deceive himself by evading the force of truth.[5]

Yet is it likely that such a man as Priestley, whose distinguished contributions to chemistry nobody can deny, could ever have been blind to the force of a crucial experiment in this field, if a genuinely crucial experiment were possible?

In point of fact, Priestley was well aware of what Lavoisier had been doing, and saw clearly what the implications of this work might be. Writing in 1783 about the new oxygen theory, he says: " The arguments in favour of this opinion, especially those which are drawn from the experiment of Mr. Lavoisier made on mercury, are so specious, that I own I was myself much inclined to adopt them." [6] Why

[5] T. E. Thorpe, *Joseph Priestley* (London & New York, 1906), 216.

[6] Priestley, "Experiments relating to Phlogiston," *Phil. Trans.* Vol. 73 (1783), 400.

then did he not adopt them?, we must surely ask. The answer to this question usually implied is, baldly, that he was an old fogey, that one cannot expect an old dog to learn new tricks. The fact of the matter is quite otherwise. It is that he, Priestley, had hit upon another experiment which, from the point of view of a Phlogistonian, supported his theory even more strongly than did the mercury experiment support Lavoisier's. What this experiment was, he proceeds to tell us in the paper of 1783, from which an extract is given below. The conclusion he drew from the experiment he had already reported in a letter to Franklin in Paris in the previous year: " In their usual state calces of metals [i.e. earthy substances of the sort we should now classify as ' metallic oxides '] do not contain air [gas], but that may be expelled by heat, and after this I reduce them to a perfect metallic state by nothing but inflammable air [hydrogen] which they imbibe *in toto* without any decomposition." [7] Priestley's experiment had convinced him that under suitable circumstances one could ' see ' phlogiston in the form of hydrogen being imbibed by a calx to form a metal even more vividly than Lavoisier's work had convinced him of the opposite.

Before we look at the experiment, one logical question requires to be underlined. There is no denying that Lavoisier's experiments are extremely suggestive, and Priestley allowed this, for in calling them " specious " he really conceded more than in the twentieth century he appears to—the word ' specious ' having come down in the world in the last 150 years. But if they had been not only convincing but logically compelling, as a truly crucial experiment should be, there the matter would have ended. However many more white swans the Dutch explorers might have seen on their return from the trip to Australia they could never reinstate the generalization about the whiteness of swans once a single black one had crossed their path; and if Lavoisier had really hit on a logically-crucial demonstration, it should not have been possible to reinstate the phlogiston theory either. Yet Priestley went off and did more experiments, and professed to find them convincing enough to outweigh Lavoisier's discoveries. Evidently these discoveries did not seem to be crucial from the point of view which Priestley adopted: it is our business to ask, how this can be.

Priestley's counter-demonstration is nicely contrived and, if reported in his own terms, looks extremely striking. " I thought," he says, " that throwing the focus of a burning lens upon a quantity of minium [i.e. the calx of lead, or in modern terms lead oxide, Pb_3O_4], surrounded with inflammable air, . . . might bring me near my object; and on making the experiment it immediately answered far beyond my expectation."

[7] Priestley to Franklin, 24th June, 1782: reprinted in Thorpe, *op. cit.*, 99–100.

For this purpose, [he goes on] I put upon a piece of a broken crucible (which could yield no air) a quantity of minium, out of which all air had been extracted; and placing it upon a convenient stand, introduced it into a large receiver, filled with inflammable air, confined by water. As soon as the minium was dry, by means of the heat thrown upon it, I observed that it became black, and then ran in the form of perfect lead, at the same time that the air diminished at a great rate, the water ascending within the receiver. I viewed this process with the most eager and pleasing expectation of the result,[8] having at that time no fixed opinion on the subject; and therefore I could not tell, except by actual trial, whether the air was decomposing in the process, so that some other kind of air would be left, or whether it would be absorbed *in toto*. The former I thought the more probable, as if there was any such thing as phlogiston, inflammable air, I imagined, consisted of it, and something else. However, I was then satisfied that it would be in my power to determine, in a very satisfactory manner, whether the phlogiston in inflammable air had any *base* or not [i.e. whether hydrogen gas was composed of phlogiston in combination with something else, or of phlogiston alone], and if it had, what that base was. For seeing the metal to be actually revived and that in a considerable quantity, at the same time that the air was diminished, I could not doubt but that the calx was actually imbibing something from the air;[9] and from its effects in making the calx into metal, it could be no other than that to which chemists had unanimously given the name of *phlogiston*.

Before this first experiment was concluded, I perceived, that if the phlogiston in inflammable air had any base, it must be very inconsiderable: for the process went on till there was no more room to operate without endangering the receiver; and examining, with much anxiety, the air that remained, I found that it could not be distinguished from that in which I began the experiment, which was air extracted from iron by oil of vitriol [i.e. the gas released by the action of sulphuric acid on iron]. I was therefore pretty well satisfied that this inflammable air could not contain any thing besides phlogiston; for at that time I reduced about 45 ounce measures of the air to five.

In order to ascertain a fact of so much importance with the greatest care, I afterwards carefully expelled from a quantity of minium all the phlogiston, and every thing else that could have assumed the form of air,[10] by giving it a red heat when mixed with spirit of nitre; and immediately using it in the manner mentioned above, I reduced 101 ounce measures of inflammable air to two.[11]

[8] Priestley, of course, means 'curiosity': the word 'expectation' has shifted in meaning as much as the word 'specious.'

[9] This is the crucial sentence.

[10] Dr. A. R. Hall argued in discussion that in this sentence Priestley begs the whole question whether minium contains any 'air' in its composition. It is, however, hard to decide whether he is here trying to decompose the minium or only to free it of adsorbed air, as we should now say. Would the distinction between adsorption and chemical combination even have been entirely clear to him? This point will be returned to at the end of the paper.

[11] *Phil. Trans.*, Vol. 73 (1783), 400–402.

Minium combines with inflammable air to form lead. In our terminology, lead oxide combines with hydrogen to form lead: that is his conclusion, though by stating it in modern terms we prejudice the question of the proper interpretation to be put upon the observation. The calx imbibes the air to form the metal, says Priestley, and I can show you this happening: the experiment which he describes is to serve as a plain demonstration of this process. And there is one thing about the experiment which makes it, if anything, six times as convincing as Lavoisier's. When oxidizing mercury in a closed container of common air Lavoisier reduced the volume of air in the container by no more than one-sixth, whereas in Priestley's demonstration, not one-sixth only, but all the gas disappears in the reaction. So even if we can account for Priestley's results in terms of our modern theories, there is at any rate no denying their apparent force.

II

What is one to say, then, about Priestley's minium experiment? It is important not to be in a hurry at this point, for there are two different questions to which the experiment directs our attention, and these we must distinguish. First, there is the chemical question, what explanation we should nowadays wish to give of the phenomenon Priestley observed; and, secondly, there is the further, philosophical or logical question, what sort of criteria we employ when we decide to back our modern interpretation of the result in preference to that put forward by Priestley.

As to the first question, we are no doubt in a position to point out one flaw in Priestley's account. The experiment was conducted in a bell-jar of hydrogen enclosed over water. The effect of heating the lead oxide was to release oxygen which combined with the hydrogen in the jar to form further water. Owing to the trifling masses involved this evolution of water escaped Priestley's attention so that, where we should write as the equation of the reaction

$$Pb_3O_4 + 4\,H_2 \rightarrow 3\,Pb + 4\,H_2O,$$

he takes the equation to be

$$Min + H \rightarrow Pb,$$

hydrogen being tentatively identified with phlogiston. If only (we are tempted to conclude) he had spotted the fact that water was being evolved in the reaction and was mingling with the water in the trough, he would have been forced to recognize the untenability of his explanation.

This last remark, however, begs the answer to the second of our questions; for it implies that, when all the ingredients in a chemical reaction have been spotted, only one interpretation of the process is open to us, and that one our own. So we must return to the history of Priestley's enquiries, and observe his next steps. Looking up his next paper in the *Philosophical Transactions*, published two years later in 1785, we find him disowning his tentative identification of hydrogen with phlogiston, but otherwise maintaining his theoretical views.[12] He does this, although he has in the meantime recognized the fact that in his minium experiment water was produced which he had at first failed to distinguish from the water in the trough. He repeats his experiment with iron, copper and mercury calx in inflammable air, but this time encloses the gas in the jar over mercury instead of water. On heating the calx, he finds the same result as before: " [The metal] began to revive, the inflammable air rapidly disappeared, and *water* was formed on the sides of the vessel in which the experiment was made." This, Priestley concludes, " seemed to afford a sufficient proof that [a metal] contains phlogiston, and that it is not revived by the mere expulsion of dephlogisticated air [i.e. oxygen], as M. Lavoisier supposes." [13]

Once more we are obliged to exercise our historical imaginations. At first we shall be tempted to complain at Priestley's continued failure to accept the modern view of this reaction; and, losing patience with the man, we may begin to look for non-rational explanations of his conservatism. It is important, therefore, to face directly the logical issue here raised, and to consider whether Priestley should really have been forced by his observations to reach the conclusions which we accept as being so obvious.

Priestley, one must notice, regards the water evolved in the reaction as a by-product: the principal phenomenon, he still declares, is the union of the calx with phlogiston to form metal. He is, of course, forced to sophisticate his explanation in order to make it still fit. Whereas, before this experiment, he had hardly thought to question the *purity* of the calces employed, he now introduces a further distinction. Common calces, such as the scales of iron he had used in this new experiment, are liable to contain a certain amount of water, which serves as-it-were as water of crystallization: only when this is driven off do we obtain the " pure earth of iron," which is now to be regarded as the true elementary substance. To quote the 1785 paper:

When iron is melted in dephlogisticated air, we may suppose that, though part of its phlogiston escapes, to enter into the composition of the small quantity of fixed air [i.e. carbon dioxide] which is then procured, yet enough remains to form *water* with the addition of dephlogisticated air which it has imbibed, so that this *calx* of iron consists of the intimate union of the pure *earth of iron* and of *water;* and therefore when the same calx, thus saturated

[12] Priestley, " Experiments and Observations Relating to Air and Water," *Phil. Trans.*, Vol. 75 (1785), 279–309.   [13] *Ibid.*, 304.

with water, is exposed to heat in inflammable air, this air enters into it, destroys the attraction between the water and the earth, and revives the iron, while the water is expelled in its proper form.[14]

Furthermore, whereas in 1783 he had been inclined to identify hydrogen with phlogiston, allowing at most that his ' inflammable air ' might contain caloric as well as phlogiston, now in 1785 he wishes to correct himself, and regards hydrogen as a union of phlogiston and water. The water evolved in the reaction, he declares, comes partly from the scales and partly from the hydrogen. In symbols:

$$Scales + H \rightarrow Fe + W$$
$$or \ E_1.W + Ph.W \rightarrow Fe + W$$

One might at this point go off down a curious side-alley, and ask how this new point of view ties up with our own views about the constitution of water. If phlogiston is minus-oxygen, then the statement that hydrogen is composed of water plus phlogiston comes remarkably close to our own view that water consists of hydrogen plus oxygen. The crucial question would now become what grounds we should require, and in fact have, for saying that hydrogen is a ' constituent ' of water, rather than saying *vice versa* that water is a ' constituent ' of hydrogen.

Leaving this aside, we must acknowledge that Priestley's interpretation of his experiment is at least consistent. Whatever grounds we have for preferring our own, Lavoisierian explanations (and I would not dream of disputing the fact that they are vastly preferable to Priestley's) the original mercury experiment is by no means the crucial or the uniquely-vivid one it at first seemed. Priestley's minium experiment was, if anything, more impressive, so that even after he had spotted the tell-tale water drops, the original conviction produced by the first discovery still remained. Where we nowadays suppose that we can ' see ' oxygen being *evolved from* heated mercury calx, Priestley was equally convinced that he could ' see ' hydrogen being *imbibed by* heated lead or iron calx. The same compelling impression of seeing a chemical formula verified before one's eyes, which was so happily suggestive to Lavoisier, was equally misleading to Priestley. And from this it follows, if nothing else does, that a telling demonstration of a chemical formula is no guarantee of its correctness. Thorpe describes Priestley's paper of 1783 in the words, " A series of experiments faultless as to execution but utterly fallacious as to interpretation." [15] If the popular doctrine of Crucial Experiments were correct, this fallaciousness must appear in the form of positive inconsistencies, indeed of self-contradictions. But these are not in evidence, for the issue is one of another kind.

[14] *Phil. Trans.* (1785), 299–300; and cf. 308n.
[15] Thorpe, *op. cit.*, 215.

III

In the second half of this paper I shall discuss some general lessons to be drawn from this particular historical episode. But before doing this it may be worth asking why historians of chemistry so rarely mention these particular experiments of Priestley's. Seeing the great importance he himself attached to them, this failure seems at least odd; and when I myself first came across Priestley's papers about them it seemed natural to put a worse interpretation on it. By neglecting to set out the facts of the case and to enquire why Priestley should have thought these experiments so important, had not historians been showing a wilful lack of sympathy and a deliberate blindness to the real issues involved? Some of them, I still think, ignore these papers simply because they find it convenient to do so: being convinced of the superiority of Lavoisier's views, they are prepared to accept the evidence of the mercury experiment as crucial, and have no patience with any contrary-looking demonstrations. But on further investigation two small bibliographical points come to light which may do something to excuse them, and since these points illustrate the pitfalls to which we amateurs of the subject are exposed, it may be worth mentioning them here.

The 1783 paper first came into my hands by chance, unbound from the rest of the *Philosophical Transactions* for that year.[16] Later on, when trying to find it again, I was at first unable to track it down. The 1785 paper came to light quickly, but that was clearly not the one required, and the allusions in it to the earlier paper were not readily intelligible without that other paper being before one. One would have thought that such a paper would have been easy to find: all one need do, surely, was to thumb through the contents at the beginning of each bound volume of the *Philosophical Transactions*, or alternatively to look up the reference to the paper in the classified contents of the standard abstracts of the *Philosophical Transactions* by Hutton, Shaw and Pearson, published by Baldwin in 1809. Yet no reference to the crucial paper, it appeared, was to be found in either place. And this is in fact the case. The 1783 paper is in the second half of the *Phil. Trans.* volume for that year, and is listed only in the contents pages bound half way through the volume; while by some mischance all reference to the paper was omitted from the classified list of papers on chemical philosophy at the beginning of volume XV of Baldwin's abstracts, although it is included in the chronological contents and referred to in the body of the abstracts on page 453.

So it is possible that some of Priestley's modern critics have simply missed seeing the 1783 paper, and have concluded that he never really

[16] It had been bought by Mr. G. Buchdahl for the Melbourne University Department of History and Methods of Science, where I was then working.

faced the implications of Lavoisier's work on mercury just because of
this. All the same, it has probably more often happened that the
existence of the paper has been recognized, but its importance and
force overlooked.

IV

To return to our main problem: Lavoisier's mercury experiment
not only *was* not in the event the crucial experiment it has often been
taken for but, in point of logic, *could* not have been crucial. Priestley
accepted Lavoisier's demonstration but interpreted it in a way which,
though to modern eyes incorrect, could nevertheless seem satisfactory
to him; and he could do so without any inconsistency. For the advance which chemistry required when Lavoisier began his work was
essentially a theoretical one, which might be suggested by a sufficiently striking experiment but could not be imposed on one by it.
Lavoisier's new system of chemistry was intended all along, not so
much to report new chemical facts, as to introduce a clearer and more
consistent set of chemical ideas,[17] and the greatest merit of the system
lay in its providing just that.

One point is particularly worth underlining. Before Lavoisier set
out his ideas, the criteria for marking off chemical substances from
other sorts of things were extremely vague, and different scientists were
inclined to include in the list of substances some or all of a wide range
of things which we would now exclude. Heat, fire, light, spirits (animal spirits and the human spirit as well as methylated spirits), airs,
principles and properties, electric, caloric and magnetic fluids were all
accepted by some chemists and rejected by others as possible participants in the natural transactions and transformations which it is the
business of the chemist to study. Phlogiston, which people think of
nowadays as the chief villain in the drama of eighteenth-century
chemistry, was in fact only one character on the scene, and not such
an important one at that. Dr. Hélène Metzger, in her profound analyses of the chemistry of this period, has brought out the extent to
which the issue was confused by the classification of (e.g.) *light* as a
chemical substance capable of entering into combination with another
substance and of affecting thereby such properties of the substance as
its refractive index.[18] It was easy enough to cite some phenomena
which seemed to support the view that each one or other of these dif-

---

[17] See, for instance, the remarks by Lavoisier in his preface to G. de Morveau
et al., *Méthode de Nomenclature Chimique* (Paris, 1787), 6–14: and also the preface
to the *Traité Elémentaire* of 1789. Cf: Hélène Metzger, *La Philosophie de la Matière chez Lavoisier* (Paris, 1935).

[18] See, for instance, Metzger, *Newton, Stahl, Boerhaave, et la Doctrine Chimique*
(Paris, 1930), 77–81.

ferent things could be thought of as being a sort of substance. What was lacking, however, was any clear criterion for deciding when, for purposes of chemical theory, it was profitable to classify them in this way.

Correspondingly, there was great obscurity about the distinction between chemical processes and physical ones: the more often that light, for instance, was thought of as a substance, the more tendency was there to treat optical phenomena as effects of combination and decomposition. Even Lavoisier himself construed the change from solid to liquid as one involving the combination of base-substance with caloric,[19] and conversely Boerhaave thought of oxidation and reduction as being no more than a physical change of state [20]—which is understandable in a generation which was aware of the chemical equivalence of diamond and graphite.

Lavoisier's main complaint against the phlogiston theory, therefore, is not that it misrepresents the facts—though no doubt he would have thought that to give an adequate representation of the facts in terms of the theory was scarcely practicable. Rather he objects that the central notions of the theory were too vague to be explanatory. In terms of phlogiston one could explain not too little, but too much: the term was a conceptual concertina, and scientists had tended to stretch it further and further in accounting for wider and wider ranges of phenomena until its effective explanatory power had become gravely attenuated. "Chemists" he wrote in his memorandum of 1783,[21] "have made a vague principle of phlogiston which is not strictly defined, and which in consequence accommodates itself to every explanation into which it is pressed. Sometimes this principle is heavy and sometimes it is not; sometimes it is free fire, and sometimes it is fire combined with the earthy element; sometimes it passes through the pores of vessels and sometimes they are impenetrable to it. It explains at once causticity and non-causticity, transparency and opacity, colours and the absence of colours. It is a veritable Proteus which changes its form every minute."

It is worth asking how we ourselves would have been inclined to proceed in this situation. E. M. Forster has written a pleasing essay in which he describes Voltaire's chemical experiments.[22] We are shown Voltaire and Madame du Châtelet living in the same castle and composing in their respective laboratories essays which are to be en-

[19] Metzger, *La Philosophie de la Matière chez Lavoisier*, 77–84, and Lavoisier, *Traité Elémentaire*, Part I, Chapters I, V, and IX.

[20] Metzger, *Newton, Stahl, Boerhaave*, 277–8.

[21] Quoted by Thorpe, *Essays on Historical Chemistry* (London, 1902), 169.

[22] E. M. Forster, "Voltaire's Laboratory" reprinted in *Abinger Harvest* (London, 1936).

tered for a competition set by the Academy of Sciences. The subject of the competition is The Nature and Properties of Fire, and Voltaire as E. M. Forster depicts him, is greatly puzzled by the inconsisten results he has got in his experiments to determine the weight of fire Looking back, we are not surprised at his failure to obtain any con sistent results, and we may even be a trifle impatient with him. once asked a scientific friend what he would have said to Voltaire to persuade him of the uselessness of his enquiries and got the reply, " should have told him to use his common sense." This answer would have been all right, if Voltaire's common sense could have been the common sense of the twentieth century; but on investigation on finds that our present common sense enshrines a good deal of the con ceptual clarification introduced by Lavoisier himself.

One thing Lavoisier did, I take it, was to use the principle of th conservation of mass as an *axiom* of chemistry: by appeal to this idea one was to determine for a start what things could be accepted as be ing ' substances ' in a chemical sense at all. Plenty of people had enunciated the principle before, or used it by implication in the course of their arguments. But the conclusions they came to were as often as not of the sort that Lavoisier himself now wanted to reject. Boyle for instance, used the principle to establish the corporeal nature of light, which he did by citing the increase in weight of a metal when calcined—the very phenomenon Lavoisier cites as proving the exist ence of oxygen.[23] In such cases, however, the weight of the intangible ingredient was never measured directly: it was, indeed, said that thi could not always be done, and that one was unreasonable in demand ing that it should be. This was the attitude taken up by Watson, fo instance, when he likened phlogiston to magnetism and gravity, and so rejected as meaningless the demand that it should be produced in iso lation from other substances and exposed to direct measurement.[24] I had been possible, accordingly, to pay lip service to the principle of the conservation of mass without clearing up the confusion between chemical and physical change, whereas Lavoisier introduced a syste matic criterion for distinguishing them. Henceforth we are to measure directly the quantities of all the ingredients entering into a reac tion, and to accept as genuine substances only those things which there is good reason to believe can be so measured: only substance passing this test are to be admitted into the equations governing

[23] Robert Boyle, " New Experiments to Make Fire and Flame Stable and Ponder able," in *Collected Works* (London, 1744), Volume III, discussed by Metzger i *Newton, Stahl, Boerhaave*, 69–71.

[24] Richard Watson, " Of Fire, Sulphur and Phlogiston," in *Chemical Essays* Volume I (London, 1782); quoted by White in his book on the phlogiston theor and by Dr. Hall in *The Scientific Revolution*. Watson's book ran through seven edi tions in less than twenty years.

chemical reactions or taken into account when working out the balance of the masses involved.

The success of this procedure is a matter of common knowledge: so much so that we are in danger of thinking of its adoption as an obvious move, when it was not. It was, in fact, a brilliant piece of analytical simplification, which served the purposes of science admirably throughout the nineteenth century, but has more recently had to be abandoned.[25] For the moment, at any rate, its effect was to cut the cackle of theoretical disputation. Watson's excuse for not producing phlogiston in a bottle had to be rejected, and, since no satisfactory independent way of establishing the quantity of phlogiston entering into a reaction was produced, one was to proceed on the assumption that " the whole doctrine of phlogiston had been founded on mistake." [26] Only by making precise in this way our criterion for telling authentic substances from other things was it possible for Lavoisier to work out a new, clear, and comprehensive set of chemical concepts, and this in fact is what the chemists of the 1780's turned to Lavoisier to provide. Being a true disciple of Condillac, he set himself to improve chemical theory by means of improvements in chemical nomenclature, and his success though incomplete was dazzling. It was incomplete, seeing that in Lavoisier's system ' caloric ' retained a foothold among the elementary substances which it did not lose till half a century later.[27] It was dazzling, because, as so often happens when great clarifications are introduced into our ideas, chemists looking back at their old speculations afterwards from the new point of view came to wonder how they could ever have thought differently. Without being clear about the nature of the change in their outlook, they decided that the phlogiston theory had been, not just hopelessly muddled, but simply false. And this is the story we have so often been told.

[25] The " nineteenth century approximation " was built up on the distinction between mass and energy, each of which was supposed to be *independently* conserved. A sharp distinction between chemical and physical processes was only maintainable for so long as this approximation held good. Now, however, we know that in many processes it is necessary to allow for the inter-conversion of matter and energy, and so to set up only a single mass-energy balance equation.

[26] Priestley's phrase: *Phil. Trans.* (1783), 399.

[27] Even then the eclipse was in part only temporary: the recognition that mass and energy are equivalent led to a return, if not to the idea of heat as a fluid, at any rate to the use of combined mass-and-energy balance equations, of which Lavoisier's equation " $2(H.Cal_2) + O.Cal_2 \rightarrow Water.Cal_1 + free\ caloric$ " is an anticipation. Of course, Lavoisier had no conversion factor for relating his calorimeter measurements of ' quantity of heat ' with his balance measurements of ' quantity of matter ', such as is provided by the expression " $E = mc^2$; " but he could certainly claim that the amount of caloric released in a reaction was observable and measurable, even if not ' ponderable.'

A crucial experiment or observation can, however, be made only when certain very strict conditions are fulfilled. What these are should be evident from a glance at the stock logic-book example which I referred to earlier in passing. The hypothesis that all swans are white, and the contrary hypothesis that not all swans are white can be decided between by a single observation, when the first authenticated report of black swans reaches the world of science. But, as a matter of logic, this is possible only as a result of the fact that the two hypotheses can be stated in such a way as formally to exclude one another. Once they have been stated in the same terms, it becomes clear what sort of observations entitle us to prefer the one to the other, and the making of such observations is crucial.

At the level of high theory, however, this can no longer be done. Rival theories present us with rival sets of terms of concepts, and the hypotheses we formulate within each theory can never directly collide. Lavoisier could not compel Priestley to agree that his demonstration with mercury settled the issue between their theories any more than Priestley's experiments could compel Lavoisier, because they could not even agree to characterize the systems they were studying in sufficiently similar ways.[28] It was always open to either of them to give an interpretation in his own terms of any experimental results that turned up, even though in some cases Priestley's explanations do begin to look (to us at any rate) somewhat strained. The superior merit of Lavoisier's theory lay in this: that it gave clear and economical explanations instead of confused ones, not that it gave true instead of false ones. One might say indeed that the supreme merit of the theory was that, in the new terms which it introduced, the issues involved in the long-disputed problems of combustion, calcination and fire could at last be stated clearly enough to be laid to rest.

V

The logical moral illustrated by the dispute between Priestley and Lavoisier is this: that over questions of scientific theory no single ex-

---

[28] This is not to say that Priestley *could* not have been convinced. The points about which he himself felt most embarrassment are clear enough: cf. the passage from the 1783 paper where he explains that because of the sublimation of the specimens of calx on heating, " I could not pretend to ascertain the weight of inflammable air in the calx, so as to prove that it had acquired an addition of weight by being metallized, which I often attempted. But were it possible to procure a perfect calx, no part of which should be sublimed or dispersed, I should not doubt but that the quantity of inflammable air imbibed by it would sufficiently add to its weight." *Phil. Trans.*, 73: 408–9. Yet when he later discovered that a loss of weight actually occurred, it was still possible for him to put this down to *water* leaving the calx. (cf. *Phil. Trans.*, 75: 284ff.)

periment can—in the logician's sense of the term—be completely 'crucial.' We are often tempted to speak of theory A predicting event a and theory B predicting event b, and of an experiment to determine whether a or b happens as settling the issue between the two theories for good and all. Yet this is in fact an abbreviated manner of speaking and one which may gravely mislead us. For it is not *theories* which make predictions but *theorists*. If Professor Alpha appeals to theory A in support of his prediction of a, he has to begin by characterizing the situation with which he is concerned in such terms that the theory A can be applied to it at all; and Professor Beta who supports theory B will normally dispute not so much the prediction as the characterization. Priestley does not dispute the facts of Lavoisier's experimental findings: what he disputes is their relevance, and his faith that calces, being elementary, contain no oxygen in turn affects his own choice of experiment. By baking the minium before beginning his experiment so as to drive off " all the phlogiston and every thing else that could have assumed the form of air " he already helps to determine in his own mind the elementary character of the calx in question, and so in part prejudges the relevance of the result he obtains to the theoretical issue he is trying to settle.[29] Just what any experiment proves at the level of theory depends, accordingly, on the interpretation we agree to give it.

This is not to deny that in two other senses an experiment may be 'crucial.' It may be historically crucial, if it sets off irreversible changes in theory. In this sense, the mercury experiment was indeed crucial: once Lavoisier had heard from Priestley what happened if one heated mercury in a confined space, he hastened to repeat the experiment and, under the stimulus of the result, the revolution in his ideas went ahead rapidly. Again, an experiment can be ' crucial ' relative to a given set of theoretical assumptions. Foucault's experiment to measure the velocity of light in a transparent substance much denser than air (1850) was regarded at the time as a crucial experiment to decide between the corpuscular and wave theories of light; but it could serve this purpose only so long as physicists shared a certain common body of theoretical ideas. Once these ideas were called in question the corpuscular theory could be revived, without Foucault's experimental results ever being disputed.

Looking back from the twentieth century as we do, it is natural for us to think of Lavoisier's mercury experiment as crucial, for we have learned to regard the phenomenon he studied as a paradigm example, and as the simplest sort of chemical reaction. To have Lavoisier's interpretation of this phenomenon questioned is, we feel, to have *all* chemistry questioned, and at this we rebel. But the task

[29] On this point cf. note 10 above.

of the philosophical historian of science *is* to probe the foundation of just these things and, if I have done so in this paper, it is not with any desire to re-instate Priestley's theories, but in order to make it rather clearer why we rightly prefer Lavoisier's. In fact, Lavoisier's achievement appears the greater when we see it for what it was. If we think of him now as 'the father of modern chemistry,' it is not because by good fortune he was the first to hit on an experiment which *obliged* one to accept the new point of view: it is rather because of the vision with which he followed out the possibilities only *suggested* to him by this experiment, and the clear-headedness with which he devised the first really comprehensive and fruitful set of chemical concepts and categories.

To return, in conclusion, to the question of *simplicity:* the dispute between Priestley and Lavoisier has important resemblances to the dispute between the Aristotelian and Galilean systems of dynamics. There, too, one can point to phenomena (such as the flight of projectiles and the motion of the planets) which seem to us, looking back, to be standing proofs of the correctness of the new outlook. The explanations given by the older thinkers seem to us particularly unsatisfactory just because they set about explaining the simplest, most natural happenings in terms of more complicated ones. What good does it do, we ask, to compare the motion of the planets through the sky with the motion of a horse and cart? A man will certainly end up with odd ideas about the heavenly bodies if that is how he proceeds. Yet to determine which phenomena in any science are to be treated as 'complex' and which as 'simple' is in fact one of the hardest problems of all, and one of the last to be resolved in any really teasing theoretical dispute. We may find it puzzling that Priestley should have wanted to explain away the results of Lavoisier's investigation. But Priestley in his turn found it strange that his contemporaries were unwilling to see the truth when it was presented before them. For him not the mercury but the minium phenomenon was the simple paradigm: any contrary-pointing phenomenon must be thought of as a more complex affair. And it is only in the framework of one or other of the rival theories that one can really ask the question whether Lavoisier's mercury phenomenon or Priestley's minium phenomenon was the *simpler* chemical reaction. We must not answer this question for ourselves first, and then go on afterwards to blame Priestley for accepting the consequences of answering it differently. He could be obliged to accept our answer to this question only if he had accepted already the vital parts of Lavoisier's theory, and this was just what he never brought himself to do.

TREMBLEY'S POLYP, LA METTRIE, AND EIGHTEENTH-CENTURY FRENCH MATERIALISM

In 1740, Abraham Trembley, a young Genevan engaged as preceptor in a noble house in Holland, while strolling in the country, chanced upon a discovery that was shortly to make his name illustrious in the eighteenth century. Below the surface of a stagnant pool, a type of water-plant attracted his attention. Upon examination, the small reed-shaped creature appeared to be composed of a uniformly gelatinous substance, having, at one end of the hollow body, a mouth-like opening, and reproducing, normally, by a series of shoots. Such were the characteristics that had led Leeuwenhoeck to class this polyp as a plant in 1703. Many had seen it since, without perceiving anything out of the ordinary. But Trembley, observing closely, noticed that his freshwater "zoophyte" had the habits of an animal. Along with its powers of locomotion, contraction and extension, eight or ten arm-like projections at its mouth-end could seize whatever prey came their way, which was then conveyed to the stomach and digested. Puzzled by this apparent contradiction between the appearance of the polyp and its behavior, Trembley experimented further before being convinced of its animality. He then communicated the facts to the great Réaumur, the authority of the age in such matters, who not only approved the young naturalist's conclusions, but became himself keenly interested in the polyp's singularity.

The most amazing fact concerning the polyp, however, first related in the usually reserved *Mémoires de l'Académie des Sciences,* is typically worded: "The story of the Phoenix who is reborn from his ashes, as fabulous as it might be, offers nothing more marvelous. . . . From each portion of an animal cut in 2, 3, 4, 10, 20, 30, 40 parts, and, so to speak, chopped up, just as many complete animals are reborn, similar to the first. Each of these is ready to undergo the same division . . . without it being known yet at what point this astonishing multiplication will cease."[1] The polyp's hydra-like regeneration, and its behavior with a type of

---

[1] *Mém. de l'Acad. d. Sciences,* 1741, (Ed. orig. in-4°), pp. 33–34. All translations in this article are by the author.

sensibility peculiar to insects when it evidently lacked all the senses and most of the organs proper to animals, caused this *"insecte singulier et merveilleux,"* as the *Encyclopédie* later summed up its reputation,[2] to be perhaps the most fascinating single curiosity of natural history in the 1740's.

Long before the publication in 1744 of Trembley's widely-circulated and classic account of the polyp,[3] talk about the new discovery had stimulated thought on a variety of subjects. Trembley, Réaumur, Henry Baker, Martin Folkes, Buffon, Jussieu, to mention only the most important, were all very much preoccupied with the several problems raised by the polyp and affecting the orientation of zoological science. What is particularly significant, however, and all the more so because of its important implications for eighteenth-century materialism, is the fact that the polyp became involved in speculations on matters ranging from the nature of the soul to the teleology of organic forms. Oddly enough, this aspect of the polyp's rôle has hitherto not been made the subject of a single study.

Paralleling the purely scientific interest for a time, the philosophical concern with the polyp continued several decades longer. Charles Bonnet, discoverer of parthenogenesis and a foremost eighteenth-century biologist; Maupertuis, the French President of the Berlin Academy of Sciences; Lyonnet, the well-known naturalist—all were aware of the broader questions, philosophical in import, implicit in the peculiarities of the polyp. Even Rousseau, in 1750, listed its manner of multiplication among the six or seven leading problems of science and philosophy in his famous *tour de force* against the vanity of searching into the secrets of the universe.[4] Many years later, Voltaire, with much curiosity and a few prejudices, observed over and over again a vase full of polyps displayed on the mantelpiece of his friend du Faï's home and did not find sufficient reason to accept their animality. About the same time, the hero of Diderot's *Rêve de D'Alembert* imagined "human polyps" inhabiting Jupiter and Saturn.

---

[2] *Encyclopédie, ou dictionnaire raisonné des sciences, des arts et des métiers,* 1751–65, XII, 945 ff. Article *Polype.*

[3] *Mémoires pour servir à l'histoire d'un genre de polypes d'eau douce, à bras en forme de cornes* (Leiden, 1744). (Also, Paris, 1744).

[4] G. R. Havens, ed., J-J. Rousseau, *Discours sur les sciences et les arts,* (1946), p. 131; also *Commentary,* pp. 215–16.

But it was Julien Offray de La Mettrie (1709–51), one of the lesser materialists of the century, who had earlier understood and utilized with originality and consistency the speculative implications of Trembley's discovery.   This integration of the polyp into the stream of materialist ideas was to effect a major change in the direction of La Mettrie's thought, culminating in the appearance of *L'Homme machine* in 1748, a work clearly divergent from his previous writings in its new approach to materialism.   In addition to what an analysis of La Mettrie's works would reveal on this point, there exists other conclusive evidence of the firm ties established, at an early date, between the nature of the polyp and the tenets of materialist philosophy.   Bonnet, who was thoroughly familiar with almost every phase of the polyp question, states this fact explicitly in the *Contemplation de la Nature* (1764).[5]   But he gives no names.   Hence when he deplores the utilization of the polyp to bolster the doctrines of materialism, Bonnet might be referring to Buffon, Maupertuis or Diderot, as well as to La Mettrie.   Be this as it may, for chronological reasons alone, La Mettrie's position must receive prior consideration in any study of French materialism during the period under scrutiny.   For the record, however, it must be noted that those who were in many ways his immediate intellectual heirs were unwilling to admit any indebtedness to him.   This was due, very likely, to La Mettrie's wholly unsavory reputation.   Moreover, his untimely death in 1751, by removing him from the scene of discussion, made it all the more easy for his successors to refuse credit where credit was due.   In recent years, an attempt has been made to restore the author of *L'Homme machine* to his merited place in the history of eighteenth-century thought.[6]   An examination, therefore, of the polyp's influence on La Mettrie and his contemporaries is most pertinent to the new revaluation.

The rôle the polyp had in the formation of La Mettrie's ideas

[5] *Contemplation de la nature* (Amsterdam, 1764), I, xxix: "On sçait combien on avoit déraisonné sur la nature de l'Ame, à l'occasion de la Découverte du *Polype*. Les Matérialistes s'en étoient saisis avec avidité pour étayer leur dogme favori." Included with the abusers of Trembley's discovery are "sceptics," who attempted thereby to strengthen "leurs vaines déclarations sur l'incertitude de nos Connaissances."

[6] Raymond Boissier, *La Mettrie, médecin, pamphlétaire et philosophe* (Paris, 1931).   Especially, pp. 163 ff.

would seem far from apparent to the critic unless *L'Homme ma
chine* were studied against the background of Trembley's work
and its various implications.[7] The first point to be established
then, is that this radical biological phenomenon, prior to 1748, had
a direct bearing on speculative matters. The impact of Trem
bley's findings, as indicated by the title of the present article, on
both scientific and philosophical orientation in the 1740's was a
very appreciable one. It is appropriate, therefore, to describe in
some detail the nature and extent of that decade's interest in the
subject.

As early as 1741, Réaumur spread and popularized the novel
facts about the polyp by repeating Trembley's experiments before
the French *Académie des Sciences,* at Court and in Paris.[8] So
great was the effect of this fresh-water hydra on popular curiosity
at the time that Réaumur wrote to Trembley: "If people in Paris
did not talk too much about war at present, they would be talking
only about the insects which, being cut in two, become complete
animals."[9] The polyp very early crossed the Channel to Eng
land. Henry Baker mentions that Buffon, in a letter written in
1741, passed the information on to Martin Folkes, the President
of the Royal Society, who in turn sought further particulars from
Holland and France, which he made public.[10] Baker himself
having made independent observations, published in 1743 *An At
tempt towards a Natural History of the Polype,* without contest
ing, however, Trembley's originality. Trembley himself satisfied
the increasing impatience of the curious when, in 1744, the long

---

[7] Boissier, for example, who fails to do this, quotes (p. 143) as part of a
longer passage La Mettrie's most revealing reference to the polyp without, how
ever, suspecting the effect on his materialism of the polyp's nature and history.

[8] *Mém. de l'Acad. d. Sciences,* 1741, p. 35.

[9] Quoted in M. Caullery, *French Science and its principal discoveries since the
seventeenth century* (New York, 1934), p. 36. An account of the discovery of the
polyp and the scientific fervor it prompted is to be found in Jean Torlais, *Réaumur*
(Paris, 1936), pp. 157–68.

[10] Henry Baker, *The Microscope Made Easy* (2d ed.; London, 1743), pp. 96–98.
Folkes's interest lasted some time, as evidenced by a letter to him from Mme. Geoffrin
(dated 16 Jan. 1743) in which, following his request, a description is given of the
latest developments in Paris concerning the polyp; cf. Harcourt Brown, "Madame
Geoffrin and Martin Folkes," *Modern Language Quarterly,* Vol. I (1940), pp. 225–
27. According to Professor Brown, moreover, the Folkes MSS examined by him
include many letters from Trembley, Bonnet, Réaumur, and others, in which the
polyp is a subject of discussion.

awaited results of his ingenious researches appeared and reached the great mass of intelligent readers.[11]   Meanwhile, Bonnet, having experimented similarly on various species of worms sharing some of the polyp's regenerative powers (although none to such a spectacular and decisive degree), published the fruits of his collaboration in the *Traité d'Insectologie* (1745).[12]   The pontifical Réaumur, unwilling to put the matter off until the proposed final volume of his unfinished monumental series, had prefaced Volume VI (1742) with a valuable summary of the state of interest and research concerning the polyp and kindred creatures.[13]   From it we learn that Bonnet's experiments had keenly aroused the curiosity of Réaumur, Lyonnet, Jussieu and Guettard, who, whetting the interest of many others, went about France cutting up all manner of worms and sea-animals to see if they would multiply like polyps.   It is important to add that the works of Réaumur and Bonnet in general, as well as the detailed studies of Trembley and Baker, had a definitely prominent place in eighteenth-century libraries, as far as scientific literature was concerned.[14]   For La Mettrie and his contemporaries the remarkable ways of the polyp were a subject of major interest.[15]

It did not take long for the nature of the polyp to give rise to speculation beyond the limits of zoology, for it was the genius of the century to make the transition very easily from the natural sciences to philosophy.   The article already cited at the outset in the *Mémoires de l'Académie des Sciences*, after introducing the new discovery, had impressed upon the literal-minded that the

[11] *See* note 3. A summary and review of the contents of this work appeared in the *Journal des Sçavants*, 1745 (in-23°), pp. 86–114, 237–68. For the widespread interest aroused by Trembley's book, cf. the results of Daniel Mornet's study of 500 catalogues of 18th-century libraries: *Les Sciences de la Nature en France, au XVIIIe siècle* (Paris, 1911), p. 248.

[12] *Traité d'Insectologie, ou Observations sur les Pucerons & sur quelques Espèces de Vers d'eau douce, qui coupés par morceaux, deviennent autant d'Animaux complets,* (Paris, 1745).

[13] *Mémoires pour servir à l'histoire des Insectes,* (Paris, 1734–42), Vol. VI (1742), Préf., xlix ff.

[14] For the very considerable diffusion of these writings, see Mornet's index figures, *op. cit.,* p. 248.

[15] La Mettrie considered that Trembley's discovery assured the passing of his name "de plein vol à l'immortalité." *Oeuvres philosophiques* (Berlin, 1796), III, 135.

polyp had biological as well as supra-biological implications, "on the generation of animals, on their extreme resemblance to plants, *and perhaps on still higher matters.*"[16] As early as 1741, the mathematician Cramer,[17] in a letter to Bonnet, argued that the polyp's manner of reproduction was a severe blow to those who defended the theory of animal-soul against the Cartesian definition of beasts as pure machines.[18] For the division of the polyp into many parts without loss of its vital principle served to prove that an animal's soul was divisible along with its body; that is, its soul was material and indistinct substantially from its physical organisation. On the same basis, Lyonnet, in the commentary adjoining his translation of the *Insecto-Theologia* of the German, Friedrich Christian Lesser, inferred that the souls of certain animals must be divisible indefinitely.[19] Such a statement, if understood by some to mean that the animal-soul is merely a function of matter, could easily suggest a dangerous analogy applicable to the *human* soul. Accordingly, following a later edition of the *Théologie des Insectes,* the *Journal de Trévoux,* reviewing the book in 1747, scented heresy, complained that Lyonnet's discussion, while in itself not unorthodox, set a bad precedent for less pious minds by emphasizing the dependence of the soul's nature on facts of natural history, rather than on revelation and the authority of the Church.[20] Not without cause were the sentinels of tradition here on guard. In their estimate of the problem raised by Lyonnet the point of departure for La Mettrie's materialism becomes in fact discernible. The same article in the *Journal de Trévoux* elsewhere went so far as to predict, very significantly, that theo-

---

[16] *Mém. de l'Acad. d. Sciences,* 1741, p. 35. (Italics are my own.)

[17] Gabriel Cramer (1704–52), friend of Jean and Jacques Bernouilli, appointed to the chair of philosophy at Geneva in 1750, and author of several works on mathematics. Cramer was in close contact with many of the great luminaries of the century, including Voltaire, D'Alembert, Buffon, and Maupertuis.

[18] Quoted in V. A. de Caraman, *Charles Bonnet, sa vie et ses oeuvres* (Paris, 1859), pp. 30–31.

[19] *Théologie des Insectes, trad. de l'allemand de Mr. Lesser avec des remarques de Mr. P. Lyonnet* (La Haye, 1742), II, 86: "Voilà donc l'ame des Insectes, au moins de quelques-uns, divisible, quel étrange paradoxe! Après ces expériences, il semble qu'on aura de la peine à s'empêcher de reconnoitre qu'il n'y ait des Insectes dont l'ame, s'ils en ont, est divisible, & même divisible en très grand nombre de parties toutes suffisantes pour animer un corps tout entier. . ."

[20] *Journal de Trévoux,* mai 1747, pp. 883–85.

ries of "spontaneous" insect generation, by departing from the fixed pattern of ordinary animal procreation, might possibly be extended by "unscrupulous" minds to include man himself and thereby play into the hands of materialist philosophy.[21] About the time of these prophetic words, *L'Homme machine,* which was to utilize the polyp's regeneration towards a decisively materialistic end, was actually being composed by La Mettrie. Many years after La Mettrie's achievement, the anti-materialist Bonnet, inveighing against those who had unwittingly abetted materialist ideas, was to reflect bitterly: "The opponents of the immateriality of animal-soul . . . did not realize that they were thus striking a blow against the spirituality of man's soul."[22]

Philosophizing about the polyp contributed all the more to materialist aims by being a widespread tendency. Speculation concerning its implications was not confined to France and the Continent. Folkes, writing to Montesquieu from England in 1742, had stated: ". . . we wish here passionately for some explanation of so extraordinary a fact."[23] He himself, in the same letter, had theorized that the polyp might prove that plants and animals share the same essential nature and that discoveries such as Trembley's might eventually correct many erroneous foundations of metaphysical opinion.[24]

In 1745, Bonnet, who in his lifetime was never to cease reflecting on the subject, had arrived at one very important conclusion in the *Traité d'Insectologie:* namely, that the polyp represented the connecting link between the forms of vegetative and animal

---

[21] *Ibid., mars* 1747, pp. 395–96: "Il n'est pas douteux . . . que la génération régulière des Insectes par voye de propagation ordinaire, dès qu'elle est vraye, ne soit la plus conforme à l'Ecriture, & à la gloire de Dieu: & il est vrai que l'opinion contraire tient du hazard, & peut rendre équivoque pour bien des esprits licentieux, la génération des autres Animaux & de l'Homme même. Rien n'est plus contraire à Spinoza, à Epicure & au système du Méchanisme pur des Modernes que la préformation nécessaire des Plantes & des Animaux, qui ne peut alors venir que de Dieu."

[22] *Essai analytique sur les facultés de l'âme* (Copenhague, 1760), p. 465.

[23] Gebelin, F., and Morize, A., *Correspondance de Montesquieu* (Paris 1914), I, 379–80.

[24] *Ibid.* Unfortunately, part of the original manuscript is torn away at precisely the most valuable point of Folkes's statement. Nevertheless, there is, we believe, sufficient evidence in the remaining portions to justify our summary of Folkes's point of view.

life.[25] As a consequence of the continuity thus established between two traditionally separate realms, Bonnet devised a tentative *"échelle des êtres."* Although the "scale of nature" had
been advanced by Locke and, in particular, generalized by the
Leibnizian "law of continuity," it was Bonnet who gave a concrete content to the metaphysical idea by grounding it in experimental fact. Even though he himself was not to accept the evolutionary hypothesis, Bonnet nevertheless elaborated, on the basis
of his interpretation of the polyp, a scientific attitude which subsequently, owing to the efforts of others, was to contribute directly
to the development of transformism. Apart from this, Bonnet
was very well aware of the several problems that the polyp's
hydra-like regeneration created for the defenders of animal-soul,
but refrained at the time from attempting a solution.[26]

The temptation to speculate broadly about the polyp's peculiarities was not limited merely to the philosophical-minded. It
was not easy, even for circumspect minds, to avoid thinking radically about Trembley's famous insect. Réaumur, the astute lover
of cold fact and the enemy of facile theorizing, discounted the
chances of ever settling the metaphysical questions raised by members of his circle.[27] Yet, unable to remain at ease about the
polyp's properties, he conceded that the most accepted ideas concerning the nature of animals had become outmoded.[28] Nor could
any but fundamentally new ideas, it seems, have explained what
Réaumur did not understand. ". . . when I saw for the first time
two polyps form gradually from one that I had cut in two, I found

[25] *Oeuvres d'Histoire naturelle et de Philosophie* (Neuchatel, 1779), I, xxx.
Arthur O. Lovejoy has stressed this aspect of the polyp's influence in his book, *The
Great Chain of Being* (Cambridge, Mass., 1936), p. 233. From the standpoint of
our study, the dating in 1745 of Bonnet's "échelle des êtres" prompted by the polyp
will have special meaning.

[26] *Oeuvres,* I, 177. "Combien . . . [de] difficultés s'offrent tout-à-coup à
l'esprit sur ce sujet! Ces Vers ne sont-ils que de pures machines, ou sont-ce des
composés dont une ame fasse mouvoir les ressorts? Et s'ils ont en eux un tel
principe, quelle est sa nature? . . . Admettra-t-on qu'il y a autant d'ames dans
chaque individu, qu'il y a de portions de ce même individu qui peuvent elles-mêmes
devenir des Vers complets?"

[27] Réaumur, *op. cit.,* VI, lxvii.

[28] *Ibid.,* li. Typical, also, of the polyp's impact is Réaumur's comment in a
letter to Bonnet, dated 30 Nov. 1741: "La plus étrange . . . & la plus embarrassante
nouveauté qui se soit jamais offerte à ceux qui étudient la Nature, est assurément la
reproduction des Animaux par boutures." Cited in Bonnet, *Oeuvres,* I, 182.

it hard to believe my eyes; and this is a fact that I cannot accustom myself to seeing, after having seen and re-seen it hundreds of times."[29]

It is evident from the foregoing account that the singularity of the polyp brought into discussion certain basic notions of philosophy. The special conditions which further accentuated its importance at the time will be treated presently. Meanwhile, the 1740's would so far seem to reveal a fermentation of ideas concerning the polyp rather than any definite crystallization of thought. What was lacking, perhaps, was audacity, or simply the readiness to reason a problem through to its ultimate results. Nevertheless, the description just given of early speculation on the polyp will assume particular significance by its relationship to what was to follow. Without it, one would be ill-prepared to evaluate correctly the influence of Trembley's findings on the thought, materialistic in nature, of La Mettrie, Maupertuis, Buffon and Diderot.

Another important element in this general background should be borne in mind. The vogue of the polyp coincided with a major modification, early in the 1740's, of the pattern of teleology with which eighteenth-century France had been nourished through the pages of Pluche's *Spectacle de la nature,* Derham's *Théologie physique* and Nieuwentyt's *L'Existence de Dieu.* The shift of accent was, specifically, from cosmology to biology; or, more explicitly, from the calculable laws of Newtonian mathematical science to the incalculable intricacies of organic nature. In this development, the part of natural history that dealt with insects (the word entomology was not yet established),[30] enjoyed a very con-

[29] *Ibid.,* lv. An impression of the polyp's effect on leading naturalists and thinkers of the day may be formed from a little book (published anonymously) by Réaumur's friend and disciple, Dr. Gilles Auguste Bazin: *Lettre d'Eugène à Clarice au sujet des animaux appelés Polypes* (Strasbourg, 1745). "Un chétif insecte vient de se montrer au monde et change ce que nous avions cru jusqu'à présent être l'ordre immuable de la nature. Les philosophes en ont été effrayés . . . enfin la tête en tourne à ceux qui le voyent." Also: "le plus étonnant spectacle qui se soit jamais présenté à l'oeil humain, une découverte en un mot qui déconcerte toute la nation des raisonneurs." Quoted in Torlais, *op. cit.,* p. 167.

[30] Bonnet preferred the more easily understandable term, *"insectologie."* Following the authority of the zoological system of Linnaeus, the class *Insecta* had at the time a much wider (and less precise) applicability than is the case in present-day usage. For Réaumur and his contemporaries, included among insects were *coelenterates* (under which polyps are now grouped), as well as other "worms" and wormlike creatures.

siderable share of influence. The convergence of several important works into a relatively short span of years corroborates this
view: Réaumur's *Mémoires* (1734–1742); Bazin's *Histoire naturelle des Abeilles* (1744); Bonnet's *Insectologie* (1745). But the
classic example of finalist interpretation in this sphere of natural
science is provided by the title alone of Lesser's work: *Théologie
des Insectes, ou Demonstration des Perfections de Dieu dans
tout ce qui concerne les Insectes.*[31] Its underlying point of view is
that "the power and wisdom of the Creator seem to shine with
the greatest degree of brilliance in the formation of the smallest
insects."[32] Diderot's *Pensées philosophiques* (1746), therefore,
merely summed up a tendency that had manifested itself for some
time when the philosopher, at the start of his career, feeling the
insufficiency of all other arguments, finally rested the burden of
his deism upon the "wing of a butterfly" and the "divinity im-
printed in the eye of a mite."[33] It will be seen that this position
is related in a special way to the orientation of La Mettrie's materialism.

It was owing to the force of this *biological teleology* that the
polyp, by shattering the accepted patterns of "animal economy,"
could insinuate itself into questions of theology and metaphysics.
According to Lesser, whose attitude was traditional and typical
of the age, God had established the distinction of the three realms
of nature and restrained their operations in such a manner that
none could encroach upon the others.[34] Moreover, it was a general law, having theological overtones, that reproduction resulted
from the coupling of the sexes, to which insects were no exception.[35] Lesser classed with materialists all those who advanced
explanations of generation which were outside these rules.[36] It is

[31] The original appeared in 1738. Lyonnet's translation attained high circulation in France; cf. Mornet, *op. cit.*, p. 248. A translation into Italian was published
in 1751.

[32] F. C. Lesser, *op. cit.*, I, 9. See also Henry Baker's rhapsodic exclamations
on the same theme, *op. cit.*, 297–300. La Mettrie himself, *op. cit.*, III, 194, substituting Nature for God, was to say: "Sa puissance éclate également, & dans la production du plus vil insecte, & dans celle de l'homme le plus superbe."

[33] Assézat, *Oeuvres complètes de Diderot*, I, 134–35.

[34] F. C. Lesser, *op. cit.*, I, 69.

[35] *Ibid.*, I, 136.

[36] *Ibid.*, I, 64. It is interesting to note how the *Journal de Trévoux* (see above,
note 21) developed Lesser's meaning in its review of the *Théologie des Insectes* by
similarly attaching theological weight to the theory of reproduction exclusively by
copulation.

not surprising, then, that the very exceptional habits of the polyp, by challenging this entire scheme of things, should favor a "speculative" approach, inclined towards materialism, to questions supposedly settled centuries earlier.

Anyone wishing to expose with method the undisciplined ramblings of La Mettrie's thought must be willing to chart one's own course. Thus, for the purpose of the present study, the starting-point of the argument of *L'Homme machine,* his *succès de scandale,* may well be identified with a *critique* of the type of *biological teleology* which Diderot elaborated and defended during the period of his adherence to deism. La Mettrie, impressed by Diderot's new finalistic approach, paused over his argument and even developed it somewhat; finally he denied its validity. In doing so, he could expect little support from the tottering remains of the Epicureanism refuted by Diderot.[37] A new materialism, which ironically was later to become Diderot's as well, was needed, a materialism which would not rest upon the threadbare "atoms-and-Chance" hypothesis of Democritus, Lucretius, and their modern successors. The ancient philosophy was contradicted on all sides by the ever-swelling mass of evidence that the processes of nature, even the minutest, were according to fixed law and undeniable design.

Let us pick up the thread of the argument of *L'Homme machine.* La Mettrie has asserted and illustrated at length the correlation of the states of the body and of the soul; a change in the former produces a change in the latter, and, conversely, a modification in the soul is accompanied invariably by a corresponding organic manifestation. In the next step, by a reasoning more dexterous than valid, man is assimilated to the Cartesian animal-machine; that is, he is denied a soul in any sense distinct from his material organization. If this is true of man, however, it must be true of all forms of life. In the whole realm of nature, therefore, the principle of "immateriality" or "spirituality" is rejected as either an efficient or a final cause. This brings La Mettrie up against the ineluctable problem: how can matter, by definition devoid of intelligence, be responsible for the order in Nature without the agency of a supreme Intelligence distinct from it? In rejecting the deism of the *Pensées philosophiques,* therefore, La

[37] The *Pensées philosophiques* in 1746 had concluded that the old materialism was no longer tenable. Diderot, *op. cit.,* I, 132–33.

Mettrie is led to show that matter possesses intrinsically the causes of its activity and organisation. It must be defined in a sense broader than both Cartesian "extension" and Aristotelian "potentiality." The ability of matter to determine its organic structure —the crux of La Mettrie's answer to Diderot—he explains in the following terms:

We do not understand Nature: causes concealed within herself [cachées dans son sein] could have brought about everything. See . . . Trembley's polyp! Does it not contain within itself the causes which produce its regeneration? What absurdity would there be, consequently, in thinking that there are certain physical causes endowed with all that is necessary to them, and to which the whole chain of this vast universe is so necessarily bound and subjected that anything that occurs could not have not occurred?[38]

This passage is of central importance in plotting the direction of La Mettrie's thinking. The intimate analogy established between the polyp's regenerative powers and the "metaphysical" properties of matter is here indicative, not only of the decisive use made of Trembley's discovery, but also of the extent to which the author of *L'Homme machine* was willing to attribute self-determination and "design" to matter. This new point of view leads directly to a determinist doctrine the basis for which are the qualities inalterably inherent in material substance. The divorce between biology and theology is thereby complete. At the same time, La Mettrie's system avoids the difficulties of the bankrupt materialism of antiquity and Gassendism which attributed to "fate" the emergence of an ordered universe out of the primordial atomic chaos, and which D'Holbach with very little originality was to perpetuate in the latter part of the century. Generalizing from the example of the polyp, therefore, it was possible for La Mettrie to conclude the above passage with the assertion that "to destroy Chance is not equivalent to proving the existence of a Supreme Being, since there could be something else that is neither Chance nor God: I mean Nature."

These words are perhaps not as atheistic as they appeared to their first readers. Whatever his personal belief might have been, it is true that La Mettrie did not take, from the vantage ground of this materialist conception, a definite stand regarding *"le pour & le contre."*[39] But if the analogy of the polyp did not

[38] La Mettrie, *op. cit.*, III, 164.   [39] *Ibid.*, 161–62, 166.

effectively apply to questions of theology and metaphysics, it did, through La Mettrie's interpretation, furnish an indispensable *rationale* for biological inquiry, the basis of a new non-Newtonian and non-theological philosophy of science much needed at the time, and which Diderot was later to work out in finer detail in the *Pensées sur l'Interprétation de la nature* (1754). Matter was envisaged as endowed with the capacity to *organise*. This, in turn, justified any enterprise that scrutinized experimentally, rather than theologically, the causes of matter's endless modifications. Such, as will be seen, was part of the preparation necessary for the subsequent achievement of Maupertuis and Diderot, and in general for the inception of evolutionary biology.

Another and most remarkable feature of *L'Homme machine* is that it announced the essentials of the theory of "muscular irritability" several years before its definitive exposition in 1752 by Albrecht von Haller, the great German physiologist. In La Mettrie's opinion, the ability of severed muscle-tissue to move in its functional manner when touched (independently of the nervous system) was evidence of the materiality of the soul or, at least, of the "vital principle" of organisms. The polyp was a crowning example, for La Mettrie, in support of this all-important phenomenon. But more than this, it not only lent itself to the theory of "irritability" but justified a fundamentally different approach to the unsolved question of generation and in a manner particularly useful to La Mettrie's thesis. The multiplication of the polyp had weakened the traditional notions of reproduction which, as has been seen, had served to maintain the distinction between soul and matter in the process by which a creature came to life. In *L'Homme machine*, the old position was completely discarded: "Polyps do more than move themselves after being cut up; they regenerate in eight days into as many animals as there are cut portions. This makes me sorry for the system of generation held by the naturalists, or rather, it pleases me very much; for how well this discovery teaches us never to conclude anything general . . .!"[40]

Matter, granted motion, according to La Mettrie, is able to determine its organisation in such a manner that "animated bodies will have all that is necessary to them in order to move, feel, think,

[40] *Ibid.*, 171.

have remorse and to conduct themselves . . . in the realm of physics as well as in that of morality which is dependent on it.'"[41] He then considers the difficulty presented by an argument such as that advanced by classical Epicureanism and, nearer his time, by Willis and Perrault, making soul generally co-extensive with body; scattered, as it were, throughout the organism instead of being centered in one place. La Mettrie is aware that the phenomenon of the polyp appears to favor, on first sight, such a view, since every portion of the polyp appears to possess as much soul or vital principle as any other part.[42] But such a definition of soul is nothing more than a poor imitation of the doctrine that has attributed "thought" to matter; in other terms, an inaccurately expressed materialism. For what would then remain in the severed parts of an organism would be not the soul simply, but a "remainder of soul."[43] The divisibility of the soul for La Mettrie, once again, is a proof of its materiality. Consequently, a notion derived from the polyp with which an earlier period of speculation was well familiar is here adroitly turned to the account of *L'Homme machine.*

In still another important sense the polyp is bound up with La Mettrie's thought. From the indistinctness of soul and body already established, it resulted that La Mettrie could elaborate a broad, fundamental analogy embracing all living types, from the vegetable to the human. The various forms of life, differing among themselves only by their *organisation,* fell in perfectly with the "natural gradation" scheme of Bonnet. The "chain of being" was thus interpreted in a materialist fashion. Behind the conception of a work such as La Mettrie's *L'Homme plante* (1748), was the assumption, consciously applied, that the whole of Nature presents a uniformity and continuity, a series of unbroken steps from the simplest organisms to the most complex. In all of this, La Mettrie not only marvelled at the "chain of being" in language reminiscent of Bonnet,[44] but assigned to the polyp, in his own re-statement of the point, a rôle similar to that in the *Traité d'Insectologie:*

[41] *Ibid.,* 169.   [42] *Ibid.,* 182.   [43] *Ibid.,* 182–83.

[44] In *L'Homme plante* (1748) La Mettrie declares: "Rien de plus charmant que cette contemplation, elle a pour object cette échelle si imperceptiblement graduée, qu'on voit la nature exactement passer par tous ses degrés, sans jamais sauter en quelque sorte un seul échelon dans toutes ses productions diverses. Quel tableau nous offre le spectacle de l'univers!" etc. *Op. cit.,* II, 69.

Such is the uniformity of Nature that one begins to feel, and such the analogy between the animal and vegetable realms, from man to the plant! Perhaps there are even animal-plants . . . which while vegetating, either fight like polyps or have other functions proper to animals.[45]

After vegetables and minerals, unanimated bodies, come beings which begin to show life: such are the polyp and all the animal-plants unknown to this day which other fortunate Trembleys will discover in time.[46]

The analogy, as one might expect, is extended to include man, and in a manner that leaves no doubt about the place of the polyp in its formulation:

If man is not a vegetative product . . . he is at least an insect who extends its roots into the womb in the same way that the fertilized seed of a plant does into its own womb. Moreover, there would be nothing surprising about this idea, since Needham observes that polyps, barnacles and other animals multiply by vegetative means.[47]

La Mettrie's use of the "scale of nature" hypothesis reveals his pivotal rôle in the progress of materialist philosophy in eighteenth-century France. The scientific application of this theory has generally been associated with the pre-Lamarckian evolutionism of Maupertuis, Diderot and Robinet in the third quarter of the century. But La Mettrie should properly be given precedence over them in a historical enumeration. Once this is done, the origins of what occurred after 1750 become clearer. For not only did La Mettrie integrate into the framework of his "system" Bonnet's revitalized *"échelle des êtres,"* but stated unmistakably, in his *Système d'Epicure* (1750), the fundamentals, however undeveloped, of transformism.[48] It is thus possible to find dispersed through *L'Homme machine, L'Homme plante* and *Le Système d'Epicure*, appearing *coup sur coup* in the brief but crucial period 1748–1750, the main elements of the century's evolutionary materialism: "matter endowed with self-determining powers," "chain of being," and "transformism." The coalescence of these lead-

[45] *Ibid.,* III, 192.   [46] *Ibid.,* II, 67.

[47] *Ibid.,* 60. Joseph Needham, spurred by Trembley's investigations, had published in 1745 an account of microscopic studies of sea-animals having some of the polyp's characteristics, which appeared in French translation in 1747 under the title: *Nouvelles Observations microscopiques.* The main purpose of the book is to determine the nature of the vital principle of organisms. It will be seen that Buffon's use of Needham's conclusions is related in a fundamental way to the polyp's rôle.

[48] R. Boissier, *op. cit.,* pp. 45–64, was the first to appreciate this important aspect of La Mettrie's thinking.

ing ideas in the thought of La Mettrie supplies, moréover, an explanation for the unexpected success of materialism from 1750 on. An excellent example of the force of this current is to be seen in the complete *volte-face* of Diderot, one of the century's keenest minds, in the relatively short period between the publication of his deistic *Pensées philosophiques* (1746) and that of his *Pensées sur l'Interprétation de la nature* (1754), oriented definitely towards materialism.   Diderot had doubtless pondered well the reference to his *Pensées philosophiques* in *L'Homme machine!* The impetus of this materialist-transformist current was in large measure due to the effective fusing together of the "chain of being" with a new vitalistic conception of matter.   The background for both of these, in turn, was a series of specific scientific discoveries during the 1740's, among which, as has been seen, the polyp had an influence that was very much felt in several directions.   Because of the speculation it provoked and the broad analogies it suggested, its rôle should be of special interest to the historian of ideas.   The polyp's sensational properties and wide popularity were particularly well suited to affect deeply the scientific imagination of the time, and to emphasize the need of a radically new approach to the phenomena of life.

The last-mentioned component of La Mettrie's thought—evolutionism—requires a separate explanation.   Raymond Boissier, in his fairly recent book on the French philosopher, admits that an enormous difficulty exists with respect to its evaluation.[49] The background of sufficient scientific data to account for La Mettrie's evolutionist insights here is lacking.   The wealth of evidence bearing on comparative anatomy that Buffon's *Histoire naturelle* was to make available in the following decade cannot be taken into consideration.   To seek in La Mettrie's early statement of transformism, as does Boissier, terms and proofs that characterized the subsequent history of the doctrine is, perhaps, an anachronism.   Its presence in La Mettrie's "system" was very probably the *logical* outcome of combining the scale of nature with a dynamic definition of matter; these two elements, likewise, were to comprise almost wholly Diderot's evolutionism in the *Pensées sur l'Interprétation de la nature.*[50] As a result of this combination, the question inevitably arose: how has matter, from a primitive, unorganised state, evolved into the complexity of forms exhibited by the grada-

[49] *Ibid.*, p. 55.   [50] Diderot, *op. cit.*, II, 15–16, 57–58.

tion among the natural species? To illustrate this, La Mettrie conveniently seized upon transformist notions that were very much 'in the air" since the publication of Benoît de Maillet's *Telliamed* in 1748, to which, however fantastic its arguments, the *Système l'Epicure* openly avowed its debt.[51] La Mettrie's evolutionism, then, may be described as the combination of two things: of ideas such as Maillet's which were common property at the time, and the philosophical import of certain scientific discoveries, notably that of the polyp.

The assumption that shortly before the appearance of *L'Homme machine* in 1748 a major shift occurred in materialist philosophy, coinciding with the period of the polyp's broadest and maturest influence, is also borne out by purely chronological facts. A comparison of the foregoing ideas of La Mettrie with the contents of an earlier work of his, *L'Histoire naturelle de l'âme* (1745), will reveal that an important development had taken place in the philosopher's thinking within a relatively short time. This very significant point has been generally ignored by scholars. The earlier work differs, on the whole, in both purpose and method. *L'Histoire naturelle de l'âme* represents an attempt, confused and unsuccessful, to combine various elements of Gassendism with the empiricism of Locke newly popularized in France by Voltaire, this mixture then being unpalatably sprinkled over with notions and terminology proper to scholasticism. In this early work one finds matter defined in Cartesian and Aristotelian terms, side by side; as *extension* exhibiting certain passive mechanical and mathematical properties, and as a substance possessing motion and the potentiality of acquiring sensation.[52] In order to explain the process by which matter becomes organised, both the *material forms* and the *substantial forms* are resorted to.[53] The fact that the relationship between matter and form is not specified, although the two are considered in a manner suggesting their independence of each other, would seem to indicate the author's indecision on this essential point.[54] Throughout the exposition of this part of the work, La

[51] La Mettrie, *op. cit.*, II, 17 f.   [52] *Ibid.*, I, 68–84, *passim*.   [53] *Ibid.*, 77, 85 ff.
[54] *Ibid.*, 68–69, 71, 72–73, 77, 78, 84. The text reproduced in the *Oeuvres* (1796) of La Mettrie is not completely reliable and omits a passage, of interest on this point, contained in the original, *L'Histoire naturelle de l'âme* (La Haye, 1745), p. 36: "Il faut cependant convenir . . . que nous ignorons si la matière a en soi la faculté immédiate de sentir ou seulement la puissance de l'acquérir par les modifications ou par les formes dont elle est susceptible; car il est vrai que cette faculté ne se montre que dans les corps organisés."

Mettrie follows closely and quotes continually classical and scholastic Aristotelian authorities for illustration and support of his doctrine. What is especially significant is the total absence of ideas even approximating the "scale of nature." On the contrary, the traditional distinction is maintained, as one might expect, between vegetative and animal soul.[55] Needless to say, nothing is mentioned that could be interpreted as being even remotely "transformistic."[56] It is not surprising, given all this, that the *Histoire naturelle de l'âme* contains no allusion to the polyp, whereas both *L'Homme machine* and *L'Homme plante* will later show a definite preoccupation with it. In the work of 1745, moreover, there is an unmistakable wavering as to its main purpose. La Mettrie does not explicitly assert the materiality of the soul, or, to be more exact, this capital problem is treated throughout in an equivocal and perplexing fashion.[57] The author appears content with demonstrating mainly the soul's dependence on the organs of the body. As an indication that this might be the principal object of the treatise, it concludes with a purely Lockean recapitulation to the effect that the senses are the source of all our ideas. *L'Histoire naturelle de l'âme*, carefully evaluated, may be classed as a close predecessor to Condillac's *Essai sur l'origine des connaissances humaines* which followed it a year later, in 1746.

La Mettrie himself, in *L'Homme machine*, gives evidence of change in his thinking by offering criticism of the earlier work. The new definition of matter as something intrinsically endowed with the causes of its organic developments renders completely useless the *substantial forms*. La Mettrie accordingly rejects, in *L'Homme machine*, this "ancient and unintelligible doctrine" of the "author of the *Histoire de l'Ame*."[58] In addition to this, the

---

[55] La Mettrie, *Oeuvres*, I, 89 ff.

[56] Leonora Rosenfield, *From Beast-Machine to Man-Machine* (New York, 1940), p. 151, sees evolutionism present in the *Histoire naturelle de l'âme*. Her view does not take into account the fact that there is an essential difference between the half-dozen commonplace similarities between humans and apes mentioned by La Mettrie in 1745 and his later attitude that the complex organisms in the scale of being have evolved by certain natural processes from simpler ones.

[57] La Mettrie's intention, of course, is to deny the existence of an immaterial substance. But his method is faulty. The attempt to combine, in this early work, a materialist definition of soul with Aristotelian concepts of "vegetative," "sensitive," and "rational" soul results only in contradictions, obscurity, and continual "hedging."

[58] La Mettrie, *op. cit.*, III, 184–85.

determinism which resulted inevitably from the materialism of *L'Homme machine* was not to be found in the *Histoire naturelle de l'âme*. In a footnote to the latter, the philosophy of Spinoza, for this and other reasons, had been treated harshly. But the attitudes of *L'Homme machine* created the need for revaluating Spinoza's determinism. In the 1751 edition of the *Oeuvres philosophiques*, revised by La Mettrie, the *Traité de l'âme* (a new title for the slightly altered contents of the work of 1745) gives a strikingly sympathetic appreciation of Spinoza's determinism. "According to Spinoza . . . man is a veritable automat, a machine subject to the most rigorous necessity, led by an impetuous fatalism, like a vessel by the current of the waters. The author of *L'Homme machine* seems to have written his book expressly in defense of this sad truth."[59]

In keeping with this, a clarification of La Mettrie's attitude towards Cartesian automatism is manifested in *L'Homme machine*. Under the pseudonym of Mr. Charp, La Mettrie had accepted in 1745 the Lockean "animal-soul" theory, about which, of course, a controversy had long since been raging in France. But his judgment of Descartes at the time had been ambiguous. While attempting, rather too ingeniously, to interpret Descartes's dualism as a mask for materialism, La Mettrie had nevertheless formally condemned Cartesian automatism as absurd and had faithfully remouthed most of Voltaire's pointed sarcasms against the Cartesian school and its founder. *L'Homme machine*, however, changed this: "Let the so-called Mr. Charp mock the philosophers who have regarded animals as machines. How differently I think!"[60] Carrying out this view, La Mettrie in 1748 considers Descartes as the real precursor of *L'Homme machine*, arguing that his doctrine of animal automatism was simply an invitation to formulate human automatism and that the whole of Cartesian metaphysics was a subterfuge designed to hoodwink the religious

[59] La Mettrie, *Oeuvres philosophiques* (Londres, 1751), p. 238. In the *Oeuvres* of 1796, the version of 1751 is followed; I, 262.

[60] La Mettrie, *Oeuvres* (1796), III, 187. Leonora Rosenfield, *op. cit.*, pp. 142 ff., is aware of the difference in La Mettrie's views between 1745 and 1748 with regard both to the general definition of soul and, in particular, to the problem of animal-soul. Her attempt to explain away these divergences by "looking beyond" the meaning of La Mettrie's words, however, becomes quite unnecessary if it is realised from the start that the philosopher's thinking actually underwent a major development in the period in question.

authorities on the question of the soul's spirituality.[61] This elevation of Descartes in *L'Homme machine* is counterbalanced by a
more critical attitude towards the school of Locke, to which La
Mettrie had owed a goodly portion of the *Histoire naturelle de
l'âme:* ". . . It is no less just that I make here a real reparation
to that great man for the sake of all those little philosophers, poor
jesters and wretched apes of Locke, who, instead of laughing im-
pudently in Descartes's face, would do better to realize that without him the field of philosophy . . . would perhaps still be lying
fallow.'"[62]

It would be reasonable to assume, on the basis of all this evidence, that between 1745 and 1748 La Mettrie's thinking underwent
a major transformation, favorable to the future of materialism in
the eighteenth century and by no means unrelated to the implications of Trembley's polyp.

In dealing with the history of the polyp in the period following
La Mettrie, one can conveniently begin with Elie Luzac's refutation of *L'Homme machine.* In *L'Homme plus que machine*
(1748),[63] after a point-by-point refutation of the new materialism,
the fundamental concept of "Nature" as the intermediary between
God and Chance and the immediate cause of the diversity of living forms, is rejected by Luzac. The passage in *L'Homme machine* quoted above, which defined this materialism almost in terms
of the polyp's relation to it,[64] is taken by Luzac to be the final position resulting from La Mettrie's argument. This being so, the
cause of the polyp's regeneration, instead of being accepted as
inherent in its physical organisation, is attributed by Luzac to the
Supreme Intelligence, in conformity with the teleological ideas of
the age. La Mettrie is thus refuted as follows: ". . . This polyp
of Trembley offers you the spectacle of a marvelous generation:
but be careful, it does not offer you within itself the first cause of
its existence. Even this sudden change which astonishes you
proves that it is necessary to seek the reason for its existence in a
cause that exists outside of it.'"[65]

*   *   *

[61] La Mettrie, *op. cit.*, III, 188.   [62] *Ibid.*, 187–88.

[63] The attribution of this book, published anonymously in 1748, has since 1900
been alternately made to La Mettrie and to Luzac. I have conclusively established,
however, the authorship of Luzac in my article, "Elie Luzac's Refutation of La
Mettrie," *Modern Language Notes,* LXIV (March, 1949), 159–161.

[64] *See* note 37.

[65] E. Luzac, *L'Homme plus que machine* (2d ed.; Goettingen, 1755), p. 136.

ল্ড Maurice Mandelbaum

SCIENTIFIC BACKGROUND OF
EVOLUTIONARY THEORY IN BIOLOGY

The aim of this paper is to show how a variety of scientific problems, and the solutions proposed concerning them, helped pave the way for the formulation and eventual adoption of the biological theory of evolution. No attempt will here be made to trace the influence of certain more pervasive philosophic doctrines on the development of evolutionary modes of thought.[1a] Nor shall I attempt to treat any one of the scientific problems here discussed in an exhaustive fashion. In spite of these limits, it is to be hoped that this paper may contribute to the understanding of the history of evolutionary theory by offering a brief conspectus of various scientific issues which were widely discussed, and each of which was relevant to the formulation of evolutionary views in biology.

To understand the significance of most of these problems it is important to remember that they were viewed in the context of their bearings on religious orthodoxy. This close connection between scientific and religious concerns was not the result of any fear of science on the part of the orthodox: on the contrary, science was quite generally viewed as lending support to orthodoxy. This harmony between science and revealed religion was a continuation of the tradition laid down by Boyle and Newton. Even those who attacked *revealed* religion, wishing to equate true religion with natural religion, did not challenge the belief that through scientific inquiry man could discover in nature the handiwork of God the Creator. Thus, for the Deist as well as for the orthodox, the sciences of nature were the allies of religion. It was therefore the case that when the specific problems which absorbed men of science were discussed, these problems were regarded as being of religious import, and were (more often than not) explicitly discussed in these terms.

The close connection between religion and those scientific developments which paved the way for biological evolutionism is most clearly evidenced in geology. The story of this connection, as well as the story of the influence of geology on the development of evolutionary theory in biology, is so well known that I shall treat it only in the most summary fashion.

[1a] The best treatment of this topic is to be found in A. O. Lovejoy, *The Great Chain of Being* (Cambridge, Mass., 1936), especially Ch. VIII and IX. For Professor Lovejoy's treatment of the more specifically biological problems, cf. his articles in *Popular Science Monthly*: " Some Eighteenth Century Evolutionists," LXV, 238ff. and 323ff.; " The Argument for Organic Evolution Before ' The Origin of Species'," LXXV, 499ff. and 537ff.; "Kant and Evolution," LXXVII, 538ff. and LXXVIII, 36ff.; " Buffon and the Problem of Species," LXXIX, 464ff. and 554ff.

I. THE HISTORY OF THE EARTH

Even before the eighteenth century there was an interest in the relations between newly discovered geologic facts and religion. This was evident in the early speculations concerning the nature and origins of fossils, and clearly evident, as their titles show, in such speculative cosmogonies as Burnet's "Sacred Theory of the Earth, containing an Account of the Original of the Earth, and of all the general Changes which it hath already undergone, or is to undergo, till the Consummation of all Things" (1684) and Whiston's "A New Theory of the Earth, wherein the Creation of the World in six Days, the Universal Deluge, and the General Conflagration, as laid down in the Holy Scriptures, are shewn to be perfectly agreeable to Reason and Philosophy" (1696). However, it is also evident in some of the forerunners of a more empirical geology, such as Hooke, Ray, and Woodward. As Lyell remarked concerning Ray: "We perceive clearly from his writings that the gradual decline of our system, and its future consummation by fire, was held to be as necessary an article of faith by the orthodox, as was the recent origin of our planet. His Discourses, like those of Hooke, are highly interesting, as attesting the familiar association in the minds of philosophers, in the age of Newton, of questions in physics and divinity." [1] And as Lyell was regretfully forced to point out in his discussion of eighteenth-century geology, the controversy between Neptunists and Vulcanists took place within an atmosphere of bitter theological recriminations. [2] Lyell felt that with the end of this dispute, and with the laying of the foundations for a new science of geology by the introduction of more accurate empirical studies of geologic formations, and by the development of the close linkage between paleontology and geology which had been inaugurated by Cuvier, a more fruitful period could begin. [3] However, Cuvier's Catastrophism stood opposed to Lyell's Uniformitarianism, and once again theological issues intruded into geological debates. In *Genesis and Geology,* C. C. Gillispie has traced in detail the later as well as the earlier stages of these controversies, but one point may here be made clear. After Lyell's *Principles of Geology* was published (1830–33) the scope of the problem became enormously widened: geo-theological debates no longer centered merely in the history of the surface of the earth, but came to include the nature of living creatures. This widening of the issues under dispute had come

---

[1] *Principles of Geology* (1st ed.), I, 36. The close connection between questions of science and theology throughout the development of evolutionary thought is amply documented both in Edwin T. Brewster, *Creation: A History of Non-Evolution Theories* (Indianapolis, 1927) and in C. C. Gillispie, *Genesis and Geology* (Cambridge, Mass., 1951).

[2] *Principles of Geology,* I, 67–69.   [3] *Ibid.,* 71–73.

about through the fact that paleontology—as both Cuvier and Lyell recognized—was the most important key for unlocking the secrets of the history of the earth.[4] Thus, the problem of the origin of different types of living creatures and their adaptation to their environments, as well as the problem of the extinction of certain species, and the distribution of those still extant, were in the forefront of attention among geologists. All these problems, of course, raised issues concerning special Creation versus Transformism (as evolution was then called), and these issues were placed in the forefront of attention by such works as Chambers' widely read *Vestiges of the Natural History of Creation* (1844) and Hugh Miller's *Footprints of the Creator* (1849). It can scarcely be wondered that when Darwin's *Origin of Species* was published in 1859, the theological implications of the work were stressed by all reviewers.

II. THE PROBLEM OF SPECIES

A second scientific problem which was instrumental in developing an interest in biological evolutionism, and which also bears the marks of the close association between theological and scientific problems in the eighteenth and early nineteenth centuries, was the problem of species.

(1) *Early Discussions*

One major aspect of Aristotle's biology was the problem of classification, and it was in this connection that the concept of "species" arose.[5] However, Aristotle's own employment of this concept as a means of classification was not consistent, and it was not until Linnaeus introduced his system of ordering plants into "class," "order," "genus," "species," "varieties" that the term "species" was a useful instrument in classification.[6] The main criterion of species, originally suggested by Aristotle and developed by Ray in 1686, was that of capacity for reproduction: only those varieties which could be crossed belonged to the same species. This criterion was adopted by Linnaeus, but his most famous utterances concerning the concept of species were couched in theological terms: there are as many species as God originally created.[7] The harmony between these two modes of definition is obvious: both rule out the possibility of transformism.

Granting this Linnaean characterization of species, the question

---

[4] Lyell, *loc. cit.*, 72f.; Cuvier, *Essay on the Theory of the Earth* (trans. by Jameson), 2nd ed. (1815), 50–51, 54.

[5] Cf. E. Perrier, *La philosophie zoölogique avant Darwin* (Paris, 1896), 12–13.

[6] Cf. Perrier, Ch. 5.

[7] For both types of definition, cf. E. Guyénot, *Les sciences de la vie aux XVIIᵉ et XVIIIᵉ siècles* (Paris, 1941), 362.

arises as to what distinguishes classes, orders, genera, and varieties. Here Linnaeus' conviction that the world constituted a perfect *Scala naturae,* with each type of plant filling a necessary niche in an overarching pattern, was an important influence on his classification. In addition to this conviction, however, Linnaeus also sought a *useful* classification of plants, and the arrangement of plants according to their modes of reproduction, and the introduction of his system of binary nomenclature, provided just such a system. Linnaeus himself did not identify his useful system with the natural system, though he always strove to make the former approximate the latter, and he hoped that the latter would at some future time be achieved. This hope rested on a faith in the strict orderliness of the divinely created world of living things. Since this created world was orderly, a perfect natural system of classification was possible, even though it had not yet been attained.[8]

The distinction between an artificial and a natural order of classification had a profound influence on later discussions of the problem of species. In the first place, it opened the door for criticism of the actual system of classification that Linnaeus had worked out,[9] and this criticism was fortified by the discovery of new specimens which demanded either an immense expansion of the number of distinct species or the lumping together of very disparate forms. In the second place, it suggested that species were not real. Those who—on general philosophic grounds—were inclined to deny the reality of universals (or who took the more moderate position of denying their importance for the empirical investigation of nature) could readily make the transition from Linnaeus' distinction between a useful and a natural classification to the thesis that all groupings into " orders," " classes," "species," and even " varieties " were man-made conventions which did not correspond to real distinctions in nature. On such a view, only the concrete individual plant or animal is real. This was the position taken by Linnaeus' contemporary and critic, the great naturalist Buffon.

Buffon shared with Linnaeus the conception of a system of nature, but for him this system was not a statically ordered array of classes, but a dynamic whole [10] in which individuals vary from each other in

---

[8] On the Linnaean system, cf. W. Whewell, *History of the Inductive Sciences* (3 vols., London, 1837), II, Bk. XVI, Ch. 4; Eric Nordenskiöld, *History of Biology* (New York & London, 1932), 203–218; Perrier, *op. cit.,* 34–8.

[9] For example, Adanson, the French botanist, found Linnaeus' system of classification arbitrary, since it was merely based on the reproductive organs, and he attempted to substitute a classification which would take into account more of the parts of the plant, and thus be less artificial.

[10] " La nature . . . est dans un mouvement de flux continuel," apud Perrier, 64.

sometimes imperceptible degrees: " la marche de la nature se fasse par nuances et par degrés." And to this he added that classification of plants or animals into " families " is our work, which we have performed only for the sake of our purposes, and that if we are unsuccessful in this task it is our fault, and not the fault of nature " qui ne connaît point les prétendues familles et ne contient, en effet, que des individus." [11] Buffon's antagonism to the reality of class concepts was so great that he even denied that our lines of demarcation between plants and animals represented a necessary break in the unity of nature.[12] In his view, Linnaeus' classifications " degraded and disfigured nature, instead of describing it." [13]

As is well known, Buffon himself came to hold the doctrine of transformism, largely through his comparative studies of the fauna and flora of different continents. His contributions to the development of evolutionary theory need not occupy us; what is here important to note is that his attack on the very concept of species was taken up and amplified by three younger biologists whom he had aided and influenced; Lamarck, Lacépède (the man whom he authorized to complete his *Histoire naturelle*),[14] and Geoffroy de Saint-Hilaire.

(2) *Lamarck*

The evolutionary views of Lamarck were closely connected with his attack on the concept of species, as that concept had been employed by Linnaeus. In the first place we may note that Lyell, who knew Lamarck's work well and introduced a knowledge of it into England, traced the origin of Lamarck's evolutionary theory to his investigations in conchology: in classifying species of fossil shells, he found that the resemblances which some of them bore to extant species were so close that the lines drawn among the extant specimens tended to break down. He was thus led to the assumption that there was a common bond of descent between the present types of individuals and formerly extant ones, and that a definition of species must include a genealogical factor as well as the factors of resemblance and capacity to reproduce.[15] Now, it is to be noted that the genealogical factor is (ideally) alone sufficient for the demarcation of species, since individuals linked by descent resemble one another and since they

---

[11] *Ibid.*, 62. The problem of Buffon's view on species is a vexed one. In his early study of this subject A. O. Lovejoy defended the view that Buffon *did* believe in the objective reality of species (*Popular Science Monthly*, LXXIX, 464ff. and 554ff. Cf. Lovejoy, *Great Chain of Being*, 229–330). On the same subject, cf. E. Rádl: *Geschichte der biologischen Theorien in der Neuzeit* (2 vols., Leipzig, 1909–.13), I, ch. XI, #3.

[12] Perrier, *op. cit.*, 67.   [13] *Ibid.*, 57.

[14] On Lacépède and species, cf. Guyénot, *op. cit.*, 408ff.

[15] Cf. Lyell, *Antiquity of Man* (2nd Amer. ed.), 389–390. Cf. Packard's con-

have obviously had the capacity to produce their descendants. But what is ideally true may not be actualized, and we may expect that from the point of view of learning about which individuals should be classified together we must rely upon the conventional criteria of resemblance and reproductive capacity. Thus, Lamarck is willing to define "species" as "Any collection of individuals which were produced by others similar to themselves." [16] Such a definition is compatible with either the older view of the fixity of species or with transformism. It is to be noted, however, that throughout the first five chapters of his *Zoological Philosophy*, which center on the problem of the classification of species, Lamarck is concerned with the distinction between *artificial* and *natural* classifications. Chapter I opens as follows:

> Throughout nature, wherever man strives to acquire knowledge he finds himself under the necessity of using special methods; 1st, to bring order among the infinitely numerous and varied objects which he has before him; 2nd, to distinguish, without danger of confusion, among this immense multitude of objects, either groups of those in which he is interested, or particular individuals among them; 3rd, to pass on to his fellows all that he has learnt, seen and thought on the subject. Now the methods which he uses for this purpose are what I call the *artificial* devices in natural science—devices which we must beware of confusing with the laws and acts of nature herself.

> It is not merely necessary to distinguish in natural science what belongs to artifice and what to nature. We have to distinguish as well two very different interests which incite us to the acquisition of knowledge.

> The first is an interest which I call *economic* . . . . From this point of view he is only interested in what he thinks may be useful to him. The other, very different from the first, is that *philosophic* interest through which we desire to know nature for her own sake, in order to grasp her procedure, her laws and operations, and to gain an idea of what she actually brings into existence. This, in short, is the kind of knowledge which constitutes the true naturalist."

The conclusion which he reached was to draw a distinction between "classifications" and "arrangements," the first being *artificial* and the second *natural*. The first "furnishes points of rest for our imagination, by means of lines of demarcation drawn at intervals in the general series"; the second "represents as nearly as possible the actual order followed by nature in the production of animals." [17]

---

firmation of Lyell's dating of this change in Lamarck's view (Packard, *Lamarck* (London and New York, 1901), 230–231).

[Cf. also Charles C. Gillispie, " The Formation of Lamarck's Evolutionary Theory," *Archives Internationales d'Histoire des Sciences*, 37 (1956), 323–38.—Editor's note.]

[16] *Zoological Philosophy* (H. Elliot translation), 35.   [17] *Ibid.*, 56.   [18] *Ibid.*, 57.

And he further points out that as knowledge advances, and more varieties are discovered, our knowledge of the natural arrangement will increase, and at the same time the utility of our artificial classifications will diminish since the intervals upon which it depends will be filled in.[18]

The motivation of this attack on the traditional view of species did not stem solely from Lamarck's own observations and from the growing difficulties in classification which he noted. Lamarck shared his age's Newtonian distrust of "systems and hypotheses," contrasting them with the results of observation.[19] His theory of knowledge is explicitly stated when he says: " Toute connaissance qui n'est pas le produit réel de l'observation ou des conséquences tirées de l'observation est tout à fait sans fondement et véritablement illusoire." [20] Furthermore, he shared his age's Lockean denial of innate ideas,[21] and its distrust of explanations which presumed that our abstract ideas mirrored reality: as he said in discussing the concept of fixed species, " in reality only individuals exist in nature." [22] These lines of linkage between Lamarck and his predecessors are often overlooked because we today tend to think of him as " a vitalist." In fact, however, Buckle was at least equally near the truth when he classified Lamarck as a materialist, because Lamarck held that the " habits of man are entirely a result of his physical organization." [23] In the light of this discrepancy between our present interpretations of Lamarck and the interpretations of those who stood closer to him in time, it may be useful to summarize his general philosophic position.[24]

As we have noted, Lamarck's theory of knowledge would seem to commit him to a rigorous " positivism." However, like many men of his age, he saw no conflict between holding that all knowledge which was not based on observation was illusory, and holding that he could know something concerning the ultimate nature of the material

[19] From the opening lecture of his course (1803); Packard, *Lamarck*, 255.

[20] *Système analytique des connaissances positives de l'homme* (1830), 84.

[21] Cf. *Zoological Philosophy*, 363ff.

[22] Packard, *op. cit.*, 230. It is also interesting to note that the contrast between the *usefulness* of abstract classifications and the *truth* to be obtained through natural classifications was paralleled in Condillac's contrast between the functions of abstract ideas and the principles of adequate explanation. Cf. "Traité des systèmes," in *Oeuvres philosophiques*, I, 122a45–b10. It is also of interest that Diderot attacked the Linnaean view of nature in Lockean terms (cf. Bréhier, *Histoire de la philosophie*, II, 437, 448).

[23] Buckle, *Miscellaneous Works*, I, 152. This is Lamarck's heritage from Cabanis. Cf. his discussions of the latter in *Zoological Philosophy*; also p. 362.

[24] A résumé of his position on about all philosophical subjects is to be found in his *Système analytique*.   [25] Cf. *Zoological Philosophy*, 183ff.

world, and could also know that God exists as Creator of the universe. When we survey the whole of created nature we find that all entities are physical, that they change state and position according to laws, and that motion accounts for these changes.[25]   However, we also find that there is a sharp distinction between the inorganic and the organic with respect to the principle of their motions: the former is characterized by passivity because its motion depends upon *transmission*, while the latter is characterized by activity because its motion depends upon *stimulus*.   Thus, it would appear that Lamarck should be regarded as a vitalist, since he draws this absolute distinction between the living and the non-living.[26]   However, it is to be noted that organic activity (the reaction to stimuli) depends upon "the vital fluids" and these are themselves physical: they are the caloric and electric fluids.[27]   Furthermore, these physical fluids act according to their physical natures, and the vitalistic view of a purposiveness immanent in all living things is explicitly rejected by Lamarck: [28]   "La vie [est] une véritable puissance qui donne lieu à des phenomènes nombreux.   Cette puissance cependant n'a ni but, ni intention, ne peut faire que ce qu'elle fait, et n'est elle-même qu'un ensemble de causes agissantes, et non un être particulier."   Teleology is therefore banned from the realm of science: even though as philosophers we may know that God created the universe, our scientific explanations must be in terms of what came to be known in the controversies which followed as "secondary causes."[29]   In the words of Buffon, Lamarck's teacher, it is the object of natural philosophy (i.e., science) to know "the *how* of things," not to search to divine the *why* of facts."[30]   And Lamarck insists, as did his evolutionary successors, that there is no reason to deny that God could have created an order of nature which gave rise to organic beings *successively* rather than having created them simultaneously with the creation of the earth.[31]   Thus, basing his theory on the difficulties which he encountered in his observations of what were supposedly distinct species, and motivated by some of the major philosophic concerns of his age, Lamarck boldly contrasted his hypothesis of evolutionary development, and of its causes, with the Mosaic account.[32]

[26] This distinction was also drawn by Buffon, who held that the ultimate particles of the inorganic and the organic were different in character, though both were material. Cf. Perrier, *op. cit.*, 69.

[27] *Zoological Philosophy*, 213 and 187–9.   [28] *Système analytique*, 37f. Cf. *Hydrogéologie*, 67, cited in John J. Judd, *The Coming of Evolution* (Cambridge, 1910), 155.

[29] *Zoological Philosophy*, 183–184.   [30] Perrier, *op. cit.*, 68.

[31] *Zoological Philosophy*, 36.   [32] *Ibid*, 126–7.

(3) *Later Developments*

While Lamarck's hypothesis was rejected by his evolutionary successors,[33] his analysis of the problem of species must be acknowledged to have had an influence even on the opponents of the doctrine of transmutation. This is to be seen in Cuvier's views on the problem of species. In the first place we may note that Cuvier's own definition of the concept of "species" introduces the genealogical element as the only rule which is not "merely hypothetical, and destitute of proof." [34] In the second place (and more importantly), Lamarck's hypothesis of the transmutation of species laid stress on the relations between species and their environments, and this adaptation of animals to their environments became the leading principle of Cuvier's fundamental principle of " the Conditions of Existence ": " As nothing can exist if it do not combine all the conditions which render its existence possible, the different parts of each being must be coordinated in such a manner as to render the total being possible, not only in itself, but in its relations to those which surround it." [35] This view, taken merely as a biological principle, is not only connected with Lamarck's insistence on viewing animals in their relations to their environments, but it echoes Lamarck's view that a true arrangement of species (as distinct from an abstract classification) depended on the affinities of the organs of individuals.[36] However, Cuvier was willing to equate his principle of " the Conditions of Existence " with the principle of "Final Causes," [37] and held fast to the view that God had created the species with relation to their environments. To be sure, Cuvier and his followers were forced to admit that, as Whewell put it, there is " a capacity in all species to accommodate themselves, to a certain extent, to a change in external circumstances . . . . There may thus arise changes of appearance and structure . . . but the mutations thus superinduced are . . . confined within certain limits. Indefinite divergence from the original type is not possible . . . . In short, *species have a real existence in nature*." [38] Thus the view was held that secondary causes accounted for the dif-

---

[33] Lyell was at first attracted to it, but then rejected it for reasons which we shall soon note. In spite of Lyell's lengthy treatment of Lamarck, Darwin viewed Lamarck's speculation with great distaste. (Cf. letters written to Hooker in 1844, as given in *Life and Letters of Darwin*, I, 384 and 390, and in *More Letters of Darwin*, I, 41; also a letter to Lyell in 1863, as given in *Life and Letters* of *Darwin*, II, 198-199.)

[34] *Theory of Earth*, 116.   [35] *Règne animale*, 6, in Whewell, *op. cit.*, II, 492.
[36] Cf. *Zoological Philosophy*, Part I, Ch. 2 and pp. 56–57.   [37] Cf. passage cited from Whewell above.
[38] *Op. cit.*, II, 565.   [39] This was also Lyell's conclusion in his *Principles of Geology* in 1832 (cf. his recapitulation at the end of the 4th chapter of Vol. II).

ferences among the *varieties* of a species, but not for the differences between species.[39]   But when the advance of observations and collections of specimens proceeded far enough—especially when comparative studies were made in new areas of the world—the early quandary of Lamarck reasserted itself, as Lamarck had prophesied it would: the lines to be drawn between species (as distinct from mere varieties) became more and more difficult to draw.

One can see this quandary at work in Hooker, whose difficulties with the question of species in his *Florae Novae-Zelandiae* prepared him to adopt Darwin's theory of transmutation, to the confirmation of which he made such great contributions.[40]   Darwin's theory furnished Hooker, and all others who accepted it, a way out of the difficulty of distinguishing " species " from " varieties," and Darwin himself (with some justice) believed that this would be of considerable help in systematic biology, i.e., it would help those who were interested in classifying biological phenomena.[41]   Through Darwin's genealogical approach, that which Linnaeus and all of his successors had sought—a natural, and not an artificial classification—seemed to have been assured.   As Lyell said: " Mr. Darwin labors to show, and with no small success, that all true classification in zoology and botany is, in fact, genealogical, and that community of descent is the hidden bond which naturalists have been unconsciously seeking, while they often imagined that they were looking for some unknown plan of creation." [42]   In these words, as well as in our survey of Linnaeus, Lamarck, and Cuvier, it is apparent how closely linked were the problem of species and questions of religion.   There is one further scientific problem of the age which also focussed interest on evolutionary theory, and which also came to be discussed against the background of religious thought.   This problem was that of the relation between the human species and the rest of the animal kingdom.

III. PROBLEMS OF MAN'S PLACE IN NATURE

The question of the relation of man to the rest of the animal kingdom had three facets.   The first concerned the problem of classification: how should the human species, regarded as a part of the

---

[40] Cf. J. Huxley, *Life and Letters of Sir J. D. Hooker*, I, Chs. 23–24 for the correspondence of Hooker relating to species in the years 1843–1859.   (Also, p. 83.)   For Hooker's view regarding species in his *Flora Novae-Zelandiae*, cf. Turrill, *Pioneer Plant Geography: The Phytogeographical Researches of Sir Joseph Dalton Hooker* (The Hague, 1953), 143ff.

[41] *Origin of Species* (1st ed.), 484; (Modern Library ed.), 371.

[42] *Antiquity of Man*, 412.   Cf. Haeckel's comment on his own *Generelle Morphologie* (1866) as the attempt to found " a natural system " of classification on the basis of Darwin's theory.   (Preface to the English edition of Haeckel, *The History of Creation*.)

Scala naturae, be defined? The second concerned the antiquity of the human species. The third, which was related to both of the others, was the problem of the races of men: did they constitute distinct species or were they merely varieties of the same species, and what was the origin of their distinctness from one another? All three of these facets of the question of man's relation to other animals were widely discussed, and all three had obvious connections with questions of religious orthodoxy. In the pre-Darwinian period, however, no general consensus of opinion developed: it was not until Darwin's general theory of biological evolution by natural selection was put forward, and its applicability to man was seen, that these problems came into the forefront of attention. I shall therefore not go into detail on the history of ideas concerning these topics, but merely indicate that they were of concern to many persons in the first half of the century. This is of importance since it throws light on two facts: (1) that even while he was developing his theory of evolution by natural selection Darwin himself frequently considered the problem of the relation of his theory to the nature and history of man; and (2) that the reception accorded *The Origin of Species* by those who condemned it was in large measure dominated by the views it entailed regarding man, rather than the views which it set forth regarding the origins of plant and animal species.

(1) With respect to the task of classifying man in the *Scala naturae,* two major possibilities were open: one could classify him as a part of the hierarchy of animal species, or one could view him as constituting a new order, distinct from the animals no less than these are distinct from plants. If the second alternative were adopted, it would be because of man's mental endowments, not because of his physical structure: as a physical structure he could be compared with other animals, and his specific differences from other species could presumably be found. Therefore, from the point of view of systematic biology it was necessary to adopt the former alternative, and this Linnaeus did. He classified man as one genus (or family) [43] among the primates. Blumenbach, however, attempted to set man apart from the apes by holding that he constituted a different order, i.e., that of *Bimana,* or two-handed animals, distinguishing them from the order of *Quadrumana* to which the apes belonged. This classificatory schema was adopted by Cuvier, but was gradually abandoned; nonetheless, as late as 1861 Huxley still felt obliged to attack it in his lecture *On the Motor Organs of Man compared with those of Other Animals.* And other attempts were made—notably by Richard

---

[43] What Linnaeus called genera were later called families, a term introduced in 1780 by Batsch: a family was wider than a genus, but narrower than an order Cf. Lyell, *Antiquity of Man,* 474, and Perrier, *op. cit.,* 38).

Owen—to separate man from the apes in terms of physiological structures; in fact, it was in terms of his theory of the differences between the human brain and the ape's brain that Owen opened his famous attack on the Darwinian theory at the 1860 meeting of the British Association.[44]

However, these debates need not occupy us.[45] Two examples should be sufficient to illustrate the point that the question of man's relation to the animal kingdom was a problem recognized to be intimately connected with the question of whether or not the transmutation theory was true. The first of these examples is from the thought of Lyell. As Lyell later wrote to Darwin, he had long believed " that the case of Man and his Races and of other animals, and that of plants, is one and the same," [46] and he later wrote that what originally had kept him from adopting Lamarck's transmutation theory was that he was put off by Lamarck's view of the continuity between man and the animals—he did not want to " go the whole orang." [47] The second example is to be found in Hugh Miller's *Footprints of the Creator,* a book written as a reply to Chambers' *Vestiges of Creation*. In opening his discussion of " the development hypothesis," [48] Miller acknowledged that an evolutionary view of species does not necessarily lead to atheism. However, he held that if this view is extended to include man, so that man is believed to be continuous with the animals, having evolved from them by small changes, then either one must ascribe immortal souls to monads and mites, fishes and reptiles, birds and beasts, or one must deny that humans have such souls. Herein lies the real danger of the development hypothesis, according to Miller, and it is for this reason that he sought to combat it by means of an examination of fossil evidences.

In brief, then, the examples of Lyell and of Miller show that the question of the truth of the theory of transmutation among plants and animals was viewed in the light of what implications it would

[44] Cf. *Life and Letters of Charles Darwin,* II, 113f.

[45] For a résumé of this material, cf. Lyell, *Antiquity of Man,* 473–494.

[46] *Life, Letters, and Journals of Lyell,* II, 325.

[47] *Ibid.,* II, 365. Cf. also *Antiquity of Man,* 406. Two further points in this letter to Darwin are worthy of comment. (1) Lyell is correct in his interpretation of Lamarck's views as a naturalist, but Lamarck hesitated (inconsistently) to espouse these same views as a philosopher, believing that man had a special origin. (Cf. Perrier, *op. cit.,* 88.) (2) In this same letter Lyell quotes a student of Cuvier's as holding that even Cuvier did not believe that species were real, but only useful modes of classification. It is difficult to reconcile this with Cuvier's writings, but it is interesting to note that Cuvier, no less than Linnaeus and Lamarck, drew a distinction between natural and artificial classifications.

[48] The second chapter in his work, 37ff. (American ed., 1851).

have for the nature of man: was his nature continuous with that of
the rest of the animal kingdom, or was it not? And, as Geoffroy de
St. Hilaire pointed out,[49] even those who debated this point with reference to man's bodily structure, were really motivated by a desire to
distinguish man as a moral being from all the rest of nature. And,
if further evidence be needed, the strength of this conviction in the
disparity and lack of continuity between man and other animals can
be seen in others as well as in Lyell and in Miller. For example, in
his very popular *Twelve Lectures on the Connexion between Science
and Revealed Religion* Nicholas Wiseman says in connection with
Lamarck's doctrine "it is revolting to think that our noble nature
should be nothing more than the perfecting of the ape's malicious-
ness";[50] and Sedgwick in his long review of *The Vestiges of Creation*
criticizes Chambers as having "annulled all distinction between
physical and moral."[51] And in 1845 Humboldt, the great naturalist,
expressed his belief in the radical discontinuity between man and
nature, saying: "A physical delineation of nature terminates at the
point where the sphere of intellect begins and a new world of mind is
opened to our view."[52] It is therefore of small wonder that Darwin's
theory of evolution, recognized as being in the "developmental"
tradition of Lamarck and of Chambers, should have had its critics
focus attention on its implications for a theory of man even though
Darwin had hoped to avoid arousing prejudice against his theory
by not discussing the question.[53]

(2) In addition to the foregoing debates concerning whether it
was possible to view man as having arisen in the course of evolution
out of remote anthropoid forebears, was the question of *when* man
had his origins. Here the question had to be decided in terms of the
discovery of human remains or human artifacts in the sequence of
geological strata. And throughout the first decades of the century,
no traces of human life were found to be anything but "recent"; on
this the Catastrophist Cuvier and the Uniformitarian Lyell were
agreed.[54] Therefore, in so far as one was to be guided by the available empirical evidence, man was of recent origin and no links were

[49] Cf. Lyell, *Antiquity of Man*, 473–475. [50] *Op. cit.* (1st Amer. ed., 1837), 126f.

[51] Gillispie, *Genesis and Geology*, 150. Cf. also the letter written by Sedgwick
(who had been Darwin's teacher in geology) acknowledging the receipt of *The
Origin of Species* (in *Life and Letters of Charles Darwin*, II, 42–45).

[52] *Cosmos*, I, p. 359. (This reference is to the English translation which appeared in the same year as the original.)

[53] Cf. *Descent of Man*, preface. Cf. his letter to Wallace (Dec. 22, 1857) in
Life and Letters of Darwin, II, 467.

[54] E.g., Cuvier, *Theory of the Earth*, 127–147; Lyell, *Principles of Geology*, II,
Ch. 16.

to be found which connected the present state of man with earlier man-like creatures. Speculations, such as those of Lamarck, on how man *might have* arisen from the anthropoid apes, were mere speculations. So too were the suggestions of Chambers, and others, that the course of human embryonic development recapitulated an evolutionary development.[55] The evidence drawn from the investigation of geological strata seemed conclusive: man had come onto the scene in relatively recent times (long after the extinction of the last prehistoric species) and had shown no development in his characteristics from the earliest times to the present. Thus, it was natural that man should have been viewed as a special creation.

As Lyell later noted,[56] the more one was impressed by the adequacy of the geologic record, the more it was necessary to assume the truth of the doctrine of the special creation of man. And the extent to which this record was trusted in so far as the history of man was concerned can be seen in Darwin. As we know, Darwin already held his theory of evolution before 1848 when he read Boucher de Perthes' *Antiquités celtiques,* which proved that man coexisted with extinct mammoths; yet Darwin dismissed it as "rubbish."[57] It was not until Darwin's friends Falconer and Lubbock visited the Abbeville excavations,[58] and Darwin, having completed *The Origin of Species,* turned his attention to the problems of *The Descent of Man,* that he came to appreciate the value of these discoveries. Thus it would seem fair to say that the question of the history of man went through two stages with relation to the development of evolutionary theory. In the first stage those who were most painstaking concerning the evidence of geologic investigations emphasized the recency of man and the need for special creation. In this state, the debate over transmutation of species was intimately connected with the question of man's origin, and the evidence seemed to indicate that with respect to this question transmutation was a less plausible view than special creation. However, at precisely the period when Darwin published *The Origin of Species,* new discoveries were being made which upset the conclusions formerly reached, and Lyell's *Antiquity of Man* (1863), which summarized the new evidence, made it clear—though

[55] In *The Vestiges of Creation,* 149, Chambers takes the doctrine of recapitulation as an established fact, citing a number of biologists from Harvey to Tiedemann. This principle that "ontogeny recapitulates phylogeny," usually associated with the name of Haeckel, was actually much discussed prior to Darwin—e.g., it was criticized by Cuvier and by Rudolph, and defended by Meckel. Cf. also Perrier, *op. cit.,* 98f.

[56] *Antiquity of Man,* 406.

[57] Cf. *Life and Letters of Darwin,* II, 200, and 198.   [58] Cf. *The Life-work of Lord Avebury,* 70ff. (John Lubbock became Lord Avebury.)

not so clear as Darwin and his friends would have liked [59]—that even with respect to man the doctrine of transmutation was in accord with the evidence.

(3) We turn now to the relation between the question of transmutation and the question of how one is to account for the differences among the races of man. The latter question was originally connected with debates concerning the classification of species, and with debates concerning the antiquity of man; however, the discussion of these problems later came to have an important relation to discussions of how " varieties " could assume the form of widely diffused and apparently fixed " species."

Two opposed theories concerning the races of mankind were possible: (1) that all races were descended from a single original stock, or (2) that different races were ultimately different in their ancestry. Either of these theories could be held by those who believed that man was directly created by God, and either could also be held by those who believed that man had an evolutionary origin. For example, Linnaeus held that all of mankind descended from a single divinely created pair of humans, whereas Cuvier, who was also a creationist, held that each of the different races was separately created.[60] On the other hand, those who rejected a separate creation for man, believing him to have evolved from other animal forms, could either hold to the unity of the human race, as did Lamarck, or they could hold to separate origins, as did Virey.[61]

However, the struggle over the unity of the human race was of short duration. Investigations in physical anthropology, inaugurated in a systematic way by Blumenbach, and carried forward by Prichard and Sir William Lawrence, had shown that the similarities between individuals of different races were far more striking than their differences. But this posed a significant problem: if all human beings had a common origin how could one account for the wide variations that we find among the different races? Prichard posed this problem for himself when he listed the facts which seemed to predispose others to believe in plural origins.[62] These facts were: (a) the differences in

[59] Cf. *Life and Letters of Charles Darwin*, II, 193–204.

[60] Cf. Prichard, *Researches into the Physical History of Mankind* (3rd ed., 1836), preface. This was also the opinion of Rudolphi, who is cited by Prichard. (On Rudolphi, cf. Nordenskiöld, *op. cit.*, 354). The method by which this type of theory could be harmonized with Biblical authority was to claim, as did Bory de Saint-Vincent, that the account of the Creation of Adam and Eve referred to only one species of man. (Cf. Wiseman, *op. cit.*, 112f., on Bory.)

[61] On Virey, cf. Wiseman, *op. cit.*, 113 (where he cites the article "Homme" in the *Dictionnaire des sciences naturelles*, Vol. XXI) and Virey, *Histoire des moeurs et de l'instinct des animaux* (Paris, 1822), I, 21 *et passim*.

[62] *Op. cit.*, 3–6.

"figure and complexion which are observed in different nations";
(b) the existence, throughout all known history, of distinct languages; (c) "moral and intellectual diversities . . . thought to characterize particular races "; (d) the existence in all newly explored
territories of uncivilized tribes " destitute of those common arts and
resources which it seems difficult to suppose that men could ever have
forgotten or have lost when once acquired." To undercut these objections Prichard took a decisive step: he attempted to show that in
both the plant and the animal kingdoms great variation in type accompanied dispersion in space without necessitating the assumption of
independent origin. After this argument he turned to a consideration of the comparative anatomy, comparative physiology, and
comparative psychology of the different races of men, and reached a
similar conclusion.[63] These investigations, as well as those of Lawrence, had an influence on the development of evolutionary theory,[64]
for the question that they attempted to answer was how distinct
varieties could be accounted for in terms of the diffusion of distinctive peculiarities ("chance variations") which cropped up in some
individuals. Still, so far as man was concerned, their views suffered
under one major handicap: the assumed time-span since the origin
of man was too short to make it plausible that the races of man had
originated in this way. It was only when Lyell and others had
pushed back the history of man that the doctrine of a single origin
lying behind all of the present races became plausible. And once this
had become plausible, it was possible to argue on the basis of evidence—and not mere speculation—whether man's origin was or was
not traceable to non-human forebears.[65]

IV. EPIGENESIS *vs.* PREFORMATION

There were two other scientific problems which, like the problems
we have already discussed, paved the way for the acceptance of evolutionary theory. Their relations to this problem were, however, less
intimate than were the struggles over the definition of species or the
attempts to place man with respect to the animal kingdom. The first
of these problems lay within the field of the theory of reproduction,
and its solution cleared away one obstacle to the acceptance of transmutation. I refer to the overthrow of the preformationist hypothesis
and the establishment of the doctrine of epigenesis.

[63] On his method, cf. *op. cit.*, 9 and vi, n.

[64] Cf. Wallace's letter to Bates in 1847, in Wallace's *Letters and Reminiscences*
(ed. by Marchant), I, 91; cf. *More Letters of Darwin*, I, 43–46 for the relations of
Darwin to Prichard's views.

[65] Cf. Lyell's discussion of these points in *Antiquity of Man*, 385–388.

The doctrine of epigenesis, i.e., that organisms developed by the successive differentiation of the fertilized ovum, was the dominant and orthodox theory of generation from the time of Aristotle. However, with the discovery of the microscope, Leeuwenhoek and Swammerdam put forward the preformationist theory, i.e., that the complete and perfect organism was already preformed in the sperm, and merely grew in size. In the late seventeenth and early eighteenth centuries this controversy was also connected with the controversy between ovists and animalculists (spermists), as to the relative importance of the egg and the sperm in the generative process. In general, the preformationists (some of whom were ovists, and some spermists) dominated the field in the eighteenth-century. The problem of accounting for the differentiation of parts in embryonic development seemed an insuperable obstacle to accepting the epigenetic view. It was not until the researches of C. F. Wolff were published (1759) that the doctrine of epigenesis was shown to be necessitated by the observable facts of embryonic developments; but Wolff's work was not widely known until 1812, when it was translated from the Latin by Meckel, another epigenesist. From that point on, the preformationist doctrine was abandoned.[66]

Now it is easy to see what bearing this controversy had upon the incipient controversies over the transmutation of species. So long as one held the preformationist doctrine, it was impossible to give up the doctrine of the fixity of species: every individual organism was simply an expanded version of that which was contained in either the egg or the sperm from which it developed, and the characteristic of this egg or sperm were completely preformed in the adult organism from which it had come. (Therefore the preformation theory was also called *emboîtement*: it was conceived on the analogy of a box-within-a-box, etc., *ad infinitum*). Thus, the possibility of individual variations from generation to generation, needed to account for transmutation, was denied by the preformationist theory: according to that theory each of the successive individuals had been implicitly created when the first male (for the spermists) or the first female (for the ovists) of that individual's species had been originally created.[67] When preformationism was abandoned, this obstacle to an acceptance of transmutation was cleared away.[68]

[66] For a brief summary of the controversies in embryology, cf. Guyénot, *op. cit.*, 209–33.

[67] Cf. *ibid.*, 359.   [68] It is worthy of note that, in general, the early transmutationists, such as Buffon and Lamarck, were hostile to the preformationist theory, though they were not in a position to substantiate epigenesis. (On Buffon, cf. Guyénot and Perrier; for Lamarck, cf. *Zoological Philosophy*, 240–243 and *Système analytique*, 117–120.) Furthermore, the doctrine of epigenesis suggested the comparison between embryonic development and the development of species. This

A further scientific problem connected with the growth of evolutionary theory was to be found in the field of political economy, viz., the problem of population. In 1798 Malthus published his *Essay on Population,* and this work (as is well known) influenced both Darwin and Wallace in their independent formulations of the theory of the origin of species by natural selection.[69]   However, it will be well to make clear why it was possible to make so easy a transition from the Malthusian doctrine to the problem of the extinction of species.

In order to make this clear we must first note that one of the major points discussed by both paleontologists and naturalists was the relation between plants and animals and their environments. That there was a close relation between them was a fact clearly attested by all of the evidence, and the problem that arose was the problem of explaining this relation. Among the transmutationists, for example, Buffon used the hypothesis of the direct action of the environment as an explanation, whereas Lamarck used the tendency of the animal to adapt itself to the environment as the key to the solution. Similarly, the Creationists held either that God had successively created the various species, fitting them to the environment which then existed, or that after the original creation of all living forms, geological catastrophes had occurred, rendering some of these species extinct and accounting for the particular localization of

comparison was not only made by Meckel, who translated Wolff's work on epigenesis, but was clearly formulated and developed by Serres, the pupil of Geoffroy de Saint-Hilaire. (On Meckel, cf. Nordenskiöld, *op. cit.,* 355–359; on Serres, cf Perrier, *op. cit.,* 259–262.) It is perhaps not too much to say that the stress which the theory of epigenesis necessarily laid on the concept of *development* itself fostered—or, at the least, was allied with—the application of the concept of development in the whole of nature. Thus Serres viewed the whole animal kingdom as if it were one developing individual, and Chambers in the *Vestiges of Creation,* relying on Serres' theory (149–152), makes the principle of development the key to what he claims to be "the first attempt to connect the natural sciences into a history of creation" (278). (On the principle of development, cf. *ibid.,* 153–155.)

[69] For Darwin's account of how he chanced to be reading Malthus, and of the influence of Malthus on the formulation of his theory, cf. *Life and Letters of Darwin,* I, 68, and *More Letters of Darwin,* I, 118. The two preliminary essays of 1842 and 1844 also contain explicit references to Malthus (*The Foundations of the Origin of Species,* ed. Francis Darwin, 7, 88, 90; cf. xv–xvi). For an account of how Wallace first struck upon the theory of natural selection and then recalled Malthus' work, which he had read twelve years earlier, cf. Alfred Russel Wallace *Letters and Reminiscences,* I, 108.

others.[70]   In all of these theories the fittingness of the species to its environment had been stressed.   The complexity of this fittingness had been stressed by Buffon in his pioneering work in geographical zoology, and it was one of the two major features of Alexander von Humboldt's studies in plant geography.   As Humboldt pointed out in the preface to his *Personal Narrative,* and in the prefaces to both the first and second editions of his *Aspects of Nature,* he was interested in conveying the feelings aroused by the grandeur of the unity of nature *and* he wanted to show " the concurrent forces and powers " which constituted this unity.[71]   These forces were the ecological factors at work in nature.   And it was widely recognized that among such factors were the interrelations of different species.[72]

Thus in 1833 the physiologist Bell, in his Bridgewater Treatise on *The Hand, Its Mechanism and Vital Endowment, as Evincing Design,* wrote as follows: " As in the present day every creature has its natural enemy; or is checked in production, sometimes by a limited supply of food, sometimes by diseases, or by the influence of seasons; and as in the whole a balance is preserved, we may reasonably apply the same principle in explanation of the condition of things as they existed in the earlier stages of the world's progress." [73]   And in the same year Lyell published the second volume of his *Principles of Geology* in which the eighth and ninth chapters were specifically devoted to the same problems.   Thus it should occasion no surprise that, in entries for the subsequent year, Darwin's *Journal of Researches* show that he too was attempting to explain the extinction of species in ecological terms; [74] this was a problem common to all who engaged in natural history at the time.   Recognizing this, and looking back upon Malthus' *Essay on Population,* one can readily see how

[70] The first of these views was typical of the Progressionists, such as Sedgwick and Hugh Miller; the second was typical of Cuvier, although his views have sometimes been equated with those of the Progressionists.   For examples of the distinctness of his views from theirs, cf. his *Theory of the Earth,* 125f., 171f., and the passage cited from his *Recherches sur les ossements fossiles* by Gillispie, *op. cit.,* 99f.

[71] Cf. also *Cosmos,* I, 23, 24.

[72] Lamarck often discussed this factor, e.g., *Zoological Philosophy,* 54-55.

[73] *Op. cit.,* 38.   Bell belonged to the group referred to as Progressionists (*ibid.,* 164–168), and rejected transmutation of species.

[74] *Op. cit.,* 178–180.   In this passage he mentions Buffon, and at the time he of course knew Humboldt's *Personal Narrative,* and frequently referred to it.   He had also previously received the second volume of Lyell's *Principles* (cf. Judd, *The Coming of Evolution,* 103), but his explicit reference to it in this passage was added between the original edition of 1840 and the revised edition of 1845.

later readers could have been struck by the application of the Malthusian doctrine to their problem: at the very outset of his work, after stating his fundamental thesis, Malthus himself immediately draws the analogy between ecological relations among plants and animals, and the question of the checks on human population.[75] Thus, the problem of population, which was a problem of interest to political economists, social theorists, and historians,[76] contributed a share in the growth of evolutionary theory by virtue of Malthus' views.

In this case, then, as in others whose histories we have here hastily sketched, a scientific problem which arose independently of the growing philosophic interest in evolutionary modes of thought did in fact contribute to the theory of biological evolution. Furthermore, the fact that Darwin's *Origin of Species* presented a view of evolutionary development toward which all of these various scientific theories had tended to converge helps to explain why the scientific and religious implications of that work were instantly understood.

[75] *Op. cit.* (Everyman ed.), I, 5–6; cf. also p. 9 on relation between the whites and the American Indians, and p. 29 for natural selection as weeding out deformities among the American Indians.

[76] The background of Malthus' own work is to be found in theories propounded by Godwin, Rousseau, and Robert Owen, but other facets of the problem were also debated by Rev. Robert Wallace and Hume. Cf. Hume's essay "On the Populousness of Ancient Nations," and E. Mossner's account of this debate in *The Forgotten Hume* (New York, 1943), 111ff.

⁓ふ Alvar Ellegård

DARWIN'S THEORY AND NINETEENTH-CENTURY PHILOSOPHIES OF SCIENCE

(1) *Object*

The object of this article is to discuss those aspects of the nineteenth-century philosophies of science which were important for determining people's attitude towards the Darwinian theories. Attention will be confined exclusively to the British scene. The views of the philosophical theorists will be represented by William Whewell and John Stuart Mill, those of the Darwinian scientists by Charles Darwin and Thomas Henry Huxley, and those of the general public by writers in English periodicals and newspapers in the decade following the publication of Darwin's *Origin of Species* in November 1859. The approach is rather from the general reader's than from the scientists' or philosophers' point of view. I hope in this way to illustrate how some principles of science and philosophy were interpreted and used by the non-specialists at the time, and thus contribute, in a modest way, to what may be called the sociology of science.

It is not contended that the non-specialists' interpretation of a doctrine or principle should be regarded as part of the meaning of that doctrine. On the other hand, neither philosophers nor scientists can well have been unaware of the use to which their various doctrines were put in the controversies which caught the attention of the general public. As the specialists were themselves members of the public and certainly not uninterested in the outcome of these controversies, it seems likely that they took some account of the general public's interpretations and misinterpretations. It has, I think, not always been sufficiently realized that some of the statements of theorists have had an implicit controversial intent: the philosophers were operating in a wider context than that of pure scientific theory. In the 1860's, the Darwinian controversy formed an important part of this wider context.

(2) *The position of the Darwinian theory*

One of the criticisms most commonly made of the Darwinian theory, in the years after the publication of the *Origin,* was that it was not *inductive;* that it was based on assumptions instead of facts. Darwin, it was said, had deserted the true British scientific tradition, inaugurated by Bacon and brought to fruition by Newton.

There was some truth in this criticism. Darwin's descent theory was largely hypothetical. He did not produce any experimental evidence to prove that an animal of one species had, through a series of generations, given rise to an animal of a distinctly different species. Indeed, no such direct evidence of the descent theory was to be obtained during Darwin's lifetime, and precisely this lack of direct proof was considered by T. H. Huxley as the chief weak spot in the Darwinian armor.

The theory of natural selection was equally hypothetical. Darwin postulated, but did not prove experimentally, that variations in nature were 'indefinite,' i.e., occurred at random, in all directions, and that accordingly there would always be material for selection to work on. The survival of the fittest could lead to progressive evolution only if at least some of the offspring were more 'fit' than the parent forms.

What Darwin did was to show that a great number of well-known facts about the resemblances of animals and their distribution in time and space could be explained *on the assumption* that they were related to each other by descent, more or less remotely. He further showed that their divergence could be explained *on the assumption* that the offspring of the same parents are not exactly alike, but vary in all directions around an average, generally coinciding with that of the parents, and that among these variations there are generally some that give their possessors a better chance to survive in the struggle for life.

Darwin's critics did not always, not even commonly, discuss these assumptions on their merits or demerits. They did not assert that they were improbable. Instead, many critics attacked the assumptions as such, denying that a scientist had any right to make assumptions at all. This led inevitably to considerations of scientific method and of the nature of scientific explanation. On both sides the Darwinian controversy brought into view some fundamental problems of the philosophy of science.

On the evidence of my material, the ideas prevailing on this subject in the middle of the nineteenth century may be classed under three heads. On one hand, there was the popular view—which was also the view of philosophers without any scientific knowledge—that science is concerned only with the collection of facts. On the other hand, there were two distinct systems due to two philosophers of science: William Whewell and John Stuart Mill. It will be convenient first to set out and compare these three positions, not indeed in their entirety,[1] but as regards the points considered important by those taking part in the Darwinian controversies. We shall then examine what opinions the leading Darwinian scientists, Charles Darwin himself, and Thomas Henry Huxley, held on these subjects. Finally, the discussion in the general periodicals will be analyzed.

[1] Whewell's philosophy of science and its relation to Mill's have recently been discussed from a more general point of view by C. J. Ducasse, " Whewell's Philosophy of Scientific Discovery," *The Philosophical Review* (1951), 56–69, 213–34; and by E. W. Strong, "William Whewell and John Stuart Mill: Their Controversy About Scientific Knowledge," *Journal of the History of Ideas* (1955), 209–31.

(3) *The popular view of science*

The popular view was a traditional one, and relied largely on the prestige of Bacon and Newton. Bacon was appealed to as the founder of the Inductive Method, and Newton as the man who had brought that inductive method to its highest achievement. The inductive method was looked upon as a peculiarly British contribution, and was contrasted with the abstract and barren deductive methods of the Continental schools, especially the French. It is evident that such a contrast fitted in perfectly with prevalent views about the national characteristics of Englishmen and Frenchmen. The Englishman's mind was practical, down to earth; the Frenchman's speculative and abstract. Thus a departure from the inductive method, which was considered to be part of the grand British heritage, could be represented popularly not only as a scientific error, but as a betrayal of the British cause. It was thus almost morally reprehensible.

The appeal to Bacon, which occurs so frequently in publications of the more popular kind whenever scientific method is discussed, must not be construed as implying any close acquaintance with that writer's work. Bacon had simply come to stand as a guarantor of safe and traditional views in science. There is little indication that the popular writers knew much about the inductive method. They seemed to understand the phrase chiefly in a negative sense: the scientist should not go beyond the facts, and above all he should abstain from framing hypotheses. Newton's *Hypotheses non fingo* was a favorite quotation, used especially against hypotheses such as the Darwinian one, which conflicted with traditional religious views. The hypothetical elements of accepted theories were not recognized.

Such an attitude could hardly further scientific progress. But the propounders of the views set forth above were not much concerned with scientific progress. Science had not, in Mid-Victorian Britain, the tremendous prestige that it has in the world today. It was the concern of a small minority only. In the schools and universities the curriculum was almost wholly classical and literary. The campaign for teaching science in the schools, in which, by the way, T. H. Huxley played a prominent part, met with strong opposition and did not bear much fruit until the end of the century. Politicians and writers, who above all others formed and gave expression to public opinion, knew little of science and less of scientific method, and cared little for either. Gladstone and Disraeli are both instances in point. The stability of society was usually their main consideration, and if scientific theories threatened that stability, so much the worse for the theories.

I have referred to this view as popular, meaning by that term that it was widely held, probably by the majority of those who gave the subject any thought at all. It was not the view of those who were acquainted with science. Of these, the active scientists as a rule did not explicitly formulate the fundamental principles underlying their work, though scattered remarks on these topics are found in the writings of most scientists of the first rank. Some—for instance, Sir John Herschel and T. H. Huxley—produced quite extensive essays on the subject. The fullest formulations of the philosophy of science, however, are due to Whewell and Mill; the former was chiefly acquainted with mathematical and physical science, the latter chiefly with the social sciences.

(4) *William Whewell*

William Whewell published his *Philosophy of the Inductive Sciences* in 1840, a third and re-arranged edition being published in 1858–60.[2]

Whewell criticized the popular view of Bacon as the final arbiter in all matters of scientific method:

But if we thus reduce the philosophy of Bacon to that portion which the subsequent progress of science has rigorously verified, we shall have to pass over many of those declarations which have excited most notice in his writings, and shall lose sight of many of those striking thoughts which has admirers most love to dwell upon. For he is usually spoken of, at least in this country, as a teacher who not only commenced, but in a great measure completed, the Philosophy of Induction. He is considered, not only as having asserted some general principles, but laid down the special rules of scientific investigation; as not only one of the Founders, but the supreme Legislator of the modern Republic of Science.[3]

He is considered as peculiarly and eminently the asserter of the value of experiment and observation. He is always understood to belong to the experiential, as opposed to the ideal school.[4]

Whewell himself, whose sympathies were with the ' ideal school,' declared that experiments by themselves could effect but little. They had to be arranged and interpreted or ' colligated ' in the light of some general principle. The active powers of the mind had to be added to the passive registration of impressions.

Now as the name of Bacon was so highly venerated by the early Victorians, Whewell was naturally anxious to show, not that Bacon was wrong, but that the popular view of Bacon was mistaken. He sought to reinterpret Bacon in a way that would make him a supporter of a less exclusively ' experiential ' philosophy:

It will appear, however, on a close examination, that he was by no means insensible or careless of this internal element of all connected speculation.

---

[2] My quotations are from the first edition, unless otherwise stated.

[3] II, 389.   [4] II, 399.

He held the balance, with no partial or feeble hand, between phenomena and ideas. He urged the Colligation of Facts, but he was not less aware of the value of the Explication of Conceptions.[5]

In the same way, Whewell was anxious to reduce the force of Newton's *Hypotheses non fingo*. First, he tried to show that Newton used the word *hypothesis* in a more restricted sense than usual, and then he pointed out that in his actual philosophizing Newton did resort to hypotheses—that indeed any scientific discovery has to be preceded by a testing of hypotheses. After quoting several passages where Newton pronounces against hypotheses, defined as ' whatever is not deduced from phenomena,' Whewell comments:

This is, in reality, a superstitious and self-destructive spirit of speculation. Some hypotheses are necessary, in order to connect the facts which are observed, some new principle of unity must be applied to the phenomena, before induction can be attempted. What is requisite is, that the hypothesis should be close to the facts.[6]

The justice of Whewell's remarks on the supreme importance of hypotheses in science is evident, and has been fully borne out by the subsequent development of science. Whether or not his interpretation of the meaning of Bacon and Newton is correct, his outspoken criticism of contemporaries using those names as sticks to beat anybody who tried to strike a new path in science, indicates how widespread that attitude had grown. And as Whewell was a recognized authority, it is probable that his decisive stand had a beneficial effect.

Whewell's treatment of several other problems in the philosophy of science was also remarkably acute—for instance, his discussion of how scientific progress depends on the explication and clarification of the concepts we use to describe and explain events. But on some points Whewell's metaphysical and religious preconceptions vitiated his judgment, especially on questions connected with biology and geology; and as our study is concerned chiefly with just those questions, it is bound to emphasize the weakness rather than the strength of Whewell's work.

Whewell's *Philosophy of the Inductive Sciences* was published before Darwin's *Origin*—even the third edition was finished by 1858—and thus does not contain any direct reference to the Darwinian theories. On the other hand, he naturally discussed the pre-Darwinian (largely Lamarckian) development theories in his books, and the arguments which Whewell employed when discussing biological and geological matters could be used, and were in fact used, equally

[5] II, 399.   [6] II, 438.

well against Darwin.   It is clear, moreover, that Whewell himself did not accept the thesis of the *Origin;* in a letter from 1863 he wrote, " The recent discussions which have taken place in geology and zoology do not appear to me to have materially affected the force of the arguments . . . I still think that what I have written is a just representation of the question." [7]

One of the weak spots in Whewell's philosophy of science was his view of causation.   Whereas empiricists considered causation as implying nothing but invariable succession, Whewell, as an idealist, looked upon it as implying more:

none of our senses or powers of external observation can detect . . . the power of quality which we call Cause.   Cause is that which connects one event with another, but no sense or perception discloses to us, or can disclose, any connection among the events which we observe.[8]   When one event gives rise to another, the first *event* is, in common language, often called the cause, and the second the effect. . . .   For our present purposes, however, we must not apply the term cause to such occurrences as this meeting and turning [e.g., of billiard balls], but to a certain conception, *force,* abstracted from all such special events, and considered as a quality or property by which one body affects the motion of the other.   And in like manner in other cases, cause is to be conceived as some abstract quality, power, or efficacy, by which change is produced; a quality not identical with the events, but disclosed by means of them.[9]

These passages show that Whewell's concept of causation cannot be equated with Kant's, whose writings he knew well.   To Whewell causation was more than a category of thought.   It was not only a construction of the mind, but an entity with some sort of real existence.   A cause, according to Whewell, was not itself to be considered as an observable phenomenon.   Accordingly, it was meaningful for Whewell to speak of and encourage the investigation of causes of phenomena which were not considered related to any antecedent ones.   Whewell seems in fact to have looked upon this corollary as a strong support for his view of causation:

[From the principle that every event must have a cause] we infer that the world itself must have a cause; that the chain of events connected by common causation, must have a First Cause of a nature different from the events themselves.   This we are entitled to do, if our Idea of Cause be independent of, and superior to, experience: but if we have no Idea of Cause

---

[7] Sir I. Todhunter, *William Whewell* (1876), 433.   Letter to D. Brown, Oct. 26, 1863.   On Whewell's attitude, see also Francis Darwin, *The Life and Letters of Charles Darwin* (London, 1888), II, 261, note.

[8] I, 160.

[9] I, 170.

except such as we gather from experience, this reasoning is altogether base-less and unmeaning.[10]

Hume . . . declared himself unable to discover any remedy for a defect so fatal to the most important parts of our knowledge.[11]

Our inference from Hume's observation is, not the truth of his conclusion, but the falsehood of his premises:—not that, therefore, we can know nothing of natural connexion, but that, therefore, we have some other source of knowledge than experience.[12]

Evidently one of Whewell's reasons for defining ' cause ' this way was that it allowed him to draw religious conclusions from it.[13] More-over, it was not only the concept of First Cause, identified with God as the Creator, that was given support by his idealistic view of cause. The concept of Final Cause, also important as a religious concept, bearing on the idea of God as Providence, could be easily assimilated with a concept of cause as ' power, or efficacy.' Whewell also thought that final causes were indispensable, at least in biology.[14] Further, if a cause was in principle unobservable, there was to him nothing re-markable in admitting the possibility that an event might be due to such similarly unobservable things as Divine interventions or mir-acles.[15] It is therefore not surprising that Whewell was reluctant to accept the so-called ' uniformitarian ' views of the scientific geologists, which excluded sudden changes that might be interpreted as Divine interpositions.[16]

Whewell's views on the nature of Induction have to be seen in rela-tion to his conception of cause. The essential difference between his and the traditional empiricist view comes out clearly in his criticism of Mill, in the third edition of his *Philosophy*: " I am obliged there-fore to dissent from Mr. Mill when he includes, in his notion of Induc-tion, the process by which we arrive *at individual facts* from other facts *of the same order of particularity*." [17]

Mill could do this because he held that " generals are but collec-tions of particulars, definite in kind but indefinite in number." [18] Whewell could not, since to him generals were more than collections of particulars, and it was this something more that he wished above all to draw attention to. He defines induction as follows:

Induction is a term applied to describe the *process* of a true Colligation of Facts by means of an exact and appropriate Conception. *An Induction* is also employed to denote the *proposition* which results from this process.[19]

[10] I, 160.   [11] I, 164.   [12] I, 72.
[13] See also on this point Ducasse, *Phil. Review* (1951), 226.
[14] I, xxxv: Aphorisms Concerning Ideas, CV.   [15] Cf. II, 116.   [16] Cf. II, 127, 134.
[17] Whewell, *Philosophy of Discovery*, 240.   [18] Mill, *Logic*, I, 328.
[19] I, xxxix: Aphorisms concerning Science, XIII.

Whewell particularly stresses the 'appropriate conception': "In every inference by Induction there is some Conception *superinduced* upon the Facts; and we may henceforth conceive this to be the peculiar import of the term *Induction*."[20]

He was also fully aware that his use of the term induction did not square with its traditional meaning. It may readily be granted that his focussing of attention on the importance of the 'conception' was a real service to science. But why should Whewell have made the introduction of the conception the chief 'import of the term *Induction*'?

Now induction was, as we have seen above, a prestige word. Induction gave firm and certain knowledge. By making the 'conception' the chief element in the induction, the same firmness and certainty might be conferred on it. Whewell was not content to show that the 'conception' was serviceable, that it facilitated our description of the observed facts, or that it might help us to visualize the connections between the facts. He was naturally aware that it did this. But he insisted that it did more: it was more than a construct of the scientist's imagination. In some cases it stood for something really existing. For while some inductions lead to Laws of Phenomena only, "Inductions founded upon other Ideas, those of Substance and Cause, for example, appear to conduct us somewhat further into a knowledge of the essential nature and real connexions of things."[21]

On this point Mill sharply disagreed with Whewell. To Mill the 'conception' was nothing but a construction of the mind, and he therefore held that "all that is true and to the purpose in Dr. Whewell's doctrine of Conceptions might be fully expressed by the more familiar term Hypothesis."[22] Mill would not accept the view that the conception could stand for some entity which Whewell insisted it did in the case of what he called the Induction of Causes.

The connection between Whewell's concepts of cause and induction should now be clear. Induction, in Whewell's sense, offered a way of representing efficient causes—the 'forces' and ultimately God that Whewell had in mind—as substantial entities.

In Whewell's account of induction there is no reference to facts as yet unknown: the inference is not from facts to facts, but from facts to a conception, or more exactly, to a proposition representing a conception. The proof of the induction therefore could not include observation of the facts hitherto unknown, but could only consist in the close correspondence of the conception with the known facts. If the rôle of the conception were purely descriptive, as, for instance, in Kepler's induction concerning the planetary movements, no other proof could be desired. The statement that the movements of the planets can be described by means of the concept of ellipticity is of course proved if they can in fact be so described. But when the induction concerned a cause, as, for instance, the force of gravity, the proof seemed to Mill incomplete. The fact that the concept of gravity served to connect the known facts of the movements of the celestial bodies could not prove the *existence* of the force of gravity as a 'power' residing in bodies. What was proved was that the concept of gravity could in fact correctly account for the movements of the celestial bodies: *if* such a thing as gravity existed, such results would follow as could in fact be observed, and besides, others not yet observed.

Whewell made a sharp distinction between two kinds of induction: one was concerned with the Laws of Phenomena, one with the Causes of Phenomena. It was, he said, one of the main achievements of Newton that he had made people aware of this distinction by his discovery of gravity as the cause of the movements of bodies. Now a cause, says Whewell, cannot be accepted as proved until inductions from two distinct classes of facts have led to the *same* cause:

> when the explanation of two kinds of phenomena, distinct and not apparently connected, leads us to the same cause, such a coincidence does give a reality to the cause, which it has not while it merely accounts for those appearances which suggested the supposition. This coincidence . . . is . . . the *Consilience of Inductions*.[23]

We note here again the insistence that induction gives 'reality to the cause.' Now a cause so established is, says Whewell, a *vera causa*. The common definition of *verae causae*, "such causes only, as *from other considerations*, we know to exist," did not find favor with him.[24] As a cause, to Whewell, was an unobservable power or quality, it could never be known to exist except by inference. It was by inference that the force of gravity was derived from terrestrial movements, and likewise by inference that it was derived from celestial movements. An empiricist could prove an inference by referring to observed phenomena, because what he inferred from phenomena were other phenomena. His inference had phenomena for objects. Whewell could not do that, since his inference had a conception for object.

Whewell's definition of *vera causa* was in fact a minimum requirement when 'cause' was taken in his sense. However, by his definition *verae causae* were to be found only in the established sciences. In the younger sciences, where no consilience of inductions had yet occurred, one had to be content with a less rigorous requirement. Whewell's recommendation was, and had to be, that scientists should accept only such 'causes as were rigorously inferred,' meaning by that

---

[23] II, 446.   [24] II, 441.

phrase, inferred by the methods employed in the established sciences, or, it would seem, in a way sanctioned by tradition. It was an eminently conservative recommendation.

Unfortunately, in the younger sciences Whewell's rule did not serve to exclude *ad hoc* explanations. Now Newton's rule of allowing only ' causes that we know to exist from other considerations ' was designed to exclude just those. We have previously seen that Whewell was prepared to accept such *ad hoc* explanations as miracles; his wholehearted advocacy of Vital Forces as causes is another example.[25] The existence of Vital Forces effected a sharp distinction between the world of physics and the world of biology. On that distinction depended Whewell's acceptance of Final Causes:

In mere Physics, Final Causes, as Bacon has observed, are not to be admitted as a principle of reasoning. But in the organical sciences, the assumption of design and purpose in every part of every whole, that is, the pervading idea of Final Cause, is the basis of sound reasoning and the source of true doctrine.[26]

This is part of what Whewell meant when he said that causes should be ' rigorously inferred.' The most valuable portion of Whewell's philosophy of science was his insistence on the value of hypotheses, and on the necessity of employing clear theoretical conceptions. But he was not content with pointing out the usefulness of theoretical concepts: he also wished to represent some of them as real entities. Indeed, it appears that theoretical concepts were acceptable to Whewell to the extent that they could be assimilated with such entities as he already believed in, mainly on religious grounds. Thus the crucial concept of cause is so defined by him to allow the use of such terms as First Cause and Miracle, and induction is so defined to support the belief in the real existence of such causes. Altogether, Whewell's religio-metaphysical preconceptions led him to a strange selectivity as regards theoretical concepts. The criteria that his idealistic philosophy offered him were such that he could make no distinction between good and bad hypotheses in the non-mathematical sciences. He therefore obviously fell back on such hypotheses as were in harmony with his religious views. Hence his rejection of uniformitarianism in geology, his acceptance of miracles to account for important changes, and his insistence on Vital Forces and Final Causes in biology.

(5) *John Stuart Mill*

Mill published *A System of Logic* in 1843 (three years after Whewell's *Philosophy*).[27] The book rapidly placed its author in the fore-

[25] II, 442; I. xxxiv: Aphorisms concerning Ideas, CI, CII; I, xlvi: Aphorisms concerning Science, LIV.　　　　　　　　　　　　　　　　　　　　　[26] II, 86.

[27] I quote from the 9th edition, published in 1875.

front of British philosophical writers. Several chapters deal with the problems of the philosophy of science. Mill here acknowledges that he has profited much from Whewell's scientific learning, and agrees with him on many important points, notably in insisting on the necessity for using hypotheses. But Mill resolutely attacks what may be called the metaphysical part of Whewell's doctrine. While Whewell was an idealist, Mill was a thoroughgoing empiricist. The difference, naturally, comes out very clearly in their respective views of causation. Mill wished to derive the idea of causation solely from experience. The more we learn about the course of nature, he held, the more evidence do we get that every fact can be connected with another fact which is its invariable antecedent. It followed that *cause* was always an observable event. or state, and that the notion of First Cause, something antecedent to all events, and thus not itself an event, was illogical, irrelevant, and meaningless. Mill disavows any such cause:

When in the course of this inquiry I speak of the cause of any phenomenon I do not mean a cause which is not a phenomenon; I make no research into the ultimate or ontological cause of anything.[28]

The Law of Causation . . . is but the familiar truth that invariability of succession is found by observation to obtain between every fact in nature and some other fact which has preceded it. . . . The invariable antecedent is termed the cause, the invariable consequent, the effect.[29]

Whereas ' force,' to Whewell, was a ' quality, power, or efficacy,' Mill looked upon it as nothing but a theoretical construct:

There is, no doubt, a tendency . . . to associate the idea of causation with the proximate antecedent *event,* rather than with any of the antecedent states. . . . And this tendency shows itself very visibly in the different logical fictions which are resorted to, even by men of science, to avoid the necessity of giving the name of cause to anything which had existed for an indeterminate length of time before the effect. Thus, rather than say that the earth causes the fall of bodies, they ascribe it to a *force* exerted by the earth, or an *attraction* by the earth.[30]

Mill would not accept Whewell's distinction between the induction of causes, and of laws of phenomena. To Mill there were only laws of phenomena of greater or less universality.[31]

When a phenomenon A was, so far as we know, unconditionally followed by another phenomenon B, Mill accepted the name ' cause ' for A. He here differed from Comte—whom Whewell had criticized—on the question of terminology. His difference from Whewell, on the other hand, was substantial. While Whewell insisted that there was

[28] I, 376.　　　　　　　　　　　　　　　　　　[29] I, 377.
[30] I, 382.　　　　　　　　　　　　　　　　　　[31] Cf. II, 394.

a 'power' in A that caused B, Mill denied that such power could be made the object of scientific inquiry. The attitude is made clear in Mill's words on explanation:

An individual fact is said to be explained, by pointing out its cause, that is, by stating the law or laws of causation, of which its production is an instance. . . . And in a similar manner, a law or uniformity in nature is said to be explained, when another law or laws are pointed out of which that law itself is but a case, and from which it could be deduced.[32]

What is called explaining one law of nature by another, is but substituting one mystery for another; and does nothing to render the general course of nature other than mysterious: we can no more assign a *why* for the more extensive laws than for the partial ones. . . . Every such operation brings us a step nearer towards answering the question which was stated . . . as comprehending the whole problem of the investigation of nature, viz.: What are the fewest assumptions, which being granted, the order of nature as it exists would be the result? What are the fewest general propositions from which all the uniformities existing in nature could be deduced? [33]

By using the term 'mystery' here Mill only wishes to draw attention to the fact that the assumptions, or hypotheses, are not such as can be proved in any ordinary sense. Mill did not hold, for example, like Whewell, that "The doctrine of the universal gravitation of matter is a simple and ultimate truth, in which the mind can acquiesce and repose." [34] To Mill the concept of gravity was a serviceable explanatory concept; it was not a really existing entity, an 'efficacy or power.' This did not by any means reduce the value of the concept. On the contrary, Mill insists as strongly as possible that 'the whole problem of the investigation of nature' depends on the invention of suitable hypothetical concepts.

As regards *vera causa* Mill naturally took a different view from Whewell:

I conceive it to be necessary, when the hypothesis relates to causation, that the supposed cause should not only be a real phenomenon, something actually existing in nature, but should also be already known to exercise, or at least to be capable of exercising, an influence of some sort over the effect . . . in [that] case alone can the hypothesis be received as true merely because it explains the phenomenon. . . . [However,] it may be very useful by suggesting a line of investigation, which may possibly terminate in obtaining real proof. But for this purpose, as is justly remarked by M. Comte, it is indispensable that the cause suggested by the hypothesis should be in its own nature capable of being proved by other evidence. This seems to be the philosophical import of Newton's maxim . . . that the cause . . . must . . . be a *vera causa*. . . . It is certainly not necessary that the cause assigned should be a cause already known; otherwise we should sacrifice our best oppor-

[32] I, 540.   [33] I, 549.   [34] Whewell. I. 264.

tunities of becoming acquainted with new causes. But what is true in the maxim is, that the cause, though not known previously, should be capable of becoming known thereafter; that its existence should be capable of being detected, and its connection with the effect ascribed to it should be susceptible of being proved, by independent evidence. The hypothesis, by suggesting observations and experiments, puts us on the road to that independent evidence if it be really attainable; and till it be attained, the hypothesis ought only to count for a more or less plausible conjecture.

This function, however, of hypotheses, is one which must be reckoned absolutely indispensable in science.[35]

Mill obviously fully agreed with Whewell in rejecting the popular view that science was concerned only with facts and not with hypotheses. But he was more liberal in regard to what hypotheses he considered allowable, and more restrictive as regards the criteria by which the hypotheses should be considered as proved. For Whewell, consilience of inductions was the only way to distinguish between *ad hoc* explanations and others. Mill denied that the fact of consilience was enough to constitute a hypothetical concept as a cause *with real existence*—a cause, in Mill's sense, meaning a phenomenon. He argued against the metaphysical part of Whewell's thesis, namely, that consilience proved that such a thing as, say, the force of gravity really existed. Mill obviously did not wish to imply that the invention of a concept which led to such consilience was not a great scientific feat. Its importance consisted in the possibility such a concept afforded of comprehending several classes of phenomena. And this was the ultimate aim of scientific inquiry: to arrive at such concepts as allowed the deduction of the greatest possible number of corollaries, testable by experience.

The fundamental difference between Whewell's and Mill's views on Induction has been explained above. A consequence of that difference was that Mill did not limit the term, as Whewell did, to those operations where a general concept was consciously introduced.[36]

Whewell had insisted that the conceptions to be used in inductions had necessarily to be clear and appropriate. Clarity was achieved, " not . . . by laying down a definition of the conception; but by acquiring such a possession of it in our minds as enables, indeed compels us, to admit along with the conception, all the axioms and principles which it necessarily implies." [37] Examples of inappropriate concepts were, for instance, mechanical concepts employed to explain vital phenomena.[38] Mill looked at these matters in another light, and offered his own explication of ' clear ' and ' appropriate ':

[35] II, 15, 16.
[36] Cf. Mill, *Logic*, I, 353.

If the conception corresponds to a real agreement among the phenomena; if the comparison which we have made of a set of objects has led us to class them according to real resemblances and differences; the conception which does this cannot fail to be appropriate, for some purpose or other.[39]

In order, then, that it [the conception] may be clear, the only requisite is, that we shall know exactly in what the agreement consists; that it shall have been carefully observed, and accurately remembered.[40]

Mill's statement of the requirements was clearly more germane to the problems of such sciences as geology, biology and sociology, whereas it is certainly somewhat jejune to say, for instance, that the concept of gravity classes terrestrial bodies with celestial ones according to real resemblances and differences. (However, Mill did not consider the Newtonian theory as established primarily by induction, but by deduction.[41]) Whewell, as we have seen, everywhere required conceptions which could be applied in a deductive system. But such conceptions were largely unattainable in the biological and social sciences. By condemning other conceptions as unscientific and premature, Whewell therefore acted as a brake on progress in these sciences. Mill indicated a method which would enable them to proceed step by step.

As we should expect from the above, Mill's views on recent developments in geology and biology differed considerably from Whewell's. He did not accept miracles as explanations,[42] and held uniformitarianism to be eminently inductive.[43] His judgment of Darwin's theory was favorable:

Mr. Darwin's remarkable speculation on the Origin of Species is another unimpeachable example of a legitimate hypothesis. What he terms ' natural selection ' is not only a *vera causa*, but one proved to be capable of producing effects of the same kind with those which the hypothesis ascribes to it; the question of possibility is entirely one of degree. It is unreasonable to accuse Mr. Darwin (as has been done) of violating the rules of Induction. The rules of Induction are concerned with the conditions of Proof. Mr. Darwin has never pretended that his doctrine was proved. He was not bound by the rules of Induction, but by those of Hypothesis. And these last have seldom been more completely fulfilled. He has opened a path of inquiry full of promise, the results of which none can foresee.[44]

(6) *Charles Darwin and Thomas Henry Huxley*

We now turn to the opinions expressed by the leading Darwinian scientists, Darwin and Huxley, on these problems of the philosophy of science.

It is evident that Darwin's and Huxley's positions differ funda-

---

[37] Whewell, II, 184.   [38] Whewell, II, 187.   [39] II, 203.   [40] II, 205.
[41] II, 536–9.   [42] Cf. II, 168.   [43] Cf. II, 26.   [44] II, 19, note.

mentally both from the popular and from the Whewellian one.   On
the other hand, it would be hard to find any point on which they disagree with Mill.   Huxley explicitly acknowledges his indebtedness to
and agreement with Mill:

I need hardly point out my obligation to Mr. J. S. Mill's *System of Logic* in
this view of scientific method.[45]

Those who wish to study fully the doctrines of which I have endeavoured to
give some rough and ready illustrations, must read Mr. John Stuart Mill's
System of Logic.[46]

Darwin expresses his general agreement with Huxley's treatment
of these matters; referring to the lectures from which the above quotation is taken he says:

I am very glad you like Huxley's lectures.   I have been very much struck
with them, especially with the ' Philosophy of Induction.' [47]

The popular view of inductive science as concerned with observation only, and not with hypotheses, was of course as unacceptable to
Darwin as to Whewell and Mill.   Here he could speak from direct
experience:

How profoundly ignorant B must be of the very soul of observation!   About
thirty years ago there was much talk that geologists ought only to observe
and not theorise; and I well remember some one saying that at this rate a
man might as well go into a gravel pit and count the pebbles and describe
the colours.   How odd it is that anyone should not see that all observation
must be for or against some view if it is to be of any service! [48]

Have you seen Hopkins in the new ' Fraser '? . . .   On his standard of proof,
natural science would never progress, for without the making of theories I
am convinced there would be no observation.[49]

Darwin fully acknowledged the hypothetical nature of his own
theory:

What you hint at generally is very, very true: that my work will be griev-
ously hypothetical, and large parts by no means worthy of being called in-

[45] *Lay Sermons,* 95.   I quote from the following editions of works by Darwin and
Huxley: Thomas Henry Huxley, *Lay Sermons* (London, 1870); *Lectures and Essays* (London, 1908); *Hume* (London, 1881); *Essays upon Controverted Questions*
(London, 1892).   Leonard Huxley, *Life and Letters of Thomas Henry Huxley* (London, 1900) [*Life*].   Charles Darwin, *The Origin of Species,* 6th ed (1872), Popular
Impression, (London, 1900); *The Origin of Species,* 1st ed. (1859), Reprint (London, 1950).   Francis Darwin, *The Life and Letters of Charles Darwin* (London,
1888) [*Letters*].   *More Letters of Charles Darwin* (London, 1903).

[46] *Lectures and Essays,* 54, note.   [47] *Letters,* III, 3, to Hooker, 1863.

[48] *More Letters,* I, 195, to Henry Fawcett, Sept. 18, 1861.

[49] *Letters,* II, 314–5, to Lyell, June 1, 1860.

duction, my commonest error being probably induction from too few facts.[50]

I have always looked at the doctrine of Natural Selection as an hypothesis which, if it explains several large classes of facts, would deserve to be ranked as a theory deserving acceptance; and this, of course, is my own opinion.[51]

In the first quotation above, from a letter to Gray, Darwin adopts, for what may be called ' tactical ' reasons, the popular view, according to which only induction was a wholly respectable scientific procedure. In the second, from a letter to Hooker, Darwin's nearest friend, he sets out his own view of the matter more clearly. It evidently agrees with Mill's. The same attitude is apparent in the following passage:

I am actually weary of telling people that I do not pretend to adduce direct evidence of one species changing into another, but that I believe that this view is in the main correct, because so many phenomena can be thus grouped together and explained. . . . I generally throw in their teeth the universally admitted theory of the undulations of light . . . admitted because the view explains so much.[52]

If light is produced by undulations, then such facts as interference will occur. *If* species are produced by natural descent and natural selection, then such facts as rudimentary organs, embryological parallelisms, and continuous distribution in space and time, will occur. In both cases they do in fact occur, therefore these views should be regarded as ' theories deserving acceptance.'

Huxley expresses his opinion on these matters very pungently:

I do protest that, of the vast number of cants in this world, there are none, to my mind, so contemptible as the pseudo-scientific cant which is talked about the ' Baconian philosophy.' [53]

Critics exclusively trained in classics or in mathematics, who have never determined a scientific fact in their lives by induction from experiment or observation, prate learnedly about Mr. Darwin's method, which is not inductive enough, not Baconian enough, forsooth, for them. But even if practical acquaintance with the process of scientific investigation is denied to them, they may learn, by the perusal of Mr. Mill's admirable chapter " On the Deductive Method," that there are multitudes of scientific inquiries in which the method of pure induction helps the investigator but a very little way.[54]

All science starts with hypotheses—in other words, with assumptions that are unproved, while they may be, and often are, erroneous; but which are better than nothing to the seeker after order in the maze of phenomena. And the historical progress of every Science depends on the criticism of hypotheses . . . until there remains only that exact verbal expression of as much as

---

[50] *More Letters*, I, 126, to Asa Gray, Nov. 29, 1859.
[51] *More Letters*, I, 139–40, to Hooker, Feb. 14, 1860.
[52] *More Letters*, I, 184, to F. W. Hutton, 1861.
[53] *Lectures and Essays*, 46.

[54] *Ibid.*, 172.

we know of the fact, and no more, which constitutes a perfect scientific theory.[55]

As regards causation it is obvious that Darwin was an empiricist, though he does not define his position in philosophical terms.   He often contrasts his own explanations in terms of *verae causae* with explanations implying a reference to an unknown agency:

the simplicity of the view that each species was first produced within a single region captivates the mind.   He who rejects it, rejects the *vera causa* of ordinary generation with subsequent migration, and calls in the agency of miracle.[56]

Vera Causa, to Darwin, seems to have meant an observable state of things: the observable fact that animals do produce offspring which diverge from the parent stock, though resembling it on the whole, and the further observable fact that more are born than the earth can feed, so that a struggle for existence results:

The belief in Natural Selection must at present be grounded entirely on general considerations, (1) On its being a *vera causa,* from the struggle for existence; and the certain geological fact that species somehow do change. . . .[57]

Tautological explanations, whose real content was no more than what was to be explained, found no favor with Darwin:

It is so easy to hide our ignorance under such expressions as the ' plan of creation,' ' unity of design,' etc., and to think that we give an explanation when we only restate a fact.[58]

The same refusal to be taken in by purely verbal explanations comes out clearly in the following quotation:

I enjoyed Tylor extremely, and the first part of Lecky; but I think the latter is often vague, and gives a false appearance of throwing light on his subject by such phrases as ' spirit of the age,' ' spread of civilization,' etc.[59]

The most explicit statement that I have been able to find in Darwin's writings on these theoretical questions is found in the 6th edition of the *Origin:*

It has been said that I speak of natural selection as an active power or Deity; but who objects to an author speaking of the attraction of gravity as ruling the movements of the planets?   Every one knows what is meant and is implied by such metaphorical expressions; and they are almost necessary for brevity.   So again it is difficult to avoid personifying the word Nature; but I mean by Nature, only the aggregate action and product of many natural laws, and by laws the sequence of events as ascertained by us.[60]

---

[55] *Hume,* 55.
[57] *Letters,* III, 25, to G. Bentham, May 22, 1863.
[59] *Letters,* III, 40, to Hooker, Sept. 27, 1865.
[56] *Origin,* 1st ed., 299.
[58] *Origin,* 1st ed., 408.
[60] *Origin,* 6th ed., 99.

Huxley wrote fairly extensively on the philosophical problems involved in science and scientific method. On causation he employed almost the same terms as Mill:

We must, in the first place, be prepared to prove that the supposed causes of the phenomena exist in nature; that they are what the logicians call *verae causae* ... in the next place, we should be prepared to show that the assumed causes of the phenomena are competent to produce such phenomena as those which we wish to explain by them; and in the last place, we ought to be able to show that no other known causes are competent to produce those phenomena.[61]

Huxley, in an article in the *Fortnightly Review* (1887), criticized at length the view of causation which identified Cause with Force, understood as a really existing entity, and not as an hypothetical concept invented to account for observable phenomena:

The tenacity of the wonderful fallacy that the laws of nature are agents, instead of being, as they really are, a mere record of experience, upon which we base our interpretations of that which does happen, and our anticipation of that which will happen, is an interesting psychological fact.[62]

But it may be useful to say, once more, that, at this present moment, nobody knows anything about the existence of a 'force' of gravitation apart from the fact; that Newton declared the ordinary notion of such force to be inconceivable; that various attempts have been made to account for the order of facts we call gravitation, without recourse to the notion of attractive force ... all we know about the 'force' of gravitation, or any other so-called 'force,' is that it is a name for the hypothetical cause of an observed order of facts.[63]

Like Mill, Huxley declared explanations in terms of unknown and unknowable causes as void. He was fully aware that neither the falsity of his opponents' views, nor the correctness of his own, could be demonstrated on *a priori* grounds. His ultimate appeal was to experience, and the proven usefulness of the empiricist attitude for scientific progress:

It is wholly impossible to prove that any phenomenon whatsoever is not produced by the interposition of some unknown cause. But philosophy has prospered exactly as it has disregarded such possibilities.[64]

The fundamental axiom of scientific thought is that there is not, never has been, and never will be, any disorder in nature. The admission of the occurrence of any event which was not the logical consequence of the immediately antecedent events, according to these definite, ascertained, or unascertained rules which we call the 'laws of nature,' would be an act of self-destruction on the part of science.[65]

[61] *Lectures and Essays*, 100.
[62] *Essays upon Controverted Questions*, 253.   [63] *Ibid.*, 287.
[64] *Life*, I, 174.   [65] *Essays upon Controverted Questions*, 247.

And be it recollected that this sort of satisfaction [derived from purely verbal explanations, such as Divine Plan] works not only negative but positive ill, by discouraging inquiry, and so depriving man of the usufruct of one of the most fertile fields of his great patrimony, Nature.[66]

Like Mill, Huxley held that scientific inquiry aimed at a description of the world of phenomena which should be consistent and as simple as possible; employing as few assumptions as possible: " In ultimate analysis everything is incomprehensible, and the whole object of science is simply to reduce the fundamental incomprehensibilities to the smallest possible number." [67]

Whewell held the principle of causation to be ' necessary ' in an absolute sense which is somewhat difficult to understand: it is apparently bound up with a view of the laws of nature as in a way dependent on the will of God. He maintained, moreover, that we are intuitively aware of the bond or necesssity connecting cause and effect. To Huxley the law of causation was ' necessary ' in a relative sense: it was necessary to postulate it in order that there might be scientific progress. Huxley's view coincides with Mill's, who looked upon the uniformity of nature as ' the ultimate major premise of all inductions.' [68] Huxley expresses it thus: " I take the conception of necessity to have a logical, and not a physical foundation." [69] He also rejected the view, held by many popular writers, that the law of causation expressed some sort of inexorable Fate—an idea which caused some people to take refuge in a belief in miracles in order to escape from the oppressive thought of either cruel Fate or blind Chance: " Fact I know; and Law I know; but what is this Necessity, save an empty shadow of my own mind's throwing? " [70]

Explanations in terms of Final Causes, or Vital Forces, were as unacceptable to Darwin and Huxley as they were to Mill. Here again they differ sharply from Whewell. Darwin's position may be inferred from the following quotations:

Herschel, in his *Physical Geography,* had a sentence with respect to the *Origin,* something to the effect that the higher law of Providential Arrangement should always be stated. But astronomers do not state that God directs the course of each comet and planet. The view that each variation has been providentially arranged seems to me to make Natural Selection entirely superfluous, and indeed takes the whole case out of the range of science. . . . Of course it may be said, when you kick a stone, or a leaf falls from a tree, that it was ordained, before the foundations of the world were laid, exactly where that stone or leaf should lie. In this sense the subject has no interest for me. . . . If you say that God ordained that at some time

---

[66] *Lectures and Essays,* 166.
[67] Article in the *Contemporary Review,* 18 (1871), 466.
[68] Mill, *Logic,* I, 356.   [69] *Life,* I, 412.   [70] *Lay Sermons,* 158.

and place a dozen slight variations should arise, and that one of them alone should be preserved in the struggle for life and the other eleven should perish in the first or few first generations, then the saying seems to me mere verbiage. It comes to merely saying that everything that is, is ordained.[71]

[Lyell asks] " Must you not assume a primeval creative power which does not act with uniformity, or how could man supervene? "—I am not sure that I understand your remarks which follow the above. We must, under present knowledge, assume the creation of one or a few forms in the same manner as philosophers assume the existence of a power of attraction without any explanation. But I entirely reject, as in my judgement quite unnecessary, any subsequent addition of ' new powers and attributes and forces ' except in so far as every character which is naturally selected or preserved is in some way an advantage or improvement, otherwise it would not have been selected. If I were convinced that I required such additions to the theory of natural selection, I would reject it as rubbish.[72]

Huxley does not waste much breath on Final Causes: " those fascinating but barren Virgins, the Final Causes, against whom a high authority has so justly warned us." [73]

We cannot understand the structure of animals or plants, unless we suppose they were contrived for special ends . . . this sort of reasoning is not very formidable. . . . It is an *argumentum ad ignorantiam*. . . . But suppose we prefer to admit our ignorance rather than adopt a hypothesis at variance with all the teachings of Nature? Or, suppose for a moment we admit the explanation, and then seriously ask ourselves how much wiser are we; what does the explanation explain? Is it any more than a grandiloquent way of announcing the fact, that we really know nothing about the matter? A Phenomenon is explained when it is shown to be a case of some general law of Nature; but the supernatural interposition of the Creator can, by the nature of the case, exemplify no law.[74]

Explanations in terms of Final Causes were always unsatisfactory; Darwin's theory made them superfluous: " For the notion that every organism has been created as it is and launched straight at a purpose, Mr. Darwin substitutes the conception of something which may fairly be termed a method of trial and error." [75] The belief in Vital Forces was severely criticized, along with the notion of Force as an existing entity:

Leibnitz . . . noted that the modern conception of Force, as a sort of atmosphere enveloping the particles of bodies, and having potential or actual ac-

---

[71] *More Letters*, I, 191–4, to Lyell, 1861.
[72] *Letters*, II, 210, to Lyell, Oct. 11, 1859.
[73] *Lectures and Essays*, 129.
[74] *Lectures and Essays*, 164.
[75] *Lectures and Essays*, 179.

tivity, is simply a new name for the Aristotelian Form . . . among those biologists who have not been asleep for the last quarter of a century [the article was written in 1887] ' vital force ' no longer figures in the vocabulary of science. It is a patent survival of realism; the generalisation from experience that all living bodies exhibit certain activities of a definite character is made the basis of the notion that every living body contains an entity ' vital force,' which is assumed to be the cause of those activities.[76]

What justification is there, then, for the assumption of the existence in the living matter of a something which has no representative, or correlative, in the not living matter which gave rise to it? What better philosophical status has ' vitality ' than ' aquosity ' ? . . . If the phaenomena exhibited by water are its properties, so are those presented by protoplasm, living or dead, its properties.[77]

(7) *The discussion among the general public*

The foregoing analysis has aimed at defining the focal points in the public discussion on the theoretical foundations of the Darwinian theory. I shall now deal with that discussion itself, as it appeared in the periodical press of the time. Only periodicals of a non-specialist kind have been included here. The purely scientific discussion is outside the scope of the present investigation.[78] This does not imply,

---

[76] *Essays upon Controverted Questions*, 260.   [77] *Lay Sermons*, 151.

[78] The following is a list of publications referred to in text and notes below, with a rough and ready description of their policy and type of readership. The circulation figures (given in thousands) are naturally mostly conjectural. The period covered is 1859–72.

Academy, weekly review, distinctly literary: circulation, *2.*
Morning Advertiser, daily newspaper, liberal–conservative: *8.*
Athenaeum, weekly review, literary and scientific: *5.*
Temple Bar, monthly magazine, mediocre intellectually: *20.*
Examiner, weekly review, liberal: *2.*
Globe, daily evening newspaper, conservative: *6.*
Guardian, weekly review, liberal-minded High Church organ: *5.*
John Bull, weekly newspaper, Tory and High Church: *3.*
Leader, weekly review, radical, positivist: *1.*
Blackwood's Magazine, monthly, literary, liberal–conservative: *10.*
Fraser's Magazine, monthly, liberal, latitudinarian in religion: *8.*
Macmillan's Magazine, monthly, liberal, latitudinarian in religion, important literary organ: *20.*
Month, monthly review, Roman Catholic organ: *2.*
Daily News, daily newspaper, liberal: *6* in 1860, *100* in 1870.
Nature, weekly review, covering natural science: *5.*
Nonconformist, weekly review, liberal, Free Church: *3.*
Intellectual Observer, monthly review, for young naturalists: *3.*
Patriot, weekly review, Congregationalist organ: *1.*
Morning Post, daily newspaper, Tory, aristocratic, fashionable: *5.*
Punch, weekly comical paper, mildly liberal: *10.*
Record, tri-weekly newspaper, Evangelical Church of England: *4.*
Methodist Recorder, weekly newspaper, Methodist organ: *20.*

however, that the opinion of the scientists has been left out of account altogether.   For even in the general publications, reviews and articles on these subjects were often written by scientific men—indeed, in the better class of periodicals, such as the three great quarterlies, the *Edinburgh*, the *Quarterly*, and the *Westminster*, by the leading scientists of the time.   Reviews written by outsiders would not have been acceptable to intelligent readers, and only writers who knew their subject could speak with any authority and thus hope to influence public opinion.   But the arguments in the general periodicals had to be somewhat different from those employed in purely scientific ones. Above all, they had to be explicitly related to wider issues.   For that reason, the discussion of the philosophical questions involved in scientific inquiry may in some ways be better followed in the general press than in the specialist one, even when the opinions of the scientific community are concerned.

However, the discussion in the general periodicals must not be expected to yield more than an indication of the state of feeling in certain sections of the public.   In other words, the discussion is often shallow, arguments are simplified, and presentation is sketchy.   In these respects, however, each periodical is likely to mirror the state of mind of its average reader.   Only a very few were in a position to know the relevant facts at first hand; and even specialists were ' average readers ' on many points outside their own particular field of study.

If the press discussion is admittedly often lacking in depth, it is certainly not defective in breadth. Most of the arguments that were brought up for discussion in books and specialist publications on the Darwinian theory were also taken up and at least briefly indicated in the general press.   Nor is this surprising.   Sides were passionately taken in the Darwinian controversy, and both opponents and sup-

---

Christian Remembrancer, quarterly review, High Church organ: *1*.

North British Review, quarterly, Scottish Church Liberal: *2*.

Contemporary Review, monthly, liberal, Evangelical religion and philosophy: *3*.

Edinburgh Review, quarterly, liberal–conservative: *5*.

Fortnightly Review, monthly, liberal, rationalist: *3*.

National Review, quarterly, latitudinarian in religion: *1*.

British Quarterly Review, quarterly, Free Church organ: *1*.

Quarterly Review, quarterly, Conservative: *7*.

London Quarterly Review, quarterly, Methodist organ: *2*.

Saturday Review, weekly, brilliant literary organ, liberal–conservative: *20*.

Popular Science Review, quarterly: *2*.

Westminster Review, quarterly, liberal–radical: *3*.

Spectator, weekly review, liberal, latitudinarian in religion: *5*.

Standard, daily newspaper, conservative: *30* in 1860, *100* in 1870.

Tablet, weekly review, Roman Catholic organ: *2*.

Times, daily newspaper, conservative, most important: *60*.

Good Words, monthly magazine, decidedly religious, Church of England: *50*.

porters sought diligently for any argument that might give them an advantage. On extensive reading the press will thus yield a nearly complete catalogue of the arguments that were current, and at the same time an indication of what arguments were considered most effective by different sections of the public.

The above analysis of Whewell's and Mill's doctrines will have indicated that the discussion of Darwin's theory from the point of view of scientific method—which is what concerns us here—was likely to follow three main lines.

(A) It was argued that the theory was deductive, not inductive; that it was based on assumptions and hypotheses, not on facts. This was the popular view, which both Whewell and Mill repudiated, but which was put forth very frequently in the non-scientific press of the time.

(B) There was the argument, for which support might be found in Whewell, that the hypothesis was premature and derived from too few facts and a one-sided selection of facts: that indeed biology and geology were as yet in a state where hypotheses about causes were not allowable. The argument was naturally often combined with a reference to the incompatibility of the hypothesis with traditional religious beliefs.

(C) Darwin was criticized for not giving any clue as to the ' real ' cause of the development of the organic world, since he did not explain how the first forms of life originated, endowed with possibilities of development, nor what forces brought about the later modifications. Natural selection, it was contended, could operate only if favorable variations occurred, and these could not be due to blind chance: they could only be explained by reference to final causes.

Darwin's opponents in the press were numerically much stronger than his supporters. Even when belief in Evolution began to prevail among the educated sections of the public, towards the end of the 'sixties, the distinctively Darwinian form of it, Evolution by Natural Selection, was acceptable to a small minority only. And it was always the Natural Selection theory that met with the strongest objections from the philosophical point of view.

The relative paucity of pro-Darwinian statements in the press, however, may also be due to the fact that Darwin's supporters relied mainly on the direct presentation of the facts, as they could fairly safely leave the interpretation of the facts to the common sense of the readers. But by the same token Darwin's opponents could *not* leave the reader to draw his own conclusions from the facts, for their criticism turned largely on the impossibility of equating scientific induction with common sense reasoning, and on the necessity of arriving at a precise conception of the fundamental, abstract ideas of biology before any scientifically valid induction at all could be attempted. The question of the philosophical foundations of Darwin's doctrine was therefore constantly brought forward by the opponents, but only incidentally by the supporters of the theory. The opponents of empiricist views had to be actively on the defensive: they considered themselves to be in a position of unfair disadvantage. This feeling is brought out in the following from a newspaper of traditionalist views:

The triumph of the materialist comes from this—that in treating upon tangible facts alone, and ignoring every power which is not palpable to the sense, he appeals successfully to practical minds, averse to ascending into the more elevated contemplations of a sounder philosophy. Great moral courage is indispensable in the opponent of views easily advanced, of a popular nature, and susceptible of refutation only by the employment of the most severe form of abstract reasoning.[79]

A. *Darwin's theory not inductive*

Bacon's and Newton's names, and the magic word induction, were very frequently invoked against Darwin's allegedly deductive method. Especially, Darwin's opponents tried to make as much capital as possible of the undeniable fact that Darwin had to make use of assumptions and hypotheses: natural scientists should consider nothing but *facts*. The organ of the Evangelicals, the *Record,* expressed this attitude in its most extreme form:

If ever a book was issued from the press which outraged all common sense, and set at nought every acknowledged principle of scientific investigation and logical deduction, it was Mr. Darwin's *Origin of Species.* Facts and assumptions, probabilities and speculations, are mingled together in it in most illogical confusion. The shallowest hypothesis becomes a basis wide enough in the author's estimation, to support the most startling and extensive conclusions. . . .[80]

The popular view was that *any* hypothesis was suspect. But the argument was used only against hypotheses that clashed with traditional beliefs. This was sometimes stated quite explicitly, as in the following pronouncement by Sir Benjamin Brodie, a distinguished scientist, F.R.S., and once President of the British Association:

There are many cases, indeed, in the history of science, where speculations, like those of Kepler, have led to great discoveries. . . . It is otherwise, however, with speculations which trench upon sacred ground, and which run counter to the universal convictions of mankind, poisoning the fountains of science, and disturbing the serenity of the Christian world. Such is doubt-

[79] *Morning Post*, Sept. 6, 1861.
[80] *Record*, Oct. 8, 1862.

less the tendency of Mr. Darwin's work.[81]

In his lecture " On the Use of Imagination in Science," Professor John Tyndall, Huxley's friend, contended for the right of scientists to follow up any hypothesis they saw fit, irrespective of ' common sense ' and traditional views. The reaction in the press was overwhelmingly negative. The *Times* wrote in a leading article:

We had been under the impression that Natural Philosophers drew no bills. We do not presume to say one word about the Evolution Hypothesis. . . . The greater part of the opposition . . . is provoked . . . not by Science, but by the imagination of men of Science. . . . We are not, after all, much concerned to know how the world was being made millions of millions of years ago. . . . we look to men of Science rather for observation than for imagination.[82]

The Darwinian answer to these attacks was forcibly put by Huxley in his review of the *Origin* in the *Westminster Review:*

There cannot be a doubt that the method of inquiry which Mr. Darwin has adopted is not only rigorously in accordance with the canons of scientific logic, but that it is the only adequate method . . . what Mr. Darwin has attempted to do is in exact accordance with the rule laid down by Mr. Mill: he has endeavoured to determine great facts inductively, by observation and experiment; he has then reasoned from the data thus furnished; and lastly, he has tested the validity of his ratiocination by comparing his deductions with the observed facts of nature.[83]

B. *Darwin's theory based on a ' hasty and imperfect ' induction*

Those anti-Darwinians who did not condemn Darwin outright for using hypotheses found support for an attack in Whewell's warning against induction from " obvious phenomena . . . collected in a loose, confused, and precarious manner." [84] Since Darwin could not state his theory in a mathematically exact way—i.e., so as to make one stage of development deducible from a previous one by means of exact laws—the theory was declared unsound. One of the clearest state-

[81] Quot. from *Good Words*, 3 (1862), Cf. also the following: *Quarterly Review*, 108 (1860), 239; *John Bull*, July 7, 1860; *Spectator* 1860, 285; *Guardian*, Feb. 6, 1861; *John Bull*, Feb. 21, 1863; *British Quarterly Review*, 38 (1863), 495; *Athenaeum*, July 28, 1866; *Contemporary Review*, 4 (1867), 48; *Globe*, Aug. 20, 1868; *Punch*, Apr. 8, 1871, 145.

[82] *Times*, Sept. 19, 1870, 9. Cf. also: *Saturday Review*, 30 (1870), 400; *English Churchman*, Sept. 29, 1870; *English Independent*, Sept. 22, 1870; *Record*, Sept. 23, 1870; *Times*, Apr. 7, 1871; *Edinburgh Review*, 133 (1871), 146–7; *John Bull*, Nov. 30, 1872.

[83] *Westminster Review*, 17 (1860), 566–7. Cf. also, for similar statements: *National Review*, 10 (1860), 214; *Temple Bar*, 1 (1860–1), 572; *Examiner*, Nov. 30, 1867.

[84] Whewell, II, 445.

ments of this requirement was made by Hopkins, a well-known biologist, in an early review of the *Origin:*

We are not denying our author's right to reason upon his hypothesis. . . . [But] we had not dreamt that because the objections to a theory could not be proved to be absolutely insuperable we were called upon to accept it as true. We had fancied that the laws of reasoning in such matters, to which Newton and Laplace, Fresnel and Faraday, in their mathematical or experimental investigations, have bowed in reverential obedience, were still in force. . . . [Darwin] constantly speaks of his theory as explaining certain phenomena, which he represents as inexplicable on any other theory. We altogether demur at this. . . . A phenomenon is properly said to be explained, more or less perfectly, when it can be clearly referred to some recognized cause. . . . But Mr. Darwin's theory can explain nothing in this sense, because it cannot possibly assign any necessary relation between phenomena and the causes to which it refers them.[85]

It was about this writer that Darwin said, " On his standard of proof, natural science would never progress." Hopkins's distinction between geometrical laws and physical causes is clearly reminiscent of Whewell.

The same attitude towards biological hypotheses appears in Sir William Thomson's (later Lord Kelvin) presidential address to the British Association in 1871, which was widely and very favorably reported in the press:

The essence of science consists in inferring antecedent conditions and anticipating future evolutions from phenomena which have actually come under observation. In biology the difficulties of successfully acting up to this ideal are prodigious. . . . I have always felt that the hypothesis of ' the origin of species through natural selection ' does not contain the true theory of evolution, if evolution there has been, in biology. . . . I feel convinced that the argument of design has been greatly too much lost sight of in recent zoological speculations.[86]

The intention of those who argued in this manner was generally to show that it was impossible to refer evolution to ordinary causation, and that Darwin's attempt to do so offered only a specious solution, since the implied concept of indefinite variability was not sufficiently precise and explicated—it was not ' clear and appropriate.' What was required was a concept, or group of concepts, whereby the present state of the organic world could be shown to be logically necessary, once its original state could be defined.[87]

[85] *Fraser's Magazine,* 62 (1860), 86.

[86] Quot. *Times,* Aug. 4, 1871. Cf. also, for similar views: *Daily News,* Dec. 26, 1859; *Fraser's Magazine,* 61 (1860), 742–7; *Spectator,* 1860, 285; *Intellectual Observer,* 1 (1862), 392; *Morning Advertiser,* Sept. 9, 1865; *Nonconformist,* Sept. 18, 1867; *British Quarterly Review,* 54 (1871), 479.

[87] Cf. *Contemporary Review,* 17 (1871), 100.

The Darwinian answer to this sort of criticism was that the chief test of a scientific theory ought to be that it connected as many facts as possible, and that the demand for a complete explanation was not only futile, but directly harmful, by discouraging inquiry. It might be granted that the Darwinian doctrine was not " a simple and ultimate truth, in which the mind can acquiesce and repose," as Whewell said of the theory of gravitation. But then that was not, for the Darwinians, the criterion to apply. Science was not concerned with ultimate truths. As Mill said: " We can no more assign a *why* for the more extensive laws than for the partial ones." The position was explained in an article by the positivist G. H. Lewes:

It is possible that the hypothesis of Natural Selection, which Mr. Darwin opposes to that of creative fiat and fixity of Plan, may be an imperfect explanation, but at any rate it has the immense merit of bringing the question within the region of research. . . . Indeed, we must protest against the frequent assumption that Darwinism is disproved because it fails to account for all the phenomena: if it interprets truly some of the phenomena, it is valuable as a colligation of facts; if it interpreted all of them, it would cease to be an hypothesis. Observe, moreover, that writers who are most contemptuous against this hypothesis because it fails—or they think so—to explain some phenomena, urge us to accept the hypothesis of creative fiats, or Divine Ideas, which absolutely explain none.[88]

C. *Darwin's explanation not a causal one*

The third line of argument concerned the concepts of cause and law themselves. Mill, as we have seen, wished to allow only observable phenomena as causes, whereas Whewell, though admitting that they were indeed popularly so regarded, insisted that this was a superficial view.

Darwin's opponents often seemingly adhered to an empiricist view of causation—Mill's prestige was at its highest in the 1860's—but it soon becomes clear that the adherence is verbal only, for while admitting that only phenomena should be regarded as causes, they declared that there were some 'phenomena' that scientists did not know of. This would have been unobjectionable had it not at the same time been added that the 'phenomena' were not only unknown, but unknowable and unobservable, such as a mere scientist could not become aware of, since they did not belong to the natural order of things, but to the supernatural. No tenable rule, unfortunately, was given to decide when an event should be explained as due to a natural cause—an observable phenomenon—and when to a supernatural one—an unobservable 'phenomenon.' In the latter case, the event in question was a miracle.

[88] *Fortnightly Review*, 3 (1868), 370. Cf. also: *Macmillan's Magazine*, 4 (1861), 237; *Westminster Review*, 32 (1867), 1; *London Review*, 1868, 179.

This direct and unashamed appeal to miracles and supernatural interferences occurs remarkably often, and by no means only in the exclusively religious publications:

[Darwin's and Lamarck's] theories recognize only those continuous physical causes which produce the ordinary phenomena of nature; whereas the latter [traditional views] in addition to these causes, recognizes a higher order of causation, acting according to some law which, in our ignorance of its nature, we are obliged to describe as discontinuous.[89]

The fundamental nature of the opposition between the natural scientists and the upholders of traditional views in religion and philosophy appears in the *Times* review of Darwin's *Descent of Man:*

What is there unreasonable in the supposition that they [all the animals in the world] have all been formed on the same general plan? Mr. Darwin's only objection is, that ' this is no scientific explanation.' But this is simply to beg the question. If Mr. Darwin starts with the preliminary assumption that every fact in Nature is capable of scientific explanation—in other words, that no causes have ever operated except natural causes, he will, of course, reject any other causes. But this assumption is the very point to be proved. To argue from it is to assume the whole doctrine of Evolution.[90]

The scientists, for their part, must have been well aware of the consequence of admitting miracles at all into their explanations. If even one was acknowledged as necessary, there would be no barrier against a further invasion:

If we require ' unknown agencies ' at all, we may surely dispense with natural selection altogether, and attribute the formation of species to these unknown agencies directly, instead of attributing it to natural selection and referring natural selection to the unknown agencies.[91]

Many writers, while unwilling to admit miraculous explanations on a par with scientific ones, insisted that the *law* itself had to be seen as an expression of God's will—a supernatural entity. The argument, for which Whewell may have provided some support, was that it was necessary to assume the existence of a Mind ' directing ' or ' manipulating ' the ' laws of nature ' for certain purposes. These ideas gained wide currency by the Duke of Argyll's *Reign of Law,* published in 1867, but based on articles which had previously appeared in such periodicals as the *Edinburgh Review* and *Good Words.*

[89] *Fraser's Magazine,* 61 (1870), 748–9.

[90] *Times,* Apr. 8, 1871.

[91] *British Quarterly Review,* 54 (1871), 469. Cf. also: *Fraser's Magazine,* 61 (1860), 748–9, and 62 (1860), 87, 89; *Quarterly Review,* 109 (1861), 300, and 110 (1861), 369; *London Quarterly Review,* 20 (1863), 272; *Patriot,* Sept. 10, 1863; *Month,* 5 (1866), 635–41; *Guardian,* Oct. 14, 1868; *Good Words,* 9 (1868), 250; *Edinburgh Review,* 134 (1871), 209.

What, then, is ' law '?   It is the generalized expression of a fact which holds good in a multitude of instances ... but even then we are as far from establishing a cause as ever. ... There is ... no proof that law has any existence save in the mind that conceives it.   When, therefore, we use the common expression that God works by general laws, we only mean, in strictness of speech, that his operations take that form to our minds.   He is still the cause, and the law is not even an interposed machinery between Him and the effect.[92]

This idealistic view was given support from the highest quarter when W. B. Carpenter, an eminent biologist, devoted almost the whole of his presidential address to the British Association in 1872 to expounding it: "When science, passing beyound its own limits, assumes to take the place of theology and sets up its own conception of the order of nature as a sufficient account of its cause, it is invading a province of thought to which it has no claim, and not unreasonably provokes the hostility of those who ought to be its best friends." [93] The religious implications of Carpenter's views were acknowledged and underlined in most press mentions of the address, and by Carpenter himself in an article in the *Contemporary Review*.[94]

The view that natural laws are the direct expression of God's will suited the theistic turn of mind of many mid-Victorians.   It was, however, possible to elaborate the idealistic argument against the Natural Selection theory in another direction, more in line with pantheistic or deistic interpretations of nature.   Instead of directly referring the ' law of development ' to God's will, it was explained in vitalistic terms.   A Vital Force, or unconscious tendency, or even conscious striving, was stated to be the efficient cause of progressive development.   Now to the empiricist a ' tendency ' is chiefly a descriptive term, useful in expressing a relation between facts; to say that, for instance, iron has a tendency to rust in damp air, is no more than saying that *if* iron should be exposed to damp air, *then* it would rust, the evidence being that iron has always been found to rust in such conditions.   It is tautological to say that this happens *because* iron has a tendency to rust.

Now Darwin's critics, when saying that an animal was endowed

---

[92] *Christian Remembrancer*, 40 (1860), 255. Cf. also, for further statements of these views: *Athenaeum*, 32 (1859), 659; *National Review*, 11 (1860), 255; *Quarterly Review*, 110 (1861), 398; *British Quarterly Review*, 33 (1861), 226; *Popular Science Review*, 1862, 273; *Edinburgh Review*, 117 (1863), 569; *Spectator*, 1864, 1413; *Inquirer*, Sep. 16, 1865; *Examiner*, Feb. 2, 1867, 69; *British Quarterly Review*, 45 (1867), 571–2; *Fortnightly Review* (1867), 514; *Blackwood's Magazine*, 101 (1867), 686–7; *Contemporary Review*, 6 (1867), 13–14; *Family Herald*, 1868–9, 652; *Quarterly Review*, 127 (1869), 136; *London Quarterly Review*, 36 (1871), 275; *Daily News*, Aug. 15, 1872; *Contemporary Review*, 20 (1872), 740.
[93] Quot. *Times*, Aug. 15, 1872.   [94] *Contemporary Review*, 20 (1872), 738–62.

with a tendency to develop into something higher, did *not* mean that such an animal would under certain specified circumstances so develop. Instead, they conceived ' tendency ' as a cause, precisely such a ' power or efficiency ' as Whewell spoke of. And the tendency itself was, it was thought, explicable only if it was put in direct relation to its final cause. This was, needless to say, in the last resort identified with the will of God. The clearest and most consistent expression of the vitalistic view was made by St. George Mivart whose *Genesis of Species,* published in 1871, made a great impression:

An internal law presides over the actions of every part of every individual, and of every organism as a unit, and of the entire organic world as a whole. It is believed that this conception of an internal innate force will ever remain necessary, however much its subordinate processes may become explicable.[95]

The ' innate tendency ' was held to be a Divine gift made at the creation:

There is the original fact of collocation, and design cleaves to that fact . . . if a systematic production is the result, [we must] infer systematic forces in the cause. . . . Such an interpretation [of the presence of Design in the organic world] of himself by Mr. Darwin would be no more than a legitimate consequence of an admission which he makes upon the very threshold of his theory. He admits that the first life germ was a creation . . . the universal result must be included in that act.[96]

The difference between this reviewer's and Darwin's views was that the reviewer wished to make the ' first created form ' contain the whole subsequent development: to him, the (unobservable) ' first created form' was made to carry the whole of the explanation, whereas to Darwin it stood only for the postulation of an organism capable of reproducing itself with small but indefinite variations. Darwin's original living form was capable of developing in any direction. His opponents' original living form was assumed to be capable of developing in one direction only: the one designed by God, and *ipso facto* the one that has been actually realized.

(8) *Conclusion*

It is quite obvious that the public discussion of the philosophical and methodological foundations of the Darwinian theory was largely motivated by its religious implications. It was impossible to accept the theory without effecting changes in a whole system of religious beliefs sanctioned by tradition, or conversely, to preserve that body of

---

[95] *Month,* 14 (1871), 529, summing up Mivart's views.

[96] *Quarterly Review,* 127 (1869), 159, 175, by Canon Mozley. Cf. also *Edinburgh Review,* 128 (1868), 450; *Month,* 11 (1869), 149, 153; *Edinburgh Review,* 134 (1871), 200; *Tablet,* Feb. 25, 1871.

beliefs intact without rejecting the theory. To the religious, the theory was an incubus which had to be cast out, or at any rate isolated and neutralized. To attack the theoretical foundations of the theory was one of the ways, and an important one, of achieving this result; in that way the theory could be, if not directly refuted, at any rate represented as no more than a loose, scientifically unjustifiable speculation.

The Darwinians, and first among them Darwin himself and Huxley, justified the theory on frankly empiricist grounds. They recognized only observable phenomena as evidence, they refused to regard hypothetical concepts as anything more than abstractions serving to comprehend the observable facts, and they judged their value solely according to their power of thus comprehending a large number of observable facts. In order to accept an explanation as a causal one, they required that one set of observable phenomena—the effect—should be connected with another set of independently observable phenomena—the cause. This ruled out explanations in terms of ' tendencies ' and ' forces,' which were, in conformity with empiricist views, no more than abstractions from the actual facts to be explained. It also ruled out final causes and miracles.

It is natural that the Darwinians should wish to lay down these empiricist methodological principles. Indeed, once they were granted, the Darwinian theory could hardly be resisted; it was possible to maintain that it was incomplete, or not conclusively established, but compared to others it must appear as a tremendous advance. A Huxley could not refrain from pointing out that it was the only theory on the subject which had any scientific status.

In order to resist the theory it was therefore practically necessary to appeal to non-empiricist principles. Not all opponents, of course, admitted this. When the theory was attacked because it was not inductive, the critics considered themselves more empirical than Darwin. But this class of critics clearly rejected empiricism at another point: they generally admitted non-observables such as Divine revelations as evidence.

The better informed critics, who admitted the right of scientists to argue hypothetically, adopted another procedure. They rejected the empiricist view that a hypothesis should be judged solely according to its power of comprehending a large number of facts; they further required that it should contain, in Whewell's phrase, a ' clear and appropriate ' conception. It was never quite clear what that phrase meant exactly, and it was therefore easy to declare arbitrarily that any hypotheses one wished to reject were inappropriate and lacking in clarity, especially in biology and the social sciences where hypotheses fall far short of the mathematical distinctness of astronomy and physics.

Moreover, the anti-Darwinians rejected the empiricist view of causation. They did not admit that it was meaningless to speak of causation except as a relation between observable phenomena; hence they were prepared to accept miracles, and to consider tendencies as expressive of final causes.

The opposition between the empiricist Darwinians and the non-empiricist anti-Darwinians was paralleled on a higher philosophical level by the opposition between Mill and Whewell. Mill, the empiricist, was a Darwinian, and Whewell, the idealist, was for *a priori* reasons an anti-Darwinian. But further search (not fully documented here) will reveal that the parallel goes still further. Just as the opposition to Darwin was largely due to religious motives, Whewell was careful to make his views on the central concept of cause compatible with his deeply-felt religious beliefs. Conversely, Mill, like Darwin and Huxley and most of their lesser supporters, agreed in rejecting this body of traditional religious beliefs.

The Mid-Victorian discussion between empiricists and idealists about the philosophy of science was only superficially concerned with theoretical problems of science. Its motives lay deeper. The parties disagreed about fundamental scales of values, symbolized by their different religious beliefs, or disbeliefs. One of the results of the appearance of Darwin's theory was to bring that underlying disagreement into full view.

~~~ *Sven Peterson*

BENJAMIN PEIRCE:
MATHEMATICIAN AND PHILOSOPHER

Although he is nearly unknown to us, Benjamin Peirce was considered to be the greatest American mathematician of his day, and was one of the first Americans to gain an international reputation for his work in applied mathematics. He taught at Harvard for nearly fifty years (1831–1880), influenced generations of students, and played an important part in broadening the Harvard curriculum of his day. Many of his pupils became well-known mathematicians; two in particular, Chauncey Wright and his own son Charles Sanders Peirce, were instrumental in giving American philosophy a decisive new turn.[1]

The close relationship between Charles Peirce and his father has been variously described. W. B. Gallie says in a recent book:

... his real education he owed to his father, who encouraged him with his precocious laboratory experiments, and, more important, taught him mathematics. Benjamin Peirce was primarily an applied mathematician, but the originality of his mind was perhaps best shown in his *Linear Associative Algebra*, the opening sentence of which, " Mathematics is the science which draws necessary conclusions," shows an approach far in advance of current conceptions in America, and indeed in Europe. The main lines of Peirce's intellectual development were laid down by his father's teaching.[2]

This view should be contrasted with Charles Peirce's own opinion:

... it was always next to impossible to induce him to take a logical view on any subject. His " broad philosophy " which could not be definitely expressed, was a mere habit of feeling. He was a creature of feeling, and had a superstitious reverence for " the square root of minus one ". . . .[3]

[1] Philip P. Wiener, in *Evolution and the Founders of Pragmatism* (Harvard University Press, 1949), has clearly demonstrated the central rôle played in the development of pragmatism by the " Metaphysical Club," that group of brilliant young intellectuals who gathered in Cambridge during the early 1870's, comprising Chauncey Wright, Charles Peirce, William James, Oliver Holmes, Jr., and several others.

[2] W. B. Gallie, *Peirce and Pragmatism* (Pelican Philosophy Series, 1952), 34.

[3] Charles Sanders Peirce, in a letter quoted by Raymond Clare Archibald, "Benjamin Peirce's Linear Associative Algebra and Charles Sanders Peirce," *American Mathematical Monthly*, 34 (1927). B. Peirce himself wrote: " The imaginary square root of algebra, from which the puzzled analyst could not escape, has become the simplest reality of Quaternions, which is the true algebra of space, and clearly elucidates some of the darkest intricacies of mechanical and physical philosophy." (*Ideality in the Physical Sciences* [Boston, 1881], 29.)

An examination of Benjamin Peirce's philosophy, however, shows it to be a far-reaching evolutionary rationalism, based on the new doctrines of material evolution which had had such an impact upon traditional theistic beliefs, and resulting finally in the ideal of a single, all-inclusive science.

I

Benjamin Peirce was born in 1809, and entered Harvard as a member of the famous class of 1829, which included such men as the elder Oliver Wendell Holmes, James Freeman Clarke, Benjamin R. Curtis, and William Henry Channing. He began teaching mathematics at Harvard in 1831, at the age of twenty-two, and continued until his death in 1880.[4]

Peirce's talent for mathematics appeared early. A glimpse of him as a student is afforded by one of his classmates:

Each class had one day a week in which to take books from the college library; and I recollect that Peirce, instead of selecting novels, poetry, history, biography, or travels, as most of us did, brought back under his arm large quarto volumes of pure mathematics.[5]

Another associate, Andrew P. Peabody, some years older than Peirce, said:

Even in our senior year we listened, not without wonder, to the reports that came up to our elevated platform of this wonderful freshman, who was going to carry off the highest mathematical honors of the University.[6]

Before he was twenty, Peirce had attracted the attention of Nathaniel Bowditch, who was translating Laplace's *Mécanique Céleste,* by pointing out an error in the proof. From then on, he assisted regularly in proof-reading the copy. There were no organized observatories in America at this time; and John Quincy Adams, in his message to

[4] Peirce married Sarah Hunt Mills in 1833: of their four sons, the eldest, James Mills Peirce, became a prominent mathematician at Harvard; Charles Sanders Peirce, first known for his work in mathematics and physics, has received belated recognition for his discoveries in logic and philosophy; Benjamin Mills Peirce, brilliant but undisciplined, died in early manhood; Herbert Henry Davis Peirce was a Cambridge businessman. In addition to his teaching, Peirce was consulting astronomer to the American Ephemeris and Nautical Almanac (1849–1867), and Superintendent of the United States Coast Survey (1867–1874), where he displayed considerable administrative skill. He served as librarian of the College library, helped form the Harvard Observatory by lecturing on Encke's Comet in 1843, and was a charter member of the famous Saturday Club, which included Agassiz, Emerson, Holmes, Henry James, Sr., and many other notable figures.

[5] James Freeman Clarke, *Autobiography, Diary, and Correspondence,* ed. Edward Everett Hale (1891), 34.

[6] Andrew P. Peabody, *Harvard Reminiscences* (Boston, 1888), 181.

Congress of 1825, had pleaded for the establishment of an American observatory so that the Western Hemisphere would not be dependent on Europe. The publication by Bowditch of Laplace's great work stimulated interest in astronomy, and soon afterwards a number of observatories were founded.

In his early years of teaching, Peirce wrote a series of elementary textbooks in the fields of Trigonometry, Sound, Geometry, Algebra, and Mechanics. All these texts were used in his own courses at Harvard as soon as they came out, but only the Trigonometry became widely popular, the failure of the others being attributed to Peirce's condensed style and innovations in notation. These textbooks had a lasting influence on the teaching of mathematics in America, however, and their innovations eventually became commonplace. So many people complained of the difficulty in understanding them, at first, that Peirce had the dubious honor of being investigated by the Harvard Committee for Examination in Mathematics. This committee eventually reported that "the textbooks were abstract and difficult, that few could comprehend them without much explanation, that Peirce's works were symmetrical and elegant, and could be perused with pleasure by the adult mind, but that books for young students should be more simple." [7]

In addition to his published textbooks and advanced treatises,[8] Peirce wrote on a wide range of topics, mostly astronomical or physical, all in an elegant mathematical style. Some of the problems he discussed were: the motion of two adjacent pendulums, the motion of a top, the fluidity and tides of Saturn's rings, orbits for Uranus, Neptune and the 1843 comet, a new form of binary arithmetic, systems of linear and associative algebra, occultations of the Pleiades, and Espy's theory of storms.[9] This list reveals the range of Peirce's thought, and the type of mathematical problem which was important in the mid-nineteenth century. American science was just coming of age, just beginning to do original, creative work that measured up

[7] Florian Cajori, *The Teaching and History of Mathematics in the United States* (Washington, 1890), 141. When a new book came off the press, Peirce would distribute proof sheets among the students, and accept the discovery of a misprint in place of a recitation. (George F. Hoar, "Harvard College Fifty-eight Years Ago," *Scribner's Magazine*, 28 [1900], 64.)

[8] Peirce's *A System of Analytic Mechanics* (1855), was praised as far as Germany as being the best book on its subject at the time. (Cajori, *op. cit.*, 144.) Toward the end of his life, one hundred copies of the *Linear Associative Algebra* were lithographed, at the insistence of Charles Peirce, who thought it represented his father's best work.

[9] Moses King, ed. *The Harvard Register*, III (1881), 29.

to European standards, and Peirce was one of the foremost leaders in this growth. One young German scholar declared in 1853 that there were no mathematicians in America, and that Peirce was the only astronomer.[10] Peirce was not himself an observer; he was inclined to think that the mathematical reduction of observations was much more important than merely looking through a telescope, and indeed, the great power of mathematical analysis was strikingly brought out by the dramatic discovery of Neptune, in which Peirce became involved.

In 1846 Leverrier, a French mathematician, seeking to explain certain perturbations of the planet Uranus, was led to calculate the approximate orbit and position of a new, trans-Uranian planet. His prediction was quickly verified by Galle in Germany, and the discovery of the new planet was everywhere hailed as a glorious triumph for Newtonian science. Peirce, however, raised a dissenting voice. He pointed out that two solutions of the initial problem were possible, consisting of two entirely distinct planetary orbits. Leverrier had worked out only one of these orbits, and the discovered planet Neptune, as it turned out, actually occupied the other orbit, and would not have been discovered at all except that by chance both predicted locations lay at that particular time in the same direction from the earth. Therefore, said Peirce, Leverrier had not in the mathematical sense discovered Neptune at all.

The ensuing controversy remained somewhat academic, since after all the planet had been found, and the theoretical preliminaries no longer mattered. Peirce insisted throughout that he did not mean to detract in the slightest from Leverrier's great and laborious calculations, and that he was convinced of the correctness of those calculations, as far as they went. The consensus of opinion by the time of Peirce's death, however, was that both men were wrong: Leverrier because he had simply made an error in his calculations which resulted in a wrong orbit; Peirce because he accepted this wrong orbit as mathematically valid, and from it derived a second solution. Leverrier had indicated the correct direction in which to look, but had predicted the wrong distance. Nevertheless, the net result of the controversy was to gain for Peirce international recognition as a mathematician and astronomer, and to increase respect for American science in European circles.

[10] Cajori, *op. cit.*, 140. Peirce, though characteristically modest, concurred in this high estimate of his genius. He was once asked what American mathematicians thought of a recent appointment to a professorship in mathematics. Peirce replied that no one had a right to express an expert opinion except himself and one former pupil, Lucien A. Wait, later professor at Cornell. (Moses King, *op. cit.*, 127.)

Peirce, with his friend Louis Agassiz as a powerful ally, devoted much time to strengthening and liberalizing the Harvard curriculum.[11] During the 1860's, while Charles Peirce and William James were students at the Lawrence Scientific School, George Herbert Palmer was attending Harvard College, which he described in unflattering terms:

Harvard education reached its lowest point during my college course. When I entered it, it was a small and local institution with 996 students in all its departments and thirty teachers in the college Faculty. . . . Nearly all its studies were prescribed, and these were chiefly Greek, Latin, and Mathematics. There was one course in Modern History, one in Philosophy, a half-course in Economics. . . . There were two or three courses in Natural Science, taught without laboratory work. All courses were taught from textbooks and by recitations. . . . All teaching was of a low order.[12]

Peirce was successful in having mathematics made an elective, first for the Senior year only, but eventually for the whole four years. One compelling motive for this action may have been his intense dislike of teaching any but the most gifted students. When mathematics was made an elective, the students stayed away in droves, and the mathematics department became known as small, difficult, and unpopular. Generations of unhappy students have recorded what they suffered at Peirce's hands, a combination of respect for his enthusiasm and genius with a total befuddlement as to what he was trying to say. Simon Newcomb, who later became a well-known astronomer, said:

As a teacher, he was very generally considered a failure. The general view he took was that it was useless for anyone to study mathematics without a special aptitude for them; he therefore gave inapt pupils no encouragement, and made no attempt to bring his instruction within their comprehension.[13]

George F. Hoar expressed a similar opinion:

He had little respect for pupils who had not a genius for mathematics, and

[11] President Norton called these two men a team of "political men in the University administration, who worked together for the advancement of the scientific interest." (Edward Waldo Emerson, *The Early Years of the Saturday Club* [1918], 101.) Likewise, President Felton's views of education "had been much influenced by long intimacy with his next-door neighbor, Benjamin Peirce." (Charles W. Eliot, *Harvard Memories* [Cambridge, 1923], 20.)

[12] George Herbert Palmer, *The Autobiography of a Philosopher* (Boston, 1930), 12–13. Also in *Contemporary American Philosophy*, ed. George P. Adams and William P. Montague, vol. I (New York, 1930), 20.

[13] Simon Newcomb, obituary notice in *Royal Society of Edinburgh, Proceedings*, XI (1880–1882), 742.

paid little respect to them.[14]

An editorial writer for the *Springfield Republican* said:

Few men could suggest more while saying so little, or stimulate so much while communicating next to nothing that was tangible and comprehensible.[15]

W. E. Byerly, a student of Peirce's who received the first Ph.D. from Harvard in 1873, had this to say:

. . . he inspired rather than taught, and one's lecture notes on his courses were apt to be chaotic. . . . Although we rarely could follow him, we certainly sat up and took notice.[16]

In view of Peirce's power to inspire and stimulate at least the more brilliant of his students, it is interesting to note what he himself considered to be of chief importance in education:

Enthusiasm, which is the highest element of successful instruction, can best be imparted nearest the fountainhead, where the springs of knowledge flow purest, and where the waters are undiluted by the weakening influence of text book literature.[17]

Peirce worked hard at his studies, and expected his students to do the same.   He maintained his originality of thought by trying to work out a new problem in his own way, before turning to standard works on the subject, and whatever question was under consideration, striving to regard it as a particular case of some more comprehensive theorem.   The one thing he distrusted most was routine method; he strove constantly to further fresh and original thinking, sometimes to the point where he failed to meet his students on any common ground.   As Oliver Wendell Holmes put it:

If a question interested him, he would praise the questioner, and answer it in a way, giving his own interpretation to the question.   If he did not like the form of the student's question, or the manner in which it was asked,

---

[14] George F. Hoar, "Harvard College Fifty-eight Years Ago," *Scribner's Magazine*, 28 (1900), 64.

[15] *Benjamin Peirce, A Memorial Collection*, ed. Moses King (Cambridge, 1881), containing obituaries from the *American Journal of Science* (Nov. 1880); *The Springfield Republican* (Oct. 23, 1880); *Woman's Journal* (Oct. 23, 1880); *Nation* (Oct. 14, 1880); and the *Boston Daily Advertiser* (Oct. 7, 1880).

[16] W. E. Byerly, in *Benjamin Peirce 1809–1880*, ed. R. C. Archibald (Oberlin, Ohio, 1925), 5.   This memorial, also printed in the *American Mathematical Monthly* (1925), contains a nearly complete bibliography, a list of Peirce's writings, and reminiscences by Charles W. Eliot, A. Lawrence Lowell, and W. E. Byerly.

[17] Benjamin Peirce, "The Intellectual Organization of Harvard University," *The Harvard Register*, I (1880), 77.

he would not answer it at all. . . .[18]

Peirce advocated more research and less teaching; the instructor should devote only two hours a day or less to formal teaching, so as to be free for new investigations. He thought the system of required courses was complicated, and prevented the students from studying under the best teachers, or learning, through the use of original memoirs, about the great investigations which were for him the life of the intellect.

The system that is adapted principally to compel attention to study is comparatively unfruitful, and fails to promote sound and original scholarship. As long as the instructions are limited to formal class teaching, the College must remain a higher school, and cannot deserve the name of University.[19]

In his later years, Peirce turned more and more to working with brilliant younger men, tutoring them and setting them a stimulating example. He had an especial fondness for finding comparative unknowns whose work had been overlooked.

The Civil War, which began when Peirce was fifty-two, left little apparent trace in his writings. He was at first a pro-slavery Democrat, and had many close friends in the South. One of his students, indicted for attempting to rescue a fugitive slave, told Peirce that if he were imprisoned, he would at least have time to read Laplace's treatise. Peirce replied ironically: " In that case, I sincerely wish you may be." [20] After the fall of Fort Sumter, however, Peirce became a strong Union supporter.[21]

[18] Oliver Wendell Holmes, Medical Essays, vol. IX, *The Works of Oliver Wendell Holmes*, Standard Library Edition (Boston, 1892), 147. Holmes also wrote a poem lauding the continued youth of the class of 1829, with the refrain " We're twenty! We're twenty! ", of which one verse refers to Peirce:

> That boy with the grave mathematical look
> Made believe he had written a wonderful book,
> And the Royal Society thought it was true!
> So they chose him right in; a good joke it was, too.

[19] Benjamin Peirce, *The Harvard Register*, I, 77.

[20] Florian Cajori, *op. cit.*, 143.

[21] Edward W. Emerson, *The Early Years of the Saturday Club* (1918), 254. Peirce's daughter remembered seeing Agassiz and her father talking over some bad news from the front, tears running down their cheeks (*ibid.*, 102). His political and social views are chiefly contained in " The National Importance of Social Science in the United States," *Documents of the American Social Science Association* (Boston, Dec. 1867), where Peirce said: " Regardless of individual as well as popular prejudice, we make truth our only aim. We search the secrets of the nation's good in the depths of experience, and our end is reached when we have

Peirce maintained throughout his life a keen interest in the arts, and in his younger days enjoyed acting in private theatricals and charades, tending to be too violent and impetuous in his acting, but always original. The Peirce and Agassiz families, friends and neighbors, would often take a carriage across the river to Boston, to see Warren at the Museum, Booth at the Boston Theatre, or perhaps to hear Fanny Kemble.[22] Peirce was always among the first to read a new poem or novel, or to attend a new opera.[23] His judgment was considered to be keen, and the following comment on the translation of poetry is perhaps typical of his literary style:

> It supposes the easy control of two languages, the full and delicate perception of the flavour of the words in both, and of the various effects of verbal combinations, as well as an ear tuned to the melodies of versification of two different peoples. The mind of the translator must consent to be formed into the mould of its original, to acquire his forms of speech, his rhetorical modulation and his musical cadence, to see with his perception and feel with his emotion.[24]

As might be expected, Peirce enjoyed chess, cards, and all sorts of intellectual puzzles. At one time he played chess every noon with Andrew Peabody, when they were teaching a class jointly, and Peabody was happy to recall an occasional victory.[25] There was an apocryphal legend among the students, however, to the effect that when Peirce played cards with his mathematical sons, no one ever actually played out a hand. Each mathematician would study his

---

ascertained the inviolable laws of human nature." Peirce held that we must guard against corrupt politics by having an enlightened electorate, and since the politicians themselves cannot be trusted to educate the people, it is up to the schools, which "should teach the children that their first duty and highest privilege is to become good citizens." Good citizens are those who are content with the station in life for which they are best fitted, and do not strive fruitlessly for power or popularity.

[22] Edward W. Emerson, *op. cit.*, 102.

[23] The extent of Peirce's reading outside the field of mathematics cannot be determined, for whatever opinions he encountered became dominated by his own thinking. He referred with respect to the opinions of Aristotle and Seneca on comets, and used Comte's three stages of science as a starting point for his own evolutionary theories. He mentioned the Bible often, but became increasingly free in his interpretation of it; he was aware of the archeological discoveries being made in Palestine, and referred to such scientists as Kepler, Galileo, Newton, Lamarck, Darwin, Cuvier, and Agassiz, but only in a general and conventional way.

[24] Unpublished note in Benjamin Peirce collection, American Academy of Arts and Sciences, Boston.

[25] Andrew P. Peabody, *op. cit.*, 185.

cards, make some calculations based on the theory of probabilities, and pay the winner.[26]

II

At the time Darwin's *Origin of Species* was published, Peirce was fifty, and though his close friend, Louis Agassiz, was a leading opponent of the Darwinian thesis, Peirce himself did not take any prominent part in the controversy, regarding it as primarily a dispute among naturalists. On the other hand, Peirce accepted wholeheartedly the larger evolutionary theories, and Laplace's Nebular Hypothesis became the basis of his systematic thinking. He held that even those, like Louis Agassiz, who rejected Darwin's hypothesis, had nevertheless been "profound believers in the laws of the succession of species . . . . The difference of doctrine is one of form rather than one of substance." [27] Peirce went on to point out that Darwin's teaching was not to be confused with Darwinism, just as Plato's teaching is not the same thing as Platonism. The disciples of Darwin would do better to go straight to the facts and find out for themselves, as Darwin did, rather than preach from his text.

The chief fault in the theory of evolution, Peirce said, is that it deifies a created power:

Is there not reason to apprehend that it is placing this very evolution upon the throne which can be occupied by no created power or any metaphysical abstraction? The force of evolution is as brute and unconscious as that of fire; there is no more royalty in it than in the log which Jupiter threw down to the frogs. In its descent it has made a frightful splash in the pool of science; but the world will recover from it, as it did from the dangerous doctrine of the earth's motion.[28]

God is immanent in the world, sustaining it from day to day, and evolution, a created power which therefore still necessitates a Creator, is simply the mode in which he appears to our eyes. Furthermore, he is a lawful God, represented to us by unchanging natural laws, and hence, argued Peirce, there could be no such thing as a miracle. Only a heathen deity who rejoiced in lawlessness would operate by

[26] Edward Emerson, *op. cit.*, 102. Another apocryphal legend was that Peirce inscribed all his books: "Who steals my Peirce steals trash." Oliver Wendell Holmes (*op. cit.*, 147) recorded the story that Peirce considered Poisson's famous *Théorie du Calcul des Probabilités* to have "a distinct Poissonish, or fishy flavor running through the whole of it."

[27] Benjamin Peirce, *Ideality in the Physical Sciences* (Boston, 1881), ed. James Mills Peirce, 135. This posthumous work is the chief source of Peirce's philosophical views.

[28] *Ibid.*, 34.

breaking the law of continuity.[29]   God proclaims himself through the rule, not through the exception; through the silent law of gravitation, not through the whirlwind or the earthquake, except insofar as these latter phenomena are also natural occurrences.   Because God has meant his eternal plan to be carried out through the laws of evolution, and has meant man to learn that plan by studying the universe, such uniformity of law is the only possible expression of God's eternal meaning.   If the universe were destitute of strict logical connection, it would be unintelligible, and hence fail to express God's will.

Peirce was a deeply religious man, with a strong emotional allegiance to certain simple theistic tenets.   Though he paid no attention to the debates of the various sects, he clung to the fundamental doctrine of a personal, loving God, to whom he made frequent reference in even his most technical books and papers.   In particular, he felt that there were certain mysteries in philosophy which were beyond the reach of science, a realm of the unknowable:

Man s speculations should be subdued from all rashness and extravagance in the immediate presence of the Creator.   And a wise philosophy will beware lest it strengthen the arms of atheism, by venturing too boldly into so remote and obscure a field of speculation as that of the mode of creation which was adopted by the Divine Geometer.[30]

Peirce argued that the Bible was necessary to science, to assure us that we were not merely bestowing an arbitrary and false structure upon a structureless chaos of atoms:

Without the faith in the Great First Cause which is derived from the Sacred Writings, the world could have taken but few steps in Science and would

[29] Being omnipotent, God did not need to operate in space and time, and the universe was not to be thought of as a self-operating machine whose creation had taken place at some fixed time.   "With him there is nothing distant: all objects, celestial and terrestrial, are in immediate proximity, and the past and the future are forever present.   Deity does not exist in time and space; but they are in him. . . ."   (*Ibid.*, 55.)

[30] Benjamin Peirce, quoted in an obituary in the *Nation* (Oct. 14, 1880).   Peirce often called upon the omnipotence of God as a premise which was not to be denied.   He held perpetual motion to be impossible, for example, because " it would have proved destructive to human belief in the spiritual origin of force, and the necessity of a First Cause superior to matter, and would have subjected the grand plans of Divine benevolence to the will and caprice of man."   (*Ideality in the Physical Sciences*, 32.)   In the same way, Peirce proved the doctrine that all possible things exist somewhere in the universe.   He argued that actuality was simply God's thought, and for God not to think of all possible things would be a limitation of His power.

have been likely to have remained forever in intellectual darkness.[31]

He gradually modified his position, however, as to the literal *truth* of the Biblical cosmology. At one time, Peirce held that the Biblical version of the Creation flatly contradicted the findings of science, that neither view was capable of being essentially modified, and that the Bible was "incomparably the higher authority, and must be sustained whatever science may report to the contrary." [32] He then went on to offer his solution, in a form not uncommon at that time, of the apparent dilemma. The scientist is entirely correct in the deductions he draws from the evidence before him—but there is nothing to prevent God from having created that evidence only yesterday! God could have created the earth in the year 4004 B.C., for example, complete with fossils, rock strata, archeological ruins, glacier deposits, and cave drawings, so that scientists studying this body of evidence could validly infer that the earth has had a long evolutionary history.

Such an attempt at reconciliation reveals the important fact that Peirce, with his training in science, could not reject outright the evidence being presented on the side of science, however much he would have liked to do so. Nor could he long cling to the theory that God had deliberately deceived his children, however pious the reason for deception might be. So in 1853 Peirce advanced another theory, namely that science and the Bible have equal authority, but in different spheres:

We acknowledge . . . that science has no authority to interfere with the Scriptures and perplex the Holy Writ with forced and impossible constructions of language. This admission does not derogate from the dignity of science; and we claim that the sanctity of the Bible is equally undisturbed by the denial that it was endowed with authority over the truths of physical science.[33]

[31] Undated manuscript entitled "Remarks to Middlesex Teachers' Association," in Benjamin Peirce collection, American Academy of Arts and Sciences, Boston. Peirce's religious feeling also overflowed into his class lectures and into his books. He would break off a demonstration in higher mathematics to prove to his astonished class the existence of God: "Gentlemen, as we study the universe we see everywhere the most tremendous manifestations of force. In our own experience we know of but one source of force, namely will. How then can we help regarding the forces we see in nature as due to the will of some omnipresent, omnipotent being? Gentlemen, there must be a God!" (W. E. Byerly, cf. note 16.)

[32] Undated manuscript entitled "Address to Massachusetts Teachers' Association," in Benjamin Peirce collection.

[33] *Address of Professor Benjamin Peirce on retiring from the presidency of the American Association for the Advancement of Science* (1853), 14. Extracts from this speech are found in Edward Waldo Emerson, *The Early Years of the Saturday Club* (1918), 105.

Under such a partition of knowledge into two non-overlapping realms, Peirce now denounced as " a monstrous absurdity " any conflict between science and religion:

How can there be a more faithless species of infidelity, than to believe that the Deity has written his word upon the material universe and a contradiction of it in the Gospel? [34]

Finally, in the last year of his life, Peirce undertook a detailed defense of the first chapter of Genesis, not as literal truth, but as a sort of poetic myth or pre-scientific account of the essential steps of the Creation, leaving man to fill in the details. Peirce listed the various sources of power or energy, declaring each in turn to be a created agent of God: 1) physical force, under the name of light; 2) the heavenly firmament, home of the regulating spiritual forces; 3) the infinite below, including the earth and its " exhaustless power of development "; 4) the infinite above, containing sun, moon, and stars, hence the source of illumination and time; 5) all created plants, animals, and man; 6) the unity, design, and harmony to be found throughout the universe. " It assures us that facts and laws are born of God; that in all fact there is law, and that the law is ascertained by the study of the fact." As to the brevity of the Mosaic creation and its apparent contradiction of the long evolutionary process, Peirce said only that God did not create in time, that his power to create must not be limited by restriction to a temporal order. Peirce's final view was that the first chapter of Genesis " may not be the revelation of an actual past, but it teaches where that revelation is to be found . . .," [35] a position considerably removed from his early insistence that the Bible was " incomparably the higher authority."

In setting forth the evolutionary pattern of the material universe, Peirce maintained that the laws of death and decay could not be extended to the spiritual realm. His main argument was that spiritual individuals, unlike physical individuals, could not be interchanged:

In the material world one atom can replace another without prejudice to the system. Tree can ever be substituted for tree, and beast for beast, each in its kind; so that species is everything, and individual nothing. . . . The spiritual individual is everything. The destruction of any soul would be an irreparable loss; nothing can be conceived more utterly at variance with the harmony of creation. It is an absolute impossibility. . . . [36]

[34] *Ibid.*, 11.
[35] *Ideality in the Physical Sciences*, 50.
[36] *Ibid.*, 187.

For the same reason, Peirce rejected the mystical ideal of spiritual release from the meshes of particular existence. The last thing he wanted was union with God, if that would mean loss of individuality; and therefore matter was an integral part of each personality, rather than a hindrance:

Were the communion between soul and soul direct and immediate, there would be no protection for thought; each man would take full possession of the thoughts of every other man, and there would be no such thing as personality and individuality. The body is needed to hold souls apart and to preserve their independence, as well as for conversation and mutual sympathy. Hence body and matter are essential to man's true existence. Without them, he must, as is supposed in the Chinese theology, be instantly absorbed into the infinite spirit. In this case, creation would be a false and unmeaning tragedy.[37]

A material body is as necessary in the next world as in this. Experience indicates that there are enough individuated souls here on earth to meet the demands of this life, but presumably in the next life there will be many more individuals required. Where will they come from? Mostly, Peirce thought, from other planets and stellar systems, where, for all we know, there are beings in a state of development far beyond our own, in whose more abundant life we may be permitted to share. Since our bodies are admirably fitted to our souls, a good man would take on a bigger and healthier body in the next life, and men like Shakespeare could be recognized at sight by their stature and nobility. Sin was not for Peirce a very serious offense, merely a violation of some material or spiritual law, and punishable by a temporary deformity of the new body, until the soul truly repents.

Thus the immutable law of evolution would lead us steadily upward, through life after life, in which we would acquire new sensory organs, new ways of experiencing things, and new possibilities of discovery and research. We could hope to transcend such minor limitations as the flickering, unstable atmosphere through which all astronomers must now make their observations, and perhaps take a ride on Halley's comet, which traverses the orbits of all the planets, and thus go on a grand tour of the solar system.[38] These speculations are important chiefly because Peirce held them to be a logical extension of the doctrine of evolution. If there is a grand, ordered sweep from the primal nebula up to today's complex yet intelligible

[37] *Ibid.*, 184.
[38] *Ibid.*, 187ff.

world, and if spiritual individuals are never destroyed, then Peirce could well look forward to the continuation of evolutionary processes in future lives, a panorama of infinite scientific research and achievement in which " the ultimate limits to which future perception and education may advance is possibly a mystery transcending the powers of research even of the archangels." [39]

Peirce held to a clear dualism between mind and matter, asserting that conscious life is different in kind from unconscious life, and could not possibly evolve from it.   Though he did not deal in any specific way with the problem of interaction between mind and matter, Peirce rejected both idealism and materialism as alternative solutions.   The mind of man could not have created the whole universe, he said, and then have shrunk to its present limited capacity. Likewise, for the conscious to have evolved out of the unconscious was to him inconceivable, for " it seems to be a gross violation of the principle of the necessity of an adequate cause for the production of an effect." [40]   This basic dualism, which involved a parallel evolutionary process in each realm, was supported by two principles: 1) the work done by the body is exactly equivalent to the material used up in metabolism, proving that the mind does no work in the scientific sense, and exerts no physical influence on the body; 2) ". . . when a man wills, his brain is heated, and his arms and feet obey the intention of his will; they have no innate power of resistance.   This is the law of harmonious action.   It is sufficient to itself and to all the demands of healthy work and inquiry." [41]

These two principles of power and harmony were considered by Peirce to be " pre-established," not to be regarded by even the boldest evolutionist as mere results of the process of evolution itself.   This Leibnizian parallelism was apparently meant to allow scope to free will, by freeing man from direct contact with the determined, mechanical universe of physics and astronomy.   On the other hand, Peirce often asserted that the intellect was bound by laws too, in the sense that perfect mathematical knowledge meant perfect harmony with the determined physical universe, and that the only freedom possible was the freedom to make errors or to fall short of the ideal of correct thinking:

Man is forced to the discovery of regions of the universe whence the arbitrary is banished, and where there remains no evidence of choice, or consciousness

[39] *Ibid.*, 192.
[40] *Ibid.*, 31.
[41] *Ibid.*, 74.

associated with power. . . . Intellect has its laws, which are as undeviating as those of the physical world. Man's conceit, stupidity, and obstinacy cannot resist them. . . .[42]

Peirce never felt any contradiction between the assertion of free will on the one hand, and a universe controlled by destiny after a strict mathematical model on the other hand. For him, this particular mathematical universe did not involve blind fatalism—it was friendly to man, and by virtue of its pre-established harmony took care of the wants of man. Its rigid, predictable unfolding fulfilled the unchanging will of God and proved his wisdom. Peirce's favorite example was the great beds of coal, laid down eons before the coming of man, certainly not exerting the slightest influence upon his coming or development, and yet obviously laid down all the time just for man's use. An inanimate universe could not do this unaided, said Peirce, hence the God whose will is thus expressed must be a God of love and mercy.

Man's particular relation to the universe is that of observer of the determined, evolutionary unfolding of its history. Peirce held that the universe was completely knowable, in the sense that man could, given enough time, find out each law and process. Questions about the origin of the laws themselves, of course, rested in the inscrutable will of God.[43]

In an intelligible world, an intellect! What is either without the other? Take away the world and what is to become of the owner of the intellect? . . . And if it were not for the intellect, the intelligible world would be a vain show, which no believing heart would attribute to the author of all good. . . . Intellect is only a possession, an attribute, it is less than faith, less than love; but it belongs to the same soul, which having higher capacities of faith and love, was saved by infinite love. The soul of love knows the soul of man and his wants, and cannot fail to supply the intellectual food which he needs.[44]

Peirce thus placed a certain emphasis on the intellect as the instrument of problem-solving and of spiritual growth. In one of his best passages he pictured the evolutionary growth of knowledge from subjective relativism to objective truth:

[42] *Ibid.*, 42. "A man can tell a lie, and thereby demonstrate his feebleness; the pagan god can deceive, because he is weak and limited. But our God, for the reason of his infinite strength and of his eternal omniscience, must forever coincide with himself. Otherwise, instead of being an infinite and necessary reality, he would be an infinite impossibility. At one and the same instant, he would be and not be God." (*Ibid.*, 184.)

[43] Unpublished notes, Benjamin Peirce collection.

[44] *Ideality in the Physical Sciences*, 38.

Each observer starts from his own peculiar position, which may be far removed from others. In the dim and uncertain light, he pursues crude theories, imbued with the minimum of fact and the maximum of fancy. He is easily diverted from his course by some delusive *ignis fatuus* or some glittering generality. When the causes are obscure and the visible agents fail, he constructs fairies and genii, demons and gods, to work out the mysteries which he perceived, but cannot understand.[45]

Peirce gave various practical examples of this relativism of knowledge. Early geologists who lived on level plains would naturally favor the sedimentary theory of rock formation, while geologists who lived in mountainous country, perhaps with volcanos around, would tend to favor the igneous theory. Today we see that both these theories were but partial truths, and the new and broader theory uses impartially the facts amassed by both sides in their historic controversy. In Egypt, the formless, life-giving inundations of the Nile would naturally suggest to the early cosmologists the concept of Chaos as the mother of all things; whereas in the far northern countries, the hard struggle for existence and the destruction of rocks by frost and sun would suggest a battle of the gods. Peirce found a common pattern in nearly all ancient cosmologies—that of a primeval egg hatching and growing into a full-fledged universe. The elements of these early views were what Peirce called Chaos and Ideality, standing silent and immovable like the sphinx by the pyramid, and the cosmos resulted when to these two, imperturbable meditation and inactive mass, was added the third necessary element, Motion. These steps of the primitive cosmologies corresponded with the steps of actual evolution, not because the ancients had any special scientific knowledge, but because they had formed the conclusions of " a sound philosophy, which is ever consistent with itself and with undying truth." [46]

Another factor that slowed up the progress of problem-solving man, was the subjective element inherent in all our contact with the world, the channeling of our knowledge through the senses:

A fact is not a sound, it is not a star. It is sound heard by the ear; it is a star seen by the eye. In the simplest case, it is the spiritual recognition of material existence. One moiety of it may be of the earth, earthy; but the other moiety is essentially mental and dependent upon the constitution of mind.[47]

By this Peirce meant that man reads something of himself into

[45] *Ibid.*, 43ff.
[46] *Ibid.*, 12.
[47] *Ibid.*, 25.

nature, as when he sees pictures in cloud shapes, or faces in a glowing fire. The beginnings of history are full of many such subjective fancies, leading to superstition, myth, and wild guesses about the nature of things. The ancients looked at the stars overhead, and formed them into bears, dogs, hunters, and heroes.

Peirce escaped both the relativity of the observer and the subjectivity of sense-knowledge by appealing to the power of the human mind, and to the belief that the universe was single, unified, and capable of reduction to an overall theory. He pointed out that a dog, with senses keener than our own, takes no part in man's spiritual or intellectual life; whereas a person like Laura Bridgman, with very limited sense-experience, lived in a spiritual universe as full of thought and knowledge as our own. The power of reason was such that man could attain to the knowledge of facts not yet perceived, and even of facts which could not be perceived. Such things as the mathematical proof of the existence of the not-yet-observed planet Neptune, or of light waves in the emptiness of outer space, were facts for Peirce, "pictures on the imagination."

Peirce's chief faith was in the ultimate agreement of all observers as to the laws of nature, however much they may differ when they first began to speculate. The ancients observed the Pleiades, for example, and composed pretty myths about the origin of the star cluster. Modern science has determined that the stars in question form a family related by a common stellar movement. This discovery Peirce held to be an objective fact, with nothing of human fancy in it, which would be true even if no humans were alive to observe the stars. Thus in the very stronghold of astrology, where human subjective interpretation was once at a maximum, there now appears indubitable evidence of intellectual order.

The conclusion in every department of science is essentially the same. Whatever may have been the play of fancy, or the delusion of superstition, or the allurement of profit, at the outset, the end has ever been a congregation of facts, organized under law, and disciplined by geometry.[48]

---

[48] The fact that we could not know God directly was no difficulty for Peirce: "The divine image, photographed upon the soul of man from the center of light, is everywhere reflected from the works of creation. . . . How could it be otherwise? Is it not a vagary of philosophy which erects one part of creation, and that the least, into the authorship of the whole?—which ignores the Deity, because he is materially invisible except in his works, wherein is his only possible mode of manifestation? We might better assert that the star, which is only known by its light, consists of mere rays. . . ." (Quoted in Merle Curti, *The Growth of American Thought* [New York, 1943], 297.)

There was thus for Peirce an intimate relation between the structure of the mind—mathematics—and the structure of the universe—ideality. The reduction of complicated and contradictory occurrences to a single inclusive law was always ultimately possible, and led to an increase in spiritual power and comprehension. Thus, in the field of religion, the plurality of oriental and classical gods gradually gave way to the deeper truth of the single Christian God.

. . . what was the perpetual intercourse between gods and men but the perception by vivid minds of the amazing intellectuality inwrought into the unconscious material world? Remove the plurality of the deities, and the absurdities vanish; the myth is transformed into a glorious truth. . . .[49]

In this way, every branch of human knowledge, beginning in superstition, myth, and illusion, ended in rigid law, mathematical discipline, and ideal structure. Law and structure was not solely a product of the scientist's mind, on the contrary, the physical universe was impregnated with ideal structure, waiting for the perceptive observer to actualize it.

When the sculptor develops his Apollo or his Venus from the quarried marble, it is his own creation, and has his image stamped upon it; but the truth which the man of science extracts has an absolute character of its own, which no power of genius can transform, and which is neither attributable to accident nor born of human parentage.[50]

The correspondence between knowledge and reality was complete in both directions. Not only was every part of the physical universe expressible in terms of relatively simple mathematical laws, but every logically consistent mathematical system necessarily had its expression somewhere in nature. Peirce's favorite illustration was that of the Greeks studying the properties of the conic sections as pure geometry, only to have Kepler, centuries later, find those same conic sections reproduced in the various orbits of the solar system. Likewise, the study of complex numbers with all their mysterious properties proved to have extremely practical applications in the study of alternating currents. This far-reaching realistic faith was thus a vindication of all theoretical and abstract studies, on the ground that if an intellectual system were internally consistent and possible, God, whose power to think all possible things could not be denied, must already have actualized that system.

Wild as are the flights of unchained fancy, extravagant and even monstrous as are the conceptions of unbridled imagination, we have reason to believe

[49] *Ibid.*, 20.
[50] *Ibid.*, 26.

that there is no human thought, capable of physical manifestation and consistent with the stability of the material world, which cannot be found incarnated in Nature.[51]

It was in this spirit that Peirce worked out his *Linear Associative Algebra,* sketching out hundreds of possible algebraic systems, of which only two or three had yet found any practical applications.

III

The intimate relation in Peirce's philosophy between the structure of thought and the structure of the physical universe meant that the parallel developments in the realms of matter and spirit formed a single cosmology, a vast orderly cosmos infused with ideality. The simplicity of the primal chaos is gradually replaced by the simplicity of the mathematical laws which express its orderly unfolding, so that in a sense nothing changes, though there is a progressive elevation from material to spiritual simplicity, as man moves steadily closer to the God who is at the heart of the whole.

The theological stage becomes perfect when all the gods are reduced to one God; the metaphysical stage is perfect when all the abstractions are comprehended in the one abstraction of Nature; the positive stage will be perfect when all facts are resolved into one fact.[52]

Far from using Comte's formula in a positivistic way, Peirce completed the circle by identifying the ultimate fact with God himself, on the ground that no other entity could contain all the infinite complexity that must go into it.

In general, Peirce's system of evolution was based on the Nebular Theory, and his detailed treatment of its elements shows the influence of his mathematical researches:

1) *Chaos* had for Peirce a definite mathematical meaning—that set of initial conditions from which, under the differential equations of dynamics, nothing followed. It was the initial uniform distribution of matter and energy throughout all space, a sort of mist without heat, light, collision of particles, change of density, or useful energy of any sort.[53]

2) *Matter* was in itself inert, and without powers or properties except that of receiving and retaining any amount of impressed mechanical force. Matter could not originate force, or modify any force applied to it; only in this way could physical bodies be faithful

[51] *Ibid.,* 29.
[52] *Ibid.,* 11.
[53] *Ibid.,* 58.

records of the forces acting upon them.[54]   In precisely the same way, the human body was inert, and incapable of resisting the human will, or else it could not be a trustworthy medium of communication between souls:

Matter must transmit thought precisely as it is received, without suspicion of transformation. It must be competent to receive all forms of thought, and incapable of resistance to any.[55]

3) *Force* was for Peirce the great wonder worker, which gave the universe all its dynamic properties, proved the existence of God, and made the world a living, friendly place. Since man can by conscious effort " exert force " and move his body, he concludes by analogy that all force has a spiritual origin. Force is in itself invisible, of course, and known only through its effects on matter.

4) *Motion* is the chief characteristic of the universe, then, because it is the sole clue to the presence of both force and matter, and because without motion there would be no events at all. The act of creation is really the creation of motion. " The earth would have remained without form, and void, if the Spirit of God had not first *moved* upon the face of the waters." [56]

Motion is the divine energy of creation; it signifies change and phenomena, and the genesis of the powers of evolution, with the controlling, planning, and warring gods. How this creative energy could itself have been born is of all mysteries the most incomprehensible. It is the inevitable impossibility inherent in any speculation which would develop everything out of nothing.[57]

5) *Equilibrium* of forces is an important element of any Newtonian system. In inorganic systems, a balance of forces produces no change in motion, whereas unstable equilibrium results in an acceleration. The striking thing about organic or living systems, Peirce

[54] A similar view of the nature of matter is found in an article by Lovering in *The Cambridge Miscellany of Mathematics, Physics, and Astronomy* (Cambridge, No. 1, April 1842, 34. This short-lived journal was edited by Peirce. Lovering wrote: " If we analyze our knowledge of matter, we shall find it to be nothing more than a record of the laws, according to which certain forces, proceeding from various centers, act upon each other. The observation and classification of these forces mark the progress of science. None of our senses ever go behind these forces, and are unable to answer the question, whether they have a substantial basis, or proceed simply from an ideal center. This is all that Berkeley, Reid, and other skilful metaphysicians could mean in denying the existence of matter."

[55] *Ideality*, 185.

[56] Benjamin Peirce, *A System of Analytic Mechanics*, 1.

[57] *Ideality*, 43.

held, was just their ability to remain in unstable equilibrium without destructive motion taking place.

Given the primal chaos with its homogeneous distribution of matter and energy, Peirce pointed out that the slightest speck of discontinuity would suffice to start nebular evolution, by providing a focus for gravitational attraction. More and more particles would be attracted to a common center, internal pressures would appear, heat would be generated, and radiant energy released. The constantly shrinking gas cloud would begin to revolve, to throw off rings of matter, and to crystallize out into suns and planets, which would then continue on their weary path of evolution.

Peirce likened this process to a pendulum free to move in a complete circle, precariously balanced at the highest point of its swing. What would now happen if an angel gave the pendulum an *infinitely small* push? For an infinitely long time, there would be no visible result, until finally, when the motion became visible, the pendulum would swing through its complete circle in a relatively short time, and appear to come to rest. In reality, however, it would be slowly approaching its point of rest, taking another infinity of time to reach it. Finally, since the pendulum still possessed its infinitesimal increment of extra energy, it would invisibly pass its equilibrium point, and the cycle would start over again, to be repeated again and again without end.

Hence, reasoned Peirce, God need only exert one infinitely small force somewhere in the primeval chaos, which would then endure without apparent change for an infinitely long time. Suddenly, in a period that would seem long to our finite calendars, but only a tick of the clock of eternity, the chaos would develop into a nebula, the nebula would condense into stars and planets, on some of which life would flash into momentary existence. In the merest blink of the cosmic eye, the suns would be dead, all energy diffused, and all creation would slowly and invisibly return to its primal state, destined to repeat the entire process, once the original impetus introduced by God had travelled its long road home.

Curiously enough, Peirce never carried his speculations to the point of considering this infinite repetition of the evolutionary process, nor did he adopt the alternative view that the cosmic unfolding would come to a halt because of the action of entropy. The action of Peirce's pendulum requires that the original energy, however small, imparted to it must be preserved not only in quantity but also in quality or form. If part of the energy goes into warming the pivot of the pendulum, or any other frictional loss, then its action will ultimately come to a halt.   Peirce mentioned the subject only once:

. . . there are paths of work which cannot be retraced, and in which there is an absorption of energy which cannot be recovered.   If this be so, there is energy that is practically lost; or, in other words, there is a continual diminution of the available energy of the physical world.[58]

If Peirce accepted this view at all, which seems unlikely in view of his belief that man's immortal soul requires at all times a material body to preserve his individuality, he must have believed that after all the plans of God for men would be carried out in a *finite* time:

The law of progress will not be suddenly interrupted; it cannot cease without previous indication and some evident diminution in the rate of advance. We have a just and abiding faith that our planet will endure for the development of our children and our children's children, to the latest generation.[59]

Peirce held that there was a parallel evolution in the realm of mind, the growth of a great organized system of knowledge about the universe, ultimately reducible to a single set of postulates.   Peirce not only had a magnificent vision of the unification of all the sciences, but he saw clearly the nature of the deductive system which must underlie such unification.   For him, a theory was simply the train of necessary consequences flowing from a given set of assumptions; hence the theory stands or falls according to its logical structure alone.   Peirce's realism appears in his profound conviction that consistent postulate systems are not empty, but are found sooner or later to correspond to physical reality.   In this way even the most abstract science is a revelation of God's ordered plan.   Science is the highest form of worship of God, a growing and evolving worship, as nature is itself an evolving and growing expression of God.

Peirce divided science into four divisions, ranged according to a progressive increase in deductive structure:

1) *History* is the collection of all facts in a given discipline.

2) *Natural history* is the reduction of history to *necessary* facts.

3) *Natural philosophy* is the reduction of natural history to the least number of necessary facts, that is, to a set of independent postulates.

4) *Mathematics,* finally, is the set of necessary inferences from the postulates, the deductive system that follows once the postulates are given.   The task of philosophy is complete when the observed

[58] *Ibid.,* 175.
[59] *Ibid.,* 181.

facts—the history—coincide throughout with the theoretical system of deductions—the mathematics.[60]

The history of astronomy is an excellent illustration of these four categories. Tycho Brahe amassed a great number of observations and empirical tables upon the motions of the planets, but had no satisfactory theory to explain those motions. Kepler reduced this "history" to a "natural history" by means of his famous three laws of motion. In another domain, Galileo reduced the history of falling objects on the earth to a natural history, by means of his laws of dynamics. Newton combined these various natural histories into a single natural philosophy, by formulating a truly universal law of gravitation. The purely mathematical deductions from this one fundamental law give us a theoretical map or image of the planetary system, and the great achievement of the nineteenth century was to prove that this theoretical map corresponded almost exactly with the real physical world. Peirce thought, along with many of his contemporaries, that the map did correspond exactly, that Newton's theoretical world *was* the world in which we live. Hence Peirce could assert with confidence that, in the field of astronomy, the main job of science was finished.

Mathematics for Peirce always meant strictly organized facts; facts without organization were nothing but curious and trivial data. "Isolated fact . . . can be committed to memory and repeated like gossip, but it overloads the intellect like green fruit in the stomach."[61] Facts combined into formulas and formulas into theory penetrate the whole domain of physical science,[62] clarifying its nature and structure, reflecting its reality.

Once established by luck and by hard work, a theory becomes a practical working device whereby to obtain new facts and new information about nature, but the theory is not itself a fact to be believed or disbelieved:

[60] Benjamin Peirce collection, unpublished manuscript.

[61] *Ibid.* In another unpublished letter, Peirce wrote: "The mathematics are an organized system of ideas, which were, however, born of facts. . . . You will perceive that my ideas of the mathematics are more comprehensive than those which are currently adopted, and that I do not restrict them to the sciences which are technically known as such. . . . I feel confident that we are sooner or later to have new kinds of mathematics and very different from those which have been hitherto developed."

[62] Peirce never held that the process of extracting theory out of a set of given facts was an automatic one, or even a simple act of intelligence. In most mathematical work, the formulation of a new theory is a genuine creative act, " . . . the intellectual result of profound thought, enduring research, and fruitful imagination."

Astronomers are frequently asked whether they believe the nebular theory. The question is logically preposterous. An hypothesis may be believed or disbelieved; but a theory is an organized system of observed phenomena, which may be accepted as good and complete, or discarded on account of its defects, but of which belief or disbelief cannot properly be predicated.[63]

The consistent goal of Peirce's philosophy is revealed in his doctrine that science simply makes actual and explicit the intelligible structure placed in the universe by God. This structure, expressible in a few differential equations, exhibits a grand cosmological scheme, unfolding from the primeval chaos, featureless and uniform, into the whole complex sequence of world events, within which man appears with his rude theories and curious beliefs, but possessed of an irreplaceable, immortal soul. The evolution of the material universe is blind, involving nothing but inert atoms thrust here and there by mechanical forces, and yet, through the basic pre-established harmony worked into it by God, it performs two essential functions. First, it underlies and sustains the spiritual universe, by making every provision for the survival and comfort of man, long before he appears on the scene. Second, the nebula unfolds in an *intelligible* fashion, so that man can look at the universe and gradually learn all the details of God's will, and thereby fulfill his glorious destiny.

It was Peirce's deepest conviction that we live in a universe that is both friendly and knowable. That fact was for him the ultimate proof of God's love for man, just as the devotion and patience of scientists was the ultimate proof of man's love for God.

---

[63] *Ideality*, 51. Peirce summarized the whole process of mathematical science as follows: "Observation supplies fact. Induction ascends from fact to law. Deduction, applying the pure logic of mathematics, reverses the process and descends from law to fact. The facts of observation are liable to the uncertainties and inaccuracies of the human senses; and the first inductions of law are rough approximations to the truth. The law is freed from the defects of observation and converted by the speculations of the geometer into exact form. But it has ceased to be pure induction, and has become ideal hypothesis. Deductions are made from it with syllogistic precision, and consequent facts are logically evolved without immediate reference to the actual events of Nature. If the results of computation coincide, not merely qualitatively, but quantitatively, with observation, the law is established as a reality, and is restored to the domain of induction. If, on the contrary, there is some inexplicable divergency between the computed and the observed facts, the law must be rejected. It cannot be accepted as an expression of the rigid theory embodied in Nature." (*Ideality*, 165.)

⚬ᢒ Milton K. Munitz

ONE UNIVERSE OR MANY?

Is the universe unique or are there many universes, perhaps infinitely many, beyond " our own "? This question has been a crucial topic of controversy and speculation in the field of cosmology from the earliest thought on the subject down to the present day. Now it may be said at once that to speak of the universe at all is by virtue of its very meaning to stipulate that we are concerned with a unique and all-inclusive system and, therefore, to speculate about, much less to affirm the existence of a plurality of universes is to exhibit a failure of proper usage, a contradiction in terms. On a purely formal level indeed the point may be granted. If one defines the universe in an abstract way (at least from the point of view of a broadly astronomical orientation) as the unique and all-inclusive system of heavenly bodies, then all cosmological systems are, as a matter of fact, in agreement; there cannot be a plurality of such systems. But the agreement is trivial. For to speak of *the* universe abstractly as the unique and all-inclusive system of heavenly bodies is at best to provide a formal schema within which significant knowledge is to be achieved by providing specific details. What *kind* of systematic connection shall we posit and of *what* heavenly bodies? Efforts at answering this question belong to particular cosmological theories and at some point or other rest upon empirical materials. Each theory offers its own particular factual identification or, if one wishes, its own material definition of *what it is to be a universe.* Significant questions throughout history about whether there is one universe or many have, in fact, revolved around the ideas presented by such concrete cosmological theories. By the same token, the referent of the term " universe," far from having a constant, univocal meaning throughout such discussions, illustrates on the contrary shifts of meaning to be understood historically only by reference to these theories. (The formulation of our question with respect to universes can be extended to cover a variety of instances in which the terms " world " or " cosmos " may be substituted for the term " universe.") One of the purposes of our investigation will be precisely to reveal the career of these shifting meanings, the way in which they are related to one another and the reasons for the changes.

There have been three broad periods in which the topic of a plurality of " universes " or " worlds " assumed crucial importance. The first period may be subdivided into two phases and includes, as the earlier, the discussions in Greek philosophy beginning with the pre-Socratics and reaching its culmination in the opposing views of Plato and Aristotle on the one hand, and the Atomists on the other. Then beginning in the thirteenth century and continuing until the end of the fifteenth century, the later phase of the discussion took place primarily under theological auspices. The second broad period is ushered in by the Copernican revolution and comes to a head in the seventeenth century. The third and last period is that which starts in the middle of the eighteenth century, stimulated by the views of Thomas Wright, Kant, and William Herschel, and continues with various ups and downs throughout the nineteenth century up to the third decade of the present century when empirical settlement of the issue, as it was discussed in this period, was finally made. Present day cosmology finds itself in what perhaps may be but a lull in this long struggle.

I

The problem of whether there is one universe or many first appears in Greek philosophy. The issue is one that not only finds the pre-Socratic cosmologists adopting one or another view, but it also receives a prominent share of attention in Plato's *Timaeus* and Aristotle's *De Caelo,* whose views on this score were to play a determining rôle throughout the post-Hellenic and medieval periods, and were to serve as the focal point of attack in late medieval and early modern thought.

There are certain common presuppositions about the nature of the cosmos which the overwhelming majority of Greek thinkers share, whatever their divergences on the problem concerning its uniqueness. In the first place, what it is to be a cosmos is contrasted with a state of " chaos "; in the second place, what it is to be a cosmos is defined by the fact that it is a physically and astronomically ordered collection of heavenly bodies, finite in spatial extent, generally conceived of as spherical in shape and centered in some single body. On the usual view the central position is occupied by a fixed, spherical earth about which move in their characteristic motions the moon, sun, five planets and the outermost sphere of the fixed stars.[1] The cosmo-

---

[1] This is not to overlook, however, the existence in Greek thought of either heterodox views of sophisticated character, or, what were in some fairly early devel-

logical schemes developed in Greek philosophy that begin with the Ionians and Pythagoreans preserve a marked continuity with the poetic and religious cosmogonical myths which antedated them, and that are represented in the writings of Hesiod, Homer and the Orphics. The dominant scheme adopted in the mythological approach is that of a cosmogony (of which a theogony forms a part); it relates the manner of genesis and development of an ordered world and all that it contains out of an antecedent, primordial state of chaos. With the advance of philosophic and especially scientific thought, the cosmogonical approach is found to recede gradually and to be replaced by an effort at giving an increasingly more accurate account of the already existing or established order to be found among the heavenly bodies. In short, we find the emergence of a cosmology looking for support to astronomy and physical theory.

The analysis of the relation of chaos to cosmos has a generally clear pattern of development from the Ionians to Aristotle. One important line of analysis consists in identifying the nature of " chaos " with the kind of material or elements out of which an ordered world is constructed. The other line of development, of special interest to us here, is the " spatial " relation of the cosmos formed with respect to the material of the cosmos thus identified. On the first count, we find at one extreme and in closest association with the mythologic stage, the view of Anaximander which identifies chaos with a " Boundless Something " out of which all determinate entities are born by a process of separation. A group of intermediate views identify this material with either a single one or a combination of four elements, earth, air, fire, water. In this group belong the views of Plato and Aristotle. The latter added a fifth element, the ether, out of which the heavenly bodies were exclusively composed, thus introducing the unfortunate and misguided cleavage between celestial and terrestrial physics that was not finally abandoned until the rise of modern

---

opments, simply extremely primitive conceptions. Of the latter, for example, some took the earth to be flat or cylindrical (Thales, Anaximander), others held the stars to be closer to the earth than the sun (Anaximander, Parmenides, Leucippus, Metrodorus of Chios). On the other hand, the Pythagorean theory that the earth, together with the sun, moon, planets and stars revolve about a " central fire," or the more brilliant, mathematically articulated views of planetary motion based on a heliocentric scheme that were later developed, are obvious instances of more sophisticated views. In both cases these represent deviants from the dominantly accepted view in the ancient period. Cf. J. L. E. Dreyer, *Planetary Systems from Thales to Kepler;* T. Heath, *Aristarchus of Samos.*

science. The logical and scientifically most fruitful culmination of this line of effort is represented by the views of the Atomists, Leucippus and Democritus, who identify the basic stuff of the universe with an infinite plurality of quantitatively defined discrete particles in constant motion and exhibiting in their behavior a pattern of mechanical necessity.

In the other direction which speculation took, the " spatial " relation of chaos to cosmos, we find a development of ideas that terminates in the rival views of Democritus and Aristotle. The major line of development from Anaximander to the Atomists is to conceive the cosmos as in some sense spatially encompassed by a surrounding chaos. The latter serves as the matrix out of which the world is born and from which, indeed, in some manner it continues to gather sustenance or nourishment, *e.g.*, as in Anaximenes and the Pythagoreans, by "breathing" the encompassing "air." Under the influence of the cosmogonical tradition, some of these earliest thinkers undertook not merely to give some account of the genesis of the present world; they envisaged, in their bold and imaginative way, a whole cycle of alternating births and destructions of worlds, so that while at any given time a single world is in existence, it represents but one of an endless sequence. Such was apparently the view of Empedocles, and, if we would trust to the reconstructive interpretations of some ancient and modern commentators, similar views were held by Anaximander, Anaximenes, Heraclitus and Diogenes of Appolonia.[2] Not until the middle of the second half of the fifth century B.C. do we meet for the first time, and unambiguously, with the radically novel doctrine of the *co-existence* of innumerable worlds.[3] This at once transforms and amplifies the previous theory which had envisaged simply the plurality of successive worlds by now viewing such plurality in spatial terms as well. For until this time no genuinely explicit or clear account is to be found among any of the pre-atomistic thinkers of the spatial extent of the surrounding chaos. It is only when we come to the atomists themselves that we find for the first time the point explicitly raised and an answer given; what extends beyond the limited confines of our world (or any world) is an *infinite* void within

[2] See E. Zeller, *Pre-Socratic Philosophy* I, 257–264, 277–278, 298; II, 61–78.

[3] See F. M. Cornford, " Innumerable Worlds in Pre-Socratic Philosophy," *Class. Quart.* XXVIII (1934), 1–16; the contrary position which would assign a belief in a plurality of co-existent worlds to pre-atomistic thinkers, a view made popular by Burnet, Taylor and their followers, finds its effective refutation in the above article.

which are to be found an infinite number of atoms moving in random ways. The atomists' theory of an infinite void was, as Cornford suggests, the counterpart in physical theory of what, in early parallel developments of a " Euclidean type " of geometry, was recognized as requisite for the elaboration of its conceptions, namely, an infinite space.[4]

Given an infinite void, there is no reason which can be assigned why matter should exist in one part and not in another, and hence matter also must be infinitely scattered. A world comes into existence at some particular place through the building up or collocation of atoms gathering together to form compound bodies, these in turn forming the macroscopic " heavenly " bodies, which by means of a " whirl " or vortex establish their rotary motions, all bounded by the outermost skin or shell that defines the limit of such a world. Having come into existence, such a cosmos will eventually disintegrate, its materials reverting to the primordial and externally existent chaos of atoms in the infinite void. Yet this process cannot be presumed to take place but once or in one portion of space; no assignable reason could be given for such a unique occurrence. Therefore what we find in our world must be presumed to have an infinite number of analogues in time and space, although with conceivable differences in detail.[5]

[4] Cornford writes: " As I read the story, what happened was briefly this. As geometry developed, mathematicians were unconsciously led to postulate the infinite space required for the construction of their geometrical figures, that space in which parallel lines can be produced 'indefinitely' without meeting or reverting to their starting-point. In the sixth and fifth centuries no distinction was yet drawn between the space demanded by the theorems of geometry and the space which frames the physical world. We know from Aristotle that the earlier Pythagoreans did not even distinguish the solid figures of geometry from the bodies we daily see and handle. Hence the considerations which led mathematicians to recognize infinite space in their science simultaneously led some physicists to recognize an unlimited Void in nature. These were the atomists, whose system was the final outcome of a tradition inspired by Pythagorean mathematics. The atomists broke down the ancient boundaries of the universe and set before mankind, for the first time, the abhorrent and really unimaginable picture of a limitless void." " The Invention of Space," in *Essays in Honor of Gilbert Murray*, 220.

[5] " Democritus said that there are worlds infinite in number and differing in size. In some there is neither sun nor moon, in others the sun and moon are greater than with us, in others there are more than one sun and moon. The distances between the worlds are unequal, in some directions there are more of them, in some, fewer; some are growing, others are at their prime, and others again declining, in one direction they are coming into being, in another they are ceasing to be. Their destruction comes about through collision with one another. Some worlds are desti-

Meanwhile both Plato and Aristotle defended and elaborated the more conservative tradition of a unique cosmos, which they now also regarded as everlasting.[6] Both attempted to cut the ground from under the atomist position by denying altogether the existence of a void or a chaos outside the cosmos, whether actually infinite or indeterminate in extent. Chaos, for Plato, is now identified with the domain of chance or necessity (the two being the same in his philosophy) and regarded as the irrational or non-purposive aspect of the universe.[7] Chaos in this sense is absorbed spatially *within* the cosmos. The latter exhausts and includes all that physically is. Not only is the co-existence of a plurality of worlds explicitly attacked, even the doctrine of successive worlds is similarly denied. With Plato the justification for this belief is essentially teleological: the model upon which the world was fashioned is that of a unique, all-inclusive " Living Creature " and the world " created " resembles its model in that respect. As unique it possesses an undeniable perfection, since if in its " creation " not all the material were " used up," but on the contrary some were left outside, it might ultimately be subject to dissolution through attack from without.[8]

With Aristotle, the argument assumes a more carefully worked out form, based on essentially physical principles.[9] Aristotle assumes the general theory of matter and motion which distinguishes elementary natural motions " away from," " toward," or " about " a center, and the corresponding simple elements out of which all bodies are composed; those of earth and water having natural motions *toward* a center, fire and air *away from* the center, ether *about* a center. Other worlds, if they exist, must contain bodies made up of the same kinds of elements, since these are the only ones possible, and therefore they

---

tute of animal and plant life and of all moisture. In our world, the earth came into being before the stars; the moon has the lowest place, then the sun (then the other planets) and after them the fixed stars. The planets themselves even are not at equal heights [*i.e.*, distances]. A world continues to be in its prime only until it becomes incapable of taking to it anything from without." Hippolytus, *Refut.* I, 13; quoted Heath, *Greek Astronomy* (1932), 38. For a general account see C. Bailey, *Greek Atomists and Epicurus* (London, 1928).

[6] Plato's adoption of the cosmogonical myth in the *Timaeus* as depicting the coming-into-being of this world is but a device of exposition and need not be taken literally as implying an absolute beginning.

[7] Cf. F. M. Cornford, *Plato's Cosmology* (1937), 161ff.

[8] *Timaeus*, 31a, 33a.   [9] *De Caelo*, 276a 18–279b 3; cf. *Met.* 1074a 32–35.

would be possessed of the same kinds of natural motion. In such a case, however, we would be faced with a contradictory situation, for it follows that a particle of earth in another world would simultaneously have to move *away from* the center of our world in order to move *towards* the center of its own. The same contradictory results would hold for all the other elements. There can be, therefore, but one absolute center and circumference, and our universe, which possesses these, contains all the matter there is. Material bodies cannot exist beyond the outermost sphere of the heavens, since they cannot exist there either naturally or by constraint: not naturally, since all natural motions of bodies are to be found *within* the sphere of the heavens (bodies cannot have more than one natural place or motion); nor yet by constraint, since if a body occupies a place by constraint or moves to it by constraint, there must be some other bodies that have such places or motions naturally, and this has already been shown to be impossible. As a corollary to all this Aristotle concludes, " outside " the cosmos, therefore, there is neither void, nor time, nor place, since all of these are in some way connected with the existence of body.

When elaborated with the geometric scheme of homocentric spheres and later with the Hipparchan-Ptolemaic system of eccentrics and epicycles, the Aristotelian approach achieved a theoretical unity and an observational support that caused its retention as the orthodox cosmology until finally overthrown in modern times. It was this very dominance of the Aristotelian philosophy and the geocentric point of view which it incorporated that led to bypassing the significant astronomic clue in ancient thought that might have helped to overthrow this whole scheme. The germinal ideas of Heraclides of Pontus (a contemporary of Aristotle), who developed the hypothesis of the earth's daily rotation on its axis, and of the revolution of Venus and Mercury around the sun as satellites; and the even more prophetic and thoroughgoing ideas of Aristarchus of Samos, that contained the equivalent of a Copernican, heliocentric scheme of planetary motions, failed to gain the recognition and elaboration they deserved. Hipparchus, the greatest astronomer of antiquity, and following him Ptolemy, adhered to the geocentric theory and thus lent their overwhelming prestige to the continuance of the entire fabric of Aristotelian cosmology.

In comparing the relative merits of the rival views of Democritus and Aristotle on the question of the uniqueness or plurality of worlds, certainly the views of Democritus must be recognized as of tremendously superior importance in terms of sheer brilliance of prophecy and suggestiveness of ideas which were to be fruitful in the subsequent history of scientific thought. Yet for the time, and within the range of the experience available, one can understand the reasons for the dominance of the more conservative views of Aristotle. On the astronomical level, for the existence or even hints of the existence of other worlds, no observational clues were then found or exploited. (Such clues were indeed at a much later period to be found in the form of the "nebulae," but of these ancient astronomy knew nothing.) Not only was there no conceivable evidence of an empirical sort that could confirm the existence of an *infinite* plurality of worlds—there was not even observational evidence to justify a belief in more than one! The intuitive genius of Democritus was premature. Similarly, the physical theory of atomism and the cosmological theory of a multiplicity of worlds went beyond the range, in both directions, of what was within the grasp and control of the instrumental techniques of ancient science. Certainly, as far as the theory of atomism is concerned, precisely because it remained too far removed from any direct experimental control then available, it could easily be supplanted by an account which more readily allowed itself, on the whole, to be tested at the time. It was precisely this more directly confirmable physical theory of Aristotle, with its foundation in the gross facts of familiar experience, which could then be brought to bear upon the astronomically identifiable facts to yield a total cosmology. It thereby made any reference to worlds beyond our own, whose existence was postulated on the basis of the other type of physics, both unwarranted and unnecessary. True, there was no inherent incompatibility between the geometrical and kinematic theory of planetary motion and the physical views of Democritus. The latter might easily have been invoked as an interpretation of the former. But the observational range of astronomy at the time, in order to account for the facts within its experience, had no need for a cosmological theory of such transcendent scope. It was at least in part then for these reasons that we may suppose Aristotelian cosmology, equally in harmony with the known astronomic facts, came to prevail.

In addition to the foregoing considerations that touch upon the immediate scientific grounds of evaluation, it is important to recognize another feature that makes its appearance in these discussions as well as in those of later periods. It is what might be called, in a broad sense, an a priori or metaphysical element; this expresses a deliberate attitude or preference of thought which determines very often the direction which scientific thought itself takes. It is clear, for example, in the case of Plato that his " reason " for looking upon the cosmos as unique is essentially teleological. Only a finite world, from his own conception of what it is to be " perfect," could claim that character. (Strikingly enough the idea of perfection was with the later rise of Hebraic-Christian theology to be identified with its exact opposite.) The lingering but effective traces of such Platonism (and ultimately of the Pythagoreanism upon which in turn it is based) are to be found in Aristotle. The cosmological theory of the finite universe rests for him upon the physical theory of natural places and motions and this in turn is derived from a conception of the ways in which types of motion are to be classified, as circular (and therefore " complete " and eternal) and as rectilinear (and therefore " incomplete " and finite). Also Aristotle in the *Metaphysics* (1074a 32) undertakes to prove that there can be only one universe on the grounds that there is but one prime mover operating as an object of " love and desire " for the whole universe. But this again is clearly beyond the scope of scientific determination and wholly at variance with the more empirical orientation of the other phases of Aristotle's cosmology. Lastly, even in the case of the atomists themselves, one finds the use of analogous a priori principles to the effect, for example that a limit to space is " inconceivable " or that no adequate " reasons " can be given why matter should occupy one part of space and not another. With respect to the adoption of all these and similar principles one can only note that the advance of science does not in any way serve to confirm or disconfirm them. Dogmatic adherence to one pole or the other of the question whether there is one universe or many that pretends to settle the issue on the basis of such extra-scientific appeals, remains wholly ineffective because incapable of effecting universal agreement.

With the revival of serious philosophic speculation in the Middle Ages, the problem of one or many worlds received a prominent share of attention. However, since there were no major significant advances in astronomy during this period that prompted any total overhauling of the traditional cosmology, the identification of what was taken to be the " world " remained essentially what it was in ancient times. The discussion of whether there is one such world or many was thus not stimulated by any fresh empirical discoveries or important shifts in physical theory, but rather by the interest in interpreting Aristotle in the light of Hebraic-Christian theology. Disputants ranged themselves on opposite sides of the question as to whether Aristotle's views were essentially compatible with correct theological doctrine. Those who attacked Aristotle came as a result by indirection to play the rôle in this context of controversy that the atomistic materialists had played in ancient thought. However, it was, of course, not as Democriteans that such thinkers now argued, but rather in support of what they took to be a correct theology.

The central issue revolved about the notion of God's omnipotence. For Aristotle, God is not essentially a source of power or creative energy, whereas in Christian theology, the necessity of understanding the world in terms of God's wisdom, goodness, and power raised problems which were altogether foreign to the older scheme. In the Democritean type of thought, given an infinite void and an infinite number of atoms scattered throughout it, there is taken to be as an *a priori* deduction, no sufficient *mechanical* reason why there should be only one world at one place, when the *physical* conditions are present at more than one place or time for the coming-into-existence of a world. By a parallel use of an equally a priori principle of God's omnipotence and goodness, the argument was offered by those who attacked Aristotle, that it would place an unjustifiable limitation on God's power and goodness to limit his creative energies to the creation of a single world. Here recourse was characteristically made to what Lovejoy has called the principle of plenitude—that God's goodness and power overflow in a boundless creation.[10]

As early as the beginning of the thirteenth century the arguments urging the irreconcilability of the Aristotelian doctrine of the uniqueness of the world and the theological dogma of God's omnipotence had been crystallized.[11] They are summarized [12] in the commentary on *The Sphere* of Sacrobosco, ascribed to Michael Scot, composed around 1225–30. The commentator, undertaking to reply to such views, argues that by making the proper distinctions, one can reconcile the two. Taken absolutely, God, of course, being omnipotent,

[10] *The Great Chain of Being* (Cambridge, Mass., 1936), esp. chs. II–IV.

[11] For historical details on which the following is based, see P. Duhem, *Études sur Leonardo Da Vinci,* " Leonardo Da Vinci et la Pluralité des Mondes " II (Paris, 1909); also P. Duhem, art. on " Physics " in *Catholic Encyc.*

[12] See L. Thorndike, *The Sphere of Sacrobosco and Its Commentators* (New York, 1949), 252ff.

could create a plurality of worlds, if He wished, but relatively to the world created, its nature is of such a character that a plurality of other worlds is rendered impossible. Similar halting attempts were made by others, including St. Thomas, in defense of the Aristotelian viewpoint, but with equally unconvincing results. St. Thomas, for example, in his *Commentary on Aristotle's De Caelo,* uses a typically Platonic mode of argument by appealing to the conception of perfection in his support of a belief in one world.[13] His argument is to the effect that had God created other worlds, either they would be duplicates of one another or not. If they were duplicates, their creation would have been futile and inconsistent with the wisdom of the Deity. On the other hand, had they been different, no one of them could be said to be perfect, and at best, therefore, their totality or collection might claim that quality. Interestingly enough, whatever might have been the objection of Thomas to the latter alternative, it was precisely that alternative which theologians at a later period were to seize upon in exhibiting what they took to be the marks of God's perfect handiwork and infinite power. Once more, therefore, we find a clear illustration of the highly ambiguous character of an a priori metaphysical principle such as the doctrine of perfection, which can be made to serve now one purpose and now another. At any rate, on the issue of God's omnipotence many writers in the late thirteenth and early fourteenth centuries (Richard of Middleton, Henry of Ghent, Guillaume Varon, Jean de Bassals, William of Ockham, Walter Burley), affirmed the principle that God could create other worlds than ours. In 1277 moreover, following instructions of the Pope, and with the advice of the theologians of the Sorbonne, Étienne Tempier, Bishop of Paris, officially condemned (together with other beliefs of a Peripatetic and astrological nature) the belief that God could not create a plurality of worlds. The gradual undermining of the Aristotelian hegemony in physics and cosmology was served not only by such a decree but by the increasingly effective attacks upon the Aristotelian scheme by the Oxford Franciscans (Richard of Middleton, Duns Scotus, and William of Ockham), and the School of Paris (John Buridan, Albert of Saxony, Nicholas of Oresme), whose influence was eventually to be felt in the works of men like Nicholas of Cusa, Leonardo da Vinci, Bruno and others, and ultimately in the founders of modern science in the sixteenth and seventeenth centuries. Of a similar character and contributing in its own way to the undermining of Aristotelian influence,

[13] Lib. I, cap. IX, Lect. XIX, 14.

was the work of Chasdai Crescas, who in his *Or Adonai* (c. 1410) laboriously and painstakingly set about to challenge the basic tenets of Aristotelian physics, and in the course of such criticism, the belief in the uniqueness of this world.[14]

Throughout all such discussions, however, until we come indeed to the sixteenth century, it must be remembered that the terms in which controversy was couched were essentially those of an Aristotelian-Ptolemaic astronomy.   Even those, therefore, who undertook to challenge the orthodox theory, did so largely in aprioristic or theological terms.   They did not as yet possess either the observational data or the elaborations of systematic theory by means of which alternative schemes could be adequately formulated and justified.   Not until the sixteenth and seventeenth centuries did these become available with the gradual building up of a body of information and ideas, based on the Copernican theory of 1543, and the use of the telescope beginning in the early 1600's.

The ancient and medieval controversy about the uniqueness or plurality of worlds, in so far as it involved the conception of a world constituted on a basically geocentric pattern, simply became irrelevant with the overthrow of this dominant astronomic scheme through the advent of the Copernican revolution.   Whether there is one world or many now took on altogether different meanings in a new setting.

II

The second general period in which the doctrine of a plurality of worlds becomes an issue was ushered in by the Copernican revolution and may be said to occupy a span of some two hundred years, from the latter half of the sixteenth century to the middle of the eighteenth.   The immediate result of the Copernican advance was to bring about a more effective theory of planetary motion.   Its wider cosmological bearings were not of special concern to Copernicus himself, who adopted on this score a conservative attitude.   He simply looked to the sun now rather than to the earth as the center of the universe. He retained the geometric scheme of epicycles and eccentrics, although the complexity required by the Ptolemaic theory could now be enormously reduced.   No longer, of course, was it necessary to postulate the daily revolution of the sphere of the fixed stars.   That there is such a sphere, however, Copernicus does not doubt, although he now

[14] Cf. H. A. Wolfson, *Crescas' Critique of Aristotle* (Cambridge, Mass., 1929), 117–118, 217, 473ff.

increases its distance from the earth by a tremendous amount in order to account for the absence of a stellar parallax in the earth's semi-annual traversal of its orbit about the sun. With respect to the extent of this sphere of fixed stars—whether it is finite or infinite—however, Copernicus refused to commit himself. That is something, he remarks, which may be left to the philosophers to speculate about.[15] Clearly the job of the astronomer, more restrained but at the same time more hopeful of solution, is the description and explanation of what comes within the limits of visual observation and mathematical articulation and control. In this general attitude Copernicus was followed by many others, including Galileo. The latter, for example, writes that "no one has proved the world to be finite and determinate or infinite and indeterminate."[16]

But the wider, more speculative effects of the Copernican theory upon the outlook of cosmology were not slow in being felt and elaborated by others. Indeed, the theory found movements already afoot (those which in the later medieval and early modern period involved criticism of the Aristotelian cosmology) which it now helped to augment. Various speculative interpretations now came to the fore, none of which could actually claim scientific verification; yet where observation and mathematics were not available, imagination and a lively sense of analogy could be called upon to help out.

Thus, for example, Thomas Digges, one of the early English translators and supporters of Copernicus, undertook to make a deliberate innovation in the picture of the universe which the new astronomy seemed to make possible. Since technically it was no longer necessary to picture the universe as limited by a finite, outermost sphere of fixed stars, as the older astronomy with its assumption of a fixed, central earth required, it could now be pictured as extending itself infinitely in all directions. Digges becomes therefore "the first modern astronomer of note to portray an infinite, heliocentric universe with the stars scattered at varying distances throughout infinite space."[17] This same idea of an infinite universe, augmented now by

[15] Cf. F. R. Johnson, *Astronomical Thought in Renaissance England* (Baltimore, 1937), 106–107; E. Rosen, *Three Copernican Treatises* (New York, 1939), 39–40.

[16] *Dialogues on Two Systems*, quoted by Boulting, *Giordano Bruno* (London, 1914), 141.

[17] Johnson, *op. cit.*, 164; cf. Johnson and Larkey, *Hunt. Lib. Bull.*, no. 5 (1934), 69–117; I cannot agree with Johnson's claim that there is an essential difference in

the doctrine of an infinite plurality of " worlds," but with the abandonment of the unique heliocentric conception—is one with which Bruno's name is forever associated. In his case, however, Copernican astronomy came to provide some of the astronomic details of a philosophy whose essential doctrines are to be understood as a fusion of Lucretius and Nicholas of Cusa, atomistic materialism combined with a pantheistic version of the principle of plenitude.[18]

A clearer and more representative scientific statement of a belief in a plurality of worlds as suggested by the new astronomy, but without a corresponding dogmatic assertion of the infinity of such systems, is to be found in Christian Huygens.[19]

For Huygens as well as for all those who in the seventeenth and eighteenth centuries were to share a belief in a plurality of worlds, such " worlds " were now to be understood as modeled on Copernican lines. The first step in the argument, and the one that was to prove

---

the speculations of Digges and Bruno on the question of the infinity of the universe, that namely, whereas Bruno was guided wholly by a priori, metaphysical considerations, Digges was wholly the " experimental scientist." It seems to me that in any case the speculation far exceeded anything justified by the available evidence and was, as far as the cosmology was concerned, an imaginative extension of the facts rather than a strict inference from them.

[18] " The one infinite is perfect, in simplicity, of itself, absolutely, nor can aught be greater or better. This is the one Whole, God, universal Nature, occupying all space, of whom naught but infinity can give the perfect image or semblance " (*De Immenso et Innumerabilibus*, Lib. II, cap. 12, quoted D. Singer, " The Cosmology of Giordano Bruno 1548–1600," *Isis* 33 [1941], 189). " It is then unnecessary to investigate whether there be, beyond the heaven, Space, Void or Time. For there is a single general space, a single vast immensity which we may freely call *Void;* in it are innumerable and infinite globes like this on which we live and grow. This space we declare to be infinite; since neither reason, convenience, possibility, sense-perception or nature assign to it a limit. In it are an infinity of worlds of the same kind as our own. For there is no . . . defect of nature's gifts. I mean either of active or of passive power to prevent the existence of other worlds throughout (universal) space, which is identical in natural character with our own space." *De L'Infinito Universo et Mondi*, Dialogue 5; quoted *loc. cit.*, 189. Cf. J. L. McIntyre, *Giordano Bruno*, London (1903), chs. III, IV. " I hold the universe to be infinite as a result of the infinite divine power; for I think it unworthy of divine goodness and power to have produced merely one finite world when it was able to bring into being an infinity of worlds " (quoted, Boulting, *op. cit.*, 267).

[19] His ideas are presented in his *Cosmotheoros* (1698) of which an English translation exists under the title *The Celestial Worlds Discovered or Conjectures Concerning the Inhabitants, Plants and Productions of the Worlds in the Planets.* Refs. in foll. are to 2nd ed. (London, 1722); for other translations, see *Oeuvres Complètes de Christian Huygens* (Hague, 1944) 21, 674.

ultimately the most significant, was to regard the sun as but one among the stars. For this, good astronomic support is to be found in the fact that the stars cannot be taken as shining by reflected light; rather they are to be conceived as luminous bodies like the sun, since their distance, as proved by the absence of any sensible parallax, must be taken as enormously great.[20] Nor is there any need to regard the stars as being in the same sphere, at the same distance from the sun; they may be taken as scattered over the immense spaces of the heavens "and are as far distant perhaps from one another, as the nearest of them are from the sun." [21] The next step, though far less convincing and resting upon the use of analogy, is taken by Huygens in common with all others who develop this point of view. If the sun is a star, then each star may be taken as a sun with its own planetary system. Indeed

there's a manifest reason why they should. For if we imagine ourselves placed at an equal distance from the sun and fixed stars, we should then perceive no difference between them. For, as for all the Planets that we now see attend the sun, we should not have the least glimpse of them, either because their light would be too weak to affect us, or that all the orbs in which they move would make up one lucid point with the sun. In this station we should have no occasion to imagine any difference between the stars, and should make no doubt if we had but the sight, and knew the Nature of one of them, to make that the standard of all the rest. We are then placed near one of them, namely, our sun, and so near as to discover six other globes moving round him, some of them having others performing them the same office. Why then may not we make use of the same judgment that we would in that case and conclude that our star has no better attendance than the others? [22]

Huygens indeed goes on to posit not only that such planetary worlds exist, but that they are all in some manner inhabited by creatures analogous to those on our own planet. It was this possibility of the existence of other *habitable* celestial bodies which exercised the popular imagination, as illustrated in Fontenelle's famous book, *Entretiens sur la Pluralité des Mondes* (1686). Because of its religious implications this was the aspect of the whole question which for many was *identified* with a belief in a "plurality of worlds." [23] As

[20] *Loc. cit.*, 145; cf. Robert Grant, *Hist. Phys. Astron.* (London, 1852), 538.

[21] *Ibid.*, 145.   [22] *Ibid.*, 149.

[23] See W. Whewell, *The Plurality of Worlds* (published anonymously, 1853); A. R. Wallace, *Man's Place in the Universe* (New York, 1903).

to the possible *number* of worlds Huygens expresses a more cautious attitude. Scientifically a more elementary desideratum is a reliable criterion of the distance of the stars, and we find him, therefore, attempting ingeniously to arrive at some estimate of what he takes to be the "nearest" star, namely Sirius. This he concludes has a distance as compared to the distance of the sun as in the ratio of 27664 to 1.[24] Further than that, one can only have an awesome sense of "the prodigious number there must be besides and of their vast distances." But of the actual number, scientific candor if not a conventional religious piety prevents any estimate.[25]

The upshot of this and similar discussions was first of all to effect a shift in the terms of the problem. No longer can we identify the meaning of "the plurality of worlds" with "the plurality of universes." For Copernicus, preserving the unique and absolute center of the universe for the sun, and conceiving the fixed stars as forming its outermost circumference, such a heliocentric world might still be identical with the unique and all-inclusive universe. Once having made the sun, however, a member of the family of stars, there is no longer strictly any need to assign a unique central position to our own sun. Moreover, with each star serving as a center to its own planetary system, a "world" comes to mean precisely such a system, or indeed in some usages, the individual members of the system themselves.[26] Like the ancient conception of a cosmos, each world is now

[24] Equal to what would now be reckoned as one-half light-year. This estimate is, however, according to present knowledge far wide of the truth—since Sirius is at a distance of 8.6 light-years.

[25] " Really, when I have been reflecting thus with my self, methought all our arithmetic was nothing, and we are versed but in the very rudiments of numbers in comparison of this great sum. For this requires an immense Treasury, not of twenty or thirty figures only in our decuple progression, but of as many as there are grains of sand upon the shore. And yet who can say that even this number exceeds that of the fix'd stars? Some of the ancients and Jordanus Brunus carry'd it further, in declaring the number infinite; he would perswade us that he has proved it by many arguments, tho' in my opinion they are none of them conclusive. Not that I think the contrary can ever be made out. Indeed it seems to me certain that the universe is infinitely extended; but what God has been pleased to place beyond the region of the stars is as much above our knowledge as it is beyond our habitation " (*loc. cit.*).

[26] Bruno, *e.g.*, sometimes uses the term "world" in this non-discriminatory sense for single heavenly bodies, as in the following: " . . . I have expounded that there is an endless number of individual worlds like our earth. I regard it, with Pythagoras, as a star, and the moon, the planets and the stars are similar to it,

finite. But this time those who upheld a belief in a plurality of worlds could appeal to the familiar and accessible facts of observation, the stars themselves, if not to their supposed planetary retinues, as evidence of the existence of " other worlds."

However, no more than in the previous attempts could there be any effective proof of the infinite number of such worlds by appeal to metaphysical principles. Once more the issue of a plurality of worlds was to be settled through the aid of astronomy. And this time such astronomy served to establish one important fact: it destroyed the privileged status of the sun by placing it within the family of stars. Our own planetary system (and any others that might exist, although to this day none has been discovered), is recognized to occupy a subordinate position in a more inclusive scheme. Indeed it becomes less confusing and technically more accurate to speak of " planetary systems " or " stars " rather than of " worlds." In any case it is the *stellar system* as an inclusive whole that is now identified as the " universe." Astronomical investigation continued, throughout the eighteenth century, for lack of precise tools of observation, to emphasize the structure and dynamics of the solar system. For cosmological speculation, however, the new frame of reference was shifted to the domain of the stars, and with this new orientation we enter upon the third phase of our story.

III

In taking the collection of stars as the most inclusive domain, as " the universe," cosmological speculation and astronomical inquiry set about to determine its structure. Does it have any particular pattern of spatial distribution, and if so are there other comparable systems, or is it rather unique? These questions and the efforts to answer them begin to come into prominence and receive increasing observational and theoretical attention in the later eighteenth century. Effective answers were in some cases not forthcoming until two centuries later, in our own generation. The man who established this branch of inquiry upon a scientific basis and gave to stellar astronomy the impetus with which it has carried on its work with ever-increasing effectiveness into our own day was William Herschel (1738–1822). Interest in cosmology, or as he calls it, " the construction of the Heavens," was from the very beginning the ruling concern to which all his tremendously detailed and numerous observations were di-

---

the latter being of endless number. All these bodies make an infinity of worlds." (Quoted, Boulting, *op. cit.*, 267.)

rected. In this domain, he remarks, in one of his earliest papers on the subject,[27] it is of the utmost importance to keep a sane balance between observation and theory.

If we would hope to make any progress in an investigation of this delicate nature, we ought to avoid two opposite extremes, of which I can hardly say which is the most dangerous. If we indulge a fanciful imagination and build worlds of our own, we must not wonder at our going wide from the path of truth and nature; but these will vanish like the Cartesian vortices, that soon gave way when better theories were offered. On the other hand, if we add observation to observation, without attempting to draw not only certain conclusions, but also conjectural views from them, we offend against the very end for which observations ought to be made.

His own work in this field sets the tone of investigation for a period of some two hundred years. Important ground-breaking ideas were provided by his contemporaries, Thomas Wright, Kant, and Lambert. The subsequent observational work in our own day of Kapteyn, Shapley and Hubble are landmarks in the same broad field of inquiry.

The first significant step in the search for a possible structure in the universe of stars was taken by Thomas Wright of Durham in 1750.[28] Instead of taking the stars as scattered at random out to indefinite distances, Wright proposed the familiar phenomenon of the Milky Way as providing the major clue. As early as the first use of the telescope by Galileo it had been confirmed that what otherwise might be taken as a streaky nebulosity, was in fact, in what is called the Milky Way, a vast congeries of individual stars. Now Wright's strikingly novel suggestion was that the whole system of stars be viewed as one enormous, finite, disc-like structure. Our own sun and its attendant planets may be considered as lying in the plane of this structure somewhere near its center. In looking out towards the top or " poles " of the arrangement, relatively few stars will be met. On the other hand, as we go towards the rim of the system, more and more stars are found, until at the rim itself what we get, because of the perspective in which this vast thickness of stars will appear to a member of the system such as ourselves, will be precisely the effect produced by the Milky Way. Along with this startling and prophetic

---

[27] " On the Construction of the Heavens " (1785), in *Collected Papers,* ed. J. L. E. Dreyer (London, 1912), I, 223.

[28] *An Original Theory or New Hypothesis of the Universe* (London, 1750). An American edition of this work was published in Philadelphia in 1837.

idea, Wright likewise conceived of the existence of other " universes " beyond our own, *i.e.*, stellar systems, or as he phrases it, " creations." That this " Plenum of Creations not unlike the known universe may be the real case," he writes, " is in some degree made evident by the many cloudy spots, just perceivable by us, as far without our starry regions in which through visibly luminous spaces, no one star or particular constituent can possibly be distinguished; those in all likelihood may be external creations, bordering upon the known one, too remote for even our telescopes to reach." [29]

To Kant, in his *Natural History and Theory of the Heavens* (1755), must go the credit for having worked out in somewhat elaborate detail, on the basis of an account of Wright's theory which he read in the Hamburg journal *Freie Urteile* of 1751,[30] yet still largely in a speculative vein, an account of the Milky Way and of comparable external systems. Making again a characteristic appeal to a combined use of Democritean ideas, Newtonian principles and the principle of plenitude, he now envisages an infinite supersystem as the outcome of the systematic interrelation of these innumerable subsystems. Kant sets up what he calls a " systematic constitution " for the universe as a whole on the analogy of what had been discovered to exist in the solar system, first by applying it to the galactic system or Milky Way of which our sun and its planetary system is but a minute part, then to systems analogous to our own Milky Way, to the various " island universes " outside our own galactic system, and finally to the total system that binds all these galaxies together in the most inclusive system of all. This total supersystem, Kant's universe, must be infinite; this follows for him from the infinite power of God, the source of all creation.

But what is at last the end of these systematic arrangements? Where shall creation itself cease? It is evident that in order to think of it as in proportion to the power of the Infinite Being, it must have no limits at all . . . the field of the revelation of the Divine attributes is as infinite as these attributes themselves. Eternity is not sufficient to embrace the manifestations of the Supreme Being, if it is not combined with the infinitude of space.[31]

[29] *Op. cit.*, 143; cf. V. Gushee, " Thomas Wright of Durham, Astronomer," *Isis* 33 (1941), 209.

[30] W. Hastie, *Kant's Cosmogony*, a trans. of the above work of Kant, 54.

[31] *Loc. cit.*, 139–140; cf. *ibid.*, 65, 154.

Comparable speculative ideas were developed, apparently quite independently, by Lambert in his *Cosmological Letters* (1761).[32]

Foregoing, however, these wholly over-extended efforts at determining the existence, let alone the possibly infinite extent of such a supersystem as Kant dreamed of, William Herschel is the first to undertake a systematic and careful observational attack on the structure of the system of stars constituting the Milky Way and of the "nebulae" he discovered with his (at-the-time) powerful telescopes. His own painstaking researches and the speculations which were guided by exact observations underwent significant changes from the earliest efforts presented in his papers of 1784–1785 to the latest in 1811.[33]   Herschel started by not only assigning a definite, finite and generally disc-like structure to the Milky Way system, but also regarding it as a " detached nebula " whose stellar structure is comparable to that of the various nebulae, in principle resolvable into stars, which he regarded as lying beyond the confines of our own system. His later observations and interpretations gradually modified this view as he discovered increasingly the complex structure of the Milky Way system itself—as not composed of "insulated" stars throughout—and the fact that some nebulae turned up which were not all resolvable into stars.   These latter Herschel took as made up of a " shining fluid " (and " of a nature wholly unknown to us ") and tried to account for the variety of telescopic objects discovered by an ingenious hypothesis of an evolutionary scheme of development—of change from diffuse nebulosities into stellar systems.   At no time, however, did he venture to make any claims about the nature and extent of the total system comprising all these sub-systems.

The subsequent history of nebular research in the nineteenth and early twentieth centuries exhibits a shifting and complicated pattern of observation and interpretation, in which the " island-universe " hypothesis is now brought into prominence and now discarded to be replaced by the view which would absorb all types of heavenly bodies within the stellar system itself.   Thus with the use of the 6-foot reflector of Lord Rosse, beginning in 1849, the island-universe hypothesis gained favor (after having been in eclipse), as a result of the ability to resolve some of the so-called spiral nebulae into stars. Writing in 1852, Grant concluded:

[32] See J. E. Gore, *The Visible Universe* (1893), 229–231.

[33] Cf. F. G. W. Struve, *Études D'Astronomie Stellaire* (1847), 21–50; H. Macpherson, *Modern Astronomy* (London, 1926), 144ff.; C. Lubbock, *The Herschel Chronicle* (New York, 1933).

Moreover, the phenomena denominated Nebulous Stars—which seemed to Herschel to be incapable of any satisfactory explanation, except by adopting the hypothesis of a self-luminous fluid—when examined with the powerful telescopes of Lord Rosse, have been found to exhibit an aspect totally different from that which appeared to Herschel so enigmatical. In fact, the greater the optical power of the telescope with which the heavens are surveyed, the more strongly do the results tend to produce the impression that all nebulae are in reality vast aggregations of stars, which assume a nebulous aspect only because the telescope with which they are observed in each instance is not sufficiently powerful to resolve them into their constituent parts and thereby disclose their real nature.[34]

Such a judgment was soon to be called into question, however, when in 1864 Huggins, with the aid of a newly invented spectroscope, discovered the bright-line or "gaseous" type spectra of several irregular and planetary-type nebulae. Opinions veered from one extreme to the other and opposition to the island-universe hypothesis continued down to the early part of the present century. Many tacitly assumed that even the so-called "white nebulae" or spirals, though giving a continuous spectrum, would also be found to be inherently gaseous.[35] Moreover, apparently anomalous facts about the distribution of nebulae, for example, that they appear predominantly in the regions about the galactic poles, avoiding the region of the galactic plane, were taken by many as indicative of their association with the galaxy itself and so part of the stellar system. As a typical expression of this point of view Herbert Spencer argued:

In that zone of celestial space where the stars are excessively abundant, nebulae are rare; while in the two opposite celestial spaces that are furthest removed from this zone nebulae are abundant. Scarcely any nebulae lie near the galactic circle (or plane of the Milky Way); and the great mass of them lie round the galactic poles. Can this also be mere coincidence? When to the fact that the general mass of nebulae are antithetical in position to the general mass of stars, we add the fact that local regions of nebulae are regions where stars are scarce, and the further fact that single nebulae are habitually found in comparatively starless spots; does not the proof of a physical connection become overwhelming? [36]

The famous historian of astronomy Agnes Clerke summed up the

[34] Grant, *op. cit.*, 568.

[35] Cf. H. B. Curtis, "The Nebulae," in *Hand. der Astrophys.* (Berlin, 1933), V, 833–834.

[36] Herbert Spencer, "The Nebular Hypothesis" (1858), in *Essays Scientific, Political and Speculative* I, 112–113.

opinion current at the time when she wrote: "The question whether nebulae are external galaxies hardly any longer needs discussion. It has been answered by the progress of research. No competent thinker, with the whole of the available evidence before him, can now, it is safe to say, maintain any single nebula to be a star system of co-ordinate rank with the Milky Way." [37]

Once more this judgment was to be reversed with further advances in observation and theory. Without going into the details of a complex story, it will suffice to state the two facts that, in our own day, finally served to establish a satisfactory solution. The one, and by far the most important, was the establishment through reliable criteria of distances of the fact that some nebulae are systems of stars and are indeed extra- galactic. This has been conclusively recognized ever since 1924, when Hubble, the leading contemporary student of the nebulae, established through the use of Cepheid variables occurring in such nebulae how their absolute distance may be estimated. The second fact that went along with the first was the securing of a basic classification of nebulae which recognized that some, like the planetary and diffuse or gaseous nebulae, are indeed parts of our own galactic system, whereas others are truly extra-galactic and belong to the predominantly regular group ranging from the compact globular types to the open-armed spirals.[38] Thus the above-noted "anomalies" are readily explained. The concentration of nebulae in the region of the galactic poles and their absence in that of the galactic plane is due to the obscuration of matter in the galaxy itself in the latter case, its relative absence in the former. Similarly, with a proper distinction between those intra-galactic nebulae that are composed of gas and dust and those extra-galactic ones that are in many instances resolved into stars, the difference in spectral data becomes readily intelligible.

Present-day observational attention in cosmology is confined to the exploration of "the realm of nebulae" as defining the purview of the observable universe. The basic elements of this domain are the extra-galactic nebulae. While the use of the Mount Palomar telescope promises even greater achievements, instruments have so far explored with varying degrees of precision a region out to some 500 million light-years in radius. Preliminary research in this domain

[37] *System of Stars* (1905), 349; cf. same author's *History of Astronomy during the 19th Century*, 422.

[38] Hubble, E., *The Realm of Nebulae* (1936).

established two broad and approximate results of great significance. First, the distribution of nebulae in space, when sufficiently large regions are considered, is uniform. In all directions and to the limits of the most deeply penetrating surveys the nebulae seem to illustrate a homogeneous distribution. Secondly, as Hubble discovered, there is a regular connection between the spectra of nebula and their distance. The greater the distance of the nebula the greater the redshift in its spectrum. This phenomenon, when interpreted along familiar lines as a Doppler effect, may be taken as indicating a velocity of recession; in that case, what observation discloses is the linear ratio of velocity to distance. From the observational point of view, continuing research with more powerful instruments will have as its major task determination of the soundness of these generalizations concerning uniformity of distribution and proportion of red-shift to distance, as increasingly larger volumes of space are opened up for exploration. Search for systematic variations or departures from such generalizations will be sought as important clues in determining the over-all structure of the universe of which the observable region is taken as a sample. Meanwhile even with respect to the region already explored complications enter into the picture that may be drawn on the basis of the interpretation given to the red-shift. Different interpretations of the data are offered in accordance with the theoretical approach adopted.

Theoretical cosmology has as its task the building up of idealized models in terms of which given data may be integrated and extrapolations beyond the already observed region may be undertaken as a guide to further research and as a means of testing such conceptual possibilities. At the present time schemes of relativistic cosmology, based on the original researches of Einstein, and more recently the approach of kinematic relativity associated with the work of E. A. Milne, are in the forefront of attention. The former, which takes its start from the use of the field-equations of the general theory of relativity, makes a fundamental assumption that the geometry of physical space is determined by its contents. This has led, after a considerable number of trials, to the introduction of a class of models defining what is characterized as a homogeneous-expanding universe. In general this is conceived as possessed of a finite density of matter and a Riemannian metric that makes it finite and unbounded but with a curvature that is a function of time. Within this schema, however, a number of alternatives are available and, without going into detail here, it may fairly well be said that the data are either not available or sufficiently precise to warrant selection from among these and so effect a determinate choice. Moreover, about the ideas upon which the whole approach is based considerable disagreement exists, so that, for example, from Milne's point of view search for a true physical geometry is altogether unwarranted. On the other hand, his own preference for decisions based on differences of time-reckoning or on a variety of " clock-graduations," cannot be said to be free from all difficulties or to have won universal acceptance.

Because of the above fundamental uncertainties the essential problems confronting cosmology at the present time do not include active debate as to whether there is more than one universe. Rather, research finds itself in a stage of consolidation and extension of its gains on an observational level with respect to what is taken as defining the universe, the collection or " realm " of nebulae accessible to exploration. Until evidence arises of the possibly finite structure of that domain, or the existence of supersystems (not simply in the form of already-known but relatively restricted clusters of galaxies) in some way comparable in magnitude to the entire domain of the observable region, no special purpose is served in speculating about the existence of such supersystems. No evidence of even a problematic observational sort at the present time suggests the warrant for such flights of imagination.[39] At the same time, responsible theory is necessarily beholden to the piecemeal advances of observation for its clues and checks. Until, therefore, the hypothesis of the finite expanding universe is in some way adequately verified, questions which might be raised now about its uniqueness are faced with even more serious difficulties. Not the least of these would be to give some accurate account in scientifically acceptable terms of what the manner of co-existence of such universes might mean and of the possibility of their verification.

We note, in conclusion, the need to recognize two levels on which the terms " world " or " universe " may be used, one where they designate what is admitted or recognized as a sub-system, the other where the terms are used to designate what is taken as the all-inclusive system. Where there is agreement reached about the status of " worlds " or " universes " as sub-systems, retention of these terms to designate such sub-systems is a terminological hang-over from the days of controversy. At best they have a kind of metaphoric signifi-

[39] See E. Hubble, *Observational Approach to Cosmology* (Oxford, 1937), 18–19.

cance. For purposes of clarity, however, it is preferable to drop their use altogether and to use such technical terms as will indicate their recognized status as sub-systems in what at a given time is taken as an acceptable scheme of classification. Thus "worlds" or "universes" become, as the case may be, "planets," "stars," "planetary systems," "stellar systems," "nebulae." When used most appropriately, the terms "world" and "universe" designate what is taken to be the all-inclusive system of heavenly bodies.

However, there is no way of knowing in advance or independently of empirical inquiry whether an established synthesis of incorporated sub-systems will prove to be the "last" or not. Widening horizons in cosmology, consequently, are always one step at a time. The equivalent of the Kantian critical notion of a regulative use of the concept of totality would amount in effect to a reinforcement of all the reminders that a given or found synthesis is not to be accepted as necessarily the last. If we take the term "universe" in its etymological sense, we may speak of cosmology as concerned with a "turning into one" of its data, with trying constantly to arrive at the goal of a systematic and inclusive ordering of its subject matter. The oneness of the universe in the minimum sense of its uniqueness is thus not something antecedently guaranteed; it rests upon empirical evidence that is by its very nature subject to correction. Uniqueness, therefore, is a regulative standard of cosmological inquiry, attainment of which may be claimed by particular theories in their description of the "universe," but which is not and never can be absolutely assured.

~ઙ Philip P. Wiener

SIR JAMES JEANS ON
PHYSICS AND PHILOSOPHY

Thales of Miletus, astronomer and philosopher, was an authority on solar eclipses, and asserted that all things were watery and "full of gods." Sir James Jeans, twenty-five hundred years later, is engaged in a similar dual rôle, enjoying, however, the rich resources of the history of physical science and philosophy from which to compose "The reflections of a physicist on some of the problems of philosophy." This should be the sub-title of the book, he tells us in his preface, which announces also that recent developments of theoretical physics make it "interesting and important" to explore questions "far beyond the technical problems of physics and philosophy which touch human life very closely, such as materialism and free-will. Thus I hope the book may interest many who are neither physicists nor philosophers by profession." Finally, the brief but illuminating preface reveals that the author's "acquaintance with philosophy is simply that of an intruder," and that he has received valuable criticisms and suggestions from Sir Arthur Eddington and Professor J. B. S. Haldane. It is well known that in their philosophic views these two eminent British scientists espouse subjective idealism and dialectical materialism respectively.

In his earlier popularizations of astronomy and physics (*The Universe Around Us, The Mysterious Universe, The Stars in Their Courses*), Jeans followed admirably and with a deserved best-seller's success the excellent tradition of British scientists who have brilliantly diffused their knowledge and the spirit of their explorations to a wide public without violating the high standards of clarity and accuracy which are the pride and glory of all men of science. The names of Boyle, Gilbert, Herschel, Faraday, Tyndall, Huxley, Clifford, Russell, and others stand for a splendid achievement in the *haute vulgarisation* of physical science in Great Britain. Yet distinguished scientists in thus serving the public have left themselves open to serious criticisms when they extend their published forays into questions beyond their special field of competence, so that we now have a right to expect some cognizance of these criticisms of their extra-scientific speculations. Such cognizance is unfortunately lacking in Jeans's invasion of epistemology and the history of physics and philosophy, which he surveys within the compass of a small volume. It is a fallacy of composition (in both the logical and literary senses) to think that a book is more interesting if it touches on a great many interesting questions, especially when scant space or consideration is given to each and when the questions border on those of technical physics and philosophy. If the result is confusing to the physicist and philosopher, the book can hardly be expected to clarify the mind of the lay reader.

So long as the history of scientific ideas and of their social and philosophical matrix have not been systematically and critically studied by their popularizers, such attempts as this one of Jeans are bound to grow wild in the uncultivated borderlands lying between a special science and other disciplines. The scientific specialist when he wishes to deal with the humanistic aspects and ramifications of his science should be ready to assume the extra burden of historical, philological, and philosophical researches required. Perhaps those who do conduct these researches have neglected the ideas vital to the history of science, so that the public will get its notions about the progress and broad implications of science from scientists of reputation disporting themselves on a philosophic holiday. In any case, Jeans's book shows that the history of scientific ideas in their wider reaches cannot be left simply to experts who have manipulated these ideas successfully within their own specialty. We look in vain for the continuity of recent developments in physics with the cumulative achievements of previous scientific thought or with the main streams of philosophic inquiry into the foundations of physical science. To substantiate these rather strong reactions to Jeans's latest book, the reviewer submits the following selected items.

1. "A direct questioning of nature by experiment has shown the philosophical background hitherto assumed by physics to have been faulty" (2). Surely the history of physics and philosophy shows more than one such background. Even if we confine ourselves to the seventeenth century, every beginning student knows of the controversies between Ptolemaists and Copernicans over "saving the appearances," between Galileo and the Aristotelians who would not look through his telescope, between Newton and Leibniz over space and time and God, between Boyle and Spinoza over the limits of experimental knowledge, between Descartes and Leibniz over *vis viva* and the essence of matter. No mention is made by Jeans of the Cambridge neoplatonism in Newton's philosophic background, nor why the French materialists found Newton more congenial to their philosophy than the Cartesian physics which was for some time more popular in England than in France. Again, the positivistic philosophy of science is treated by Jeans as represented solely by Comte, to the complete neglect of the much more important physical theories of Mach and Duhem who had different philosophical backgrounds and very different interpretations of the history of science, differing from one another as well as from Comte.

2. After quoting Huyghens, who wrote in 1690: "In true philosophy, the causes of all natural phenomena are conceived in mechanical terms. We must do this, in my opinion, or give up all hope of ever understanding anything in physics," Jeans adds: "Today the average man probably holds very similar opinions" (13). Surely the "average man" has but the roughest comprehension of what Huyghens or his contemporaries understood by a mechanical explanation, if we recall that to them it meant explanation

in geometric terms of transmission of motion by contact and of central forces. The electro-magnetic theories of Maxwell and Faraday clung with difficulty to this type of explanation, but the difficulty is not made clear by Jeans (120 ff.). Does Jeans think he can really convince "the average man" why all mechanical explanation "has failed and must fail" if the grounds for its alleged complete failure are provided by the technical considerations of relativity and quanta theory? The fact is that apart from the special phenomena covered by these technical theories, the classical Newtonian mechanics is still valid for most of the phenomena ordinarily encountered where velocities do not approach that of light. It is extremely doubtful that all physicists or philosophers, let alone the "average man," will find at all convincing Jeans's arguments that the new physics of large-scale and small-scale phenomena imply a mentalistic view of space, time, and "ultimate reality." While it is true that the "common-sense" of "the average man" does reflect the uncriticized repository of ancient metaphysical and scientific theories embedded in language, it is important to show the conflicting diversity of these theories and the need for critical clarification of them when employed in explanations. No jury would excuse a heinous crime deliberately committed, on the ground alleged by Jeans that the "average man" believes in prerelativity mechanistic determinism and hence that criminals cannot act of their own free-will. Nor did "mechanistic philosophers" who accepted mechanical explanations *in physics* (as 'non-teleological'), find it necessary to accept the same sort of explanation for human actions. This is amply evident in Descartes, Newton, Kant, and even in Hobbes whose political sagacity rests on his psychological insights rather than on his professed mechanistic materialism.

3. Jeans never intimates that the fact that physicists today still find Newtonian mechanics adequate to deal with many "man-sized facts," is evidence that there is a fundamental continuity in the history of their science. Hence it is sheer unwarranted mystification for Jeans to talk about the complete failure of classical physics in the way dialectical materialists and other theologically-minded critics of science do in their discussions of the "failure and crisis of contemporary culture." When a fundamental change occurs in the theoretical framework of a science it is not because of some external social revolution or spiritual or epistemological crisis, but because certain experimental findings are not logically explained by the prevailing theories within the science itself. No school of philosophy has ever been able to undermine the cumulative logical continuity of science.

4. Many points in the history of philosophy are grossly misstated; the following are only samples: (a) Thales, Epicurus, Heraclitus, and Bruno are cited as great names in science as well as in philosophy (17, 20); (b) Hegel is reported as regarding the "workshop of the philosopher" to be "his own brain" (17); (c) Plato, we are repeatedly told, presented the

Ideas as ultimate realities residing only "in our minds" (33 ff.); (d) the "rationalists" are all assigned to the Continent (38) and held to maintain that the highest truths reside in our own minds, whereas the "empiricists" are all consigned to Great Britain and made to affirm that truth lies outside our minds (34). Poor Kant suffers most of all in Jeans's handling of "certain threads which run clearly through the history of philosophy" (17), when we are told that Kant claimed that it ought to be possible "to construct 'a pure science of nature,' which should be independent of all experience of the world," and "attempted a reasoned discussion of this question in his famous *Critique of Pure Reason*" (35), a similar view being held, according to Jeans, by Plato and Eddington. Although Kant did seek a metaphysic of nature in his *Metaphysische Anfangsgründe der Naturwissenschaft* (published posthumously long after the *Critique* and differing essentially from it as well as from Kant's precritical or Leibnizian philosophy of science), everybody knows that the whole aim of Kant's *Critique* was to show the impossibility of any scientific knowledge of objects beyond possible experience, such as Plato's Ideas or Eddington's Mind or Jeans's "ultimate reality." Kant worked in vain when he thought he had proved by means of his antinomies the impossibility of determining the size of the material universe or its duration, for Jeans finds the hyphen inserted between space and time in recent physics has done away with all of Kant's arguments! There is no historical or logical justification for Jeans's inference that Roemer's measurement in 1676 of the speed of light and Bradley's discovery in 1725 of aberration "show that space and time are not totally independent of one another as Kant and many others seem to have imagined" (63), on the ground alleged by Jeans that Kant did not appear to know that light takes time to travel through space. Anybody knowing how close a student Kant was of the astronomical literature of his day (Newton, Maupertuis, Bradley, Euler), would scarcely suspect Kant of such ignorance, even though Adickes has shown in his two-volume work on *Kant als Naturforscher* (Berlin, 1924–5) that Kant was no more than a brilliant amateur when it came to matters of scientific detail.[1] In any case, a closer study of Kant on Jeans's part would have helped him avoid making amateurish errors concerning Kant. It is well known also that "space-time" could not come into scientific use until the work of Riemann and Minkowski, and that no relativity considerations have any bearing on many of Kant's epistemological questions about space and time unhyphenated.

[1] An exact and direct reference to the velocity of light in Kant was pointed out to me by my friend, Jerome Rosenthal, who shared my suspicions about Jeans's inaccuracies, and to whom I owe very much in matters of intellectual history. The reference is to be found in the first footnote to Kant's short essay, published in 1794, *Etwas über den Einfluss des Mondes auf die Witterung*, where Kant tells us it takes *about* 1 1/5 seconds for light to reach us from the moon. This accords with Roemer sufficiently to refute Jeans's statement (63) of Kant's ignorance of the fact.

In his criticisms of Eddington's misguided attempt to revive a priorism in physics after it has become discredited in philosophy (72), Jeans fails to make clear why a priori knowledge has become discredited in philosophy. A proper understanding of Kant would have helped here also.

5. A most flagrant type of confusion that occurs in Jeans's book is his account of the differences between science and philosophy both with regard to method and subject-matter. "The tools of science are observation and experiment; the tools of philosophy are discussion and contemplation" (81). This over-simplified contrast leaves us in the dark with regard to the rôle of logical discourse in science and of experience in philosophy. The "two voices of philosophy and science" cannot be, as Jeans claims, expressions of "facts as they are revealed by our primitive senses" *versus* facts "revealed by instruments of precision" (84), since theories and hypotheses play a large rôle in the formulation of both types of facts in science and philosophy. Nor is it correct to say that "the philosopher usually thinks in terms of qualities, the scientist in terms of quantities" (89). Here Jeans missed a chance to contribute to the historical epistemological controversy over primary and secondary qualities. He could have explained why Galileo, Descartes, and their contemporaries treated the geometric properties for which they had worked out methods of measurement as *primary* or inherent properties of bodies, whereas the remaining properties for which they had no ordering rules were relegated to the vaguer subjective world. Nowadays, as Jeans should know, mathematical science is not restricted to quantity. In these matters Jeans should have referred to the historical development of scientific logic from its classical subject-predicate form to the more general relational logic.

6. Jeans's treatment of Zeno's paradoxes leads him to reject the law of excluded middle as well as the "strait path of formal logic" (95). Dialectical materialism may be the source of Jeans's confusion here.[2] The same source may account also for his attempt to define causality in terms of "the whole previous state of the world" or "the state of the world at this instant," so that for him there is "no justification for dividing the happenings of the world into detached events" (103). What scientist or sane person has ever tried to find the cause of anything by considering the state of the whole world at an instant? And how does anybody proceed to solve a causal problem without detaching relevant from irrelevant events?

The more trustworthy portions of the book are to be found in the discussion of the contributions of Planck, Rutherford, Bohr, Heisenberg, De

[2] Jeans never alludes to the more important critics of the law of excluded middle, namely, Brouwer and his school of constructionists, who far from abandoning the "strait path of formal logic," insist on more formally rigorous foundations for mathematical proofs.

Broglie, Schrödinger, and Dirac to the new physics, where Jeans is more at home. The *evolution* of this new physics is everywhere subordinated by Jeans to its novel aspects, and in this regard, is treated much more clearly in the popular but accurate work of Einstein and Infeld, *The Evolution of Physics.* It can only confuse the layman when he is told by Jeans: "The theory of relativity deals with measures of things, and not with things themselves, and so can never tell us anything about the nature of the things with the measures of which it is concerned. In particular it can tell us nothing as to the nature of space and time" (68), and "the physical theory of relativity has now shown (134, 137) that electric and magnetic forces are not real at all; they are mere mental constructs of our own" (200). Are not mental constructs also "real"? But of course only those who follow Jeans's transcendental epistemology would call an electric shock a "mental construct."

The last chapter on the problem of free-will reveals the high but futile idealism of the author. He assumes that the progress of physics throws light on the ethical problem. "The old physics showed us a universe which looked more like a prison than a dwelling-place. The new physics shows us a universe which looks as though it might conceivably form a dwelling-place for free men, and not a mere shelter for brutes" (246). The ancient poets and philosophers had no need to resort to physical theories in order to know the bondage of the passions and of social injustice, and our war-torn world will not find the freedom it seeks in the new physics. In his popular survey of an important segment of the history of thought, Jeans has made a fundamental error in transferring the locus of the problem of human freedom from its social context to a dubious philosophy of physics.

~§ *André Lalande*

HENRI POINCARÉ: FROM *SCIENCE AND HYPOTHESIS* TO *LAST THOUGHTS* *

It was at the close of the nineteenth and the beginning of the twentieth century that Henri Poincaré wrote the articles brought together in the series of his works *Science and Hypothesis* (Paris, 1902), *The Value of Science* (Paris, 1905), *Science and Method* (Paris, 1909), *Last Thoughts* (Paris, 1913). Of these four volumes [1] the first is the most negative. Its leading idea may be summarized in two theses: first, that science cannot know any absolute truth concerning nature since all it can establish with certainty is the relation of certain principles to certain consequences, or of a hypothesis to what it implies; secondly, that a great many results claimed by science have nothing necessary about them and result from " conventions " adopted by scientists not without reason and yet by free choice, for among many possible conventions they have selected those that were " convenient " (*commodes*), although others could be substituted without any contradiction. Classical geometry is not more *true* than non-euclidean geometries; the only advantage of the former is that of being simpler. Is it a fact that the Earth turns around the Sun? It is really a hypothesis accepted by the astronomer and handed down to common sense where it is crystallized into a fact. By accepting it, despite appearances contrary to our senses, we have a more aesthetic picture of the world and our calculations are facilitated. But nothing would strictly prevent our leaving the Earth stationary; only that would produce a complication too cumbersome for a complete cosmography.

The expressions " convention " and " convenience " (*commodité*) caused consternation, but Poincaré was not vexed by it. However, these terms were exploited by the enemies of science who were delighted to see its authority weakened; but Poincaré refused to admit that. In the aftermath of his publications, during a very lively session of the *Société de philosophie*, he reacted vigorously against those who wished to convert his critical reservations into a weapon against the value of experiment and reasoning; whence the title of his second volume, *The Value of Science*.

Paradoxical though some of his formulations might appear, they still adhered to a broad stream of thought which can be traced back to the

* Translated by Philip P. Wiener [from Professor Lalande's article in *Le Monde* (Paris, 18 mai, 1954), p. 9, issue dedicated to the Hundredth Anniversary of the Birth of Henri Poincaré] with the kind permission of Professor Lalande and the Editor of *Le Monde*.

[1] The first three of these four books were translated (1905-1907) by George Bruce Halsted (a student of C. S. Peirce at Johns Hopkins) and published together as *The Foundations of Science* by The Science Press in 1913, with a special preface by H. Poincaré and an introduction by Josiah Royce (1855-1916), a second edition was published in 1946 by The Science Press (Lancaster, Pa.).

scientific philosophy of Whewell and even to the " Copernican revolution " of Kant. Poincaré was not ignorant of the philosophy of his time. He was acquainted with the doctoral thesis of his brother-in-law Emile Boutroux (1845-1921) on *La Contingence des Lois de la Nature* (Paris, 1874) [*The Contingency of the Laws of Nature*]. He had probably read the articles in which Charles S. Peirce founded ' pragmatism,' [1a] developed so brilliantly (but not without distortion) under the later influence of William James. Poincaré freely quoted Ernst Mach and his ingenious theory of the " economy of thought." It was also the time when Gaston Milhaud (1858-1918) was writing his *Essai sur les conditions et les limites de la certitude logique* (Paris, 1898, 2d. edition) [*Essay on the Conditions and Limits of Logical Certainty*] and Pierre Duhem (1861-1916) was writing his *Théorie physique: son objet, sa structure* (Paris, 1905).[2] When we reinsert Poincaré's bold philosophical utterances into this intellectual atmosphere, they are far from appearing excessive.

Moreover, they were subordinated in his thought to a solid faith in truth and reason. If it is necessary and important to make room in our knowledge of nature and even in geometry for the will, convention, and intellectual convenience, that does not take anything away from science's moral value or power. " The search for truth," he writes " should be the aim of our activity; it is its only worthy goal . . . . And when I speak of truth, undoubtedly I mean first of all scientific truth, but I also mean moral truth, what is called justice being one of its aspects. It is for the very same reasons that we are led to love and doubt them." Many pages of *Dernières Pensées* [*Last Thoughts*] might be found which develop this aspect of his philosophy.

When we recall his philosophy today, we must accordingly be wary of reducing it to a few formulas which have become famous for their novelty. Neither scientists nor philosophers speak any longer in terms of " convenience " or " convention," although M. Dupréel in a very well balanced and precise article [3] has shown the full import of this term. But the character of science which Poincaré wished to express has not disappeared, and has perhaps even become the acquisition of thinking men.

In the first place, what Poincaré felt strongly is that man's science is not a more and more exact copy of a body of laws already made and inscribed beforehand in the structure of things around us or in the anthropomorphic

---

[1a] The French translation of Peirce's two articles on " The Fixation of Belief " and " How To Make Our Ideas Clear " (*Pop. Sci. Monthly*, 1877–78) appeared in the *Revue Philosophique* (Dec. 1878 and Jan. 1879) without the word ' pragmatism ' occurring in either the original or French versions. Peirce himself objected to Poincaré's nominalist, pragmatist, and finitist philosophy of science, and sided with Cantor against Poincaré's attack on Cantorian realistic views of infinity.—P. P. W.

[2] *The Aim and Structure of Physical Theory*, transl. by Philip P. Wiener (Princeton University Press, 1954) from the second edition (Paris, 1912).

[3] " Convention et Raison," *Revue de Métaphysique et de Morale* (juillet 1925).

intelligence of a Great Architect of the Universe, but a work analogous to that of our morality, of our art, or of our languages involving, no doubt, fundamental norms but also contingencies and decisions which might be different. The world which science causes us to become acquainted with is but the most recent stage of the constructions raised in common by scientists and philosophers on the basis of our sense impressions and in accordance with the guidance of our reason.

In the second place, he brought out vividly the fundamental procedure in all the sciences of reasoning, experimental or otherwise; this procedure, he showed, consists of setting up a definitive " axiomatic " system, as we now say, from which consequences follow whose value is then judged retroactively by their agreement with what exists independently of us. Nobody has done more than he in France to bring home to educated men the idea that Euclid's system of axioms is not endowed with metaphysical truth, and that on this point it does not differ in any way from Riemann's or Lobatchevski's axiomatic systems. In that respect he was one of the precursors of what M. Bachelard has ingeniously called " the philosophy of No [*La philosophie du Non*, Paris, 1940]," of the critical method which systematically explores the regions to which we would be led by the hypothetical negation of such and such a principle accepted traditionally.

Poincaré has often been reproached for having believed that classical geometry would always remain the most " convenient," and that it would be preferable, should an adverse case arise, to admit actions by new physical forces rather than change the geometry. But that proves only that, as Meyerson used to say, " we do not put reason to task right away on the first trial." And so Poincaré's error in his prognosis even confirms his main thesis: for it is precisely because it was found more convenient to use a space of constant or variable curvature that non-Euclidean space was preferred.

And if we were to object that the chief reason for abandoning the simplest axiom-system, *i.e.*, Euclid's, despite its analytical advantages and despite common-sense habits, is primarily the assimilation or identification thus obtained among domains originally very distinct, there again a normative idea even if not in the foreground of Poincaré's thought, nevertheless appears to have been present in his thought: the supreme value of identity. With respect to the assimilation of things among themselves, he offered the remark that the great aim of science was to discover invariants, and if the evolution of creatures were admitted, we could not suppose an evolution of laws without rendering all knowledge impossible. But it is above all with respect to the assimilation of minds to one another that he recognized the sovereignty of identity:

" Whether we adopt the viewpoint of ethics, aesthetics, or science, it is always the same thing: nothing is objective except what is identical for all."

I. Bernard Cohen

SOME RECENT BOOKS ON THE HISTORY OF SCIENCE

I

The historian of science faces a problem of audience (for whom are his books and articles written?) which is not encountered, at least on the same scale, by scholars in other disciplines. Modern physics, for example, is written in a mathematical language that non-scientists cannot understand and is based on concepts and experiments that are outside their range of knowledge. Thus a history of electrical theories from Franklin's concept of a single "fluid" to quantum electrodynamics, if simply addressed to the subject without thought of the reader and written on the scholarly plane expected of studies in other fields, would be intelligible only to scientists (and not to all scientists, not even all physical scientists) and unintelligible to almost all historians, philosophers, and students of the history of ideas. And the paradox in this situation is that by and large the scientists who could understand such a history would not be much interested in reading it. It is all very well to say contributions to the history of science should be addressed to other historians of science, but then we are faced with a whole complex of further problems. Not the least of these is the bare fact that the number of professional historians of science is too small to justify publication. But even if the number were larger, the very scope of the history of science would indicate a limitation of audience for all but the most general works. An historian of science specializing in, let us say, ancient astronomy or mediaeval mechanics might be as hard put to understand the data of the history of electrical theory as the student of nineteenth-century French literature or eighteenth-century political theories. The history of science, by definition, includes the development of all aspects of scientific activity from the earliest times to the present, and the cultivation of science or a proto-science in all lands and all sorts of cultures; and if we add to that the study of the social and cultural matrices in which this scientific activity occurred, and also the effects of science on other human activities, the discipline of the history of science is found to encompass nothing less than practically the whole of human history. So we can understand why George Sarton has come, more and more, to think of the history of science as the major part of "the history of civilization."

Now most students of the history of ideas would not agree that the history of "civilization," or even the history of thought, can be reduced to the development of scientific ideas and their sources and influences. While appreciating that scientific ideas are an essential part of the complex of ideas in any given portion of history—and more essential in some periods or cultures than in others—the historian of ideas in general is more apt to value the history of science as an ancillary discipline to his own than as the be-all and end-all of historical research or even as an independent sphere of activity. Thus, the historian of science, if he wishes to make his re-

627

search have the impact on scholarship it deserves, must consciously strive to make his results intelligible to others, a word that includes " other " historians of science just as much as " other " kinds of historians. Even so, the historian of ideas must not expect the historian of science to provide him with an easy and popular introduction to science; if the historian of science had to write a scientific primer into each of his works, he would never get around to presenting the research the learned world expects of him. The student of nineteenth-century ideas, after all, must learn the major ideas of that century, including the scientific ideas, as a part of his primary frame of reference. But he has the right to expect that the historian of science can, at least, help him by indicating the nature and significance of the major concepts and their relevance to the chief problems of science at that time and to the development of science in the coming age. The historian of ideas who studies the effects or influences of science in, let us say, the age of Newton should study Newtonian science in the very books which actually were the sources of knowledge to the thinking men and women of the eighteenth century; the latter, by and large, did not " read " the *Principia,* save for a bit here and there, but learned about its doctrine in splendid vulgarizations written by Pemberton, Maclaurin, and Voltaire, or in textbooks by 'sGravesande, Desaguliers, and Clarke's edition of Rohault. But students of Newtonianism need the historian of science to evaluate the presentations of Pemberton, Maclaurin, Voltaire, 'sGravesande, Desaguliers, and Clarke, and to correct the distortions that arise from the fact that these writers were too close to the time of Newton. Historians of science have ably illuminated the meaning of the Newtonian achievement in terms of the main currents of physics and astronomy in the centuries antecedent to Newton, but as yet they have not fulfilled the obligation to indicate the failures of the *Principia,* its mistakes and its unresolved problems, which constituted a major challenge to the scientists of the eighteenth and even the nineteenth century. We may search in vain throughout the general literature on Newton and Newtonianism for a fully adequate analysis of Book Two of the *Principia;* this " book," comprising about a third of Newton's *opus majus,* was devoted entirely to the subject of fluid mechanics. Although " almost all of the results are original, . . . but few [are] correct," and the program " of deriving all results rationally from the ' axioms, or laws of motion,' while fairly successful for mass-points in Book I, broke down completely in Book II, where a fresh hypothesis starts up at every turn." [1] Thus the history of modern rational fluid mechanics begins in the questioning and ultimate rejection of Newton's results and their replacement by new principles. Other problems faced by Newton's successors, and not fully explored by historians of science, include the doctrine of the æther proposed by Newton to account for gravitation, chemical action, optical and physiological effects, and the physical properties or behaviour of bodies—how did Newton's imperfect speculations react on the production of explanations in electricity, heat, and

---

[1] C. Truesdell, preface to L. Euler, *Opera Omnia,* series 2, vol. 12, to be published shortly in Zürich by Füssli for the Swiss Society of Natural Sciences.

so on, and how were they related to the " field " theories of Faraday and Clerk Maxwell? And what was the scope of influence of Newton's atomism and his writings on chemistry: how did his successors attempt to resolve the problems he raised and could not solve?

The familiar example of Newtonian science serves to indicate the kind of illumination to the historian of ideas that can, or should, be provided by the monographs written by specialists in the history of science; a like situation could be indicated in a consideration of almost every aspect of science and practically every period. I believe it is no exaggeration to say that current misunderstandings about the science of the past, wrong emphases, lack of information, and faulty interpretations in the literature of the history of ideas may serve as one of the best guides to the historian of science in formulating his program of research and writing, and indicating some of the major areas where work needs to be done. This statement is not intended as a criticism of the literature of the history of ideas so much as a description of a state of affairs that has been caused by the general lack of adequate secondary works in so many fields of the history of science. I believe it true that, however critical historians of science may be of other historians who deal with science, most historians of science cannot help but admire the general historians who attempt to explore the implications of science without the aid they have come to expect from every other discipline save the history of science.

This situation is in good measure a result of the relative newness of the history of science [2] as a professional subject: a point to which I shall have to refer more than once in the following pages. Of course, research in the history of science is at least as old as modern science itself; certain genuine works on the history of science were produced by the battle of the books, or the quarrel of the ancients and the moderns, such as Wotton's *Reflections on Ancient and Modern Learning*. In the seventeenth century, editions were made of important scientific classics, such as Halley's Apollonius and Wallis's Aristarchus. In the eighteenth century there were produced many works of a high quality: Delambre's writings on the history of astronomy, Priestley on the history of electricity and of optics, Montucla on mathematics, and others come immediately to mind. Many of these older histories are still valuable tools of research today, and some of them may even display a better grasp of the development of science than part of the literature produced in the twentieth century. It may be noted, furthermore, that the best of these works, like many of the most original scholarly contributions in our own day, were not general histories so much as histories of

---

[2] Many historians do not fully appreciate the extreme youth of the history of science as a professional academic discipline. At present only three American universities have full-scale graduate programs leading to a doctorate in the history of science (Cornell, Harvard, Wisconsin), although there are others where the history of medicine (Johns Hopkins, Wisconsin, Yale) and ancient mathematics and astronomy (Brown) may be studied. Cf. the writer's editorial in *Science*, vol. 114, No. 2973, Dec. 21, 1951.

special subjects or works that dealt with special areas or periods. One presumes that the readers for whom these works were intended were scientists, and it is notable that the authors of the works mentioned above—notably Wallis, Halley, Delambre, and Priestley—were scientists of the first rank. Their books, therefore, can probably be described correctly as studies on the historical development of the sciences written by scientists for other scientists. Today, the scientists are not as interested in the history of science, and in many cases even in the history of their own disciplines, as their prototypes apparently were in the seventeenth and eighteenth centuries. The history of science is, by the same token, not written today so much by practicing scientists as by historians of science, and other types of historians who have become interested in the development of science as it relates to their own field of activity.

The heroic pioneers of the history of science—like Paul Tannery, Moritz Cantor, Karl Sudhoff, George Sarton, Lynn Thorndike, Pierre Duhem, Charles H. Haskins, Charles Singer, and many others—were to a considerable degree self-taught and self-trained in the history of science, and those of the next generation, while necessarily critical, can afford to be so because these founders have begun to establish new standards from which— as scholarship moves forward—their very works can be examined and reassessed. Even so, the number of professionally trained historians of science who devote themselves exclusively to the subject are few in number, and they are spread over a wide spectrum of research. The history of science is so broad an area that the problem of communication is as great, and possibly greater, than in the sciences themselves. Those who study the history of mathematics may have neither the training nor the background to understand the problems in the history of biology, which may hold no interest for them; and in the same way, a student of pre-Greek science may not be particularly interested or concerned with research in, let us say, the rise of scientific societies in nineteenth-century America. A work written on ancient astronomy might, therefore, be of greater interest to those who study ancient history, ancient literature, or ancient philosophy than those who are scientists or who are interested in the history of modern science; but the great difficulty is that scholars in these areas of ancient history or ancient culture are often poorly equipped to understand the technical aspects of Greek astronomy. A similar situation exists in the study of the scientific writings of Isaac Newton; although many scholars are interested in " Newtonianism," only a small number of them have sufficient training in mathematics, physics, astronomy, and the history of science to be able to read with profit and understanding a technical study of this subject.

The student of the history of ideas is apt to value most those works in the history of science which are intelligible to him even though the most penetrating and original research may be difficult to understand, even to the point of incomprehensibility. Since the historian of science is apt to be in the same situation as the historian of ideas with regard to subjects and periods which are not within his own primary field of specialty, such general works are apt to be as valuable to the historian of science as to the historian of ideas. Yet those who are making the greatest progress in advancing our knowledge of the history of science appreciate the fact that although their works may be readily accessible to only a small number of readers, this number is constantly increasing: a concomitant of the growing realization that an understanding of the rôle of science, even in its cultural aspects, demands and is worth serious and time-consuming study.

One of the primary jobs of the historian of science is, of course, to correct the inadequacies of earlier writings in the history of science, which were in so many instances produced by amateurs who labored heroically to produce a subject called the history of science, where none had existed before. And, in the same way, the writings of historians of science will probably always need the corrective efforts of specialists in other areas. The historian of science can never hope to be the equal of, say, a classical philologist in his own field, and the latter will no doubt be able to call attention to errors in erudition or background in any work on classical antiquity produced by an historian of science. But, even so, such a work should inform and illuminate all classical studies which deal with ideas—else it were a failure.

Examples have been given above of the difficulty in understanding the historical aspects of modern physics, but they could easily be multiplied by considering any other part of the science of the last 300 years. For example, the vast literature on Darwinism, more of it written by general historians and social scientists than by biologists and historians of science, is apt to betray a woeful ignorance of what has happened during the last half-century (the rise of genetics and its application to evolution); all too often we are apt to encounter a parody of science itself in the reduction of Darwin to a minor position (was not every one of his ideas stated at least once at some earlier time from ancient Greece to the eighteenth century?). There is also current a mistaken idea that the science of modern times may be difficult to comprehend, but anyone can understand the science of antiquity. Well, ancient science can be as technical as modern science. Most philosophers and classicists have shown themselves capable of discussing Plato's cosmology or the scientific atomism of Lucretius, but an astronomer was needed to show in detail the production of retrograde motion in the system of concentric spheres of Eudoxus, and I venture to say that to know the properties of the hippopede, as explained by Schiaparelli, is as difficult as Newton's proof that a homogeneous sphere acts gravitationally as if all its mass were concentrated at its center. The Babylonian treatment of number theory is not, after all, readily comprehensible to the non-mathematician and the Ptolemaic system [3] (or even the system described by Copernicus) requires a formidable study if the scholar really wishes to understand it and to appreciate adequately what it accomplished: its beauties, its achievements, and even its limitations. Nor is the technical science of the middle ages an open book for anyone to read without preparation. Any mediaeval

[3] Cf. the remarks below, apropos of Neugebauer's recent book on ancient mathematics and astronomy, in section V.

treatise on the system of the world, or motion, or statics, or optics, or the latitude of forms is as difficult for the non-specialist as the methods of " integration " of Archimedes.

The general historian or the historian of ideas can no more hope to read many of the major original scientific treatises of the past than he can those of the present. So, for the most part, he must rely on the monographs and general surveys produced by the historians of science. The latter have, as a result, an obligation to their other scholarly colleagues to make available from time to time the results of the research in their field. Every historian of science has, in other words, a double obligation: to produce original scholarly research which may or may not be generally understandable to those without his own special competences, and also to help to make his work and that of his colleagues a part of the knowledge of every historian who may be concerned in any way with the culture in which that science was produced or which was affected by it. I believe that in this way the historian of science may serve himself as well as others, not only by making the fruits of research in his own field more widely used, but also by in this way calling attention to the essential worth of his own specialty and thereby gaining support for it. Although on occasion the monographic literature of the history of science may be ably and brilliantly summarized and interpreted by the general historian,[4] there can never be a substitute for the presentation of any subject by its master, as countless examples show.[5]

In the following presentation of some of the recent literature of the history of science, I have attempted to show the significance of each work for the student of the history of ideas. I have, largely, limited myself to general presentations or specialized monographs that contain general interpretive surveys.[6] Some works discussed below contain new or little known material or a novel point of view, but others go over familiar ground in a way that may equally be of use to historians of science and historians of ideas. Some of the books are initiations into the subject. The list is, of course, by no means exhaustive and is not meant to include a complete guide to the literature of the history of science of the last several years, nor even of the " best " recent books in the history of science. Omissions, therefore, do not indicate a gross inferiority in the books presented but rather their fitting poorly into the general scheme of the essay. Except in one instance, all of the books discussed are written in English. Most of the kinds of current writing in the history of science are represented.

---

[4] Cf. the remarks below, apropos of Butterfield's recent book on the origins of modern science, in section III.

[5] *E.g.*, J. L. Heiberg's *Mathematics and Physical Science in Classical Antiquity* (London, 1922); Sir Thomas Little Heath's *Archimedes* and *The Copernicus of Antiquity* (London, 1920).

[6] Books reviewed are listed in footnotes with the number of pages and illustrations and thus may be easily distinguished from books to which reference is made but which are not reviewed.

II

At a time in world history characterized by anxiety and insecurity, we may see a symbol of encouragement in the projects begun by the two acknowledged leaders in their respective fields—George Sarton in the history of science and Henry E. Sigerist in the history of medicine—who have both retired from all other professional duties to devote themselves to writing surveys of their subjects on a scale and a high level of scholarship and readability never before attempted by a single individual. George Sarton,[7] founder of *Isis* [8] and its editor until his resignation in 1952, founder and editor of the companion volume *Osiris*,[9] and Professor Emeritus of the History of Science at Harvard University, is known to the world of scholarly letters for many valued articles, monographs, and books,[10] but chiefly for his indispensable *Introduction to the History of Science*.[11] He has planned

---

[7] See *Studies and Essays in the History of Science and Learning offered in homage to George Sarton* (New York: Henry Schuman, [no date]); biographical data by Mrs. Sarton [E. M. S.] appear on pp. xi–xiv.

[8] *Isis* was founded in 1912 and became the official organ of the History of Science Society in 1924. From the start, the unique feature of *Isis* has been that, in addition to articles, notes, queries, and book reviews, there have been published periodic " critical bibliographies " covering every possible aspect of the history of science. The last of these to be compiled by Sarton was No. 79 (published in *Isis* *44:* 102–204, 1953) and contained an estimate by Sarton that he had processed over 100,000 entries, many of which were short reviews! Future critical bibliographies are to be prepared by an editorial committee.

[9] *Osiris* was founded in 1936, as a companion to *Isis,* to publish articles and monographs which were too long for the latter. An unusual feature of this series is that each volume was dedicated to a living historian of science and contained his biography and a complete list of his publications. Historians of science so honored by Sarton have been: David Eugene Smith (1936), Sir Thomas Little Heath (1936), Edmund O. v. Lippmann (1937), Paul and Marie Tannery (1938), Julius Ruska (1938), Joseph Bidez (1939), Gino Loria (1939), Paul Ver Eecke (1948), Max Meyerhof (1950), Henri Berr (1952), Lynn Thorndike (in press).

[10] The Sarton *Festschrift* (n. 7) does not contain a bibliography of his published writings—almost 500 articles and books. In addition to his *Introduction* (n. 11, *infra*), his guide to the history of science (n. 30, in section III, *infra*), and his recent volume on Greek science (n. 22, *infra*), Sarton's major books include *The History of Science and the New Humanism* (New York, 1931; Cambridge, 1937), *The Study of the History of Science* (Cambridge, 1936), *The Study of the History of Mathematics* (Cambridge, 1936), *The Life of Science: Essays in the History of Civilization* (New York, 1948), *The Appreciation of Ancient and Medieval Science during the Renaissance* (Philadelphia: University of Pennsylvania Press, [in press]), *Galen of Pergamon* (Lawrence, Kansas: University of Kansas Press [in press]).

[11] *Introduction to the History of Science*, 3 vols. in five parts. Publication No. 376 of the Carnegie Institution of Washington. Vol. 1, " From Homer to Omar Khayyam " (Baltimore, 1927); vol. 2, " From Rabbi ben Ezra to Roger Bacon," pts. i & ii (*Idem*, 1931); vol. 3, " Science and Learning in the Fourteenth Century,"

a series of volumes which will cover the material he presented in his introductory courses at Harvard: these courses were designed for undergraduate students who had taken at least one course (often not more) in the physical or the biological sciences, and the sequence occupied four semesters. Sarton's schedule calls for eight volumes (two per semester) and a ninth to carry the series up to the present. Henry E. Sigerist,[12] founder and editor until 1947 of the *Bulletin of the History of Medicine*,[13] and the companion series *Supplements to the History of Medicine*,[14] William H. Welch Professor of the History of Medicine and Director of the Institute of the History of Medicine at Johns Hopkins until his resignation in 1947, is known for many publications—not only on the history of medicine, but also what we may call medical sociology and medicine in the Soviet Union.[15] He has planned an eight-volume survey of the rise of medicine that is addressed to physicians and historians and that begins with primitive medicine and will end at the present.

The first volumes of the Sarton and Sigerist series have already appeared, but it is fitting to note that the dean of British historians of science, Dr. Charles Singer, for many years associated with the history of science program at University College London,[16] and author of many publications on the history of science (especially the history of biology and of anatomy) and the history of medicine,[17] has planned for early publication a five-

---

pts. i & ii (*Idem*, 1947, 1948). Sarton's *opus majus*, this work contains brief biographical sketches (and bibliographies of primary and secondary sources) of all men and women in any way related to science in every major culture from Homer to A.D. 1400, plus general surveys of the state of science and learning in each half-centurial period.

[12] Cf. the " Henry E. Sigerist Valedictory Number " of the *Bulletin of the History of Medicine*, 22, 1 (Jan.–Feb. 1948), 1–93, and " Henrico E. Sigerist Sexagenario," *Gesnerus* 8 (1951), fasc. 1–2.

[13] The *Bulletin* is the organ of the American Association of the History of Medicine and the Johns Hopkins Institute of the History of Medicine; it was founded in 1933.

[14] The " Supplements " are a series of small books, really long articles. Sigerist has also edited several other series, " Monographs," " Texts and Documents," " The Hideyo Noguchi Lectures," and " Bibliotheca Medica Americana "; cf. n. 12, *supra*, pp. 66–69, for an account of them.

[15] A bibliography of most of Sigerist's publications is given in note 12, *supra*, pp. 70–73, 81–91. Some of his major historical books are: *Man and Medicine: An introduction to medical knowledge* (New York, 1932), *The Great Doctors: A biographical history of medicine* (New York, 1933), *American Medicine* (New York, 1934), *Civilization and Disease* (Ithaca, 1943).

[16] A Singer *Festschrift*, edited by E. Ashforth Underwood, is in press.

[17] Singer's major books are: *The Discovery of the Circulation of the Blood* (London: G. Bell, 1922), *The Evolution of Anatomy: A short history of anatomical and physiological discovery to Harvey* (London: Kegan Paul, 1925), *A Short History*

volume survey of the development of technology, to be issued by the Clarendon Press, of which the first volume is in press and is due to be published in April 1954.[18] And while on the subject of many-volumed series, we may note that Lynn Thorndike, Professor Emeritus of History at Columbia University,[19] known for many valuable tools for the study of mediaeval science,[20] is continuing his famous *History of Magic and Experimental Science* [21] and is currently completing for publication the volumes on the seventeenth century.

Both Sarton and Sigerist have produced volumes that may be called syntheses, in that both of them write from a unified view of the whole development of their respective subjects from earliest beginnings to the present, and the presentations are illuminated by the insight and wisdom acquired in a life-time of devotion to their studies. Both authors have written intensely personal documents, giving way to their prejudices, their enthusiasms, and their values in life generally as well as in science and in history. Finally, both books are written so that the non-specialist may understand them and both present the material in a readable and attractive style.

Sarton's survey of ancient science through the " golden age of Greece " [22]

---

of Medicine: Introducing medical principles to students and non-medical readers (Oxford: Clarendon Press, 1928), *From Magic to Science: Essays on the scientific twilight* (New York: Boni and Liveright, 1928), *A Short History of Science to the Nineteenth Century* (Oxford: Clarendon Press, 1941), with C. Rabin *A Prelude to Modern Science: Being a discussion of the history, sources and circumstances of the " Tabulae Anatomicae Sex" of Vesalius* (Cambridge University Press, 1946), *The Earliest Chemical Industry: An essay in the historical relations of economics and technology illustrated from the alum trade* (London: Folio Society, 1948), *A History of Biology*, (2nd ed., New York: Henry Schuman, 1950), and *Vesalius on the Human Brain* (London: Oxford University Press, 1952).

[18] It is described at the end of section IV, *infra*.

[19] A bibliography of Thorndike's writings will be published in vol. 11 of *Osiris* (cf. n. 9, *supra*).

[20] We may note, especially, *Science and Thought in the Fifteenth Century* (New York, 1929), *A Catalogue of Incipits of Mediaeval Scientific Writings in Latin*, with Pearl Kibre (Cambridge: The Mediaeval Academy of America, 1937), *University Records and Life in the Middle Ages* (New York, Columbia University Press, 1944), *The Herbal of Rufinus*, with Francis S. Benjamin, Jr. (University of Chicago Press, 1945), *The "Sphere" of Sacrobosco and its Commentators* (University of Chicago Press, 1949), *Latin Treatises on Comets between 1238 and 1368 A.D.* (University of Chicago Press, 1950).

[21] *A History of Magic and Experimental Science*. Vols. 1 & 2, " During the first thirteen centuries of our era " (New York, 1923), vols. 3 & 4, " Fourteenth and fifteenth centuries " (New York, 1934), vols. 5 & 6, " The sixteenth century " (*idem*, 1941).

[22] George Sarton, *A History of Science: Ancient science through the golden age of Greece* (xxvi + 646 pp., 103 ills. Cambridge: Harvard University Press, 1952).

deals with the Near East and the Greek world from the earliest times to about the end of the fourth century B.C. Although Sarton proceeds more or less by centurial periods, he divides each period by subject—not that each such sub-division is a specialized history, but rather these sub-divisions enable him to stress one aspect of science and its cultural background rather than another. As a matter of fact, Sarton's strong desire to avoid specialism has caused him to treat only *en passant* many of the technical achievements of ancient science, such as the Babylonian solution of the quadratic equation, pre-Greek knowledge of the " Pythagorean theorem." [23] Sometimes the materials on the cultural and social background actually crowd out the technical aspects of the science of ancient times and, in this sense, that science is actually presented as less than it actually was, although Sarton does fulfill his expressed aim of presenting the history of science as an amalgamation of the "technical and aesthetic pursuits of man." Lest ideas and theories become too abstract and divorced from their creators, Sarton has included brief sketches of the lives of the main characters and has reproduced their portraits whenever possible. Furthermore, so that the reader may see that the ancient thinkers have not merely an antiquarian interest, Sarton always indicates how their writings were introduced into Europe and reproduces, in facsimile, pages of first printed European editions: incunabula and sixteenth- and seventeenth-century texts.

Although Sarton traces the rise of the several branches of sciences—*e.g.*, mathematics, astronomy, physics, geography, botany, zoology, and to some extent medicine and technology—his purpose is never to recount the development of any one of them so much as to consider ancient science in its "wholeness." His main interest is "ancient culture, the whole of it, but focused, as it should be, on ancient science, ancient wisdom." So it is that Sarton has not produced a reference book nor an encyclopaedia but a lively story, well told, of the more or less continuous expansion of man's view of the universe and of himself.

The personal style of this book enables the reader to share Sarton's enthusiasms, *e.g.*, for Aristotle, but not all readers will equally share his prejudices, *e.g.*, against philologists and especially historians of medicine who " have the notion that medicine is the center of science " and who have produced the "main misunderstandings concerning the history of science." Sarton's animosity towards Plato is so deep that Plato almost seems to be living amongst us (Sarton points out that this may actually be the case owing to the " bad " influence of Eddington). From the strict point of view of positive science, Sarton is, of course, correct in attacking Plato's deprecation of actual observation of nature, but the only way to describe his

---

[23] O. Neugebauer (n. 64, *infra*), p. 35, has shown that the "Pythagorean" theorem was known "more than a thousand years before Pythagoras." In other words, " it was known during the whole duration of Babylonian mathematics that the sum of the squares of the lengths of the sides of a right triangle equals the square of the length of the hypotenuse."

judgment that most writers on Plato have been guilty of hypocrisy (in a dishonest veiling of his homosexuality) is to observe that great scholars are entitled to have personal prejudices.[24]

It is, however, all too easy to criticize [25] a mammoth sized book and ignore its virtues. Never before has the whole panorama of ancient science been so displayed for the general reader in its mighty dimensions. The many illustrations are well chosen and beautifully reproduced and the bibliographical notes are extensive. No matter what correctives any specialist may desire, Sarton's book on ancient science will long stand as an extraordinary monument of love for the subject and of learning on a vast scale, unequalled in the annals of scholarship. I doubt whether anyone, no matter what his field of specialization, can read this history without great profit to his knowledge and understanding. All who are drawn to its pages will anxiously await the succeeding volumes in the series.

Sigerist's book on ancient medicine [26] is a fit companion to Sarton's, although quite differently conceived. It consists of four separate essays dealing, respectively, with primitive or archaic medicine, medicine in ancient Egypt, medicine in ancient Mesopotamia, and a general study of the methods, scope, and possible usefulness of the history of medicine. Sigerist has taken into account the fact that a history of medicine is both " a medical book and a history book " and has written his in such a way as to make it most useful to historians and medical men.

Unlike Sarton, who proceeds in the order of strict chronology, Sigerist deals in discrete units. Although " medicine developed at an early date not only in Egypt and Mesopotamia but also in India and China," Sigerist has not included the latter two in his first volume, because " ancient Indian and Chinese medicine are still fully alive and are practiced today on millions of people," while " Egyptian and Babylonian medicine completed their courses long ago." [27] Although the title of the volume is " Primitive and Archaic Medicine," Sigerist does not include " folk medicine " along with the " primitive." Primitive medicine is timeless and could, we are told, have been considered in the last volume as well as the first, but folk medicine, even though it helps to understand primitive medicine, is a " strange mixture of primitive views and reminiscences of scientific systems of the past "; its treatment is reserved by Sigerist to a later volume,

[24] Sarton introduces, 426–430, a history of the " cult of Plato," including a facsimile reproduction of the title page of the " first attack on Platonic philosophy " —by Charles Crawford (London 1773)—and excerpts from personal correspondence with Warner Fite.

[25] For example, Sarton nowhere fully explores the calendarial origins of astronomy.

[26] Henry E. Sigerist, *A history of medicine.* Volume I: Primitive and archaic medicine (xxi + 564 pp., 104 ills. New York: Oxford University Press, 1951).

[27] Furthermore, as Sigerist points out, " The earliest Indian and Chinese medical texts that we possess are . . . decidedly younger than those of Egypt and Mesopotamia."

therefore, since " it recapitulates the entire history of medicine." [28]

All historians of ideas will be interested in the two parts of the general introduction, in which Sigerist discusses " The historical approach to medicine " and " Diseases in time and space." Medical history includes, of course, the growth of medical systems and their relations to philosophical movements and general scientific ideas, but in contrast to the general history of science it lays a greater stress on social history than the development of ideas. Sigerist points out that medicine itself has four major tasks: 1, promotion of health; 2, prevention of illness; 3, restoration of health; 4, rehabilitation. " Medical history, therefore, will study health and disease through the ages, the conditions for health and disease, and the history of all human activities that tended to promote health, to prevent illness, and to restore the sick, no matter who the acting individuals were."

Sigerist introduces the subject of medicine in Egypt and in Mesopotamia by a description of the geographical setting, a brief chronology, and a discussion of the social and economic conditions. Among the Egyptians he finds a highly developed craft of surgery and medical practice, both rational and empirical to some degree, and also speculative theories that " represent the beginning of medical science, a science which was different from our sober natural science but still one which endeavored to explain the phenomena of life and death, of health and disease, rationally without having recourse to the gods. It was a way of thinking in terms of a philosophy of nature, and in doing it the Egyptians anticipated views and methods of the pre-Socratic philosophers of Greece." Thus, Sigerist concludes, it was probably " no accident that the first of them, Thales of Miletos, traveled in Egypt, where he had experience that influenced his philosophy in a decisive way. . . ." Although rational and empirical elements also appear in Mesopotamian medicine, the latter was more magical or religious, relying on divination: illness was " a result of sin or [that] for some other reason an evil spirit had taken hold of [a man and made] him [ill]." The interpretation of omens was the " chief method employed . . . to make diagnosis and prognosis ": hepatoscopy being a major practice. Sigerist only barely mentions the related subject of judicial astrology, and does not address himself at all to the comparison between medicine and exact science in Egypt and Mesopotamia. Whereas Egyptian medicine was rational and empirical, Egyptian astronomy and mathematics was crude and rudimentary. By contrast, the Babylonians developed an intricate and complex mathematics, and their achievements, only recently fully appreciated, still leave us breathless. In astronomy, too, the Babylonians were far in advance of the Egyptians. The historian of science thus finds a paradox in the advanced science of Mesopotamia in contrast to the low state of science in Egypt and Sigerist's discovery of the beginnings of a natural philosophy in Egyptian medicine but not in Mesopotamian.

[28] But primitive medicine seemed to belong in volume one, Sigerist writes, " because it has many elements in common with the medical systems of ancient civilizations."

The student of the history of science, therefore, quits Sigerist's magnificent volume with a sense of admiration mingled with some disappointment. The treatment of Egyptian and Babylonian medicine as more or less discrete units does not permit Sigerist to make an extended contrast between the two. The concentration on medical treatment, health conditions, and their social and economic backgrounds, without much address to the character of Egyptian and Babylonian natural and exact science, isolates the subject from the major considerations of man and nature. In this sense Sigerist has given us an account of man's environment and condition to a greater extent than a contribution to the history of ideas. This brilliant panorama of the state of man in terms of his health and position in the world provides the background to the growth of science, but illuminates the latter only by implication. Sigerist has given a hint that in the later volumes, the emphasis will be altered and we eagerly await his unfolding of the relation of medicine to the major currents of scientific and philosophic ideas.

III

Both the Sarton and the Sigerist volumes satisfy the criteria of readability and intelligibility that make them of exceptional value to the historian of ideas. We may presume that historians generally will always turn to one of the volumes of these series (when completed) for primary illumination on the period or region that they are studying. The footnotes and literature lists in these volumes will also provide an admirable introduction to the sources (both original texts and secondary works).[29] But, not content to await the completion of his series, George Sarton has prepared a general survey of the literature of the history of science which has been published as a mammoth appendix to his London lectures on " Science and Tradition " and which is intended to serve as " A First Guide for the Study of the History of Science." [30] These lectures comprise a personal testament in the form of an answer to two questions: (1) Is it worthwhile to teach the history of science? (2) Is it possible to teach the history of science? Sarton claims that the " first modern " history of science was William Whewell's *History of the Inductive Sciences* (1837) [31] and that the first " satisfactory textbook " in this field was Friedrich Dannemann's *Die Naturwissenschaften in ihrer Entwicklung und in ihrem Zusammenhange* (1910–13).[32] What Sarton admires most in Dannemann's book is that he " really

---

[29] Sigerist has included (499–541) a systematic introduction to the literature of the history of medicine, a job made somewhat simpler by the availability of Walter Artelt, *Einführing in die Medizinhistorik, ihr Wesen, ihre Arbeitsweise und ihre Hilfsmittel* (Stuttgart, 1949).

[30] *Horus: A Guide to the History of Science; A first guide for the study of the history of science, with introductory essays on science and tradition* (xviii + 316 pp., Waltham, Mass.: Chronica Botanica Publishing Co., 1952).

[31] But Sarton points out that Whewell's " purpose was philosophical rather than historical."

[32] It should be noted that Dannemann's history, based largely on primary

tried to explain, as the title put it, 'science in its evolution and "hanging together" (wholeness).'" Sarton has always insisted that the history of science be studied as a unit and not be broken down into a set of histories of each branch of science, although he admits—of course—that general history must always depend on the special histories. But Sarton's major thesis, which should be of exceptional interest to historians of ideas, is that the history of science should serve " to explain the development of mankind or the organization of knowledge " and that this aim forces the historian of science to transcend the narrow limitations of scientific specialism in history.

The " First Guide " prepared by Sarton (with the assistance of Claudius F. Mayer for some sections) is divided into four major parts: history; science; history of science; organization of the study and teaching of the history of science. Historians of ideas will find the third part (history of science, occupying almost 150 pages) of greatest value. The many subdivisions will enable them to find readily the printed works (in the major languages) on almost any aspect of the history of science imaginable. Such a compilation has, however, obvious disadvantages. Limited to books, it omits those crucial articles in journals that often outweigh by far the many books in the lists (some of which may even be worthless). Furthermore, the absence of biographies [33] is to be regretted since a biographical study is apt to be a rich source of information on the subject in which that person worked. It may also be observed that the limitation of strict compartments [34] has caused the omission of many major works, *e.g.*, under the history of mechanics the reader will not find the names of Anneliese Maier or Alexandre Koyré.[35]

---

sources, " was composed partly to serve as a framework to the *Klassiker der exakten Wissenschaften*," edited by Wilhelm Ostwald.

[33] Cf. Thomas J. Higgins, Book-length Biographies of engineers, metallurgists and industrialists, *Research Publications of the Illinois Institute of Technology*, No. 7, 1949. Higgins has compiled similar checklists for mathematicians (*American Mathematical Monthly*, 51 (1944), 433–445; 56 (1949), 310–312), physicists and astronomers (*American Journal of Physics*, 12 (1944), 234–36), and chemists (*School Science and Mathematics*, [Oct. 1944], 650–665).

[34] Although Sarton has always inveighed against compartmentation of the history of science, the critical bibliographies prepared by him for *Isis*—like this one—are broken down into strict categories.

[35] The reason is that Koyré's penetrating studies on the pre-Galilean and Galilean mechanics do not comprise a general history of mechanics, nor do works of A. Maier on such subjects as the theory of impetus in the fourteenth century.

It must be pointed out that Sarton has prepared only a " first guide," a list of general books on the chief divisions of the history of science. Sarton has devoted a major part of his life to giving other scholars an easy access to *all* the literature on every aspect of the history of science: in the bibliographical sections which comprise a major feature of his *Introduction* (see n. 11, *supra*) and the 76 Critical Bibliographies he has prepared and published in *Isis*.

A guide to the history of science of a somewhat different sort has been prepared by Henry Guerlac, Professor of the History of Science at Cornell University. Intended as a syllabus for a two-semester course dealing with "Science in Western Civilization," [36] it consists of 91 topics presented in outline (each to serve a lecture in the course), beginning with the prehistory of Western culture and concluding with the physical science of the mid-twentieth century. Wholly apart from its use in courses in the history of science, this syllabus serves admirably as a general outline of the development of scientific ideas and their consequences; and its usefulness is greatly enhanced by the list of readings included under each topic and the general bibliography at the end. A companion volume, entitled *Selected Readings in the History of Science*,[37] issued in a preliminary edition, covers the period from antiquity to the time of Galileo. Like the syllabus, the readings embody a new point of view which distinguish them from earlier compilations.[38] In a word, they are marked from beginning to end by a true sense of history which not only has guided the choice of readings within each subject, but also the determination of the subjects themselves and the proportion of space allotted. Whereas the predecessors of this volume were intended to present major discoveries in the very words of the discoverers, or to display portions of the "great" works of science, or even to provide an introduction to the literature of science, Guerlac's book is an attempt to show science as a part of the great stream of history. It includes many sorts of documentary material—scientific texts, of course, but also portions of diaries and letters—and each major section contains one or more selections from modern scholarship, so that the student is brought face to face with the problems of critical interpretation and thus helped to avoid the pitfalls of attributing too modern a sense to the English rendering of earlier texts. Among the notable features of this collection are the generous amounts of material on technology (although it must be observed that mining is a bit overdone) and agriculture, the inclusion of the writings of minor figures, as well as major, to fill in the general picture, and many descriptions of the state of science written in the past.[39]

[36] Henry Guerlac, *Science in Western Civilization: A Syllabus* (197 pp. New York: Ronald Press, 1952).

[37] H. Guerlac, *Selected Readings in the History of Science*. Volume One: From Antiquity to the Time of Galileo. (x + 464 pp. Ithaca, N. Y.: published by the editor, 1950). A revised edition is scheduled to appear under the imprint of the Ronald Press in 1954.

[38] In chronological order, the major ones in English are as follows: William Cecil Dampier Whetham and Margaret Dampier, *Cambridge Readings in the History of Science* (Cambridge, England, 1924); William S. Knickerbocker, *Classics of Modern Science* (Copernicus to Pasteur) (New York, 1927); Forest Ray Moulton and Justus J. Schifferes, *The Autobiography of Science* (New York, 1945); Harlow Shapley, Samuel Rapport, and Helen Wright, *A Treasury of Science* (New York, 1948).

[39] Guerlac's views on the history of science in relation to general history may be found in Comité International des Sciences Historiques, *Rapports* (Paris, 1950), 182–211.

Certain omissions will certainly be corrected in the new edition; among them we may note Tycho's account of his methods of observation (in many ways more revolutionary than his account of the new star) and a description of his system, some portions of Galileo's *Dialogue on the Great World Systems;* some mediaeval mechanics (statics and dynamics), a sample of Babylonian astronomy (to accompany the astrology); Kepler, apparently excluded from the first volume so as to appear in the second, would—it would seem—more properly belong to the "time of Galileo."

The texts presented by Guerlac were chosen for readability as well as for their importance in illustrating the growth of science. I believe, however, that a certain number of explanatory notes and comments might prove helpful to the non-scientist. Guerlac's reader ends with the astronomical work of Galileo. Galilean and Newtonian dynamics, the full flowering of science in the seventeenth and eighteenth centuries, and the science of the nineteenth and twentieth centuries are reserved for a second volume. From the point of view of history, *i.e.,* the choice of materials to illustrate what "science" was before Galileo and how the many various threads that led up to Galileo's science were related to each other and were a part of the growth of civilization, the first volume raised problems which will not be so urgent in the second volume. Yet the second volume, if carried out on anything like the scale of the first one, must be a mammoth enterprise that will, at every turn in its preparation, provide a test of the historian's craft. Selection for intelligibility will be difficult enough, apart from the major task of encompassing the whole of modern science within a single bound book. But we know that the rise of modern science can be intelligible to historians and an earnest of this possibility has been provided in Herbert Butterfield's *Origins of Modern Science.*[40]

Butterfield, Professor of Modern History at Cambridge, is not an historian of science and yet he has written one of the most remarkable introductions to the subject ever produced. Leaning heavily on the monographic literature, he has created an account of the growth of science, beginning with the impetus dynamics of the late middle ages and ending somewhere in the eighteenth century, that will delight and inform anyone who is interested in the creative activities of the human mind. A well informed, sensitive, and highly literate historian, Butterfield was able to bring to bear a distinguished array of talents and the result is an extraordinary picture of science during the formative two centuries before Galileo and its triumph during the next two centuries. The presentation of late mediaeval physics and the world of Galileo is breath-taking and in many ways more satisfactory to the historian of science than the later part. It would be grossly ungenerous to carp at some inaccuracies of detail or distortions of perspective that arise from the fact that Butterfield is not an historian of

[40] Herbert Butterfield: *The Origins of Modern Science* (x + 217 pp. London: G. Bell & Sons, 1949; an American edition has been brought out by the Macmillan Co. in New York).

science, since it is likely that this very fact has given him the detachment necessary to write of science with the penetrating simplicity that will make his book cherished by the general historian and the historian of science alike as a lucid story of the major issues in the formation of modern science set against a continuous background of social and intellectual history. If we had a similar volume on the past two centuries, the place of science in history would be available for the whole gamut of modern science and its mediaeval background. Yet it must be stated again that to deal with the science of the last two centuries will prove to be a Herculean task for which the monographic literature is at present vastly inadequate.[41]

IV

Although the historian of ideas does not usually concern himself with technology, the technical aspects of civilization cannot be neglected by the historian of science. Furthermore, the state of the technical arts is not only intimately associated with science, but affords an index of the state of any given society and as such belongs to the social and economic matrix of ideas. In some ways, therefore, the history of technology plays the same rôle for the history of ideas as does the history of clinical medicine. Only a beginning has been made in the study of the ideational significance of inventions and technological change [42] and we may, therefore, welcome the availability of monographs and general books on these subjects.

For decades A. P. Usher's *History of Mechanical Inventions* [43] has been the standard work on this subject. Long out of print, and available only in a Spanish translation,[44] it has now been completely revised for publication in a second edition early in 1954.[45] In the meanwhile, a somewhat differently conceived one-volume work has been written by R. J. Forbes, Professor of the History of Science in Amsterdam.[46] At once more popular

[41] It may appear paradoxical, in the light of my earlier discussion of the possibility of the history of science being written by the general historian, to find so excellent a book produced on the history of science by a non-specialist. It must be observed, therefore, that Butterfield's book is best where he deals with subjects that have adequate secondary literature (*e.g.*, mediaeval dynamics) and poorest where he deals with modern science (*e.g.*, the eighteenth century), in which case the concepts become more difficult as the guides become less frequent.

[42] Two examples may be cited: Lynn White, Jr., " Technology and Invention in the Middle Ages," *Speculum* 15 (1940), 141–159; John U. Nef, *War and Human Progress: An Essay on the Rise of Industrial Civilization* (Harvard University Press, 1950).

[43] Albert Payson Usher, *A History of Mechanical Inventions* (New York, 1929).

[44] *Historia de las invenciones mecánicas* (México, 1941).

[45] Under the imprint of the Harvard University Press.

[46] Forbes has compiled a most useful bibliography (up to 1939) of ancient technology and related subjects in ten parts, under the general title of *Bibliographia Antiqua—Philosophia Naturalis*, published in Leyden by the Nederlandsch Instituut

and more comprehensive than Usher's history, *Man the Maker* [47] attempts to display every aspect of technology from earliest times to the present as a driving force in the advance of civilization. Unfortunately this treatment produces a volume in a style more suited for undergraduate collateral reading than for the serious scholar; the latter will wish for more detailed information, especially the facts that might serve to buttress Forbes's statements about the inventions or devices that originated in the West and moved eastward, only to be *re*-introduced into Europe.[48] The historian of ideas will especially miss any discussion of the vexing unsolved questions about the origin and transmission of certain devices which are studied, in the absence of historical documents, by methods of archaeology, folklore, and even philology. Yet *Man the Maker* does provide the only readily available survey of the technological aspects of civilization and we are grateful for it.

Forbes has written two technical monographs which are also of interest to the historian and may even prove more useful to him. *Metallurgy in Antiquity* [49] was conceived as " a notebook for archaeologists and technologists," and its main purpose was " to bring the archaeologist and the technologist in contact with each other's results, to help them over the gulf that still separates them from co-operating in the study of a fascinating aspect of ancient civilization." Historians of ideas are familiar with the sequence of " metal ages " used to denote the progress or decline of mankind by such writers as Hesiod, Plato, Claudianus, Cicero, Juvenal, and Ovid, and found in the Avesta and in Buddhist doctrines and in Daniel 2.31–45. But in general historians are not conversant with the degree, if any, to which the symbolic sequences of metal ages may reflect the story of man's actual conquest of metals. Forbes presents a synopsis of early metallurgy and an historical survey of mining, followed by a sketch of the " evolution of the smith, his social and sacred status " and of the tools and

---

van het Nabije Oosten, 1940–1950, containing 10,751 entries classified under the following heads: 1—mining and geology (1940), 2—metallurgy (1942), 3—building materials (1944), 4—pottery, faience, glass, glazes, beads (1944), 5—paints, pigments, varnishes, inks and their applications (1949), 6—leather, manufacture and application (1949), 7—fibrous materials, preparation and industries (1949), 8—paper, papyrus and other writing materials (1949), 9—man and nature (1949), 10—science and technology (1950).

[47] R. J. Forbes, *Man the Maker: A History of Technology and Engineering* (41 ills., xiv + 355 pp. New York: Henry Schuman, 1950).

[48] No discussion of the literature in the history of technology can afford to ignore the monumental book of J. R. Partington, *Origins and Development of Applied Chemistry* (London, 1935), a general survey of all ancient chemico-technical processes prior to the invention of chemical theory.

[49] R. J. Forbes, *Metallurgy in Antiquity: A Notebook for Archaeologists and Technologists* (iv + 489 pp., 98 figs. Leiden: E. J. Brill, 1950).

methods of early metallurgy; then come chapters on gold and copper in the ancient Near East, silver, lead, tin, antimony, arsenic, zinc and brass in antiquity, and the early story of iron. Since progress in the metallurgical arts is an important part of the " prelude to urban civilization "—V. Gordon Childe's phrase for the transition from the stone to the metal ages—Forbes has written of metals not only in a technical way, but also as a part of early literate and pre-literate civilization. At the same time he is careful to avoid exaggeration and "pronounce metallurgy to be the prime factor in the transition from stone to metal ages."

Forbes's *Short History of the Art of Distillation* [50] sketches the development of this art from its primitive beginnings until the middle of the nineteenth century in the first full-length history of the " oldest and still most important method of producing chemically pure substances." The history of distillation is part of the history of chemistry and chemical technology, it cannot be understood without them, just as they must be read in the context of their cultural background; this philosophy has dictated a history of one aspect of technology set against the history of civilization. We must remember that distillation was not only the method of producing chemically pure substances for various technological arts, and for the physician and alchemist, but it was also the means of making potent alcoholic beverages; furthermore, as Forbes amply documents, notions of change of state and the separation of substances by distillation were always closely linked to concepts of the nature of matter. In studying the history of distillation, therefore, as in the early history of metallurgy, Forbes constantly throws out hints for the historian of science and the general historian.

Although this review has been limited to books in English, an exception must be made for the two recent Swiss publications dealing with automata. One, written by Alfred Chapuis and Edmond Droz, is a monograph on the history and technology of artificial figures of men and animals; the other, by Chapuis, deals with automata in works of " imagination," a term that includes philosophy, literature, and the social sciences. Chapuis has written many books on the history and technology of watches, Swiss history, and the history of Swiss manufacturing, as well as some works of fiction and drama, and was a co-author of two volumes published in 1928 on *Les mondes des automates*, which contained a chapter on automata in literature. *Les automates dans les oeuvres d'imagination* [51] is not a contribution to the history of ideas; like Forbes's two monographs, it only serves to indicate a rich field as yet unexploited by the historian of ideas. Chapuis has merely collected together all references to automata that he has encountered in his

[50] R. J. Forbes, *Short History of the Art of Distillation from the Beginnings up to the Death of Cellier Blumenthal* (vi + 405 pp., 203 figs. Leiden: E. J. Brill, 1948).

[51] Alfred Chapuis, *Les automates dans les oeuvres d'imagination* (269 pp., figs. Neuchâtel: Editions du Griffon, 1947).

wide reading in folklore, philosophy, and literature. Each such automaton is described, or presented in quotation, with no attempt made to study fashions or trends nor even the obvious psychological significance of the ways in which they are used. But the list of authors cited is impressive—containing major and minor figures from the late Middle Ages to the present—and the book may serve as a series of notes for some scholar who will make a penetrating analysis of the ideational significance of mechanical animals and persons, robots, in modern creative thought. The companion volume deals with the history of all sorts of automata and quasi-automata: masks with moving jaws, clock-driven figures, models, and mechanical " brains " or complex computing machinery.[52] It is lavishly illustrated with photographs of devices (many in color), reproductions of paintings and prints, and diagrams: an impressive record of the heroic labor and ingenuity that have, since ages past, been expended on the production of mechanical devices to simulate living functions. This book thus provides the evidence to document the importance of the subject as a whole and makes us wish for a plausible history of man's efforts to reproduce the activities of life on a mechanical basis and to reduce them to mechanical action.

On a wholly different level is a recent study of chemical technology: Archibald and Nan Clow's *The Chemical Revolution*,[53] winner (in manuscript) of the Senior Hume-Brown Prize of the University of Edinburgh. Subtitled " A contribution to social technology," its aim is to present the evolution of chemical technology " as an important concomitant of the industrial revolution," and as such it explores a ground common to economic history and the history of applied chemistry during the 80 years from 1750 to 1830. That this is a useful exploration of the adaptation of scientific discoveries to economic needs cannot be denied, but the authors—despite the general title—have limited their discussion to Scotland, and we have no idea as to whether or not Scottish conditions were typical of those that obtained elsewhere at the same time. I found the continued use of the Lewis Mumford–Patrick Geddes language (" eotechnic," " palaeotechnic," " neotechnic ") irksome and misleading. The Scottish emphasis apart, the Clows have produced a book that—perhaps for the first time—is devoted entirely to the practical consequences of scientific ideas and it is, therefore, a reminder of another important field not as yet explored.

Another work that deals with technology, but that has broad implications for the historians of ideas, is A. R. Hall's *Ballistics in the Seventeenth Century*.[54] Hall, University Assistant Lecturer in the History of Science

---

[52] Alfred Chapuis and Edmond Droz, *Les automates: figures artificielles d'hommes et d'animaux—histoire et technique* (430 pp., 506 ills., 18 color plates. Neuchâtel: Editions du Griffon, [no date]).

[53] Archibald and Nan Clow, *The Chemical Revolution: A Contribution to Social Technology* (xvi + 680 pp., 101 ills., 16 diagrams. London: The Batchworth Press, 1952).

[54] A. R. Hall, *Ballistics in the Seventeenth Century: A Study in the Relations of Science and War* (viii + 186 pp., 8 figs., 4 pl. Cambridge, England: At the University Press, 1952).

at Cambridge University, has written what may come to be considered a classic monograph of its kind. It is an accurate survey of the foundation, in the seventeenth century, " of the science of ballistics as a mathematical interpretation of some physical problems upon a basis of exact experimental investigation." As such, it deals necessarily with pre-seventeenth century approaches to the subject and embraces both the ideas and practices of gunnery men and the investigations of first-rate men of science, like Galileo and Newton. But what will appeal particularly to the historian of ideas is Hall's consistent endeavour " to relate this series of researches in applied mathematics to its background, social, economic and scientific, as a contribution to the history of science in society " and the subject of ballistics was chosen " as a critical example of early science being directed by utilitarian considerations." How far could such progress as was actually made in this subject be " imputed to governmental interest, to the experience of a warlike age, or to the not uncommon feeling that the fruits of knowledge ought to be useful? " Hall's carefully documented conclusion is that " the purposeful application of science to the art of war (and, it may be, to any technique or useful art) at any period before the nineteenth century is much less than at first appears from non-professional accounts," and that " the conservative traditions of practical men yielded very slowly to the enthusiasm of inventive amateurs, whether scientists or not." So it is that Hall has thrown into sharp relief that vexing question of attempting to square men's deeds with their words. While so many of the scientists of the seventeenth and eighteenth century continually expressed sentiments like those of Descartes and Bacon, about how science was to be valued for the practical applications it would produce, they did not in general see such applications made nor were they particularly bothered that they did not. So the historian of ideas must be very wary in taking at their face value the statements made about science by scientists of the past, and must always apply to them a corrective factor obtained by analyzing the kind of scientific research they did and its actual consequences.

Enough has been said to indicate that the history of technology may be of some interest to the historian of ideas, and this section may be concluded with a brief description of Dr. Charles Singer's project. Dr. Singer and Dr. E. J. Holmyard—editor of *Endeavour* and an historian of chemistry—are joint editors of the *History of Technology;* A. R. Hall is deputy editor. Five volumes are planned, having " to do rather with cultures than with periods." [55] The first deals with " technology from the earliest times up to and including the ancient empires," the second with " the Mediterranean civilizations and their sequelae in the European middle ages," the third with " the first impact of science," the " period of the great voyages of discovery, together with the impact of science on technology in the 16th and 17th centuries," the fourth with " north-west Europe up to about the

[55] From a private communication (9 June 1953) from Dr. Singer to the writer. Some account of this project may be found in Dr. Singer's " L. T. Hobhouse Memorial Trust Lecture of 23 October 1951," *Technology and History* (London, 1952).

French Revolution," and the last with "the great period of industrial expansion up to about the middle of the 19th century." Each volume is being composed of a series of essays by specialists and thus follows the familiar pattern of the Cambridge histories—with their respective strengths and weaknesses.

V

One of the marks of the youthfulness of the history of science as a professional discipline is, of course, the paucity of secondary works on many topics and the lack of standard texts. For instance, the most influential book in modern science—Newton's *Principia*—has never been printed in a decent edition; by this I mean that there does not exist a critical edition in which the changes introduced by Newton into successive editions are delineated, nor has Newton's masterpiece ever been printed (either in the original Latin or in English translation) with an adequate index or an analytical table of contents.[56] There is no full collection available of the correspondence of Faraday, Clerk Maxwell, Lavoisier,[57] or Priestley, and although magnificent editions exist, or are in progress, of the complete works and correspondence of Fermat, Huygens, Descartes, Euler, Kepler, Leeuwenhoek, Tycho Brahe and Galileo,[58] the editing and publishing of Newton's correspondence has only recently got under way (under the sponsorship of the Royal Society of London)[59] and there is at present no plan to publish systematically his many scattered manuscripts or to issue critical editions of his published works.[60]

[56] The edition prepared by Florian Cajori, a revision of Andrew Motte's 18th-century translation, published by the University of California Press in 1934, has no table of contents, no index, and no critical apparatus whatever. The unwary reader is never warned as to which portions were revised by Newton in later editions, and which portions remain substantially as first written. Presumably, had Cajori lived to prepare the text for publication, it would not have been printed in this form.

[57] The International Union of the History of Science announces that "La Correspondance de Lavoisier est sous presse," F. J. M. Stratton, ed.: *Reports of Proceedings: The Sixth General Assembly of the International Council of Scientific Unions* (Cambridge, England, 1953), Rapport de l'Union Internationale d'Histoire des Sciences, p. 50.

[58] The Royal Netherlands Academy of Sciences is sponsoring an edition of the writings of Simon Stevin in which his major works will be presented in the original language (chiefly Dutch) and also in English translation. For details, see *Isis*, 44 (1953), 98.

[59] The correspondence is being edited by Professor H. W. Turnbull and the first volume, containing a foreword by Professor E. N. daC. Andrade, will be published shortly by the Cambridge University Press.

[60] A collection of the scattered letters and papers on natural philosophy published by Newton in his lifetime or issued soon after his death, together with related documents, is available as *Isaac Newton's Letters and Papers on Natural Philosophy* (Norwalk, Conn.: Burndy Library, 1953). Each item is reproduced in facsimile from the original printing and explanatory matter has been added by Marie Boas, I. Bernard Cohen, Thomas S. Kuhn, Perry Miller, and Robert E. Schofield.

Naturally enough, many historians of science have approached the subject systematically *a capite ad calcem*. So it is that we have witnessed of late a great flurry of scholarly activity in many fields of science before the time of Galileo; there have been produced such notable results as the unveiling of pre-Greek mathematics and astronomy and a better knowledge of the scientific culture of Islam and the developments in mechanics prior to Galileo's "Two New Sciences." Professor O. Neugebauer of Brown University and the Institute for Advanced Study has long been the major figure in the interpretation of ancient exact science [61] and we owe to him a large collection of published Babylonian texts which should have changed many a pious statement about the "miracle" of Greek science.[62] Some years ago, Neugebauer wrote a general account of pre-Greek mathematics [63] and he has complemented his more recent scholarly publications by a challenging study of "Exact Science in Antiquity," [64] in which he has made available the fruits of his own researches and those of others, and his interpretation of the development of mathematics and astronomy in Babylonia, Egypt and "Hellenistic" Greece. The title of this book is not intended to "suggest an exhaustive discussion of this vast subject," since Neugebauer has presented only "a survey of the historical interrelationship between mathematics and astronomy in ancient civilizations"; the "main emphasis is laid on mathematics and astronomy in Babylonia and Egypt in their relationship to Hellenistic science." [65] Neugebauer has shown that in the "Hellenistic" period, there was developed "a form of science" which spread eastward out over the world to India and westward to Europe and "which was dominant until the creation of modern science in the time of Newton," and which had "roots in the oriental civilizations." So that the science of these oriental civilizations may become at once relevant to students of European history, Neugebauer begins his book with a discussion of the "Book of the Hours" made for Jean de France, Duc de Berry (died 1416), in which the astronomical data and the numerals show their oriental origins.

[61] Cf. G. Waldo Dunnington, "Otto Neugebauer: Biographical Sketch," *National Mathematics Magazine*, vol. 11, pp. 1–2, 1936.   [62] Alas! they have not.

[63] O. Neugebauer, *Vorgriechische Mathematik*, Erster Band of *Vorlesungen über Geschichte der Antiken Mathematischen Wissenschaften* (Berlin, 1934).

[64] O. Neugebauer, *The Exact Sciences in Antiquity* (xvi + 191 pp., 29 figs., 14 plates. Princeton: Princeton University Press, 1952). The text is based on the "Messenger Lectures on the Evolution of Civilization" given at Cornell in 1949; the book was originally printed in 1951 in Copenhagen as volume nine of the Acta Historica Scientiarum Naturalium et Medicinalium, published by the University Library, Copenhagen, Scientific and Medical Department.

[65] Neugebauer writes: "Since the works of Sir Thomas L. Heath provide an excellent guide for Greek mathematics, I see no need to summarize their contents in a series of lectures. For Greek astronomy no similar presentation exists, but its highly technical character makes it impossible to discuss any details in the present book."

One of the finest aspects of Neugebauer's book, surely to be appreciated by the historians of ideas, is that the facts of ancient science and their interpretation are constantly woven into the weft of an historical discussion of how our knowledge was obtained. "The Sources: their decipherment and evaluation," chapter three of this book, reads like a detective story.[66] No one who is interested in the history of science, whether ancient science or the science at the time of Copernicus, can afford to miss this stimulating book. Not only is it a critical corrective to the standard discussions of ancient science (usually centered around classical Greece), but it is a mine of information and challenging statements: *e.g.,* "Plato's doctrines undoubtedly have had great influence upon the modern interpretation of Greek sciences. But, if modern scholars had devoted as much attention to Galen or Ptolemy as they did to Plato and his followers, they would have come to quite different results and they would not have invented the myth about the remarkable quality of the so-called Greek mind to develop scientific theories without resorting to experiments or empirical tests." [67]

Although many scholars will wish to criticize the title of Neugebauer's book because his ". . . in antiquity " does not include the mathematics and astronomy of classical or "Hellenic " Greece, the fact is that Neugebauer has shown that the "Hellenistic " astronomy and mathematics—and its transmission to Europe—can best be understood by a consideration of its Babylonian, and to a lesser extent, Egyptian sources and influences. But the title is, in one real sense, misleading since nowhere in the book can one find any discussion of the "exact " parts of physics, such as they were in antiquity.[68]

One of Neugebauer's often-voiced complaints is the state of texts in ancient science,[69] and also in the exact science of the middle ages and

[66] Particular attention may be called to Neugebauer's pungent story of the myth of a "Babylonian Saros " (134).

[67] All students of the history of ideas will be interested in Neugebauer's conclusions about the origins and transmission of astrology, so often said to be the "mother " of astronomy, a statement for which Neugebauer can "see no evidence " (cf. 161).

[68] It may be noted that the series of "Source Books in the History of Science" begins with "Greek Science" (cf. Ludwig Edelstein, "Recent Trends in the Interpretation of Science," pp. 90–121), so that this series as a whole will perpetuate the myth that science began in ancient Greece.

[69] Neugebauer has pointed out that "much remains to be done to repair the harm caused by classical philologists who made their editions inaccessible to modern scientists by translating them into Latin instead of a modern language. Great opportunities have been spoiled by this absurd attitude. It has fortunately never occurred to Orientalists to translate their texts into Hebrew. It should be mentioned, however, that the Arabic version of Euclid's *Elements* was published in Latin (!) translation by Besthorn, Heiberg and others " (final note to O. Neugebauer, "The History of Ancient Astronomy—Problems and Methods," *Publications of the Astronomical Society of the Pacific*, 58 [1946], 17–43, 104–142; reprinted, with additions and corrections, from *Journal of Near Eastern Studies*, 4 [1945], 1–38).

Renaissance.[70] I have mentioned above that recent decades have witnessed much research in pre-Galilean dynamics; but the writers on this subject, Duhem, Maier, Dijksterhuis,[71] and others, have not served us quite as well as Neugebauer has, since Neugebauer has published not only interpretations and commentaries, but also the original texts themselves (in photographic reproduction, with drawings to make the characters clear, and with transliterations and translations.) [72] The non-specialist studying pre-Galilean mechanics has, up until now, had largely to rely on the interpretations of texts in secondary works, save for those extracts quoted here and there for illustrative purposes. So it is with a sense of special gratitude that we welcome the publication by Marshall Clagett and Ernest A. Moody of a series of late mediaeval treatises on mechanics, each published in its entirety for the first time (from manuscript sources) with a translation into English. *The Medieval Science of Weights*,[73] as its name suggests, is devoted entirely to statics and its publication sharpens our desire to see in print a similar volume devoted to dynamics, or the latitude of forms generally, so that we might gain some more exact perspective on the flowering of ideas concerning motion and physical change in the era before Galileo produced the modern formulation of the laws of acceleration of freely falling bodies.

[70] He writes (n. 64, *supra*) : " The history of the transmission of Hellenistic science throughout the Islamic world need not be told here. The general trend is no longer in doubt and has often been described. What is less generally known, however, is the fact that for every specific question of astronomical or mathematical theory we are still groping in the dark because of a most deplorable lack of edited source material. With the splendid exception of al-Battānī's tables, none of the great astronomical tables of the Middle Ages—Arabic or Latin, Hebrew or Greek— is available in modern editions for the period between Ptolemy and Copernicus. The history of the ancient mathematical sciences is a field in which one need not go far to find fertile soil ready to be cultivated."

[71] Of course, all such authors present extracts and even short texts, but they have not given us editions of the major writers whose ideas they discuss, with proper critical apparatus and a translation into a modern language. Since the subject of linguistic barriers has been raised, it may be noted that the works of E. J. Dijksterhuis are in Dutch, which means that those of us who read reviews of them cannot hope to comprehend the originals; they include: *Die Mechanisering van het Wereldbild* (Amsterdam, 1950), *Simon Stevin* ('s Gravenhage, 1943), *Val en Worp: Een Bijdrage tot de Geschiedenis der Mechania van Aristoteles tot Newton* (Groningen, 1925).

[72] O. Neugebauer, Mathematische Keilschrift-Texte, 3 vols., *Quellen und Studien zur Geschichte der Mathematik, Astronomie und Physik*, Abteilung A: Quellen, 3. Band, 1935; *Mathematical Cuneiform Texts*, American Oriental Series, vol. 29, 1945; a volume of *Astronomical Cuneiform Texts* is in preparation.

[73] *The Medieval Science of Weights (Scientia de Ponderibus): Treatises ascribed to Euclid, Archimedes, Thabit ibn Qurra, Jordanus de Nemore and Blasius of Parma.* Edited with introductions, English translations, by Ernest Moody, Marshall Clagett (x + 438 pp., diagrams. Madison: University of Wisconsin Press, 1952).

As we learn more about pre-Galilean science, we come to appreciate Galileo's genius in a wholly new light. His gigantic stature is not really diminished by an awareness that many of the ideas he used are to be found in the writings of his predecessors; for the fact remains that even if certain fundamental concepts and principles were " in the air," no one else saw how they might be integrated into a system of modern dynamics; Galileo alone, of all his contemporaries, saw how to put together the science of mechanics in a fruitful way. Even so, the long-cherished (and still oft-expressed) view that modern science began with Galileo [74] can no longer be held, just as that other view of science beginning with Greek philosophers can no longer meet the test of scholarship. The texts presented by Clagett and Moody and the illuminating introductions and commentaries call to our attention the fact that there was mediaeval progress in statics as well as in dynamics; they thus inform the prevailing ignorance concerning Archimedean physics in the middle ages.

In an earlier section of this review, mention was made of the admirable review of impetus mechanics in Butterfield's *Origins of Modern Science*,[75] and the reader's attention may also be called to two books on the development of science prior to Galileo by A. C. Crombie (Lecturer in the History and Philosophy of Science, University College, London,[76] and Editor of the *British Journal for the Philosophy of Science*). The first of these is a general survey of scientific activity from about A.D. 400 to 1650, from Augustine to Galileo,[77] and the other is a monograph on Roger Bacon's teacher, Robert Grosseteste, and his influence in the development of an experimental science from 1100 to 1700.[78]

Crombie has told the story of science from Augustine to Galileo, " from its decay after the collapse of the Roman Empire in the West to its full reflowering in the 17th century," with an emphasis on what he believes to be " the most striking result of recent scholarship, the essential continuity of the Western scientific tradition from Greek times to the seventeenth century and, therefore, to our own day." Throughout the book an attempt has been made to place the scientific material in its historical context of philosophical and theological ideas; Crombie, quite properly, has included musi-

[74] See, for example, Herbert Dingle, *The Scientific Adventure* (New York, 1953) *passim*.

[75] See footnote 41, above.

[76] In 1953–54, Dr. Crombie is visiting professor at the University of Washington and, upon his return to England, will be Senior Lecturer in the History of Science at Oxford.

[77] A. C. Crombie, *Augustine to Galileo: The History of Science A.D. 400–1650* (xv + 436 pp., 48 ills., charts. London: Falcon Educational Books, 1952).

[78] A. C. Crombie, *Robert Grosseteste and the Origins of Experimental Science 1100–1700* (xii + 369 pp., 15 figs. Oxford: Clarendon Press, 1953).

cal theory or harmony among the sciences and has presented an unusually large amount of information on technology. We must repeat once again that any survey must, of necessity, contain opinions which will be challenged by specialists and certain emphases which each reader may question. But, in the main, Crombie's presentation appears sound and well informed and displays an encyclopaedic learning of high order. Particularly brilliant is the exposition of the somewhat independent growth of experimental and mathematical methods which developed within a " predominantly Aristotelian system of scientific thought "; Crombie sees in Gilbert's *De Magnete* (1600), which was non-mathematical in treatment although it did contain some measurements, the " most striking illustration of the independence of the experimental and mathematical traditions in the 16th century." Written in an engaging and readable style, Crombie's thoughtful book should go far toward advancing his thesis that " no construction of the mind can be used to set limits to the mind's activity "; he is firmly convinced that " the illumination that natural science has given in the modern world has depended precisely upon the practical recognition of this fact." Thus science can " provide no capital for either theologians or atheists, moralists or libertines " and it " has nothing to say about aesthetics or ethics, about the existence of God or miracles." Crombie claims that even before the twentieth century men believed (to some extent) that " a scientific theory of itself never provides grounds for denying a belief held in context outside the range of the scientific method," and further that " although scientific theories are themselves conceptual and hypothetical, there is nothing in the scientific method that either denies or affirms the validity of other methods of making sense of experience, or the attainability of objective truth." Yet from the time of Augustine to Galileo, and even Newton, science was conceived as " capable of discovering, in its theories, the real causes of phenomena," and was not merely a source of ingenious devices to " save the appearances." But " the scientific revolution of the sixteenth and seventeenth centuries," as conceived by Crombie, came about not merely because men had ceased to consider nature wholly as sacramental and as symbolic of spiritual truths (as Augustine had done), but because they asked " questions within the range of an experimental answer, by limiting their inquiries to physical rather than metaphysical problems, concentrating their attention on accurate observation of the kinds of things there are in the natural world and the correlation of the behaviour of one with another rather than on their intrinsic natures, on proximate causes rather than substantial forms, and in particular on those aspects of the physical world which could be expressed in terms of mathematics."

Crombie's other work is mainly a monograph on the science of Grosseteste and its immediate influences. Following a sketch of the philosophical and technological background to the science of the thirteenth century, Crombie presents Grosseteste's ideas on the nature and logic of the sciences and the character of his studies of nature (primarily mathematics as applied to physics, chiefly optics, and astronomy) and the extension of his conceptions in the work of the " Oxford School " and the later Continental scholars. In considering the influence of Grosseteste, Crombie displays the work of Roger Bacon, Witelo, and Theodoric of Freiburg—practically writing a history of experimental and theoretical optics, especially the research into the cause of the rainbow. Crombie's main thesis here is that "the natural philosophers of Latin Christendom in the thirteenth and fourteenth centuries created the experimental science characteristic of modern times " as a result of " their attempts to answer the Greek question: How is it possible to reach with the greatest possible certainty true premises for demonstrated knowledge of the world of experience? " Crombie documents the proposition that although the " conception of scientific explanation accepted, for example, by Galileo, Harvey, and Newton, was the theory of formal proof developed by the Greek geometers and logicians," the distinctive feature of the science of the seventeenth century was non-Greek in origin, a " scientific method " based on a " conception of how to relate a theory to the observed facts it explained, the set of logical procedures . . . for constructing theories and for submitting them to experimental tests "— and that " the modern, systematic understanding of at least the qualitative aspects of this method was created by the philosophers of the West in the thirteenth century." Although this proposition is, as I have just said, amply documented, the sense in which we may discern in the thirteenth century some " qualitative aspects " of a seventeenth-century " method " that is essentially quantitative may seem puzzling. Qualitative theories—in the physical sciences, at any rate—have been most valuable when they proved susceptible of translation into mathematics, as Franklin's theory of the electric fluid, mathematicized by Æpinus and Cavendish, or Faraday's theories of lines of force, rendered into elegant mathematics by Clerk Maxwell. We are apt to suspect that Franklin and Faraday thought in terms of an unexpressed, intuitive mathematics, for how else could their concepts so readily have lent themselves to mathematical formulation? How nonquantitative methods may become quantitative is apparent only by implication in Crombie's monograph and perhaps merits an independent discussion.

But we must always be careful in reading the past, and we cannot hope to find modern science during the middle ages. Crombie—correctly, to my mind—insists that there *was* a great scientific revolution in the sixteenth and seventeenth centuries, but he has shown that in the preceding 400 years there had been begun a tradition that was becoming increasingly empirical, and that out of appeals to experience in founding explanations and in testing theories there grew up an attitude about explanations of natural phenomena which is one of the important roots of modern experimental science. Unlike those who would deny the originality of Galileo and who would see the revolutionary science of his day already existing centuries earlier, Crombie quite correctly does not allow his historical perspective and his critical scientific judgment to become warped by his enthusiastic researches;

no one who reads his two books can escape the conclusion that although many elements of modern science are discernible long before the age of Galileo, modern science as such was forged in that great revolution of the sixteenth and seventeenth centuries. With the emergence of Newton, the face of science was completely altered. " In mathematical astronomy," for example, as Neugebauer points out, " ancient methods prevailed until Newton and his contemporaries opened a fundamentally new age by the introduction of dynamics into the discussion of astronomical phenomena. One can perfectly well understand the *Principia* without much knowledge of earlier astronomy [though, be it noted, not without knowledge of early mathematics] but one cannot read a single chapter in Copernicus or Kepler without a thorough knowledge of Ptolemy's *Almagest*. Up to Newton all astronomy consists in modifications, however ingenious, of Hellenistic astronomy."

VI

The now-classic introductions to the science of the sixteenth and seventeenth centuries,[79] and the science of the eighteenth century,[80] written by A. Wolf, have been reissued with revisions by Douglas McKie, Reader in the History and Philosophy of Science, University College, London, and a distinguished historian of science in his own right.[81] The new edition has been produced by offset, so that McKie was limited in his revisions to alterations only within a given page, and the changes he has made occur chiefly in the references to the secondary literature. Turning over the pleasant pages of Wolf's books is a delight to the eye, although the critical reader will wish that the many handsome illustrations had been prepared more uniformly (some are taken from the original books and papers, others from mediocre reproductions in secondary sources, and still others from new drawings that are out of keeping with the spirit of the age to which they should properly belong). One of the great merits of these two books is that they contain long introductory sections on scientific instruments, their makers, and the way in which they were used. Another is the close juxtaposition of the history of science and the history of technology. Curiously enough, although the author was a professional philosopher,[82] the sections on philosophy invite the most criticism; they are tucked in at the end of each volume as a sort of appendage and are far too brief to be of any use. Had they been conceived as providing a general account of the main currents of ideas for each period, they would have illuminated the discussions

[79] A. Wolf, *A History of Science, Technology and Philosophy in the 16th and 17th Centuries* (ed. 2, xxvii + 692 pp., 316 ills. New York: The Macmillan Co., 1951).

[80] *A History of Science, Technology and Philosophy in the Eighteenth Century* (ed. 2, 814 pp., 345 ills. New York: The Macmillan Co., 1952).

[81] His most recent book is *Antoine Lavoisier: Scientist, Economist, Social Reformer* (New York, 1952).

[82] His books on Spinoza and on logic are especially noteworthy.

of scientific thought which would then have followed. So separated are they from the rest of each book that even the obvious connections between science and philosophy—as Lavoisier's admitted indebtedness to Condillac —are not present. Perhaps the treatment of philosophy is but one result of the plan of the author, in which wholly separate sections are devoted to the major fields of science and their subdivisions (*e.g.*, magnetism, electricity, heat, meteorology, mechanics, mathematics, etc.).[83]

Wolf's two histories may properly be considered as accounts of the major discoveries and theories in each branch of science, rather than a unified history of science as a whole in, say, the eighteenth century. Even so, these volumes are rich treasure-houses of useful information and are indispensable tools for the historian of science or the historian of ideas; they make it possible to learn the main developments in any area of scientific activity in as painless a fashion as possible, and they are written with a simplicity and clarity that often belie the difficulties in the subjects presented.

But once we pass the boundary between the eighteenth and nineteenth centuries, we encounter no general surveys written in a way that will serve the historian of ideas. Merz's older work,[84] dull, myopic, and often poorly informed, is still the major presentation of the science of the nineteenth century. The fourth volume of Ernst Cassirer's *Erkenntnisproblem* [85] is sketchy and far too technical for the average historian. Standard histories of physics, chemistry, biology, etc., contain much of the information but it needs to be digested and interpreted in the main stream of scientific ideas. Only the future can tell whether the history of science in the nineteenth century can be presented in a meaningful way for the general historian.[86]

---

[83] Thus, the work of a single individual may be discussed in many places.

[84] John Theodore Merz, *A History of European Thought in the Nineteenth Century* (Vols. 1 & 2, ed. 3. Edinburgh, 1907). These two volumes make up " Part One," devoted to " The History of Scientific Thought in the Nineteenth Century."

[85] Ernst Cassirer, *The Problem of Knowledge: Philosophy, Science, and History since Hegel*. Trans. by W. H. Woglon and C. W. Hendel (334 pp. New Haven, 1950). Reviewed in the *J. H. I.* by Philip Wiener (April 1951), 305ff.

[86] Of course, this subject is discussed in every survey volume of the history of science.

BIOGRAPHICAL NOTES ON THE CONTRIBUTORS

MARIE BOAS teaches the history of science at the University of California at Los Angeles. She has written on Robert Boyle and seventeenth-century "mechanical philosophy."

JOHN E. BOODIN (1869–1950) is the author of several books on philosophy, including *A Realistic Universe* (1931), *Three Interpretations of the Universe* (1934), and *Man in His World* (1939).

I. BERNARD COHEN, Professor of the History of Science at Harvard University and the editor of *Isis,* has published a number of studies on the history of physical thought and on science in America. He is the author of *Roemer and the First Determination of the Velocity of Light* (1942), *Science, Servant of Man* (1948), *Benjamin Franklin: His Contribution to the American Tradition* (1953), and *Franklin and Newton: An Inquiry into Speculative Newtonian Experimental Science and Franklin's Work as an Example Thereof* (1956).

A. C. CROMBIE is University Lecturer in the History of Science at Oxford University and the author of *Augustine to Galileo: The History of Science A.D. 400–1650* (1952) and *Robert Grosseteste and the Origins of Experimental Science, 1100–1700* (1953).

LUDWIG EDELSTEIN, Professor of Humanistic Studies at Johns Hopkins University, is the editor of *The Hippocratic Oath, Text, Translation and Interpretation* (1943), the co-author of the two-volume study, *Asclepius, A Collection and Interpretation of the Testimonies* (1945), and the author of *Wielands 'Abderiten' und der deutsche Humanismus* (1950).

ALVAR ELLEGÅRD teaches English at Gotenburg University and writes on the sociology of science.

MELBOURNE G. EVANS, Visiting Lecturer in Philosophy at the

University of New Mexico, is a specialist on the history and philosophy of physical science and mathematics.

HEINRICH GOMPERZ (1873–1943) taught philosophy at the University of Vienna and the University of Southern California. Among his numerous books and articles are *Grundlegung der neusokratischen Philosophie* (1897), *Sophistik und Rhetorik* (1912), *Die Wissenschaft und die Tat* (1934), and *Philosophical Studies* (1953).

THOMAS S. HALL is the co-author of *Life Science: A College Textbook of General Biology* (1955).

WALTER E. HOUGHTON, JR., Professor of English Literature at Wellesley College, is the author of *The Formation of Thomas Fuller's Holy and Profane States* (1938) and *The Art of Newman's Apologia* (1945).

FRANCIS R. JOHNSON, Professor of English at Stanford University, is a specialist on Renaissance English literature and science and the author of *Astronomical Thought in Renaissance England* (1937).

A. C. KELLER teaches French at the University of Washington and has published articles on French intellectual history.

ALEXANDRE KOYRÉ, Professor at the Sorbonne (*Ecole Pratique des Hautes Etudes*), is the author of several studies in the historical relations of science to philosophy. Among his publications are *Etudes galiléennes* (1939), *Discovering Plato* (1945), *A Documentary History of the Problem of Fall from Kepler to Newton* (1955), and *From the Closed World to the Infinite Universe* (1957).

ANDRÉ LALANDE, Member of the French Institute and *Professeur honoraire* at the Sorbonne, is the author of several studies of the philosophy of science, including *Les théories de l'induction et de l'expérimentation* (1929). He is the editor of the *Vocabulaire technique et critique de la philosophie,* a standard work that has gone through four printings, the most recent in 1951.

RICHARD MCKEON, Charles F. Grey Distinguished Service Professor of Philosophy and of Greek at the University of Chicago, is the author of *The Philosophy of Spinoza* (1928), "The Empiricist and Experimental Temper in the Middle Ages: A Prolegomenon to the Study of Medieval Science," in *Essays in Honor of John Dewey* (1929), and "Aristotle and the Origins of Science in the West," in *Science and Civilization* (1949). He is also the editor of *The Basic Works of Aristotle* (1941).

ROBERT MCRAE is Professor of Philosophy at the University of Toronto, specializing in the development of British empiricism.

MAURICE MANDELBAUM is Chairman of the Department of Philosophy at Johns Hopkins University and the author of *The Problem of Historical Knowledge: An Answer to Relativism* (1938), *The Phenomenology of Moral Experience* (1955), and one of the editors of *Philosophic Problems* (1957).

ERNEST A. MOODY taught philosophy at Columbia University. He is the author of *The Logic of William of Ockham* (1935) and the co-editor of *The Medieval Science of Weights* (1952).

MILTON K. MUNITZ, Associate Professor of Philosophy at New York University's Graduate School, has recently published two cosmological studies: *Space, Time, and Creation* (1957), and *Theories of the Universe: From Babylonian Myth to Modern Science* (1957).

MARJORIE NICOLSON, Professor of English and Executive Officer of the Department of English and Comparative Literature at Columbia University, has made major contributions to the study of the "interplay of science and literature." Among her publications are the following: *Newton Demands the Muse; Newton's Opticks and the Eighteenth Century Poets* (1946), *The Breaking of the Circle; Studies in the Effect of the 'New Science' upon Seventeenth Century Poetry* (1950), and *Science and Imagination* (1956).

SVEN PETERSON teaches philosophy at Union College and specializes in the history and philosophy of science.

MOODY E. PRIOR, Dean of the Graduate School of Northwestern University, is the author of *Joseph Glanvill, Witchcraft, and Seventeenth-Century Science* (1932) and *The Language of Tragedy* (1947).

JOHN HERMAN RANDALL, JR., Frederick J. E. Woodbridge Professor of Philosophy at Columbia University and an editor of *The Journal of Philosophy,* is the author of numerous studies in the history of ideas, the history of science, and metaphysics. Among his various publications are *The Making of the Modern Mind* (1926), "Dualism in Metaphysics and Political Philosophy," in *Essays in Honor of John Dewey* (1929), *Our Changing Civilization: How Science and the Machine are Reconstructing Modern Life* (1929), and *Nature and Historical Experience: Essays in Naturalism and in the Theory of History* (1957).

EDWARD ROSEN, Associate Professor of History at The City College, New York, is the translator and editor of *Three Copernican Treatises* (1939) and the author of *The Naming of the Telescope* (1947), "The Invention of Eyeglasses," *Journal of the History of Medicine and Allied Sciences* (1956), and numerous articles on the history of astronomy.

EDWARD W. STRONG is Professor of Sociology and Social Institutions at the University of California and the author of *Procedures and Metaphysics: A Study in the Philosophy of Mathematical-Physical Science in the Sixteenth and Seventeenth Centuries* (1936).

LYNN THORNDIKE is Professor Emeritus of History at Columbia University and a prolific writer on medieval history and science. Some of his noteworthy publications are *The History of Medieval Europe* (1949), *The Sphere of Sacrobosco and Its Commentators* (1949), *Latin Treatises on Comets between 1238 and 1368 A.D.* (1950), and the monumental eight-volume *A History of Magic and Experimental Science* (1923–57).

STEPHEN E. TOULMIN, Professor of Philosophy at the University of Leeds, is the author of *An Examination of the Place of Reason in Ethics* (1950), *The Philosophy of Science* (1953), and numerous articles in *Mind, Proceedings of the Aristotelian Society* and other philosophical journals.

ARAM VARTANIAN, Associate Professor of French Language and Literature at the University of Minnesota, is the author of "Elie Luzac's Refutation of La Mettrie," *Modern Language Notes* (1949), and *Diderot and Descartes: A Study of Scientific Naturalism in the Enlightenment* (1953).

PHILIP P. WIENER, Professor of Philosophy at The City College, New York, has written on the history and philosophy of science. Among his publications are "The Tradition Behind Galileo's Methodology," *Osiris* (1936), *Evolution and the Founders of Pragmatism* (1949), *Readings in the Philosophy of Science* (1952), Duhem's *Aims and Structure of Physical Theory* (1954), and *Values in a Universe of Chance* (1957).

EDGAR ZILSEL (1891–1944) wrote extensively on the sociology of science. Some of his publications in the field are *Entstehung des Geniebegriffes* (1926), "The Sociological Roots of Science," *The American Journal of Sociology* (1941–42), and "The Genesis of the Concept of Physical Law," *The Philosophical Review* (1942).

INDEX